Congratulations! You have purchased a 12-month, prepaid subscription to the Special Edition of *The Biology Place* for *BIOLOGY*, Fifth Edition, by Campbell, Reece, and Mitchell, a web learning environment for general biology that includes learning activities, study and testing aids, and a wide range of content to help you succeed in your biology course.

To activate your prepaid subscription:

1. Point your web browser to **www.biology.com/campbell**

2. Select *The Biology Place* Special Edition login

3. Enter your preassigned activation ID and password exactly as they appear below in the user ID and password fields:

Activation ID	BIPPST12070700
Password	cornea

4. Select "Login"

5. Complete the online registration form to establish your personal user ID and password.

6. Once your personal ID and password are confirmed, go back to **www.biology.com/campbell** to enter the site with your new ID and password.

Your activation ID and password can be used only once to establish your subscription, which is not transferable.

If you did not purchase this book new and in a shrink-wrapped package, this activation ID and password may not be valid. However, if your instructor is recommending or requiring use of *The Biology Place*, you can find more information on purchasing a subscription directly online at **www.biology.com/campbell**, or you can purchase a subscription at your local college bookstore if your professor has specifically requested it.

BIOLOGY
FIFTH EDITION

Custom Edition for the University of Colorado

Campbell • Reece • Mitchell

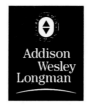

Addison
Wesley
Longman

Pearson
Custom
Publishing

Cover photo: Courtesy of Tony Stone Images

Taken from:

Biology, Fifth Edition,
by Neil A. Campbell, Lawrence G. Mitchell, and Jane B. Reece
Copyright © 1987, 1990, 1993, 1996, 1999 by Benjamin/Cummings
An imprint of Addison Wesley Longman
A Pearson Education Company
Menlo Park, California 94025

This special edition published in cooperation with Pearson Custom Publishing

Printed in the United States of America

10 9 8 7 6 5 4 3 2 1

Please visit our web site at www.pearsoncustom.com

ISBN 0–536–62342–2

BA 992786

PEARSON CUSTOM PUBLISHING
75 Arlington Street, Suite 300, Boston, MA 02116
A Pearson Education Company

DETAILED CONTENTS

UNIT ONE

UNIT TWO

ABOUT THE AUTHORS

Neil A. Campbell combines the investigative nature of a research scientist with the heart of an experienced and caring teacher. He earned his M.A. in zoology from UCLA and his Ph.D. in plant biology from the University of California, Riverside. Dr. Campbell has published numerous research articles on how certain desert and coastal plants thrive in salty soil and how the sensitive plant (*Mimosa*) and other legumes move their leaves. His 30 years of teaching in diverse environments include general biology courses at Cornell University, Pomona College, and San Bernardino Valley College, where he received the college's first Outstanding Professor Award in 1986. Dr. Campbell is currently a visiting scholar in the Department of Botany and Plant Sciences at the University of California, Riverside. In addition to his authorship of this book, he coauthors *Biology: Concepts and Connections* with Drs. Mitchell and Reece.

Jane B. Reece has worked in biology publishing since 1978, when she joined the editorial staff of Benjamin/Cummings. Her education includes an A.B. from Harvard University, an M.S. from Rutgers University, and a Ph.D. in bacteriology from the University of California, Berkeley. At UC Berkeley and later as a postdoctoral fellow in genetics at Stanford University, her research focused on genetic recombination in bacteria. She has taught biology at Middlesex County College (New Jersey) and Queensborough Community College (New York). During her years at Benjamin/Cummings, Dr. Reece played major roles in a number of successful textbooks, including *Microbiology: An Introduction*, by G.J. Tortora, B.R. Funke, and C.L. Case; *Molecular Biology of the Gene*, Fourth Edition, by J.D. Watson et al.; and earlier editions of this book. She is a coauthor of *The World of the Cell*, Third Edition, with W.M. Becker and M.F. Poenie, and of *Biology: Concepts and Connections*.

Lawrence G. Mitchell has 21 years of experience teaching a broad range of life science courses at both undergraduate and graduate levels. He holds a B.S. in zoology from Pennsylvania State University and a Ph.D. in zoology and microbiology from the University of Montana. Following postdoctoral research with the National Institute of Allergy and Infectious Diseases, Dr. Mitchell joined the biology faculty at Iowa State University in 1971. He received the Outstanding Teacher Award at Iowa State in 1982. In addition to numerous research publications in aquatic parasitology, Dr. Mitchell has coauthored the textbooks *Zoology* and *Biology: Concepts and Connections*. He has also developed television courses in general biology and has written, produced, and narrated programs on wildlife biology for public television. Dr. Mitchell is currently an affiliate professor in the Division of Biological Sciences at the University of Montana. Since 1989, he has devoted most of his time to writing and environmental activism.

PREFACE

by Neil A. Campbell

Students of biology are in the right place at the right time. Biology has emerged as the central science, a junction of all the natural sciences and the busiest intersection between the natural sciences and the humanities and social sciences. Biology is daily news. Advances in biotechnology, health science, agriculture, and environmental monitoring are just a few examples of how biology weaves into the fabric of society as never before. Biology is as inspirational as it is important. We are moving ever closer to understanding how a single cell develops into a plant or animal, how the human mind works, how myriad interactions among organisms structure biological communities, and how the enormous diversity of life on Earth evolved from the first microbes. For biology students and their instructors, these are the best of times.

These are also the most challenging times to learn and teach biology. The same information explosion that makes modern biology so exhilarating also threatens to suffocate students under an avalanche of facts and terminology. Most students in an introductory course do not yet own a framework of biological concepts into which they can fit the many new things they learn. More than ever, a biology textbook must help students synthesize a coherent view of life that will serve them throughout their introductory course and during their continuing education. *BIOLOGY* has always reflected my belief that education is all about making connections.

This fifth edition of *BIOLOGY* builds upon the earlier versions' dual goals: to help students construct a conceptual appreciation of life within the context of integrating themes and to inspire students to develop more positive and realistic impressions of science as a human activity. Those teaching values evolved in the classroom, and it is gratifying that the book's conceptual approach and emphasis on science as a process have had such widespread appeal for biology courses all over the world. It is a privilege to help instructors share biology with so many students, but the book's success also brings a responsibility to serve the biology community even better. Thus, in 1996, as I began planning this new edition, I visited dozens of campuses to listen to what students and their professors had to say about their biology courses and textbooks. Those conversations with faculty and students helped shape this fifth edition of *BIOLOGY*, by far the most ambitious revision in the history of the book.

My New Coauthors

In planning this new edition, I was humbled by the task ahead and had to admit that it was finally time to seek the help of coauthors. Biology is a much bigger subject than it was when the first edition of the text was published in 1987, but in adapting to the growth of biology, I did not want the book to become bigger or encyclopedic. Adding content is not very hard, but deciding what to leave out is much tougher. Authoritative renewal across the whole book would require expert reevaluation of the current state of each field of biology and judicious decisions about which ideas are most important to develop in depth in an introductory textbook. Given the breathtaking progress of biology on its many fronts, I was concerned that if I continued as sole author, the text could no longer deliver the educational integrity and scientific accuracy that the biology community expects from the book.

Once I decided to recruit help, it was easy to choose coauthors: Jane Reece and Larry Mitchell. They are my longtime collaborators on our nonmajors textbook, *Biology: Concepts and Connections*, and they have contributed in various ways to earlier editions of *BIOLOGY*. Dr. Reece's knowledge of genetics and molecular biology and Dr. Mitchell's expertise in zoology and ecology complement my own research background in cell biology and botany. More importantly, Jane and Larry share my commitment to "getting it right" and to having a positive impact on biology education.

My new coauthors brought fresh ideas and reenergized me and the whole *BIOLOGY* team. Among Jane's many contributions are two new chapters: Cell Communication (Chapter 11) and The Genetic Basis of Development (Chapter 21). Larry's extensive work on this edition includes the book's new capstone chapter, Conservation Biology (Chapter 55).

Even with the help of my coauthors, I worked as hard as ever on this edition of *BIOLOGY*. In addition to writing chapters, I edited the entire book to ensure consistent voice and level. Because of my confidence in Jane and Larry as partners in the book, I also finally had more time to help plan the supplements, especially the new CD-ROM and web site. All that is new in this fifth edition of *BIOLOGY* and its supplements is firmly stamped with the hallmarks that have distinguished earlier editions.

BIOLOGY's Hallmark Features

Unifying Themes and Key Concepts. A thematic approach continues to distinguish *BIOLOGY* from an encyclopedia of life science. Chapter 1 introduces 11 themes that resurface throughout the text to help students make connections in their study of life. The core theme, the theme of all themes, is evolution, the thread that ties all of biology together.

On the scale of individual chapters, an emphasis on key concepts keeps students focused on each topic's most important ideas. For example, Chapter 9, Cellular Respiration, teaches about 10 key concepts, including "Feedback mechanisms control cellular respiration." Each chapter's key concepts appear in three places: in an overview of key concepts on the first page of the chapter; within the body of the chapter as the headings of the main subsections under broader topic headings; and in the review of key concepts at the end of the chapter. In placing such emphasis on a manageable number of big ideas in each chapter, we do not equate "conceptual" with "superficial." Oversimplifying a complex topic is a disservice to students, for without the support of sufficient detail, key concepts collapse into meaningless factual statements and lose their value as organizing principles. We avoid trying to cover everything, but if a concept is essential to include, we believe it should be developed in enough depth to leave a lasting impression on students.

BIOLOGY's key concepts and unifying themes work together to help students develop a coherent view of life. Notice, for example, that "Feedback mechanisms control cellular respiration" is a concept specific to the topic of a particular chapter. However, one of the book's overarching themes, the theme of regulation, helps students fit the concept of controlling respiration into a broader context that applies to many other biological processes. The key concepts give form to each chapter; the integrating themes connect the concepts and give form to the whole book.

Science as a Process. As one of the book's unifying themes, the nature of science is introduced at some length in Chapter 1, but *BIOLOGY*'s commitment to featuring science as a human activity does not end there. Case studies announced by the subtitle "Science as a Process" enrich many chapters throughout the book by balancing "what we know" with "how we know" and "what we do not yet know." *BIOLOGY* also features many Methods Boxes, which demystify science by walking students through laboratory and field methods in the context of experiments. For example, a new Methods Box in Chapter 21, "Using Mutation to Study the Genetic Basis of *Drosophila* Development," explains the rationale behind experiments that have revolutionized developmental biology. Another example is a new Methods Box in Chapter 55 that illustrates the use of computerized mapping techniques in

conservation biology. Eight new interviews with influential scientists, which introduce the eight units of the book, help personalize science and portray it as a social activity of creative men and women. Many of the Challenge Questions at the ends of chapters also engage students in the process of science.

Another one of *BIOLOGY*'s themes, the relationship of science and technology to society, helps students connect biology to their other college courses and to their daily lives. It is important for students to realize that ethics has a place in science, even in basic research, and that the benefits of technology also bring the need to examine values and make choices. At the end of each chapter, Science, Technology, and Society questions encourage students to fit the biological concepts they have learned into their broader view of the world.

A Marriage of Text and Illustrations. Biology is a visual science, and many of our students are visual learners. We take as much care in creating new ways to illustrate the story of life as we do in writing the narrative. I have always authored the illustration program for *BIOLOGY* side by side with the text, and Drs. Reece and Mitchell take the same approach. Beginning with the first draft of this edition, we collaborated with the designer, artists, photo researchers, and developmental editors to embed the illustrations and their legends into the flow of each chapter. Compared to the more common publishing model of deferring work on the illustration program until the text manuscript is completed, our approach creates logistical challenges. There is a benefit, however: a union of words and pictures that makes each chapter an integrated lesson.

With this commitment to integrating text and graphics, earlier editions of *BIOLOGY* pioneered many innovations in how science textbooks are illustrated. For example, many chapters in *BIOLOGY* use a sequence of orientation diagrams as road signs to help students keep track of where they are in biological processes such as photosynthesis (Chapter 10) and gene expression (Chapter 17). In figures that walk students through stepwise processes, circled numbers in the illustration are keyed to circled numbers in the figure legend or text. We think this approach works better than cluttering the illustration itself with too much text. Throughout the book, color coding and icons help students connect concepts from chapter to chapter. For example, proteins are generally purple, and ATP always appears as a yellow sunburst. These and other features of *BIOLOGY*'s illustration tradition have had a noticeable impact on many other excellent textbooks, but we have continued to refine our model to raise the standard even higher. In addition to the many new diagrams that support the narrative in this fifth edition, we have found subtle ways to improve the teaching effectiveness of a great number of the other figures in the book.

An "Overview-Closer Look" Teaching Style. *BIOLOGY* begins the development of many complex topics, such as cellular respiration (Chapter 9) and gene expression (Chapter 17), with a panoramic view—an overview—of what the whole process accomplishes. Text and figures then invite the student inside the process for a closer look at how it works. The orientation diagrams, miniature versions of the overview illustration, with appropriate parts highlighted as "you are here" aids, keep the overall process in sight even as its steps unfold. This teaching approach complements *BIOLOGY*'s other hallmarks in helping students navigate through their biology course.

BIOLOGY's Versatile Organization

BIOLOGY makes no pretense that there is one "correct" sequence of topics for a general biology course. No two syllabi match, and the individual approaches of biology instructors are one of the strengths of biology education. Therefore, we have built *BIOLOGY* to be versatile enough to serve diverse courses, whether the instructor chooses to start with molecules or ecosystems or somewhere in between. The eight units of the book are largely self-contained, and most of the chapters can be assigned in a different sequence without substantial loss of continuity. For example, instructors who integrate plant and animal physiology into a systems approach can merge chapters from Units Six and Seven to fit their courses. As another example, instructors who begin their course with ecology and continue with a "top-down" approach can assign Unit Eight right after Chapter 1. It is the themes introduced in Chapter 1 that make the book so versatile in organization by providing students with a biological context no matter what the topic order of the syllabus.

An Overview of *BIOLOGY* and a Few Examples of What's New in the Fifth Edition

Unit One: The Chemistry of Life. Many students struggle in general biology courses because they are uncomfortable with basic chemistry. Chapters 2–4 help such students by developing just the chemical concepts that are essential to success in a beginning biology course. This edition features improved explanations of atomic and molecular electron orbitals and their influence on molecular shape and function. We designed the chapters of Unit One so that students of diverse educational backgrounds can use them for self-study, reducing the amount of valuable class time instructors need for reviewing chemistry before they move on to biology. However, Chapter 5 (The Structure and Function of Macromolecules) and Chapter 6 (An Introduction to Metabolism) provide important orientation even for students with solid chemistry backgrounds.

Unit Two: The Cell. Chapters 7–12 build the study of cells upon the theme of correlation between structure and function. For example, the role of membranes in ordering cell functions is emphasized throughout the unit. In the fifth edition, this unit includes a completely new chapter, called Cell Communication (Chapter 11). This chapter synthesizes our current understanding of the functions and mechanisms of cell communication and signal transduction, giving students a conceptual foundation that applies to many processes at the cellular and organismal levels.

Unit Three: Genetics. Chapters 13–21 trace the history of genetics, from Mendel to DNA technology, with the process of science as a major theme. In this edition, the chapters on molecular genetics (Chapters 16–20) have undergone a major revision, entailing both updating and organizational improvements. For instance, the explanations of transcription and translation in Chapter 17 (From Gene to Protein) have been reorganized into two distinct sections that should help students keep these two important stages of gene expression clear in their minds. The material in Chapter 19, The Organization and Control of Eukaryotic Genomes, has been extensively revised and expanded; it includes updated coverage of chromatin structure, repetitive DNA, transcriptional regulation, and cancer. Chapter 20, DNA Technology, features updated discussion of the Human Genome Project and introduces students to some exciting new techniques for studying gene function. As in previous editions, *BIOLOGY*'s extensive coverage of human genetics is integrated throughout the unit. Concluding the unit is a new chapter on one of the most important areas in biology, The Genetic Basis of Development (Chapter 21). This chapter builds on molecular, cellular, and genetic principles to introduce concepts of development that apply to both animals and plants. *Drosophila*, the nematode *C. elegans*, and the plant *Arabidopsis* provide the main case studies here. (More extensive coverage of vertebrate development and plant development appears in later units.)

Unit Four: Mechanisms of Evolution. As the core theme of *BIOLOGY*, evolution figures prominently in all parts of the book, but Chapters 22–25 focus specifically on how life evolves and how biologists study evolution and test evolutionary hypotheses. Chapter 22, Descent with Modification: A Darwinian View of Life, sets the stage for the unit by grounding evolutionary biology in the process of science. Students will then find many examples throughout the unit of research and debate about mechanisms of evolution. For instance, a new section in Chapter 24 summarizes the ongoing debate about how to define a species. An expanded discussion of systematics in Chapter 25 emphasizes current efforts to meld classification and evolutionary history. New and updated sections highlight molecular and cladistic methods and their use in formulating phylogenetic hypotheses.

Unit Five: The Evolutionary History of Biological Diversity. Chapters 26–34 view the diversity of life in the context of key evolutionary junctures, such as the origin of prokaryotes; the evolution of the eukaryotic cell; the genesis of multicellular life; the colonization of land; and the adaptive radiation of plants, fungi, and animals. This evolutionary theme contrasts with a "parade of phyla" approach. The scientific view of biological history and diversity is being transformed by discoveries of new fossils, increased application of molecular biology in systematics, and a growing consensus for cladistic classification. These trends demanded extensive revision of this unit. Chapter 26 sets the stage by comparing several classification schemes, including the traditional five-kingdom system, an eight-kingdom system, and a superkingdom, three-domain system. Chapters 27 and 28 reflect the view that the enormous diversity among prokaryotes and protists deserves recognition at the highest levels of classification. Unit Five centers on current thinking and ongoing debates about kingdoms and superkingdoms while retaining its applicability to courses with labs based on the five-kingdom system. Extensive emphasis on biodiversity is making a comeback in many courses, and we expanded our coverage of the evolution and diversity of plants (now two chapters instead of one) and animals (now three chapters instead of two.)

Unit Six: Plant Form and Function. Chapters 35–39 showcase plants in the evolutionary context of adaptation to terrestrial environments. Much of the new material emphasizes how plant cell biologists and molecular biologists are reshaping our understanding of plant morphology, physiology, and development. Just one example is the progress in our understanding of disease resistance in plants, now a major section in Chapter 39 (Control Systems in Plants). Throughout the unit in this edition, there is also more emphasis on symbiotic relationships between plants and bacteria and fungi.

Unit Seven: Animal Form and Function. The interaction between organisms and their environment is the focus of Chapters 40–49, which take a comparative approach to exploring adaptations that have evolved in diverse animal groups. The themes of regulation and bioenergetics are accented throughout, and many figures have been reconstructed to bring out these themes. Some highlights include new information on fat metabolism in Chapter 41, current findings about coreceptors and protease inhibitors relevant to HIV in Chapter 43, more about the role of cell adhesion in animal development in Chapter 47, an updated account of human brain development in Chapter 48, and an expanded section on locomotion in Chapter 49.

Unit Eight: Ecology. Chapters 50–55 emphasize the connections between ecology and evolution. The unit also reflects the urgent need for basic ecological research in an era when the growing human population and its technology are threatening the biosphere. Highlighting this issue, and serving as a capstone for the unit and the entire book, is a new chapter on conservation biology (Chapter 55). Firmly grounded in modern ecological science, this chapter examines the significance of biodiversity and discusses conservation strategies at the species, population, community, ecosystem, and landscape levels.

Learning Aids at the Ends of Chapters

At the end of each chapter is a **Review of Key Concepts**, which restates each concept with a short explanation. With each concept are page numbers and figure numbers telling students where to return if they are having trouble understanding that concept. A **Self-Quiz** helps students assess their comprehension of key concepts, and many of these questions also require students to apply concepts or solve problems. **Challenge Questions** give students opportunities to verbalize their interpretations of key concepts, to extrapolate from what they have learned to new situations, to think and write critically about controversies, to apply quantitative skill to biological problems, and to generate testable hypotheses of their own. The **Science, Technology, and Society** questions encourage students to think about biology's place in our culture and to confront the potential consequences of applied biology. A short, annotated **Further Reading** list directs students to articles and books that explore some of the chapter's topics in more depth. New to this edition is a list of **Web Links**, Internet resources selected and annotated by Dr. Iain Miller of the University of Cincinnati.

A Complete Teaching and Learning Package

This full range of supplements is highlighted by breakthrough media tools that have been developed specifically for use with *BIOLOGY*, Fifth Edition. They have been crafted with the same careful attention to scientific accuracy and teaching effectiveness found in the text. In each case, the value to instructor and student is based on integration with the text.

New! **Interactive Study Partner CD-ROM** by Richard Liebaert of Linn-Benton Community College. Packaged with the textbook at no additional charge, the Study Partner includes 120 interactive exercises, animations, and lab simulations. Icons 🔵 appear throughout the textbook to guide students to the applicable activity on the CD-ROM. Also featured are a glossary and 20 quiz questions per chapter, with feedback for all answers and page references to the relevant explanations in the textbook. The CD-ROM is also the student's gateway to the special edition of *The Biology Place*, the web site that now complements this textbook.

New! **The Special Edition of** *The Biology Place* **for** *BIOLOGY,* **Fifth Edition.** For the past three years, I have been working with several other educators and Peregrine Publishers to develop *The Biology Place,* a web-based learning environment for general biology students. A subscription to the customized version of *The Biology Place,* specifically keyed to the fifth edition of *BIOLOGY,* is now available to all students (see www.biology.com/campbell for more details). *The Biology Place* includes BioCoach (interactive tutorials with self-assessment), investigative learning activities, LabBench (lab simulations), TestFlight (customizable practice exams), Biology News (summaries of newsworthy research breakthroughs), chapter-specific web links, and access to a web version of the Interactive Study Partner. An instructor's entrance to the special edition of *The Biology Place* provides access to fifth edition art, resources, and a new on-line Course Management System.

New! **Course Management On-Line.** The Addison Wesley Longman Course Management System allows the instructor to offer on-line quizzing and to create a course-specific web site for posting a syllabus and/or lecture schedule. The instructor can also use the system to conduct discussion groups and administer the course.

New! **Instructor's Presentation CD-ROM.** Over 100 animations and QuickTime movies and the complete art program from *BIOLOGY* are included. A presentation program enables instructors to design a slide show of images, import illustrations and photos from other sources, transfer figures into other software programs, and edit the figures for content.

New! **More Transparency Acetates.** For the first time, all of the drawings in the text are available, more than 600 figures in full color.

New! **Instructor's Guide to Media** by Iain Miller, University of Cincinnati. This useful guide to media supplements provides guidance on how best to utilize the electronic tools available with the text and how to integrate them into your course. It contains information on web sites, course management software, presentation software, the special edition of *The Biology Place,* and the Interactive Study Partner.

Instructor's Guide by Mark Sheridan, North Dakota State University. Tailored to match the content in *BIOLOGY,* Fifth Edition, the guide offers teaching assistance that is especially helpful for first-time instructors.

Student Study Guide by Martha Taylor, Cornell University. This printed learning aid provides a concept map of each chapter, chapter summaries, a variety of interactive questions, and chapter tests.

Investigating Biology, **Third Edition,** by Judith Giles Morgan, Emory University, and M. Eloise Brown Carter, Oxford College of Emory University. This investigative laboratory manual asks students to pose their own hypotheses, design their own experiments, and then analyze their data. Also available: *Investigating Biology,* **Third Edition, Annotated Instructor's Edition** and **Preparation Guide.**

35-mm Slides. This package contains approximately 300 slides keyed to the text.

Printed Test Bank and **Computerized Testing Software for Macintosh and Windows,** edited by Dan Wivagg, Baylor University. Featuring more questions than ever, a new program allows the professor to view and edit electronic questions, transfer them to tests, and print them in a variety of formats.

■　　　■　　　■

The real test of any textbook is how well it helps instructors teach and students learn. We welcome comments from the students and professors who use *BIOLOGY.* Please address your suggestions for improving the next edition directly to me:

Neil Campbell
Department of Botany and Plant Sciences
University of California
Riverside, California 92521

ACKNOWLEDGMENTS

Every edition of *BIOLOGY* has been an immense journey for many people, and the authors of this fifth edition wish to extend heartfelt thanks to the numerous instructors, researchers, students, editors, and artists who have contributed to this and previous editions. It is a privilege to be part of a global community dedicated to excellence in science education.

Special thanks go to several biologists who contributed in major ways to the revision of fourth edition chapters or helped with the creation of new chapters for the fifth edition. Chapter 21, The Genetic Basis of Development, greatly benefited from the advice of Ann Reynolds (University of Washington), Jeff Hardin (University of Wisconsin), and Nancy Hopkins (MIT) and from early drafts of new material that Ann and Jeff created. Jeff Hardin also helped reshape and refine Chapter 47, Animal Development, and was the main contributor of updated material for that chapter. Mary Jane Niles (University of San Francisco) did a superlative reorganization and updating of Chapter 43, The Body's Defenses. Steven Lebsack (Linn-Benton Community College) provided a number of new review questions for the ends of chapters. We thank these contributors for helping us make our fifth edition more accurate, up to date, coherent, and pedagogically effective. It was a pleasure to work with them.

Further helping us improve *BIOLOGY*'s scientific accuracy and pedagogy, 50 scholars and teachers, cited on page x, provided detailed reviews of one or more chapters for this edition. Numerous other professors and their students offered suggestions by writing directly to Neil Campbell. Those correspondents include: Anne Ashford (University of New South Wales), Peter Atsatt (University of California, Irvine), Anton Baudoin (Virginia Polytechnic Institute), Bruce Chorba (Mercer County Community College), Raymond Damian (University of Georgia), Marshall Darley (University of Georgia), Marianne Dauwalder (University of Texas), Earl Fleck (Whitman College), Joseph Frankel (University of Iowa), Warren Gallin (University of Alberta), Larry Giesman (Northern Kentucky University), Bruce Grant (Widener University), Albert Hendricks (Virginia Polytechnic Institute), Becky Houck (University of Portland), Roger Lloyd (Florida Community College of Jacksonville), Ernst Mayr (Harvard University), Matthias Ochs (Georg-August-Universitat Gottingen), Barry Palevitz (University of Georgia), Tom Rambo (Northern Kentucky University), Thomas Reimchen (University of Victoria, Canada), Cyril Thong (Simon Fraser University), Gordon Ultsch (University of Alabama), Itzick Vatnick (Widener University), and Cherie Wetzel (City College of San Francisco).

Of course, the authors alone bear the responsibility for any errors that remain in the text, but the dedication of our contributors, reviewers, and correspondents makes us especially confident in the accuracy of this edition.

Many colleagues have also helped shape this fifth edition by discussing their research fields and ideas about biology education. Neil Campbell thanks numerous UC Riverside colleagues, including Katharine Atkinson, Elizabeth Bray, Richard Cardullo, Mark Chappell, Timothy Close, Darleen DeMason, Norman Ellstrand, Robert Heath, Anthony Huang, Tracy Kahn, Elizabeth Lord, Carol Lovatt, Robert Neuman, Eugene Nothnagel, John Oross, Kathryn Platt, Mary Price, David Reznick, Rodolfo Ruibal, Clay Sassaman, Irwin Sherman, Vaughan Shoemaker, William Thomson, Linda Walling, Nickolas Waser, and John Moore (whose "Science as a Way of Knowing" essays have had such an important influence on the evolution of *BIOLOGY*). Neil also is grateful to Pius Horner, who taught him by example during their many years of team-teaching at San Bernardino Valley College. Among the scientists elsewhere who shared their expertise and ideas with us are Wayne Becker (University of Wisconsin), Deric Bownds (University of Wisconsin), Nicholas Davies (Cambridge University), Daniel Gagnon (Université du Quebec), David Glenn-Lewin (Wichita State University), Peter Grant (Princeton University), Ira Herskowitz (UC San Francisco), Nancy Hopkins (MIT), Richard Hutto (University of Montana), Robert Lambrecht (U.S. Forest Service), Christopher Murphy (James Madison University), Andrée Nault (Biodôme de Montréal), David Patterson (University of Sydney), Mitchell Sogin (Marine Biological Laboratory), and Kirwin Werner (Salish Kootenai College).

Interviews with prominent scientists have been a hallmark of *BIOLOGY* since its inception, and conducting these interviews was one of the great pleasures of revising the text. To open the eight units of this fifth edition and help put human faces on our science, we are proud to include interviews with Mario Molina, Bruce Alberts, Mary-Claire King, Richard Dawkins, Elisabeth Vrba, Gloria Coruzzi, Terence Dawson, and Michael Dombeck.

BIOLOGY, Fifth Edition, results from an unusually strong synergism between a team of scientists and a team of publishing professionals. A fresh design, ambitious revision of the art and photo program, and the nesting of key concepts into a pedagogical hierarchy are three examples of goals for this edition that created challenges for the publishing team. Heading Addison Wesley Longman's Biology Group, publisher Jim Green brought his high publishing standards and flair for team-building to our endeavor; we are grateful for his leadership. Linda Davis, general manager of Benjamin/Cummings Publishing, has shared the book team's commitment to excellence and provided strong support over the long haul. Our former editor Lisa Moller worked closely with the authors and book team in the planning and early draft stages. The authors are extremely grateful to Laura Kenney, production managing editor, who has been a key member of the book team since those early stages. Senior production editor Angela Mann brought her professional expertise and can-do attitude to the book's production; moreover, she brought calm and good cheer to the often-turbulent later stages of the production process. Two senior developmental editors, the incomparable Pat Burner and Shelley Parlante, worked closely with the authors through all phases of manuscript and art preparation; we are deeply grateful for their countless contributions to the book and for their professionalism, obsessive dedication, and exceptional patience. Our copyeditor and fellow biologist Alan Titche brought a rare mix of content knowledge and editing skills to late stages of the manuscript.

Art and design are key elements of *BIOLOGY*'s teaching effectiveness. Don Kesner, art and design manager of the AWL Biology Group, and book designer Mark Ong worked closely and patiently with us until we had the right design to make each chapter a better teaching tool. Senior art supervisor Donna Kalal shepherded all of our art through production. We are grateful to the artists who worked on the new and revised figures for this edition, including Mary Ann Tenorio, Karl Miyajima, Carla Simmons, and the artists of Precision Graphics. On the four previous editions Carla was a major

shaper of the art program, which continues to serve students well. Photo researchers Kathleen Cameron and Roberta Spieckerman searched for just the right photos to reinforce key concepts. Yvo Riezebos designed a handsome cover that reflects the freshness of this new edition yet remains true to the elegant simplicity that distinguished the covers of earlier editions.

We are all indebted to our supreme leader for the project, executive editor Erin Mulligan. Erin brought her leadership ability, publishing expertise, native intelligence, and down-to-earth sense of humor to the *BIOLOGY* team in 1997. She immediately began mustering the forces that gave rise to the fifth edition's outstanding supplements package. Erin's fierce dedication to this project and to excellence in educational publishing has touched us all.

Working closely with Erin and with authors of the supplements, associate editor Thor Ekstrom and associate producer Claire Cameron coordinated the print and electronic supplements, respectively. Key players on the supplements included senior developmental editor Pat Burner, senior production editor Larry Olsen, project editor Kathy Yankton, and publishing assistant Maureen Kennedy. Important contributions to the electronic components of the package were made by Russell Chun (with his threefold expertise in art, computer animation, and biology), designer Peilin Nee, several freelancers, and our incomparable media lab manager, Guy Mills. We also thank Laura Maier, executive editor at Peregrine Publishers, and Claire Cameron for their collaborative leadership in developing the special edition of *The Biology Place* as a web site coordinated with our book. Guy Mills, Lee Stayton, Rachel Collett, Betsy Burr, and Todd Rodgers also played key roles in customizing *The Biology Place* for *BIOLOGY*, Fifth Edition. As a result of the efforts of all these people, students and professors have available a marvelous assemblage of support materials for their biology courses.

Dorothy Zinky is hands-down the most efficient and unflappable administrative assistant the authors have ever had the pleasure of depending upon. Publishing assistants Kelly Millon, Claire Cameron (before her promotion), Natalia Cortes and Maureen Kennedy provided essential support to the authors and the book team. Hilair Chism helped us by editing the transcripts of some of the interviews. Anita Wagner and Carol Lombardi were careful proofreaders for the fifth edition, and Charlotte Shane created a very useful index. Prepress manager Lillian Hom and prepress supervisor Vivian McDougal worked wonders to bring about the culmination of all our efforts—a bound book. The entire publishing group worked together to craft a book that teaches biological concepts even better than earlier editions.

Both before and after the publication of the book, we are fortunate to have the support of AWL's marketing professionals. We gratefully acknowledge the contributions of market development manager David Horwitz and members of Stacy Treco's marketing team, especially biology marketing manager Gay Meixel. We also thank Lillian Carr and Bob Leone for creating effective promotional materials.

The field staff that represents *BIOLOGY* on campus is our living link to the students and professors who use the text. The field representatives tell us what you like and don't like about the book, and they provide prompt service to biology departments. The field reps are good allies in science education, and we thank them for their professionalism in communicating the merits of our book without denigrating other publishers and their competing texts.

Finally, we wish to thank our families and friends for their encouragement and for enduring our obsession with *BIOLOGY*. In particular, we are grateful for the support of Rochelle and Allison Campbell (N.A.C.); Deborah Gale, Dan Gillen, Robin Heyden, Sharmon Hilfinger, Jeff Reece, Susan Weisberg, and Hugues d'Audiffret (J.B.R.); and Wesley, Paul, and Paula Mitchell (L.G.M.).

Neil Campbell
Jane Reece
Larry Mitchell

Reviewers of the Fifth Edition

Martin Adamson	University of British Columbia
Robert Atherton	University of Wyoming
Judy Bluemer	Morton College
Deric Bownds	University of Wisconsin, Madison
Charles H. Brenner	Berkeley, California
Mark Browning	Purdue University
Bruce Chase	University of Nebraska, Omaha
David Cone	Saint Mary's University
Marianne Dauwalder	University of Texas, Austin
Michael Dini	Texas Tech University
Andrew Dobson	Princeton University
Susan Dunford	University of Cincinnati
Carl Frankel	Pennsylvania State University, Hazleton
Simon Gilroy	Pennsylvania State University
David Glenn-Lewin	Wichita State University
Elliott Goldstein	Arizona State University
Linda Graham	University of Wisconsin, Madison
Mark Guyer	National Human Genome Research Institute
Ruth Levy Guyer	Bethesda, Maryland
Jeff Hardin	University of Wisconsin, Madison
Colin Henderson	University of Montana
Ira Herskowitz	University of California, San Francisco
R. James Hickey	Miami University
Charles Holliday	Lafayette College
Steven Hutcheson	University of Maryland, College Park
Robert Kitchin	University of Wyoming
Jacqueline McLaughlin	Pennsylvania State University, Lehigh Valley
Paul Melchior	North Hennepin Community College
Brian Metscher	University of California, Irvine
Michael Misamore	Louisiana State University
Deborah Mowshowitz	Columbia University
Gavin Naylor	Iowa State University
Raymond Neubauer	University of Texas, Austin
Caroline Niederman	Tomball College
Maria Nieto	California State University, Hayward
Patricia O'Hern	Emory University
Daniel Pavuk	Bowling Green State University
Debra Pearce	Northern Kentucky University
Martin Poenie	University of Texas, Austin
Deanna Raineri	University of Illinois, Champaign-Urbana
Gary Reiness	Lewis & Clark College
Walter Sakai	Santa Monica College
Gary Saunders	University of New Brunswick
Erik Scully	Towson State University
Edna Seaman	Northeastern University
Elaine Shea	Loyola College, Maryland
Susan Singer	Carleton College
John Smol	Queen's University
Mitchell Sogin	Woods Hole Marine Biological Laboratory
Kathryn VandenBosch	Texas A & M University

Reviewers of Previous Editions

Kenneth Able (State University of New York, Albany), John Alcock (Arizona State University), Richard Almon (State University of New York, Buffalo), Katherine Anderson (University of California, Berkeley), Richard J. Andren (Montgomery County Community College), J. David Archibald (Yale University), Leigh Auleb (San Francisco State University), P. Stephen Baenziger (University of Nebraska), Katherine Baker (Millersville University), William Barklow (Framingham State College), Steven Barnhart (Santa Rosa Junior College), Ron Basmajian (Merced College), Tom Beatty (University of British Columbia), Wayne Becker (University of Wisconsin, Madison), Jane Beiswenger (University of Wyoming), Anne Bekoff (University of Colorado, Boulder), Marc Bekoff (University of Colorado, Boulder), Tania Beliz (College of San Mateo), Adrianne Bendich (Hoffman-La Roche, Inc.), Barbara Bentley (State University of New York, Stony Brook), Darwin Berg (University of California, San Diego), Werner Bergen (Michigan State University), Gerald Bergstrom (University of Wisconsin, Milwaukee), Anna W. Berkovitz (Purdue University), Dorothy Berner (Temple University), Annalisa Berta (San Diego State University), Paulette Bierzychudek (Pomona College), Charles Biggers (Memphis State University), Robert Blystone (Trinity University), Robert Boley (University of Texas, Arlington), Eric Bonde (University of Colorado, Boulder), Richard Boohar (University of Nebraska, Omaha), Carey L. Booth (Reed College), James L. Botsford (New Mexico State University), J. Michael Bowes (Humboldt State University), Richard Bowker (Alma College), Barry Bowman (University of California, Santa Cruz), Jerry Brand (University of Texas, Austin), Theodore A. Bremner (Howard University), James Brenneman (University of Evansville), Donald P. Briskin (University of Illinois, Urbana), Danny Brower (University of Arizona), Carole Browne (Wake Forest University), Herbert Bruneau (Oklahoma State University), Gary Brusca (Humboldt State University), Alan H. Brush (University of Connecticut, Storrs), Meg Burke (University of North Dakota), Edwin Burling (De Anza College), William Busa (Johns Hopkins University), John Bushnell (University of Colorado), Linda Butler (University of Texas, Austin), Iain Campbell (University of Pittsburgh), Deborah Canington (University of California, Davis), Gregory Capelli (College of William and Mary), Richard Cardullo (University of California, Riverside), Nina Caris (Texas A & M University), Doug Cheeseman (De Anza College), Shepley Chen (University of Illinois, Chicago), Henry Claman (University of Colorado Health Science Center), Lynwood Clemens (Michigan State University), William P. Coffman (University of Pittsburgh), J. John Cohen (University of Colorado Health Science Center), John Corliss (University of Maryland), Stuart J. Coward (University of Georgia), Charles Creutz (University of Toledo), Bruce Criley (Illinois Wesleyan University), Norma Criley (Illinois Wesleyan University), Richard Cyr (Pennsylvania State University), Marianne Dauwalder (University of Texas, Austin), Bonnie J. Davis (San Francisco State University), Jerry Davis (University of Wisconsin, La Crosse), Thomas Davis (University of New Hampshire), John Dearn (University of Canberra), James Dekloe (University of California, Santa Cruz), T. Delevoryas (University of Texas, Austin), Diane C. DeNagel (Northwestern University), Jean DeSaix (University of North Carolina), John Drees (Temple University School of Medicine), Charles Drewes (Iowa State University), Marvin Druger (Syracuse University), Betsey Dyer (Wheaton College), Robert Eaton (University of Colorado), Robert S. Edgar (University of California, Santa Cruz), Betty J. Eidemiller (Lamar University), David Evans (University of Florida), Robert C. Evans (Rutgers University, Camden), Sharon Eversman (Montana State University), Lincoln Fairchild (Ohio State University), Bruce Fall (University of Minnesota), Lynn Fancher (College of DuPage), Larry Farrell (Idaho State University), Jerry F. Feldman (University of California, Santa Cruz), Russell Fernald (University of Oregon), Milton Fingerman (Tulane University), Barbara Finney (Regis College), David Fisher (University of Hawaii, Manoa), William Fixsen (Harvard University), Abraham Flexer (Manuscript Consultant, Boulder, Colorado), Kerry Foresman (University of Montana), Norma Fowler (University of Texas, Austin), David Fox (University of Tennessee, Knoxville), Otto Friesen (University of Virginia), Virginia Fry (Monterey Peninsula College), Alice Fulton (University of Iowa), Sara Fultz (Stanford University), Berdell Funke (North Dakota State University), Anne Funkhouser (University of the Pacific), Arthur W. Galston (Yale University), Carl Gans (University of Michigan), John Gapter (University of Northern Colorado), Reginald Garrett (University of Virginia), Patricia Gensel (University of North Carolina), Chris George (California Polytechnic State University, San Luis Obispo), Robert George (University of Wyoming), Frank Gilliam (Marshall University), Todd Gleeson (University of Colorado), William Glider (University of Nebraska), Elizabeth A. Godrick (Boston University), Lynda Goff (University of California, Santa Cruz), Paul Goldstein (University of Texas, El Paso), Anne Good (University of California, Berkeley), Judith Goodenough (University of Massachusetts, Amherst), Ester Goudsmit (Oakland University), Robert Grammer (Belmont University), Joseph Graves (Arizona State University), A. J. F. Griffiths (University of British Columbia), William Grimes (University of Arizona), Mark Gromko (Bowling Green State University), Serine Gropper (Auburn University), Katherine L. Gross (Ohio State University), Gary Gussin (University of Iowa), R. Wayne Habermehl (Montgomery County Community College), Mac Hadley (University of Arizona), Jack P. Hailman (University of Wisconsin), Leah Haimo (University of California, Riverside), Rebecca Halyard (Clayton State College), Penny Hanchey-Bauer (Colorado State University), Laszlo Hanzely (Northern Illinois University), Richard Harrison (Cornell University), H. D. Heath (California State University, Hayward), George Hechtel (State University of New York, Stony Brook), Jean Heitz-Johnson (University of Wisconsin, Madison), Caroll Henry (Chicago State University), Frank Heppner (University of Rhode Island), Paul E. Hertz (Barnard College), Ralph Hinegardner (University of California, Santa Cruz), William Hines (Foothill College), Helmut Hirsch (State University of New York, Albany), Tuan-hua David Ho (Washington University), Carl Hoagstrom (Ohio Northern University), James Hoffman (University of Vermont), James Holland (Indiana State University, Bloomington), Laura Hoopes (Occidental College), Nancy Hopkins (Massachusetts Institute of Technology), Kathy Hornberger (Widener University), Pius F. Horner (San Bernardino Valley College), Margaret Houk (Ripon College), Ronald R. Hoy (Cornell University), Donald Humphrey (Emory University School of Medicine), Robert J. Huskey (University of Virginia), Bradley Hyman (University of California, Riverside), Alice Jacklet (State University of New York, Albany), John Jackson (North Hennepin Community College), Dan Johnson (East Tennessee State University), Wayne Johnson (Ohio State University), Kenneth C. Jones (California State University, Northridge), Russell Jones (University of California, Berkeley), Alan Journet (Southeast Missouri State University), Thomas Kane (University of Cincinnati), E. L. Karlstrom (University of Puget Sound), George Khoury (National Cancer Institute), Robert Kitchin (University of Wyoming), Attila O. Klein (Brandeis University), Greg Kopf (University of Pennsylvania School of Medicine), Thomas Koppenheffer (Trinity University), Janis Kuby (San Francisco State University), J. A. Lackey (State University of New York, Oswego), Lynn Lamoreux (Texas A & M University), Carmine A. Lanciani (University of Florida), Kenneth Lang (Humboldt State University), Allan Larson (Washington University), Diane K. Lavett (State University of New York, Cortland, and Emory University), Charles Leavell (Fullerton College), C. S. Lee (University of Texas), Robert Leonard (University of California, Riverside), Joseph Levine (Boston College), Bill Lewis (Shoreline Community College), John Lewis (Loma Linda University), Lorraine Lica (California State University, Hayward), Harvey Lillywhite (University of Florida, Gainesville), Sam Loker (University of New Mexico), Jane Lubchenco (Oregon State University), James MacMahon (Utah State University), Charles Mallery (University of Miami), Lynn Margulis (Boston University), Edith Marsh (Angelo State University), Karl Mattox (Miami University of

Ohio), Joyce Maxwell (California State University, Northridge), Richard McCracken (Purdue University), John Merrill (University of Washington), Ralph Meyer (University of Cincinnati), Roger Milkman (University of Iowa), Helen Miller (Oklahoma State University), John Miller (University of California, Berkeley), Kenneth R. Miller (Brown University), John E. Minnich (University of Wisconsin, Milwaukee), Kenneth Mitchell (Tulane University School of Medicine), Russell Monson (University of Colorado, Boulder), Frank Moore (Oregon State University), Randy Moore (Wright State University), William Moore (Wayne State University), Carl Moos (Veterans Administration Hospital, Albany, New York), Michael Mote (Temple University), John Mutchmor (Iowa State University), Elliot Myerowitz (California Institute of Technology), John Neess (University of Wisconsin, Madison), Todd Newbury (University of California, Santa Cruz), Harvey Nichols (University of Colorado, Boulder), Deborah Nickerson (University of South Florida), Bette Nicotri (University of Washington), Charles R. Noback (College of Physicians and Surgeons, Columbia University), Mary C. Nolan (Irvine Valley College), David O. Norris (University of Colorado, Boulder), Cynthia Norton (University of Maine, Augusta), Bette H. Nybakken (Hartnell College), Brian O'Conner (University of Massachusetts, Amherst), Gerard O'Donovan (University of North Texas), Eugene Odum (University of Georgia), John Olsen (Rhodes College), Sharman O'Neill (University of California, Davis), Wan Ooi (Houston Community College), Gay Ostarello (Diablo Valley College), Barry Palevitz (University of Georgia), Peter Pappas (County College of Morris), Bulah Parker (North Carolina State University), Stanton Parmeter (Chemeketa Community College), Robert Patterson (San Francisco State University), Crellin Pauling (San Francisco State University), Kay Pauling (Foothill Community College), Patricia Pearson (Western Kentucky University), Bob Pittman (Michigan State University), James Platt (University of Denver), Scott Poethig (University of Pennsylvania), Jeffrey Pommerville (Texas A & M University), Warren Porter (University of Wisconsin), Donald Potts (University of California, Santa Cruz), David Pratt (University of California, Davis), Halina Presley (University of Illinois, Chicago), Rebecca Pyles (East Tennessee State University), Scott Quackenbush (Florida International University), Ralph Quatrano (Oregon State University), Charles Ralph (Colorado State University), Brian Reeder (Morehead State University), C. Gary Reiness (Pomona College), Charles Remington (Yale University), David Reznick (University of California, Riverside), Fred Rhoades (Western Washington State University), Christopher Riegle (Irvine Valley College), Donna Ritch (Pennsylvania State University), Thomas Rodella (Merced College), Rodney Rogers (Drake University), Wayne Rosing (Middle Tennessee State University), Thomas Rost (University of California, Davis), Stephen I. Rothstein (University of California, Santa Barbara), John Ruben (Oregon State University), Albert Ruesink (Indiana University), Don Sakaguchi (Iowa State University), Mark F. Sanders (University of California, Davis), Ted Sargent (University of Massachusetts, Amherst), Carl Schaefer (University of Connecticut), Lisa Shimeld (Crafton Hills College), David Schimpf (University of Minnesota, Duluth), William H. Schlesinger (Duke University), Erik P. Scully (Towson State University), Stephen Sheckler (Virginia Polytechnic Institute and State University), James Shinkle (Trinity University), Barbara Shipes (Hampton University), Peter Shugarman (University of Southern California), Alice Shuttey (DeKalb Community College), James Sidie (Ursinus College), Daniel Simberloff (Florida State University), John Smarrelli (Loyola University), Andrew T. Smith (Arizona State University), Andrew J. Snope (Essex Community College), Susan Sovonick-Dunford (University of Cincinnati), Karen Steudel (University of Wisconsin), Barbara Stewart (Swarthmore College), Cecil Still (Rutgers University, New Brunswick), John Stolz (California Institute of Technology), Richard D. Storey (Colorado College), Stephen Strand (University of California, Los Angeles), Eric Strauss (University of Massachusetts, Boston), Russell Stullken (Augusta College), John Sullivan (Southern Oregon State University), Gerald Summers (University of Missouri), Marshall Sundberg (Louisiana State University), Daryl Sweeney (University of Illinois, Champaign-Urbana), Samuel S. Sweet (University of California, Santa Barbara), Lincoln Taiz (University of California, Santa Cruz), Samuel Tarsitano (Southwest Texas State University), David Tauck (Santa Clara University), James Taylor (University of New Hampshire), Roger Thibault (Bowling Green State University), William Thomas (Colby-Sawyer College), John Thornton (Oklahoma State University), Robert Thornton (University of California, Davis), James Traniello (Boston University), Robert Tuveson (University of Illinois, Urbana), Maura G. Tyrrell (Stonehill College), Gordon Uno (University of Oklahoma), James W. Valentine (University of California, Santa Barbara), Joseph Vanable (Purdue University), Theodore Van Bruggen (University of South Dakota), Frank Visco (Orange Coast College), Laurie Vitt (University of California, Los Angeles), Susan D. Waaland (University of Washington), William Wade (Dartmouth Medical College), John Waggoner (Loyola Marymount University), Dan Walker (San Jose State University), Robert L. Wallace (Ripon College), Jeffrey Walters (North Carolina State University), Margaret Waterman (University of Pittsburgh), Charles Webber (Loyola University of Chicago), Peter Webster (University of Massachusetts, Amherst), Terry Webster (University of Connecticut, Storrs), Peter Wejksnora (University of Wisconsin, Milwaukee), Kentwood Wells (University of Connecticut), Stephen Williams (Glendale Community College), Christopher Wills (University of California, San Diego), Fred Wilt (University of California, Berkeley), Robert T. Woodland (University of Massachusetts Medical School), Joseph Woodring (Louisiana State University), Patrick Woolley (East Central College), Philip Yant (University of Michigan), Hideo Yonenaka (San Francisco State University), John Zimmerman (Kansas State University), Uko Zylstra (Calvin College).

iology, the study of life, is rooted in the human spirit. People keep pets, nurture houseplants, invite avian visitors with backyard birdhouses, and visit zoos and nature preserves. Biology is the scientific extension of this human tendency to feel connected to and curious about all forms of life. It is a science for adventurous minds. It takes us, personally or vicariously, into jungles, deserts, seas, and other environments, where a variety of living forms and their physical surroundings are interwoven into complex webs called ecosystems. Studying life leads us into laboratories to examine more closely how living things, called organisms, work. Biology draws us into the microscopic world of the fundamental units of organisms known as cells, and into the submicroscopic realm of the molecules that make up those cells. Our intellectual journey also takes us back in time, for biology encompasses not only contemporary life, but also a history of ancestral forms stretching nearly four billion years into the past. The scope of biology is immense. The purpose of this book is to introduce you to this multifaceted science. It is unlikely that any biology course could or should cover all 55 chapters, but this textbook is designed to help you succeed in your general biology course and to serve as a durable reference in your continuing education.

You are becoming involved with biology during its most exciting era. Using fresh approaches and new research methods, biologists are unraveling some of life's most engaging mysteries. Though stimulating, the information explosion in biology is also intimidating. Most of the biologists who have ever lived are alive today, and they add about a half-million new research articles to the scientific literature annually. Each of biology's many subfields changes continuously, and it is very difficult for a professional biologist to remain current in more than one narrowly defined specialty. How, then, can beginning biology students hope to keep their heads above water in this deluge of data and discovery? The key is to recognize unifying themes that pervade all of biology—themes that will still apply decades from now, when much of the specific information presented in any textbook will be obsolete. This chapter introduces some broad, enduring themes in the study of life. The list on this page previews these themes.

LIFE'S HIERARCHICAL ORDER

In this very first section, we introduce one of life's most distinctive features, its order. Life is highly organized into a hierarchy of structural levels, with each level building on the levels below it. As we examine the hierarchy, we will see that special qualities, called emergent properties, result from the structure at each level. Life itself is associated with a set of properties that depend on structural order.

The cell is the lowest structural level in which all of life's properties, including reproduction, can occur. Within each

INTRODUCTION: THEMES IN THE STUDY OF LIFE

Life's Hierarchical Order
- The living world is a hierarchy, with each level of biological structure building on the level below it
- Each level of biological structure has emergent properties
- Cells are an organism's basic units of structure and function
- The continuity of life is based on heritable information in the form of DNA
- Structure and function are correlated at all levels of biological organization
- Organisms are open systems that interact continuously with their environments
- Regulatory mechanisms ensure a dynamic balance in living systems

Evolution, Unity, and Diversity
- Diversity and unity are the dual faces of life on Earth
- Evolution is the core theme of biology

Science as a Process
- Testable hypotheses are the hallmarks of the scientific process
- Science and technology are functions of society
- Biology is a multidisciplinary adventure

(a) Mary-Claire King, geneticist

(b) Elisabeth Vrba, paleontologist

(c) Gloria Coruzzi, plant molecular biologist

(d) Terry Dawson, physiologist

FIGURE 1.1 ▪ **Biologists study life on many different scales of size and time.** **(a)** Geneticist Mary-Claire King studies mutations in DNA that contribute to human disorders such as familial breast cancer and hereditary deafness. **(b)** Paleontologist Elisabeth Vrba investigates human evolution by studying relationships between the history of life as chronicled by the fossil record and environmental changes of the past. **(c)** Plant molecular biologist Gloria Coruzzi, photographed here with one of her student researchers, uses genetics and DNA technology to investigate key processes in plants. **(d)** Terry Dawson studies the structural and physiological adaptations of Australian organisms.

cell, life's order is coded at the molecular level. Molecules of DNA contain genes, units of inheritance, that enable organisms to reproduce, providing continuity from one generation to the next.

Biologists study life on many different levels (FIGURE 1.1). At the end of this section, we take a brief look at the regulatory mechanisms that keep living systems ordered and thereby functioning smoothly.

The living world is a hierarchy, with each level of biological structure building on the level below it

You can see order in the intricate pattern of veins throughout a leaf or in the colorful pattern of a bird's feathers. Biological order exists at all levels (FIGURE 1.2), even those invisible to the unaided eye. Starting at the lowest level, atoms, the chemical building blocks of all matter, are ordered into complex biological molecules. Many of the molecules of life are arranged into minute structures called organelles, which are in turn the components of cells.

Cells are subunits of organisms, and organisms are the units of life. Some organisms, such as amoebas, consist of single cells, but others are multicellular aggregates of many specialized types of cells. What an amoeba accomplishes with a single cell—the uptake and processing of nutrients, excretion of wastes, response to environmental stimuli, reproduction, and other functions—a human or other multicellular organism accomplishes with a division of labor among specialized cells. Unlike the amoeba, none of your cells could live for long on its own. The organism we recognize as an animal or plant is not a random collection of individual cells, but a multicellular cooperative.

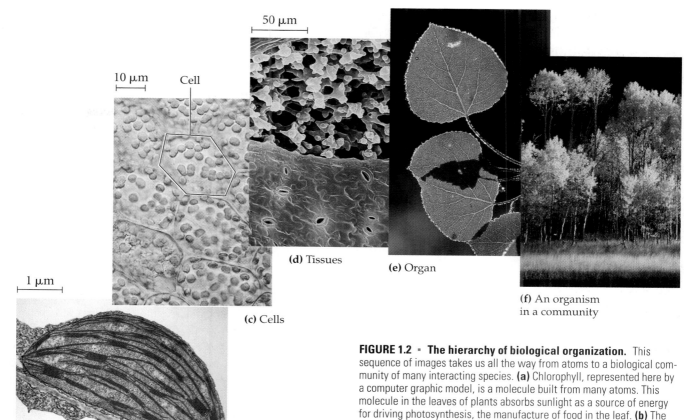

50 μm

10 μm

Cell

(d) Tissues

(e) Organ

1 μm

(f) An organism
in a community

(b) Organelle
(chloroplast)

Atoms

(a) Molecule (chlorophyll)

(c) Cells

FIGURE 1.2 ▪ The hierarchy of biological organization. This sequence of images takes us all the way from atoms to a biological community of many interacting species. **(a)** Chlorophyll, represented here by a computer graphic model, is a molecule built from many atoms. This molecule in the leaves of plants absorbs sunlight as a source of energy for driving photosynthesis, the manufacture of food in the leaf. **(b)** The process of photosynthesis requires the participation of many other molecules organized within the cellular organelle called the chloroplast (the greenish structure in this micrograph, a photograph taken with a microscope). **(c)** Many organelles cooperate in the functioning of the living unit we call a cell. Chloroplasts are evident in these leaf cells. **(d)** In multicellular organisms, cells are usually organized into tissues, groups of similar cells forming a functional unit. The leaf in this micrograph has been cut obliquely, revealing two different specialized tissues. The honeycomblike tissue (upper half) consists of photosynthetic cells within the leaf. The dark green tissue with the small pores (lower half) is the epidermis, the "skin" of the plant. The pores in the epidermis allow carbon dioxide, a raw material that is converted to sugar by photosynthesis, to enter the leaf. **(e)** The aspen leaf, a plant organ, has a specific organization of many different tissues, including photosynthetic tissue, epidermis, and the vascular tissue that transports water from the roots to the leaves. **(f)** These aspens are members of a biological community that includes many other species of organisms.

Multicellular organisms exhibit three major structural levels above the cell. Similar cells are grouped into tissues, specific arrangements of different tissues form organs, and organs are grouped into organ systems. For example, the signals (nerve impulses) that coordinate your movements are transmitted along specialized cells called neurons. The nervous tissue within your brain has billions of neurons organized into a communications network of spectacular complexity. The brain, however, is not pure nervous tissue; it is an organ built of many different tissues, including a type called connective tissue that forms the protective covering of the brain. The brain is itself part of the nervous system, which

also includes the spinal cord and the many nerves that transmit messages between the spinal cord and other parts of the body. The nervous system is only one of several organ systems characteristic of humans and other complex animals.

In the hierarchy of biological organization, there are tiers beyond the individual organism. A population is a localized group of organisms belonging to the same species; populations of different species living in the same area make up a biological community; and community interactions that include nonliving features of the environment, such as soil and water, form an ecosystem.

Identifying biological organization at its many levels is fundamental to the study of life. This text essentially follows such an organization, beginning by looking at the chemistry of life and ending with the study of ecosystems and the biosphere, the sum of all Earth's ecosystems. However, we will also see that biological processes often involve several levels of biological organization. For example, when a rattlesnake explodes from its coiled posture and strikes a mouse, the snake's coordinated movements result from complex interactions at the molecular, cellular, tissue, and organ levels within its body. This behavior also affects the biological community in which the snake and its prey live. Such episodes of predation can have an important cumulative impact on the sizes of both the mouse and the rattlesnake populations. Most biologists specialize in the study of life at a particular level, but they gain broader perspective when they integrate their discoveries with processes occurring at lower and higher levels.

Life resists a simple, one-sentence definition because it is associated with numerous emergent properties. Yet almost any child perceives that a dog or a bug or a tree is alive and a rock is not. We recognize life by what living things do. FIGURE 1.3 illustrates and describes some of the properties and processes we associate with the state of being alive.

Because the properties of life emerge from complex organization, scientists seeking to understand biological processes confront a dilemma. One horn of the dilemma is that we cannot fully explain a higher level of order by breaking it down into its parts. A dissected animal no longer functions; a cell reduced to its chemical ingredients is no longer a cell. Disrupting a living system interferes with the meaningful explanation of its processes. The other horn of the dilemma is the futility of trying to analyze something as complex as an organism or a cell without taking it apart. Reductionism—reducing complex systems to simpler components that are more manageable to study—is a powerful strategy in biology. For example, by studying the molecular structure of a substance called DNA that had been extracted from cells, James Watson and Francis Crick deduced, in 1953, how this molecule could serve as the chemical basis of inheritance. The central role of DNA was better understood, however, when it was possible to study its interactions with other substances in the cell. Biology balances the reductionist strategy with the longer-range objective of understanding how the parts of cells, organisms, and higher levels of order, such as ecosystems, are functionally integrated.

Each level of biological structure has emergent properties

With each step upward in the hierarchy of biological order, novel properties emerge that were not present at the simpler levels of organization. These emergent properties result from interactions between components. A molecule such as a protein has attributes not exhibited by any of its component atoms, and a cell is certainly much more than a bag of molecules. If the intricate organization of the human brain is disrupted by a head injury, that organ will cease to function properly, even though all its parts may still be present. And an organism is a living whole greater than the sum of its parts.

The concept of emergent properties accents the importance of structural arrangement and applies to inanimate material as well as to life. Neither the head nor the handle of a hammer alone is very useful for driving nails, but put these parts together in a certain way, and the functional properties of a hammer emerge. Diamonds and graphite are both made of carbon, but they have different properties because their carbon atoms are arranged differently. The emergent properties of life reflect a hierarchy of structural organization without counterpart among inanimate objects.

Cells are an organism's basic units of structure and function

The cell is the lowest level of structure capable of performing *all* the activities of life. All organisms are composed of cells, the basic units of structure and function.

Robert Hooke, an English scientist, first described and named cells in 1665, when he observed a slice of cork (bark from an oak tree) with a microscope that magnified 30 times ($30\times$). Apparently believing that the tiny boxes, or "cells," that he saw were unique to cork, Hooke never realized the significance of his discovery. His contemporary, a Dutchman named Anton van Leeuwenhoek, discovered organisms we now know to be single-celled. Using grains of sand that he had polished into magnifying glasses as powerful as $300\times$, Leeuwenhoek discovered a microbial world in droplets of pond water and also observed the blood cells and sperm cells of animals. In 1839, nearly two centuries after the discoveries of Hooke and Leeuwenhoek, cells were finally acknowledged as the ubiquitous units of life by Matthias Schleiden and Theodor Schwann, two German biologists. In a classic case of inductive reasoning—reaching a generalization based on many concurring observations—Schleiden and Schwann summarized

(a) Order

(b) Reproduction

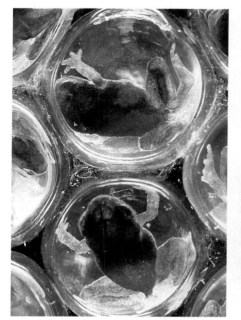

(c) Growth and development

(d) Energy utilization

(e) Response to the environment

(f) Homeostasis

(g) Evolutionary adaptation

FIGURE 1.3 ▪ **Some properties of life.**
(a) *Order:* All other characteristics of life emerge from an organism's complex organization, which is apparent in this closeup of a sunflower.
(b) *Reproduction:* Organisms reproduce their own kind. Life comes only from life, an axiom known as biogenesis. Here, a Japanese macaque protects its offspring. **(c)** *Growth and development:* Heritable programs in the form of DNA direct the pattern of growth and development, producing an organism that is characteristic of its species. Shown here are embryos of a Costa Rican species of frog. **(d)** *Energy utilization:* Organisms take in energy and transform it to do many kinds of work. This bat obtains fuel in the form of nectar from the saguaro cactus. The bat will use energy stored in the molecules of its food to power flight and other work. **(e)** *Response to the environment:* This soon-to-be-digested cricket "tripped" the Venus flytrap when it stimulated hair cells on the surface of the modified leaves that make up the trap. The plant responded to this environmental stimulus with a rapid closure of the trap. **(f)** *Homeostasis:* Regulatory mechanisms maintain an organism's internal environment within tolerable limits, even though the external environment may fluctuate. This regulation is called homeostasis. In this example, regulation of the amount of blood flowing through the blood vessels of this blacktail jackrabbit's large ears constantly adjusts heat loss to its surroundings. This contributes to homeostasis of the animal's body temperature. **(g)** *Evolutionary adaptation:* Life evolves as a result of the interaction between organisms and their environments. One consequence of evolution is the adaptation of organisms to their environment. The white feathers of the white-tail ptarmigan in winter plumage make it nearly invisible against the animal's snowy surroundings.

their own microscopic studies and those of others by concluding that all living things consist of cells. This generalization forms the basis of what is known as the cell theory. This theory was later expanded to include the idea that all cells come from other cells. The ability of cells to divide to form new cells is the basis for all reproduction and for the growth and repair of multicellular organisms, including humans.

All cells are enclosed by a membrane that regulates the passage of materials between the cell and its surroundings. Every cell, at some stage in its life, contains DNA, the heritable material that directs the cell's many activities.

Two major kinds of cells—prokaryotic cells and eukaryotic cells—can be distinguished by their structural organization (FIGURE 1.4). The cells of the microorganisms commonly called bacteria are prokaryotic. All other forms of life are composed of eukaryotic cells. Much more complex than the prokaryotic cell, the eukaryotic cell is subdivided by internal membranes into many different functional compartments, or organelles. In eukaryotic cells, the DNA is organized along with certain proteins into structures called chromosomes contained within a nucleus, the largest organelle of most eukaryotic cells. Surrounding the nucleus is the cytoplasm, a thick fluid in which are suspended the various organelles that perform most of the cell's functions. Some eukaryotic cells, including those of plants, have tough walls external to their membranes. Animal cells lack walls.

In the much simpler prokaryotic cell, the DNA is not separated from the rest of the cell in a nucleus. Prokaryotic cells also lack the cytoplasmic organelles typical of eukaryotic cells.

Almost all prokaryotic cells (bacteria) have tough external cell walls.

Although eukaryotic and prokaryotic cells contrast sharply in complexity, we will see that they have some key similarities. Cells vary widely in size, shape, and specific structural features, but all are highly ordered structures that carry out complicated processes necessary for maintaining life.

The continuity of life is based on heritable information in the form of DNA

Order implies information; instructions are required to arrange parts or processes in an organized way. Biological instructions are encoded in the molecule known as DNA (deoxyribonucleic acid). DNA is the substance of genes, the units of inheritance that transmit information from parents to offspring (FIGURE 1.5).

Each DNA molecule is made up of two long chains each composed of four kinds of chemical building blocks called

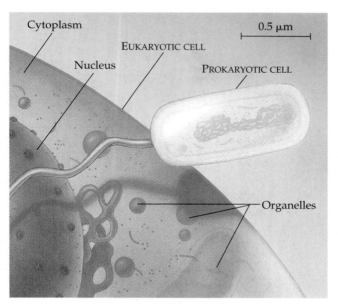

FIGURE 1.4 · **Structural organization of eukaryotic and prokaryotic cells.** The eukaryotic cell, found in plants, animals, and all other organisms except bacteria, is characterized by an extensive subdivision into many different functional compartments called organelles. The prokaryotic cell, unique to bacteria, is much simpler, lacking most of the organelles found in eukaryotic cells. Compared to eukaryotic cells, most prokaryotic cells are also much smaller.

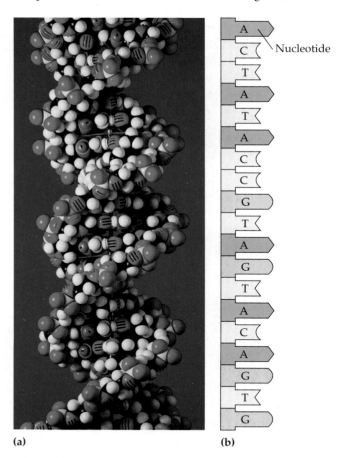

(a)   (b)

FIGURE 1.5 · **The genetic material: DNA.** DNA molecules carry biological information from one generation to the next. **(a)** This model shows each atom in a segment of DNA. Made up of two long chains of building blocks called nucleotides, a DNA molecule takes the three-dimensional form of a double helix. **(b)** This diagram uses geometric shapes to represent the nucleotides in a small section of one of the two nucleotide chains in a DNA molecule. Each nucleotide is made up of many atoms. Genetic information is encoded in specific sequences of the nucleotides.

nucleotides. The way DNA conveys information is analogous to the way we arrange the letters of the alphabet into precise sequences with specific meanings. The word *rat*, for example, conjures up an image of a rodent; *tar* and *art*, which contain the same letters, mean quite different things. Libraries are filled with books containing information encoded in varying sequences of only 26 letters. We can think of nucleotides as the alphabet of inheritance. Specific sequential arrangements of these four chemical letters encode the precise information in a gene. If the entire library of genes stored within the microscopic nucleus of a single human cell were written in letters the size of those you are now reading, the information would fill more than a hundred books as large as this one. The complex structural organization of an organism is thus specified by an inherited script conveying an enormous amount of coded information.

All forms of life employ essentially the same genetic code. A particular sequence of nucleotides says the same thing to one organism as it does to another; differences between organisms reflect differences between their nucleotide sequences. The diverse forms of life are different expressions of a common language for programming biological order.

Inheritance itself depends on a mechanism for copying DNA and passing its sequence of chemical letters on to off-spring. As a cell prepares to divide to form two cells, it copies its DNA. A mechanical system that moves chromosomes then distributes the DNA copies equally to the two "daughter" cells. In species that reproduce sexually, offspring inherit copies of DNA from the parents' sperm and egg cells. The continuity of life over the generations and over the eons has its molecular basis in the replication of DNA.

Structure and function are correlated at all levels of biological organization

Given a choice of tools, you would not loosen a screw with a hammer or pound a nail with a screwdriver. How a device works is correlated with its structure: Form fits function. Applied to biology, this theme is a guide to the anatomy of life at its many structural levels, from molecules to organisms. Analyzing a biological structure gives us clues about what it does and how it works. Conversely, knowing the function of a structure provides insight about its construction.

An example of this structure-function theme is the aerodynamically efficient shape of a bird's wing (FIGURE 1.6). The skeleton of the bird also has structural qualities that contribute to flight, with bones that have a strong but light

(a)

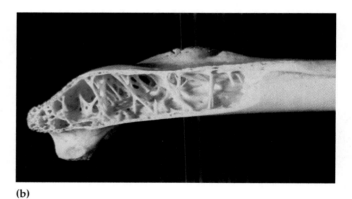

(b)

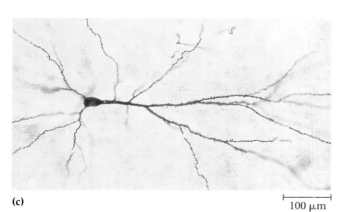

(c)

|————| 100 μm

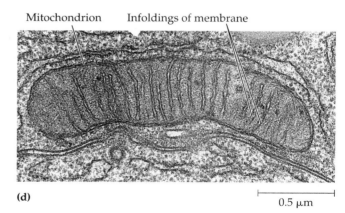

Mitochondrion   Infoldings of membrane

(d)

|————| 0.5 μm

FIGURE 1.6 ▪ Form fits function. (a) A bird's build makes flight possible. The correlation between structure and function can apply to the shape of an entire organism, as you can see from this white tern in flight. **(b)** The structure-function theme also applies to organs and tissues. For example, the honeycombed construction of a bird's bones provides a lightweight skeleton of great strength. **(c)** The form of a cell fits its specialized function. Nerve cells, or neurons, have long extensions (processes) that transmit nervous impulses. **(d)** Functional beauty is also apparent at the subcellular level. This organelle, called a mitochondrion, has an inner membrane that is extensively folded, a structural solution to the problem of packing a relatively large amount of this membrane into a very small container.

honeycombed internal structure. The flight muscles of a bird are controlled by neurons (nerve cells), which transmit impulses. With long extensions, neurons are especially well structured for communication. The flight muscles need plenty of energy, which they obtain from organelles called mitochondria. These organelles are the sites of cellular respiration, the chemical process that powers the cell by using oxygen to help tap the energy stored in sugar and other food molecules. A mitochondrion is surrounded by an outer membrane, but it also has an inner membrane with many infoldings. Molecules embedded in the inner membrane carry out many of the steps in cellular respiration, and the infoldings pack a large amount of this membrane into a minute container (FIGURE 1.6d). In exploring life on its different structural levels, we will discover functional beauty at every turn.

Organisms are open systems that interact continuously with their environments

Life does not exist in a vacuum. An organism is an example of what scientists call an open system, an entity that exchanges materials and energy with its surroundings. Each organism interacts continuously with its environment, which includes other organisms as well as nonliving factors. The roots of a tree, for example, absorb water and minerals from the soil, and the leaves take in carbon dioxide from the air. Solar energy absorbed by chlorophyll, the green pigment of leaves, drives photosynthesis, which converts water and carbon dioxide to sugar and oxygen. The tree releases oxygen to the air, and its roots change the soil by breaking up rocks into smaller particles, secreting acid, and absorbing minerals. Both organism and environment are affected by the interaction between them. The tree also interacts with other life, including soil microorganisms associated with its roots and animals that eat its leaves and fruit.

The many interactions between organisms and their environment are interwoven to form the fabric of an ecosystem. The dynamics of any ecosystem include two major processes. One is the cycling of nutrients. For example, minerals acquired by plants will eventually be returned to the soil by microorganisms that decompose leaf litter, dead roots, and other organic debris. The second major process in an ecosystem is the flow of energy from sunlight to photosynthetic life (producers) to organisms that feed on plants (consumers) (FIGURE 1.7). The theme of organisms as open systems that exchange materials and energy with their surroundings is essential to understanding life on all levels of organization.

The exchange of energy between an organism and its surroundings involves the transformation of one form of energy to another. For example, when a leaf produces sugar, it converts solar energy to chemical energy in sugar molecules. When an animal's muscle cells use sugar as fuel to power movements, they convert chemical energy into kinetic energy,

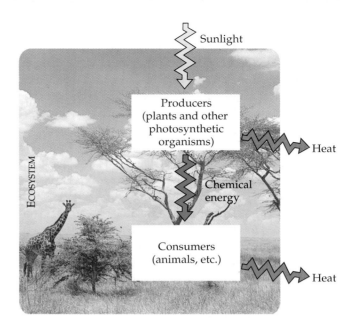

FIGURE 1.7 ▪ An introduction to energy flow and energy transformation in an ecosystem. Living is work, and work requires that organisms obtain and use energy. Most ecosystems are solar-powered. Plants and other photosynthetic organisms convert light energy to the chemical energy stored in sugar and other complex molecules. By breaking these fuel molecules down to simpler molecules, organisms can harvest the stored energy and put it to work. Photosynthetic organisms are called producers because the entire ecosystem (schematically represented here) depends on their photosynthetic products. Animals and other consumers acquire their energy in chemical form by eating plants, by eating animals that ate plants, or by decomposing organic refuse, such as leaf litter and dead animals. The energy that enters an ecosystem in the form of sunlight exits in the form of heat, which all organisms dissipate to their surroundings whenever they perform work.

the energy of motion. All of the work of cells involves the transformation of chemical energy (which is ordered) into heat, which is the unordered energy of random molecular motion. Life requires continual uptake of ordered energy and the release of some unordered energy to the surroundings.

Regulatory mechanisms ensure a dynamic balance in living systems

If you strike a match, it undergoes a chemical reaction in which the chemical energy in its molecules is transformed into heat and light. Burning is unregulated energy transformation, obviously not a suitable way for living cells to transform energy. Organisms are able to obtain useful energy from fuel molecules such as sugar because cells break the molecules down in a series of closely regulated chemical reactions.

Regulation of the chemical reactions within cells centers on protein molecules called enzymes. Produced by the cells in which they function, enzymes are catalysts, substances that speed up chemical reactions. When your muscle cells need a lot of energy during exercise, enzymes catalyze the rapid breakdown of sugar (glucose) molecules, releasing energy that

can be put to work. In contrast, when you rest, other enzymes catalyze the formation of glucose, which may be added to the body's fuel reserves. With one group of enzymes catalyzing the breakdown of glucose and another group catalyzing its formation, how is order maintained in the cell? A big part of the answer is that regulatory mechanisms determine precisely when, where, and how fast certain reactions occur in a cell.

Many biological processes are self-regulating, operating by a mechanism called feedback, in which an output or product of a process regulates that process. Negative feedback, also called feedback inhibition, slows or stops processes; positive feedback speeds a process up (FIGURE 1.8).

Mammals and birds have a negative feedback system that keeps body temperature within a narrow range, despite wide fluctuations in their surroundings. A control center in the brain holds the temperature of the blood close to a set point (about 37°C in mammals). For instance, when the human body starts getting hot, signals from the control center increase the activity of sweat glands and the diameter of blood vessels in the skin. Evaporative cooling results as sweating increases, and heat radiates from the blood vessels as they fill with warm blood. Negative feedback occurs as soon as the blood cools back to the set point, causing the control center to stop sending signals to the skin. If the blood temperature drops below the set point, the brain's control center inactivates the sweat glands and constricts the skin's blood vessels. This shunts blood to deeper tissues, reducing heat loss. When the blood warms back to the set point, negative feedback occurs again, and signals from the control center cease.

The clotting of blood is one example of positive feedback. When a blood vessel is injured, structures in the blood called platelets start accumulating at the site. Positive feedback occurs as chemicals released by the platelets attract more platelets, and the platelet cluster initiates a complex sequence of chemical reactions (called a cascade) that seals the wound with a clot. Regulation by positive and negative feedback is a pervasive theme in biology, and we will see numerous examples throughout this text.

EVOLUTION, UNITY, AND DIVERSITY

Evolutionary change has been a central feature of life since it arose about 4 billion years ago. The evolutionary connections among all organisms explain the unity and diversity of life.

Diversity and unity are the dual faces of life on Earth

Diversity is a hallmark of life. Biologists have identified and named about 1.5 million species, including over 260,000 plants, almost 50,000 vertebrates (animals with backbones), and more than 750,000 insects. Thousands of newly identified species are added to the list each year. Estimates of the total diversity of life range from about 5 million to over 100 million species.

If life is so diverse, how can biology have any unifying themes at all? What, for instance, can a mold, a tree, and a human possibly have in common? As it turns out, a great deal! Underlying the diversity of life is a striking unity, especially at the lower levels of organization. We can see it, for example, in certain similarities of cell structure (FIGURE 1.9 on p. 10). Unity is also evident in the universal genetic code shared by all organisms. Different expressions of this genetic code, however, result in the diversity of life.

Biological diversity is something to relish and preserve, but it can also be a bit overwhelming. To make diversity less daunting, people tend to group similar species together. For instance, we may talk about squirrels without distinguishing among the many different species of squirrels. Taxonomy, the branch of

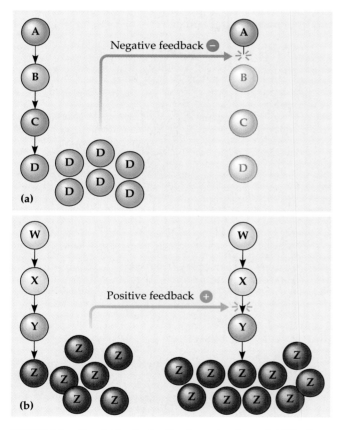

FIGURE 1.8 · **Regulation by feedback mechanisms.** **(a)** This simple model illustrates the principle of negative feedback, or feedback inhibition, in the regulation of a chemical reaction sequence in a cell. The sequence involves four molecules (A–D). The black arrows represent three different enzymes catalyzing the conversion of one molecule to the next. The final product (D) inhibits the first enzyme in the sequence; when the concentration of D rises to a certain point, the reaction shuts itself down. Self-regulation by negative feedback is common in living systems. **(b)** In positive feedback, a product of the reaction sequence enhances the action of one of the enzymes, increasing the rate of production of the product.

biology concerned with naming and classifying species, groups organisms according to a more formal scheme. The scheme consists of different levels of classification, each more comprehensive than those below it (FIGURE 1.10).

Traditionally, biologists divided the diversity of life into five kingdoms. All prokaryotic organisms, commonly called bacteria, were placed in the kingdom Monera. Eukaryotes were divided into the kingdom Protista (unicellular eukaryotes and their relatively simple multicellular relatives), the kingdom Plantae (plants), the kingdom Fungi (fungi), and the kingdom Animalia (animals).

Today, many biologists prefer classification schemes that recognize six, eight, or more kingdoms and that group kingdoms into a higher category, the domain. Reflecting strong evidence developed over the past two decades, prokaryotes are divided into two fundamentally different groups, the domains Bacteria (formerly called Eubacteria) and Archaea (formerly called Archaebacteria). These groups of prokaryotes seem to be at least as different from each other as either is from any eukaryote. The eukaryotes are grouped into a third domain, Eukarya (FIGURE 1.11).

Among the Eukarya, the enormous diversity among the protists (Kingdom Protista) has most researchers convinced that the group should be divided into several kingdoms. We will take a close look at these new developments in taxonomy at the kingdom and domain levels in Unit Five. Meanwhile, we follow the convention of referring to single-celled eukaryotes and closely related multicellular organisms as protists. The other eukaryotes, the kingdoms Plantae, Fungi, and Animalia, consist mainly of multicellular organisms. One way to distinguish them from one another is by their contrasting modes of nutrition (see FIGURE 1.11).

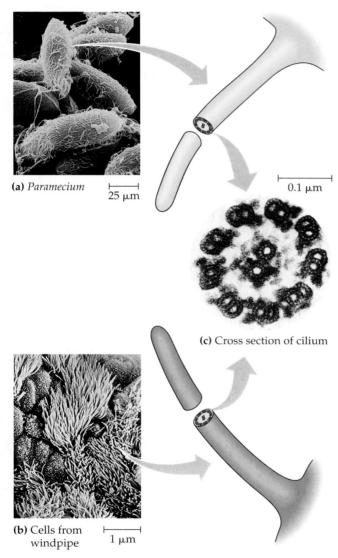

(a) *Paramecium*   25 μm   0.1 μm

(c) Cross section of cilium

(b) Cells from windpipe   1 μm

FIGURE 1.9 · An example of unity underlying the diversity of life: the architecture of eukaryotic cilia. Eukaryotic organisms as diverse as the single-celled organism *Paramecium* and animals possess cilia, locomotory "hairs" that extend from cells. **(a)** The cilia of *Paramecium* propel the cell through pond water. **(b)** The cells that line the human windpipe are also equipped with cilia, which help keep the lungs clean by moving a film of debris-trapping mucus upward. **(c)** Comparing cross sections of cilia from diverse eukaryotes reveals a common structural organization. Such striking similarity in complex components contributes to the evidence that organisms as different as *Paramecium* and humans are, to some degree, related.

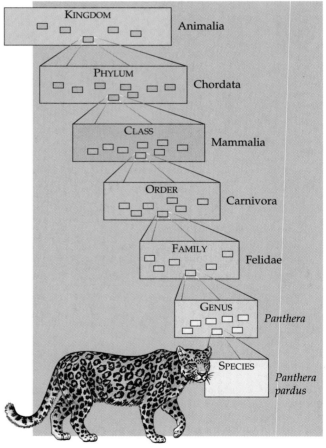

FIGURE 1.10 · Classifying life. The taxonomic scheme classifies species into groups subordinate to more comprehensive groups. Species that are very similar are placed in the same genus, genera are grouped into families, and so on, each level of classification being more comprehensive than those it includes. This example classifies the species *Panthera pardus*, the leopard.

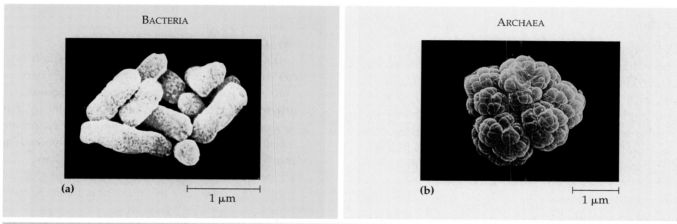

BACTERIA

ARCHAEA

1 μm

1 μm

EUKARYA

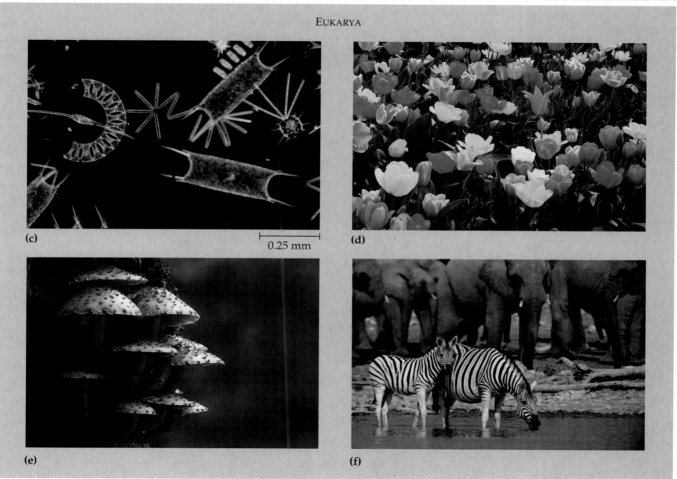

(a)

(b)

(c)

0.25 mm

(d)

(e)

(f)

FIGURE 1.11 ▪ **Domains of life.** The domains Bacteria, Archaea, and Eukarya represent three fundamentally different kinds of organisms. Their most basic differences appear at the molecular level, in their nucleic acids. The domains Bacteria and Archaea are composed of prokaryotes. The more traditional five-kingdom system of classification recognized all prokaryotes as members of one kingdom, the Monera, plus the four kingdoms in the domain Eukarya shown here. **(a)** Members of Domain Bacteria (formerly called Eubacteria) are the most diverse and widespread prokaryotes. A unique set of molecular traits dis-tinguishes them from other prokaryotes and eukaryotes. **(b)** Most Archaea (formerly called Archaebacteria) live in Earth's extreme environ-ments, such as salty lakes and boiling hot springs. Molecular evidence indicates that archaeans have at least as much in common with eukaryotes as they do with members of Domain Bacteria. Within the domain Eukarya, **(c)** King-dom Protista consists of unicellular eukaryotes and their relatively simple multicellular relatives. Pictured here is an assortment of protists inhab-iting pond water. Scientists are currently debat-ing how to split the protists into several kingdoms that better represent evolution and diversity. **(d)** Kingdom Plantae consists of multi-cellular eukaryotes, such as these tulips, that carry out photosynthesis. **(e)** Kingdom Fungi is defined, in part, by the nutritional mode of its members, organisms, such as these mushrooms, that absorb nutrients after decomposing organic material. **(f)** Kingdom Animalia consists of multi-cellular eukaryotes that ingest other organisms. You will learn more about the scientific debate over classification at the domain and kingdom levels in Unit Five.

Evolution is the core theme of biology

The history of life is a chronicle of a restless Earth billions of years old, inhabited by a changing cast of living forms (FIGURE 1.12). Life evolves. Just as an individual has a family history, each species is one twig on a branching tree of life extending back in time through ancestral species more and more remote. Species that are very similar, such as the horse and zebra, share a common ancestor that represents a relatively recent branch point on the tree of life. But through an ancestor that lived much farther back in time, horses and zebras are also related to rabbits, humans, and all other mammals. And mammals, reptiles, birds, and all other vertebrates share an even more ancient common ancestor. Trace evolution back far enough, and there are only the primeval prokaryotes that inhabited Earth more than three billion years ago. All of life is connected. Evolution, the processes that have transformed life on Earth from its earliest beginnings to its vast diversity today, is the one biological theme that ties together all others.

Charles Darwin (FIGURE 1.13) brought biology into focus in 1859 when he published *The Origin of Species*. Darwin's book presented two main themes. First, Darwin argued convincingly from several lines of evidence that contemporary species arose from a succession of ancestors through a process of "descent with modification," his phrase for evolution. (The evidence for evolution is discussed in detail in Chapter 22.) The second theme of Darwin's book was his theory for *how* life evolves. This proposed mechanism of evolution is called natural selection.

Darwin synthesized the concept of natural selection from observations that by themselves were neither new nor profound. Others had the pieces of the puzzle, but Darwin saw how they fit together. He inferred natural selection by connecting two observations:

OBSERVATION #1: *Individual variation.* Individuals in a population of any species vary in many heritable traits.

OBSERVATION #2: *Struggle for existence.* Any population of a species has the potential to produce far more offspring than the environment can possibly support with food, space, and other resources. This overproduction makes a struggle for existence among the variant members of a population inevitable.

FIGURE 1.12 ▪ The fossil record is one type of historical documentation that chronicles evolution. *Archaeopteryx,* the animal documented in this fossil, lived about 150 million years ago. It had feathers (a hallmark of birds), but unlike any modern bird, *Archaeopteryx* had teeth, claws on its wings, and a bony tail. *Archaeopteryx* actually resembled certain dinosaurs more than it did any modern bird. The fossil record is compatible with other types of evidence supporting the hypothesis that birds evolved from dinosaurs.

FIGURE 1.13 ▪ Charles Darwin (1809–1882). Darwin and his son William posed for this photograph in 1842. The author of numerous books and monographs on topics as diverse as barnacles, plant movements, and island geology, Darwin would be remembered as one of the greatest naturalists of the nineteenth century even if he had never published on the topic of evolution. But it was *The Origin of Species* that established Darwin's place as the most influential scientist in the development of modern biology. He is buried next to Isaac Newton in London's Westminster Abbey.

INFERENCE: *Differential reproductive success.* Those individuals with traits best suited to the local environment generally leave a disproportionately large number of surviving, fertile offspring. This differential reproductive success of some individuals over others means that certain heritable traits (those carried by the best-suited individuals) are more likely to appear in each new generation. Darwin called differential reproductive success natural selection, and he envisioned it as the cause of evolution.

We see the products of natural selection in the exquisite adaptations of organisms to the special problems posed by their environments (FIGURE 1.14). Notice, however, that natural selection does not *create* adaptations; rather, it screens the heritable variations in each generation, increasing the frequencies of some variations and decreasing the frequencies of others over the generations. Natural selection is an editing process,

FIGURE 1.14 ▪ Evolutionary adaptation is a product of natural selection. This sea horse lives among kelp (seaweed). The fish looks so much like a seaweed that it lures prey into the seeming safety of the kelp forest and then eats them. In the Darwinian view of life, the best-camouflaged members of the sea horse population have the greatest probability of obtaining food and escaping predators—and thus the greatest probability of surviving and leaving offspring. By this mechanism of differential reproductive success, or natural selection, the interaction between environment and the heritable variation among members of the sea horse population gradually refined and maintained the camouflage over the generations.

with heritable variations exposed to environmental factors that favor the reproductive success of some individuals over others. The camouflage of the sea horse in FIGURE 1.14 did not result from individuals changing during their lifetimes to look more like their backgrounds and then passing that improvement on to offspring. The adaptation evolved over many generations by the greater reproductive success in each generation of individuals who were innately better camouflaged than the average member of the sea horse population.

Darwin proposed that natural selection, by its cumulative effects over vast spans of time, could produce new species from ancestral species. This would occur, for example, when a population fragments into several populations isolated in different environments. In these various arenas of natural selection, what begins as one species may gradually diversify into many as the geographically isolated populations adapt over many generations to different sets of environmental problems. Descent with modification accounts for both the unity and the diversity we observe in life. In many cases, features shared by two species are due to their descent from common ancestors, and differences between the species are due to natural selection modifying the ancestral equipment in different environmental contexts. Evolution is the core theme of biology—a unifying thread that ties every chapter of this text together.

SCIENCE AS A PROCESS

Biology is a natural science. Having identified unifying themes that apply specifically to the study of life, we now examine some general features of science as a process.

Like life, science is better understood by observing it than by trying to create a precise definition. The word *science* is derived from a Latin verb meaning "to know." Science is a way of knowing. It emerges from our curiosity about ourselves, the world, and the universe. Striving to understand seems to be one of our basic drives. At the heart of science are people asking questions about nature and believing that those questions are answerable. Scientists tend to be quite passionate in their quest for discovery. Max Perutz, a Nobel Prize–winning biochemist, put it this way: "A discovery is like falling in love and reaching the top of a mountain after a hard climb all in one, an ecstasy induced not by drugs but by the revelation of a face of nature that no one has seen before."

Testable hypotheses are the hallmarks of the scientific process

A process known as the scientific method outlines a series of steps for answering questions, but few scientists adhere rigidly to this prescription. Science is a less structured process than most people realize. Like other intellectual activities, the best

science is a process of minds that are creative, intuitive, imaginative, and social. Perhaps science is distinguished by its conviction that natural phenomena, including the processes of life, have natural causes—and by its obsession with evidence. Scientists are generally skeptics. As you begin each unit of study in this text, you will meet such scientists through personal interviews and come to understand a bit more about how they think and why they enjoy their work.

Although it is counterproductive to reduce science to a stereotyped method, we *can* identify a common theme of the scientific process: *hypothetico-deductive thinking*. The first part of this term refers to *hypothesis,* which is a tentative answer to some question—an explanation on trial. Consider, for example, this imaginary scenario: Scott and Ian, identical twins, are sleepy every day in their 1:00 history class; they want to know why, so they can prevent the drowsiness and improve their history grades. Maybe eating a big lunch just before going to history every day makes them sleepy. Or maybe the classroom is too warm. Maybe Scott and Ian are listless because they sit in the back of their history class and are less involved than they are in their other classes, where they always sit in front. Or maybe it's just the time of day. These are all hypotheses, possible explanations for this daily behavior of sleeping through history class. It is possible to test these hypotheses.

The *deductive* in hypothetico-deductive thinking refers to the use of deductive reasoning to test hypotheses. Deduction contrasts with induction, which is reasoning from a set of specific observations to reach a general conclusion (as in "All organisms are composed of cells"). In deduction, the reasoning flows in the reverse direction, from the general to the specific. From general premises we extrapolate to specific results we should expect if the premises are true: If all organisms are made of cells (premise #1) and humans are organisms (premise #2), then humans are composed of cells (prediction about a specific case). In the scientific process, deduction usually takes the form of predictions about the results of experiments or observations we should expect *if* a particular hypothesis (premise) is correct. We then test the hypothesis by performing the experiments or making observations to see whether or not the predicted results occur. This deductive testing takes the form of *"If . . . then"* logic:

HYPOTHESIS #1: *If* the twins get sleepy because they eat lunch before their 1:00 class,

EXPERIMENT: and Scott postpones lunch until class ends at 2:00 (but Ian still eats at noon),

PREDICTED RESULT #1: *then* Scott should be less sleepy than Ian in history class.

This symbol links topics in the text to interactive exercises in the CD-ROM that accompanies the book. The number indicates the appropriate activity in the CD.

1.1

PREDICTED RESULT #2: *then* Scott should get sleepy in his 3:00 class instead.

OR

HYPOTHESIS #2: *If* the twins get sleepy in their 1:00 class because they sit in the back of the room,

EXPERIMENT: and Scott (but not Ian) moves to the front of the class,

PREDICTED RESULT: *then* Scott should be more alert than Ian during the 1:00 class.

Now, suppose the result of the first experiment is that Scott is still as sleepy as Ian (but hungrier) in their 1:00 class. The twins try the second experiment, with the result that now Scott dozes in the front row of class instead of the back row. The twins continue to test and reject various hypotheses. And then they are the subjects of an experiment they did not even plan—daylight savings time begins. Scott and Ian (and most of their classmates) notice that for a day or two, they have more trouble than usual waking up in the morning. However, the twins find that they are more alert than usual in their 1:00 class and instead hit their low point during the 2:00–3:00 break in their schedule. Within a few days, patterns are back to normal, and Scott and Ian are drowsy during their 1:00 class again. The twins conclude that they are just naturally sleepy at this time of day and decide not to schedule 1:00 classes in future semesters.

Although this example is fanciful and there are flaws in the experiments, five important points about hypotheses are evident:

1. *Hypotheses are possible explanations.* A generalization based on inductive reasoning is not a hypothesis. The twins may conclude, "We are sleepy every day at about 1:00," but that conclusion merely summarizes a set of observations. A hypothesis is a possible *explanation* for what we have observed. "The warm temperature of the classroom puts Scott and Ian to sleep" is a hypothesis.
2. *Hypotheses reflect past experience.* Sometimes hypotheses are described as *educated* propositions about cause. For example, the hypothesis that a warm classroom causes drowsiness may be based on a general experience of sleepiness under such conditions. Although we should consider any hypothesis that is a possible explanation for what we have observed, the hypotheses we test first should be those that seem the most reasonable, based on what we already know.
3. *Multiple hypotheses should be proposed whenever possible.* Proposing alternative explanations that can answer a question is good science. If we operate with a single hypothesis, especially one we favor, we may direct our investigation toward a hunt for evidence in support of this hypothesis.

4. *Hypotheses should be testable via the hypothetico-deductive approach.* Hypotheses should be phrased in a way that enables us to make predictions that can be tested by experiments or further observation. "Scott falls asleep in history class because the devil makes him do it" is not a testable hypothesis and therefore does not lend itself to the scientific process. Requiring that hypotheses be testable limits the scope of questions that science can answer.

5. *Hypotheses can be eliminated but not confirmed with absolute certainty.* If moving to the front of his 1:00 class does not reduce Ian's drowsiness, this casts doubt on one hypothesis. A hypothesis can be falsified by experimental tests, especially if the experiments are repeated with the same results. The onset of daylight savings time supported the "sleepy time of day" hypothesis, and our confidence in this explanation grows if the hypothesis continues to stand up to various kinds of experimental tests. But we can never *prove* that this hypothesis is the true explanation. It is impossible to repeat an experiment enough times to be absolutely certain that the results will *always* be the same. And some false hypotheses make accurate predictions. Consider this hypothesis: "Night and day are caused by the sun orbiting around Earth in an east-west direction." This hypothesis predicts that the sun will rise each morning in the east, move across the sky, and set in the west, which is exactly what we observe. However, the "geocentric universe" hypothesis makes many other predictions that enable us to falsify the hypothesis. Of the many hypotheses proposed to answer a particular question, the correct explanation may not even be included. Even the most thoroughly tested hypotheses are accepted only conditionally, pending further investigation.

The "sleepy twins" scenario introduces another important feature of the scientific process: the controlled experiment. In a *controlled experiment,* the subjects (Scott and Ian, in this case) are divided into two groups, an *experimental group* and a *control group.* Ideally, the two groups are treated exactly alike except for the one variable the experiment is designed to test. This provides a basis for comparison, enabling us to draw conclusions about the effects of our experimental manipulation. Scott and Ian attempted to control their experiments. When Scott moved to the front of the 1:00 class as the experimental, Ian remained in the back of the room as the control.

There are, of course, serious deficiencies in this experiment. If the twins were trying to test the effect of seating locale on sleepiness in class generally, then a single individual is an inadequate sample size for either a control group or an experimental group. Note also that this experiment included uncontrolled variables. Temperature and other unknown factors may have varied between the front and back of the classroom. Some experiments are easier to control than others, but setting up the best possible controls is characteristic of good experimental design.

Now that we have analyzed the hypothetico-deductive approach by using an imaginary example, you should be able to recognize the process in an elegant study reported in the scientific literature. For many years, David Reznick of the University of California, Riverside, and John Endler of the University of California, Santa Barbara, have been investigating differences between populations of guppies in Trinidad, a Caribbean island (FIGURE 1.15). Guppies *(Poecilia reticulata)* are small freshwater fishes you probably recognize as common aquarium pets. In the Aripo River system of Trinidad, guppies live in small pools as populations that are relatively isolated from one another. In some cases, two populations inhabiting

FIGURE 1.15 ▪ **David Reznick conducting field experiments on guppy evolution in Trinidad.**

the same stream live less than 100 meters (m) apart, but they are separated by a waterfall that impedes the migration of guppies between the two pools.

When Reznick and Endler compared guppy populations, they observed differences in what are called *life history characteristics.* These characteristics included the average age and size of guppies when they reach sexual maturity and begin to reproduce, as well as the average number of offspring per brood. The researchers were able to correlate variations in these life history characteristics with the types of predators present in different locations. In some pools, the main predator is a small fish called a killifish, which preys predominately on small, juvenile guppies. In other locations, a larger predator called a pike-cichlid preys more intensely on guppies and mainly eats relatively large, sexually mature individuals (FIG-URE 1.16). Guppies in populations exposed to these pike-cichlids have larger broods, reproduce at a younger age, and are smaller at maturity, on average, than guppies that coexist with killifish.

What causes these life history differences between the guppy populations? Correlation with the type of predator present is suggestive, but a correlation does not necessarily imply a cause-and-effect relationship. The type of predator present and the life history characteristics of the guppy populations in a particular location may be independent consequences of some third factor. In fact, Reznick and Endler tested the hypothesis that the life history variations were due to differences in water temperature or other features of the physical environment. Notice the "*If . . . then*" logic characteristic of the hypothetico-deductive approach:

HYPOTHESIS #1: *If* differences in physical environments cause variations in the life histories of guppy populations,

EXPERIMENT: and samples from different wild guppy populations are collected and maintained for several generations in identical environments in predator-free aquaria,

PREDICTED RESULT: *then* the laboratory populations should become more similar in their life history characteristics.

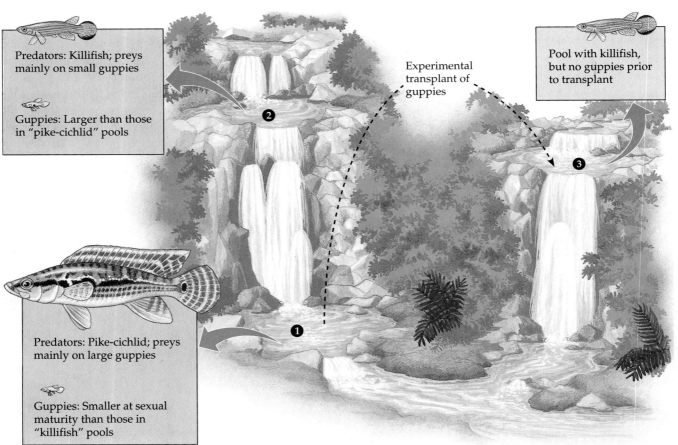

Predators: Killifish; preys mainly on small guppies

Guppies: Larger than those in "pike-cichlid" pools

Experimental transplant of guppies

Pool with killifish, but no guppies prior to transplant

Predators: Pike-cichlid; preys mainly on large guppies

Guppies: Smaller at sexual maturity than those in "killifish" pools

FIGURE 1.16 · Testing the hypothesis that selective predation affects the evolution of guppy populations. This drawing represents three pools along streams of Trinidad's Aripo River system. ① In one pool, pike-cichlids prey intensively on guppies, mainly eating relatively large individuals. ② In another pool, the predators are killifish, which prey less intensively than pike-cichlids and feed mainly on relatively small guppies. In this and other killifish pools, guppies are larger and older at sexual maturity than guppies in pike-cichlid pools. This observation led to Reznick and Endler's hypothesis that selective predation was affecting the evolution of life history characteristics of the guppy populations. One way the researchers tested this hypothesis was to transplant guppies from pike-cichlid pools to pools that contained killifish but had no nat-ural guppy populations ③. Reznick and Endler then tracked the evolution of life history in the experimental guppy populations for 11 years. They compared average age and size of mature guppies in the experimental pools to these life history characteristics of guppies in control pools inhabited by pike-cichlids. FIGURE 1.17 summarizes the results of these experiments.

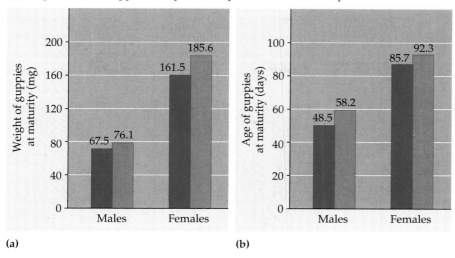

■ Control: Guppies from pools with pike-cichlids as predators

■ Experimental: Guppies transplanted to pools with killifish as predators

(a)

(b)

FIGURE 1.17 ■ Experimental evidence for natural selection in action: results of the guppy transplant experiments. These data represent average measurements for two life history characteristics in guppy populations: **(a)** weight at sexual maturity and **(b)** age at sexual maturity. The vertical bars of the histograms compare control guppy populations to experimental populations. Controls were populations native to pools in which the main predator is the pike-cichlid, which feeds predominately on large, sexually mature guppies. The experimental populations consisted of guppies that were removed from pike-cichlid pools and transplanted to guppy-free pools inhabited by killifish (see FIGURE 1.16). Killifish prey mainly on small, immature guppies. After just 11 years in this study, the transplanted guppy populations had evolved measurably. More recent studies show that similar changes can occur in as few as 4 years in male guppies and 7.5 years in females.

When the researchers performed this experiment, the differences persisted for many generations. This result eliminates hypothesis #1 and also indicates that the life history differences in guppy populations are inherited. Based on the assumption that natural selection can lead to genetic differences in populations, Reznick and Endler tested the following explanation:

HYPOTHESIS #2: *If* the feeding preferences of different predators caused contrasting life histories in different guppy populations to evolve by natural selection,

EXPERIMENT: and guppies are transplanted from locations with pike-cichlids (predators of mature guppies) to guppy-free sites inhabited by killifish (predators of juvenile guppies),

PREDICTED RESULT: *then* the transplanted guppy populations should show a generation-to-generation trend toward later maturation, larger size, and smaller broods—life history characteristics typical of natural guppy populations that coexist with killifish.

In 1976, Reznick and Endler introduced guppies from locations with pike-cichlids to sites that had killifish but no guppies (see FIGURE 1.16). These transplanted populations were the researchers' experimental groups, and they studied them for 11 years, measuring age and size at maturity, brood size, and other life history characteristics. The scientists compared these measurements to data collected over the same period on control groups, guppies that remained in the original locations inhabited by pike-cichlids. To be certain that only heritable differences were counted, the measurements were made after samples from the experimental and control populations had been reared for two generations in identical aquarium environments. Over 11 years, or 30 to 60 generations, the average weight at maturity for guppies in the introduced (experimental) populations increased by about 14%

compared to the control populations. Other life history characteristics also changed in the direction predicted by hypothesis #2 (FIGURE 1.17).

Without a control group for comparison, there would be no way to tell whether it was the killifish or some *other* factor that caused the transplanted guppy population to change. But because control sites and experimental sites were often nearby pools of the same stream, the main variable was probably the presence of different predators. And these careful researchers observed similar results when guppy populations were reared in artificial streams that were identical except for the type of predator.

Of the several hypotheses Reznick and Endler have tested (we examined only two), they are left with natural selection due to differential predation on larger versus smaller guppies as the most likely explanation for the observed differences between guppy populations. Apparently, when predators such as pike-cichlids prey mainly on reproductively mature adults, the chance that a guppy will survive to reproduce several times is relatively low. The guppies with greatest reproductive success should then be the individuals that mature at a young age and small size and produce at least one brood before growing to a size preferred by the local predator.

The popular press gave Reznick and Endler's research a lot of attention because it documents evolution in a natural setting over a relatively short time (within only 11 years in the study we have followed). In more recent studies, Reznick and others have documented similar evolutionary changes in guppies in as few as four years. We have examined the guppy experiments in some detail because they also provide a fine example of the key role of hypothetico-deductive thinking in science.

Another key feature of science is its progressive, self-correcting quality. A succession of scientists working on the same problem build on what has been learned earlier. It is also

common for scientists to check on the conclusions of others by attempting to repeat observations and experiments. Both cooperation and competition exist among scientists working on the same question. Scientists share information through publications, seminars, meetings, and personal communication. They also subject one another's work to careful scrutiny.

Many people associate the word *discovery* with science. Often, what they have in mind is the discovery of new facts. But accumulating facts is not really what science is about; a telephone book is a catalog of facts, but it has little to do with science. It is true that facts, in the form of observations and experimental results, are the prerequisites of science. What really advances science, however, is a new idea that collectively explains a number of observations that previously seemed to be unrelated. The most exciting ideas in science are those that explain the greatest variety of phenomena. People like Newton, Darwin, and Albert Einstein stand out in the history of science not because they discovered a great many facts, but because they synthesized ideas with great explanatory power. Such ideas, much broader in scope than the hypotheses that pose possible causes for one set of observations, are known as theories. Because theories are comprehensive, they only become widely accepted if they are supported by a large body of evidence. Natural selection qualifies as a theory because of its broad application to so many situations. And the theory of natural selection is widely accepted because researchers working in the many fields of biology continue to validate the theory with new observations and experiments, including those of Reznick and Endler.

This book is only partly about the current state of biological knowledge. It is also important for you to learn, by example and by practice, how the process of science works. The power of hypothetico-deductive thinking is one of the themes of this text, and you will read many examples of how biologists have applied it in their research. However, it is mainly your own experience in the laboratory and in the field that will teach you how to do science. And your practice with the hypothetico-deductive approach will help you think more critically in general.

Science and technology are functions of society

Science and technology are associated. In many cases, technology results from scientific discoveries applied to the development of goods and services. Watson and Crick discovered the structure of DNA through the process of science. This breakthrough sparked an explosion of scientific activity that led to better understanding of DNA chemistry and the genetic code. These discoveries eventually made it possible to manipulate DNA, enabling genetic technologists to transplant foreign genes into microorganisms and produce such valuable products as human insulin. The new biotechnology is revolution-

izing the pharmaceutical industry, and DNA technology has also had an enormous impact in other areas, including the legal profession (FIGURE 1.18). Perhaps Watson and Crick envisioned that their discovery would someday have technological applications, but that was probably not what motivated their research; nor could they have predicted exactly what the applications would be. Scientist/writer Lewis

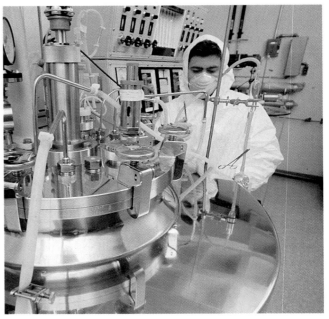

(a)

(b)

FIGURE 1.18 · Two examples of DNA technology. (a) This employee of a biotechnology company is monitoring a tank for growing yeast cells that have been engineered to carry genes of the virus that causes hepatitis B. The genetically engineered cells produce large amounts of a protein molecule that is found on the surface of the virus. The protein is used to make a vaccine against the virus. **(b)** Forensic technicians can use traces of DNA extracted from a blood sample or other body fluid to produce a molecular "fingerprint." The stained bands visible in this photograph represent fragments of DNA, and the pattern of bands varies from one person to another. The legal applications of DNA technology have become very public in recent years. You will learn more about DNA technology in Chapter 20.

Thomas put it this way in his essay "Making Science Work": "We cannot say to ourselves, we need this or that sort of technology, therefore we should be doing this or that sort of science. . . . Science is useful, indispensable sometimes, but whenever it moves forward it does so by producing a surprise; you cannot specify the surprise you'd like."*

Not all technology can be described as applied science. In fact, technology predates science, driven by inventive humans who built tools, crafted pots, mixed paints, designed musical instruments, and made clothing—all without necessarily understanding why their inventions worked. Science catalyzes certain technologies by complementing trial and error with more informed design. But the direction technology takes depends less on science than it does on the needs of humans and the values of society.

Technology has improved our standard of living in many ways, but it is a double-edged sword. Technology, especially technology that keeps people healthier, has enabled the human population to grow more than tenfold in the past three centuries. The environmental consequences are enormous. Acid rain, deforestation, global warming, nuclear accidents, ozone holes, toxic wastes, and extinction of species are just a few of the repercussions from more and more people wielding more and more technology. Science can help us identify problems and provide insight about what course of action may prevent further damage. But solutions to these problems have as much to do with politics, economics, culture, and values as with science and technology.

Now that both science and technology have become such powerful functions of society, it is more important than ever to distinguish "what we would like to understand" from "what we would like to build." Scientists should not distance themselves from technology but instead try to influence how society applies scientific discoveries. And scientists have a responsibility to help educate politicians, bureaucrats, corporate leaders, and voters about how science works and about the potential benefits and hazards of specific technologies. The crucial relationship among science, technology, and society is a theme that increases the significance of our study of life.

Biology is a multidisciplinary adventure

In some ways, biology is the most demanding of all sciences, partly because living systems are so complex and partly because biology is a multidisciplinary science that requires a knowledge of chemistry, physics, and mathematics. Modern biology is the decathlon of natural science. If you are a biology major or a preprofessional student, you have an opportunity to become a versatile scientist. If you are a physical science major or an engineering student, you will discover in the study of life many applications for what you have learned in your other science courses. If you are a nonscience student enrolled in biology as part of a liberal arts education, you have selected a course in which you can sample many scientific disciplines. And of all the sciences, biology is the most connected to the humanities and social sciences.

No matter what brings you to biology, you will find the study of life to be challenging and uplifting. Do not let the details of biology spoil a good time. The complexity of life is inspiring, but it can be overwhelming. To help you keep from "getting lost in the forest because of all the trees," each chapter of this book is constructed from a manageable number of key concepts. The concepts are listed at the beginning of the chapter, displayed throughout the chapter, and then reappear in the review at the end of the chapter. The details of a chapter enrich your understanding of the concepts and how they fit together. This introductory chapter is the exception; instead of presenting the key concepts of a particular area of biology, this chapter introduced themes that cut across all biological fields—ways of thinking about biology. These themes, along with the key concepts in each chapter, will provide you with a framework for fitting together the many things you will learn in your multidisciplinary exploration of life—and will encourage you to begin asking important questions of your own.

---

* Thomas, L. "Making Science Work." *Late Night Thoughts on Listening to Mahler's Ninth Symphony.* New York: Viking Press, 1983, p. 28.

THE CHEMISTRY OF LIFE

Mario Molina personifies two of this textbook's integrating themes: the multidisciplinary nature of biology and the relationship of science and technology to society. His research on the chemistry of the atmosphere's ozone layer and how certain pollutants are damaging that protective layer led to international awareness about a serious threat to life on Earth. In 1995, Dr. Molina was awarded the Nobel Prize in chemistry, along with Paul Crutzen and F. Sherwood Rowland. The Nobel citation clearly connected these chemists' research to biology and society: "By explaining the chemical mechanisms that affect the thickness of the ozone layer, the three researchers have contributed to our salvation from a global environmental problem that could have catastrophic consequences." I interviewed Dr. Molina in his office at the Massachusetts Institute of Technology, where he is a professor in the Department of Earth, Atmospheric, and Planetary Sciences.

Let's start with the atmosphere's ozone layer. Why is it important to life on Earth?

The ozone shield is important to biological systems because it shields the Earth's surface from powerful ultraviolet radiation that comes from the sun. This UV radiation is harmful to organisms, including humans. For example, UV radiation causes sunburn, and skin cancer can be a cumulative result of exposure. There is also evidence that UV can damage crops, such as soybeans. Certain developing animals, such as the larvae of fish, seem to be particularly sensitive. The atmosphere's ozone layer prevents most of this harmful UV radiation from reaching Earth. But it is the Achilles' heel of the atmosphere.

In what way?

The ozone shield, so crucial to life, is relatively thin and fragile. In fact, the whole atmosphere is thin, with most air located within about 30 miles of Earth. Compared to the size of the Earth, the atmosphere is like the skin of an apple. And within this thin atmosphere, ozone is very scarce, measured in parts per million. Most of that ozone is located about 15 miles from Earth, in the stratosphere. The ozone forms when high-energy solar radiation breaks apart oxygen molecules and frees oxygen atoms. These oxygen atoms then react with unbroken oxygen molecules, which consist of two bonded oxygen atoms. This forms ozone, which has three oxygen atoms. So ozone is continuously forming by the action of sunlight on the atmosphere, but this is bal-

anced by continuous destruction of the unstable ozone molecules when they react with other chemical compounds that are naturally present in the atmosphere. We've disrupted that balance by releasing certain industrial chemicals that damage the fragile ozone layer.

That's a good segue to the story of your Nobel Prize. Tell us about that research.

In 1974 we published our first paper on the CFC-ozone depletion theory. We made a prediction based on laboratory experiments on atmospheric chemistry. We predicted that our continuous release of chlorofluorocarbons, or CFCs, such as Freon, which is a brand name,

INTERVIEW

MARIO MOLINA

would damage the protective ozone layer. These compounds were used as refrigerants, as propellants in spray cans, as solvents, and in the process for making plastic foams. The CFCs were actually developed as replacements for toxic refrigerants. In fact CFCs are very stable, or unreactive, which is why they are not toxic. You can even breathe them, and nothing happens. But it is also the stability of CFCs that allows them to reach the ozone layer. Most other pollutants released into the air are removed before they reach the stratosphere. Water-soluble pollutants come back to the Earth very fast. And most pollutants that are not soluble in water, such as hydrocarbons, are oxidized by other gases in the lower atmosphere and are converted to water-soluble compounds. So the atmosphere has a pretty efficient cleansing mechanism, but only at low altitudes. The problem is that CFCs make it up to the stratosphere, where solar

radiation finally converts them to very reactive chemical species called free radicals. Those free radicals then destroy the ozone.

So, when you and your colleagues sounded this alarm in 1974, what was the reaction of the scientific community and the general public?

At first, there was very little reaction because not many people were aware of the importance of invisible things like the ozone layer and UV radiation. Experts in our research field quickly realized that the prediction of the CFC–ozone depletion theory was something to worry about, but many other scientists were skeptical, which is natural for scientists. Then as we and others in our field began doing experiments to test the idea, the case for the CFC–ozone depletion theory became strong and more and more people, including politicians, became concerned about the issue of ozone depletion. There was also growing awareness about the role of UV radiation in skin cancer and in other biological damage. Then, in 1985, scientists documented a drastic depletion of the ozone layer over the Antarctic, an ozone hole. This caused the United Nations to act in 1987.

And what was that action?

The UN Montreal Protocol of 1987 was an international agreement to reduce by one-half the amount of CFCs released into the atmosphere. Then, as evidence in support of the ozone depletion theory continued to grow, the Protocol was strengthened to require a complete phasing out of CFC production by developed countries by 1995. So that's already happened. Industrial countries are no longer manufacturing CFCs. Instead, these countries now use other refrigerants, which are destroyed in the atmosphere before they reach the ozone layer. The Montreal Protocol allowed a grace period for developing countries, a bit more time and some help from the industrial countries in the transition to CFC-free technology. That's in the works now, and CFCs will be phased out everywhere within the next decade.

Is the damage we've already inflicted on the ozone layer reversible?

Yes, because ozone is forming continuously in the atmosphere. But because CFCs are so stable and because they take so long to reach the ozone layer, the damage that we're seeing today is actually caused by CFCs released a decade ago. And CFCs will remain in the stratosphere for several more decades. So, we

predict that the ozone layer won't recover until about the middle of the next century.

Your commitment to the relationship of science to society includes your service on the President's Committee of Advisors on Science and Technology. What have you learned from that experience about the interface between science and politics?

One lesson is that science is not always something that politicians care very much about. Often, supporting science is considered a luxury. But I think the scientific community has succeeded to some extent in putting science in the limelight. Supporting science is a good investment. Another challenge is that many issues related to science and technology are long-term issues that require patience and long-term commitment. An example is our excessive production of carbon dioxide and the related possibility of global warming. Let's say that ten to twenty years from now, we realize that we really are in trouble because of global warming. We will seem foolish if we did not invest in research now if global warming does turn out to be a serious problem, which we think is a reasonable possibility.

In terms of mounting an international effort, the global warming problem is an even tougher challenge than the ozone depletion problem, right?

Fortunately, we have the precedent of the Montreal Protocol, but, yes, the climate change issue is more complicated. First of all, the accumulation of gases that could warm the planet by what is known as the greenhouse effect is occurring mainly in the lower part of the atmosphere, which is a more complex system than the stratosphere. So, there are many more scientific uncertainties than we have for the ozone problem. But it is reasonable to predict that there will be consequences of our adding these greenhouse gases to the atmosphere. We can also tell that temperatures are indeed increasing, but it's not yet that clear that this is a consequence of human activities. One could argue that much of the change is natural, although there is more and more evidence that the planet's climate is being affected by human activities. But we don't have a smoking gun yet, like we did with the ozone hole over the Antarctic. The second important difference is that reducing the release of greenhouse gases requires much more social and economic change than does reducing the release of CFCs.

Tell us more about this challenge.

The most important greenhouse gas is the carbon dioxide we're releasing by burning fos-

sil fuels and burning forests. This activity is related to energy sources, which are so important for society. Conserving energy and developing alternative energy requires much bigger change in our patterns than using other compounds in place of CFCs. What we're talking about is preserving a high standard of living and increasing the standard of living in developing countries. But we may be able to do that in clever ways, without consuming so much energy. We have some examples. Energy consumption per person in Europe is a lot less than it is in the United States. Clearly, there are some different habits. For one thing, gasoline for cars is very cheap here in the United States, so there is no incentive to be more efficient. With rapid, drastic change in energy use, we can predict that the economy would suffer. But with more gradual change and the right kind of planning and incentives, we can deal with the climate change issue. In fact, recent international agreements could change the way we use energy.

Will this seem like "changing rules" to the developing countries that are trying to improve their living standard?

That's an issue, but there is another important element that I've observed from my own experience. When I was a young person going to the university in Mexico, no one cared about pollution. Dealing with pollution seemed like a luxury. Today, everybody in Mexico City cares about pollution, so solving this problem no longer seems like something the industrialized countries want to impose upon them. The costs of pollution are enormous in Mexico City, where I was born. If only there had been insight about what would happen to the city, pollution could have been

reduced at a much lower cost. It's much more difficult to repair the environment now, but I think there is a strong incentive to do that in developing countries. It's not easy because of the complications of social and economic issues. Science and technology are very important components, but not the only ones, so scientists will have to be humble and realize their limits.

You came to MIT in 1989 after several years as a researcher at the Jet Propulsion Lab in California. Why did you decide to return to the academic community?

The main reason was to have more interaction with students. I find it very stimulating both to teach undergraduate students in the classroom and also work with graduate students in research.

What general advice can you share with the undergraduate students reading this book?

First, students should be conscious about how fun it can be to study and learn, which is difficult to realize when there are so many hurdles to go over and the work sometimes seems overwhelming. But believe me, studying can be fun. To some extent, university education is changing. There are so many things to learn and so many new developments that there is no hope of covering everything. We are not just teaching facts, but teaching how to learn. Students should discuss ideas with their professors and become engaged. Try not to be just a passive student listening to lectures, but participate actively in the process of learning.

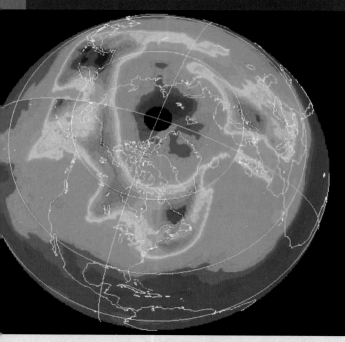

CHAPTER 2

THE CHEMICAL CONTEXT OF LIFE

Chemical Elements and Compounds

■ Matter consists of chemical elements in pure form and in combinations called compounds

■ Life requires about 25 chemical elements

Atoms and Molecules

■ Atomic structure determines the behavior of an element

■ Atoms combine by chemical bonding to form molecules

■ Weak chemical bonds play important roles in the chemistry of life

■ A molecule's biological function is related to its shape

■ Chemical reactions make and break chemical bonds

*A*long with Mario Molina, whom you met in the preceding interview, many other scientists are studying the Earth's ozone layer and its importance to life on the planet. (In this image of the northern hemisphere at the left, the areas of thinnest ozone are blue and purple.) This research involves specialists in a number of different disciplines, for unlike a college catalog of courses, nature is not packaged into biology, chemistry, physics, and the other natural sciences. Biologists are scientists who specialize in the study of life, but organisms and the world they live in are natural systems to which basic concepts of chemistry and physics apply. Biology is a multidisciplinary science.

This unit of chapters introduces key concepts of chemistry that will apply throughout our study of life. We will make many connections to the themes introduced in Chapter 1. One of those themes is the organization of life on a hierarchy of structural levels (FIGURE 2.1), with additional properties emerging at each successive level. In this unit, we will see how the theme of emergent properties applies to the lowest levels of biological organization—to the ordering of atoms into molecules and to the interactions of those molecules within cells. Somewhere in the transition from molecules to cells, we will cross the blurry boundary between nonlife and life.

CHEMICAL ELEMENTS AND COMPOUNDS

Matter consists of chemical elements in pure form and in combinations called compounds

Organisms are composed of **matter**, which is anything that takes up space and has mass.* Matter exists in many diverse forms, each with its own characteristics. Rocks, metals, wood, glass, and you and I are just a few examples of what seems an endless assortment of matter.

Some of the ancient Greek philosophers believed that the great variety of matter arises from four basic ingredients, or elements. They imagined these elements to be air, water, fire, and earth—supposedly pure substances that could not be decomposed to other forms of matter. All other substances were thought to be formed by blending various proportions of two or more of the elements. Even though these classical philosophers proposed the wrong elements, their basic idea was correct.

---

* Sometimes we substitute the term *weight* for *mass*, although the two are not equivalent. We can think of mass as the amount of matter an object represents. The weight of an object measures how strongly that mass is pulled by gravity. An astronaut in orbit in a space shuttle is weightless, but the astronaut's mass is the same as it would be on Earth. However, as long as we are earthbound, the weight of an object is a measure of its quantity of matter; so for our purposes, we can use the terms interchangeably.

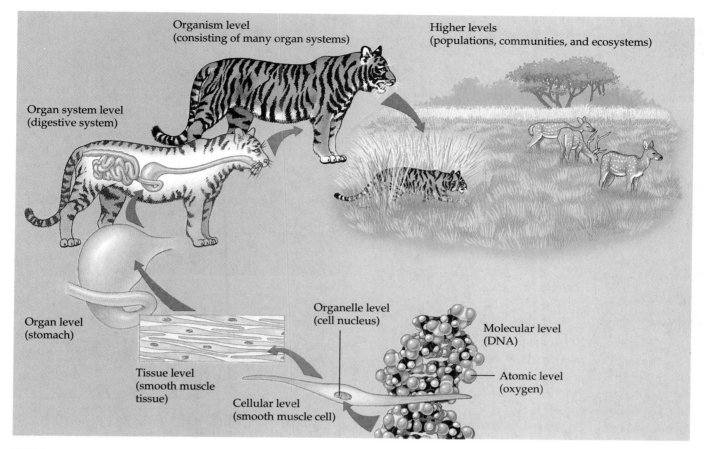

FIGURE 2.1 · The hierarchy of biological order.

An **element** is a substance that cannot be broken down to other substances by chemical reactions. Today, chemists recognize 92 elements occurring in nature; gold, copper, carbon, and oxygen are examples. Each element has a symbol, usually the first letter or two of its name. Some of the symbols are derived from Latin or German names; for instance, the symbol for sodium is Na, from the Latin word *natrium.*

A **compound** is a substance consisting of two or more elements combined in a fixed ratio. Table salt, for example, is sodium chloride (NaCl), a compound composed of the elements sodium (Na) and chlorine (Cl) in a 1:1 ratio. Pure sodium is a metal and pure chlorine is a poisonous gas.

Chemically combined, however, sodium and chlorine form an edible compound. This is a simple example of organized matter having emergent properties: A compound has characteristics beyond those of its combined elements (FIGURE 2.2).

Life requires about 25 chemical elements

About 25 of the 92 natural elements are known to be essential to life. Just four of these—carbon (C), oxygen (O), hydrogen (H), and nitrogen (N)—make up 96% of living matter. Phosphorus (P), sulfur (S), calcium (Ca), potassium (K), and a few other elements account for most of the remaining 4% of an

Sodium + Chlorine → Sodium chloride

FIGURE 2.2 · The emergent properties of a compound. The metal sodium combines with the poisonous gas chlorine to form the edible compound sodium chloride, or table salt.

Table 2.1 ■ Naturally Occurring Elements in the Human Body

SYMBOL	ELEMENT	ATOMIC NUMBER (See p. 25)	PERCENTAGE OF HUMAN BODY WEIGHT
O	Oxygen	8	65.0
C	Carbon	6	18.5
H	Hydrogen	1	9.5
N	Nitrogen	7	3.3
Ca	Calcium	20	1.5
P	Phosphorus	15	1.0
K	Potassium	19	0.4
S	Sulfur	16	0.3
Na	Sodium	11	0.2
Cl	Chlorine	17	0.2
Mg	Magnesium	12	0.1

Trace elements (less than 0.01%): boron (B), chromium (Cr), cobalt (Co), copper (Cu), fluorine (F), iodine (I), iron (Fe), manganese (Mn), molybdenum (Mo), selenium (Se), silicon (Si), tin (Sn), vanadium (V), and zinc (Zn).

FIGURE 2.4 ■ Goiter. The enlarged thyroid gland of this Malaysian woman is due to an iodine deficiency.

organism's weight. TABLE 2.1 lists by percentage the elements that make up the human body. FIGURE 2.3 illustrates a deficiency of the essential element nitrogen in plants.

Trace elements are those required by an organism in only minute quantities. Some trace elements, such as iron (Fe), are needed by all forms of life; others are required only by certain species. For example, in vertebrates (animals with backbones), the element iodine (I) is an essential ingredient of a hormone produced by the thyroid gland. A daily intake of only 0.15 milligram (mg) of iodine is adequate for normal activity of the human thyroid. An iodine deficiency in the diet causes the thyroid gland to grow to abnormal size, a condition called goiter (FIGURE 2.4). Where it is available, iodized salt has reduced the incidence of goiter.

FIGURE 2.3 ■ Nitrogen deficiency in corn. In this controlled experiment, the plants on the left are growing in soil that was fertilized with compounds containing nitrogen, an essential element. The soil on the right is deficient in nitrogen. If the poorly nourished crop growing in this soil is harvested, it will yield less food—and less nutritious food—than the crop on the left.

ATOMS AND MOLECULES

The properties of chemical elements and of the compounds they form, including the compounds crucial to life, ultimately result from the structure of atoms.

Atomic structure determines the behavior of an element

2.1 Each element consists of a certain kind of atom that is different from the atoms of any other element. An **atom** is the smallest unit of matter that still retains the properties of an element. Atoms are so small that it would take about a million of them to stretch across the period printed at the end of this sentence. We symbolize atoms with the same abbreviation used for the element made up of those atoms; thus, C stands for both the element carbon and a single carbon atom.

Subatomic Particles

Although the atom is the smallest unit having the properties of its element, these tiny bits of matter are composed of even smaller parts, called subatomic particles. Physicists have split the atom into more than a hundred types of particles, but only three kinds of particles are stable enough to be of relevance here: **neutrons**, **protons**, and **electrons**. Neutrons and protons are packed together tightly to form a dense core, or **atomic nucleus**, at the center of the atom. The electrons, moving at nearly the speed of light, form a cloud around the nucleus (FIGURE 2.5).

Electrons and protons are electrically charged. Each electron has one unit of negative charge, and each proton has one

2.1 This symbol links topics in the text to interactive exercises in the CD-ROM that accompanies the book. The number indicates the appropriate activity in the CD.

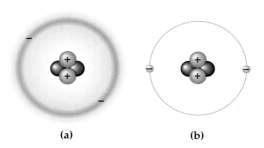

(a)   **(b)**

FIGURE 2.5 ▪ Two simplified models of a helium (He) atom. The helium nucleus consists of two neutrons (gray) and two protons (magenta). **(a)** The nucleus is surrounded by a cloud of negative charge (blue), owing to the rapid movement of two electrons. **(b)** The circle indicates the average distance of the electrons from the nucleus, although this distance is not drawn to scale compared to the size of the nucleus. (Our model of an atom will be refined as the chapter progresses.)

unit of positive charge. A neutron, as its name implies, is electrically neutral. Protons give the nucleus a positive charge, and it is the attraction between opposite charges that keeps the rapidly moving electrons in the vicinity of the nucleus.

The neutron and proton are almost identical in mass, each about 1.7×10^{-24} grams (g). Grams and other conventional units are not very useful for describing the mass of objects so minuscule. Thus, for atoms and subatomic particles, we use a unit of measurement called the **dalton**, in honor of John Dalton, the British scientist who helped develop atomic theory around 1800. Neutrons and protons have masses close to 1 dalton (1.009 and 1.007, respectively). Because the mass of an electron is only about $1/2000$ that of a neutron or proton, we can ignore electrons when computing the total mass of an atom.

Atomic Number and Atomic Weight

Atoms of the various elements differ in their number of subatomic particles. All atoms of a particular element have the same number of protons in their nuclei. This number of protons, which is unique to that element, is referred to as the **atomic number** and is written as a subscript to the left of the symbol for the element. The abbreviation $_2$He, for example, tells us that an atom of the element helium has two protons in its nucleus. Unless otherwise indicated, an atom is neutral in electrical charge, which means that its protons must be balanced by an equal number of electrons. Therefore, the atomic number tells us the number of protons and also the number of electrons in an electrically neutral atom.

We can deduce the number of neutrons from a second quantity, the **mass number**, which is the sum of protons plus neutrons in the nucleus of an atom. The mass number is written as a superscript to the left of an element's symbol. For example, we can use this shorthand to write an atom of helium as $^4_2$He. Because the atomic number indicates how many protons there are, we can determine the quantity of neutrons by subtracting the atomic number from the mass number: A $^4_2$He atom has 2 neutrons. An atom of sodium,

$^{23}_{11}$Na, has 11 protons, 11 electrons, and 12 neutrons. The simplest atom is hydrogen, $^1_1$H, which has no neutrons—a lone proton with a single electron moving around it constitutes a hydrogen atom.

Almost all of an atom's mass is concentrated in its nucleus, because the contribution of electrons to mass is negligible. Because neutrons and protons each have a mass very close to 1 dalton, the mass number is an approximation of the total mass of an atom, usually called its **atomic weight**. Thus, we might say that the atomic weight of helium ($^4_2$He) is 4 daltons, although more precisely it is 4.003 daltons.

Isotopes

All atoms of a given element have the same number of protons, but some atoms have more neutrons than other atoms of the same element and therefore weigh more. These different atomic forms are referred to as **isotopes** of the element. In nature, an element occurs as a mixture of its isotopes. For example, consider the three isotopes of the element carbon, which has the atomic number 6. The most common isotope is carbon-12, $^{12}_6$C, which accounts for about 99% of the carbon in nature. It has 6 neutrons. Most of the remaining 1% of carbon consists of atoms of the isotope $^{13}_6$C, with 7 neutrons. A third, even rarer isotope, $^{14}_6$C, has 8 neutrons. Notice that all three isotopes of carbon have 6 protons—otherwise, they would not be carbon. (The number usually given as the atomic weight of an element is actually an average of the atomic weights of all the element's naturally occurring isotopes.)

Both ^{12}C and ^{13}C are stable isotopes, meaning that their nuclei do not have a tendency to lose particles. The isotope ^{14}C, however, is unstable, or radioactive. A **radioactive isotope** is one in which the nucleus decays spontaneously, giving off particles and energy. When the decay leads to a change in the number of protons, it transforms the atom to an atom of a different element. For example, radioactive carbon decays to form nitrogen.

Radioactive isotopes have many useful applications in biology. In Chapter 25 you will learn how researchers use measurements of radioactivity in fossils to date those relics of past life. Radioactive isotopes are also useful as tracers to follow atoms through metabolism, the chemical processes of an organism (see the Methods Box, p. 30). Cells use the radioactive atoms as they would nonradioactive isotopes of the same element, but the radioactive tracers can be readily detected. Radioactive tracers have become important diagnostic tools in medicine. For example, certain kidney disorders can be diagnosed by injecting small doses of substances containing radioactive isotopes into the blood and then measuring the amount of tracer excreted in the urine.

Although radioactive isotopes are very useful in biological research and medicine, radiation from these decaying isotopes also poses a hazard to life by damaging cellular molecules. The

FIGURE 2.6 • The Chernobyl accident. In 1986, an explosion and fire at a nuclear power plant in Chernobyl, Ukraine, released clouds of dangerously radioactive materials into the air, producing widespread contamination downwind. The militiaman in this photo controls access to an evacuated town in the region.

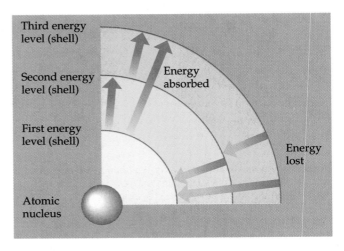

FIGURE 2.7 • Energy levels of an atom's electrons. Electrons exist only at fixed levels of potential energy. An electron can move from one level to another only if the energy it gains or loses is exactly equal to the difference in energy between the two levels. Arrows indicate some of the stepwise changes in potential energy that are possible. These energy levels are also called electron shells.

severity of this damage depends on the type and amount of radiation an organism absorbs. One of the most serious environmental threats is radioactive fallout from nuclear accidents (FIGURE 2.6).

The Energy Levels of Electrons

The simplified models of the atom in FIGURE 2.5 greatly exaggerate the size of the nucleus relative to the volume of the whole atom. If the nucleus were the size of a golf ball, the electrons would be moving about the nucleus at an average distance of approximately 1 kilometer (km). Atoms are mostly empty space.

When two atoms approach each other during a chemical reaction, their nuclei do not come close enough to interact. Of the three kinds of subatomic particles we have discussed, only electrons are directly involved in the chemical reactions between atoms.

An atom's electrons vary in the amount of energy they possess. **Energy** is defined as the ability to do work. **Potential energy** is the energy that matter stores because of its position or location. For example, because of its altitude, water in a reservoir on a hill has potential energy. When the gates of the reservoir's dam are opened and the water runs downhill, the energy is taken out of storage to do work, such as turning generators. Because potential energy has been expended, the water stores less energy at the bottom of the hill than it did in the reservoir. Matter has a natural tendency to move to the lowest possible state of potential energy; in this example, water runs downhill. To restore the potential energy of a reservoir, work must be done to elevate the water against gravity.

The electrons of an atom also have potential energy, because of their position in relation to the nucleus. The negatively charged electrons are attracted to the positively charged

nucleus; the more distant the electrons are from the nucleus, the greater their potential energy. Unlike the continuous flow of water downhill, changes in the potential energy of electrons can occur only in steps of fixed amounts. An electron having a certain discrete amount of energy is analogous to a ball on a staircase. The ball can have different amounts of potential energy, depending on which step it is on, but it cannot spend much time between the steps.

The different states of potential energy for electrons in an atom are called **energy levels**, or **electron shells** (FIGURE 2.7). The first shell is closest to the nucleus, and electrons in this shell have the lowest energy. Electrons in the second shell have more energy, electrons in the third shell more energy still, and so on. An electron can change its shell, but only by absorbing or losing an amount of energy equal to the difference in potential energy between the old shell and the new shell. To move to a shell farther out from the nucleus, the electron must absorb energy. For example, light energy can excite an electron to a higher energy level. (Indeed, this is the first step when plants harness light energy for photosynthesis, the process that produces food from carbon dioxide and water.) To move to a shell closer in, an electron must lose energy, which is usually released to the environment in the form of heat. For example, when sunlight excites electrons in the paint of a car roof to higher energy levels, the roof heats up as the electrons fall back to their original levels.

Electron Orbitals

Early in the twentieth century, the electron shells of an atom were visualized as concentric paths of electrons orbiting the nucleus, somewhat like planets orbiting the sun. It is still convenient to use concentric-circle diagrams to symbolize elec-

tron shells, as in FIGURE 2.7. The atom is not this simple, however. In fact, we can never know the exact path of an electron. What we can do instead is describe the volume of space in which an electron spends most of its time. The three-dimensional space where an electron is found 90% of the time is called an **orbital** (FIGURE 2.8).

No more than two electrons can occupy the same orbital. The first energy shell has a single orbital and can thereby accommodate a maximum of two electrons. This orbital, which is spherical in shape, is designated the 1s orbital. The lone electron of a hydrogen atom occupies the 1s orbital, as do the two electrons of a helium atom. Electrons, like all matter, tend to exist in the lowest available state of potential energy, which they have in the first shell. An atom with more than two electrons must use higher shells because the first shell is full.

The second electron shell can hold eight electrons, two in each of four orbitals. Electrons in the four different orbitals all have nearly the same energy, but they move in different volumes of space. There is a 2s orbital, spherical in shape like the 1s orbital, but with a greater diameter. The other three orbitals, called 2p orbitals, are dumbbell-shaped, each oriented at right angles to the other two. (At higher energy levels, the orbitals are referred to as 3s, 3p, and so on.)

Electron Configuration and Chemical Properties

The chemical behavior of an atom is determined by its electron configuration—that is, the distribution of electrons in the atom's electron shells. Beginning with hydrogen, the simplest atom, we can imagine building the atoms of other elements by adding one proton and one electron at a time (along with an appropriate number of neutrons). FIGURE 2.9, p. 28, an abbreviated version of what is called a periodic table, shows this distribution of electrons for the first 18 elements, from hydrogen ($_1$H) to argon ($_{18}$Ar). The elements are arranged in three rows, or periods, corresponding to the sequential addition of electrons to orbitals in the first three electron shells. The main point is that the chemical properties of an atom depend mostly on the number of electrons in its *outermost* shell. We refer to those outer electrons as **valence electrons**, and to the outermost electron shell as the **valence shell**.

An atom with a completed valence shell is unreactive; that is, it will not interact readily with other atoms it encounters. At the far right of the periodic table are helium, neon, and argon, the only three elements shown that have full valence shells. They are termed inert elements because they are chemically unreactive. All other atoms shown in FIGURE 2.9 are chemically reactive because they have unfilled valence shells. This reactivity actually arises from the presence of unpaired electrons in the valence shell. As we "build" the electronic

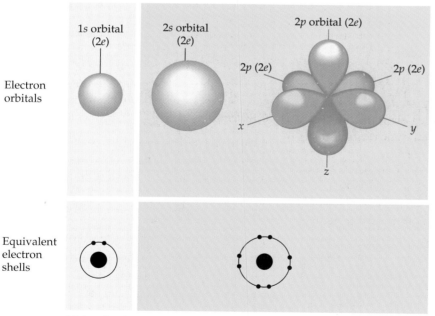
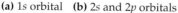

(a) 1s orbital   (b) 2s and 2p orbitals

(c) Neon ($_{10}$Ne): 1s, 2s and 2p

FIGURE 2.8 ▪ **Electron orbitals.** These three-dimensional shapes represent the volumes of space where the constantly moving electrons of an atom are most likely to be found. Each orbital holds a maximum of two electrons. **(a)** The first electron shell has one spherical *(s)* orbital, designated 1s. Only this orbital is occupied in hydrogen, which has one electron, and helium, which has two electrons. **(b)** The second and all higher shells each have one larger *s* orbital (designated 2s, in the case of the second shell) plus three dumbbell-shaped orbitals called *p* orbitals (2p for the second shell). The three 2p orbitals are arranged at right angles to one another along imaginary *x, y,* and *z* axes of the atom. The third and higher electron shells can hold additional electrons in orbitals of more complex shapes. **(c)** To symbolize the electron orbitals of the element neon, which has a total of ten electrons, we superimpose the 1s orbital of the first shell and the 2s and three 2p orbitals of the second shell. (Each orbital, remember, can hold two electrons.) The small dots in the electron-shell diagrams represent electrons.

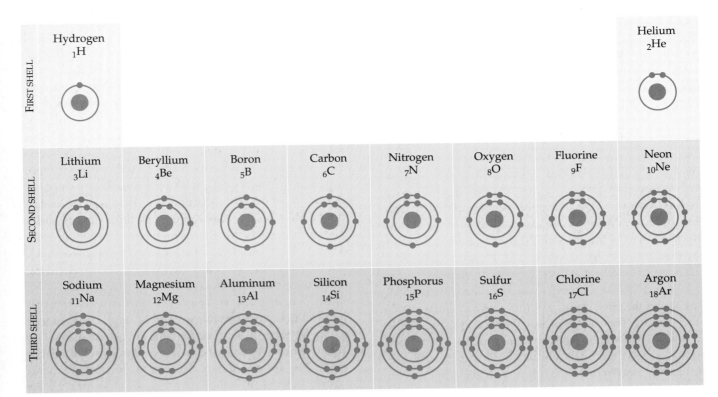

2.1
FIGURE 2.9 ▪ Electron configurations of the first 18 elements. In these diagrams, electrons are shown as blue dots and energy levels (electron shells) as concentric rings. (The orbitals of each shell are not shown, but two electrons occupying the same orbital are drawn as a pair.) The elements are arranged in rows, each representing the filling of an electron shell. As electrons are added, they occupy the lowest available shell. Hydrogen's one electron and helium's two electrons are located in the first shell. The next element, lithium, has three electrons. Two electrons fill the first shell while the third electron occupies the second shell (not some higher shell). This behavior of electrons illustrates the general tendency for matter to exist in its lowest state of potential energy. The outermost energy level occupied by electrons is called the valence shell. Of these first 18 elements, only helium, neon, and argon have atoms with full valence shells; such elements are called inert because they are unreactive. All other elements in this figure consist of atoms with incomplete valence shells; these atoms are chemically reactive. Note that, within a shell, one electron goes into each orbital before any orbital gets a second. The reactivity of an atom is due to unpaired electrons. Elements with the same number of valence electrons—fluorine and chlorine, for instance—have similar chemical properties.

configurations in FIGURE 2.9 by adding electrons, we first place just one electron in each orbital of the valence shell; only then do the orbitals begin to receive a second electron.

Atoms with the same number of electrons in their valence shells exhibit similar chemical behavior. For example, fluorine (F) and chlorine (Cl) both have seven valence electrons, and both combine with the element sodium to form compounds.

Atoms combine by chemical bonding to form molecules

Now that we have looked at the structure of atoms, we will move up in the hierarchy of organization and see how atoms combine to form molecules. Atoms with incomplete valence shells interact with certain other atoms in such a way that each partner completes its valence shell. Atoms do this by either sharing or transferring valence electrons. These interactions usually result in atoms staying close together, held by attractions called **chemical bonds**. The strongest kinds of chemical bonds are covalent bonds and ionic bonds.

Covalent Bonds

2.3
A **covalent bond** is the sharing of a pair of valence electrons by two atoms. For example, let's consider what happens when two hydrogen atoms approach each other. Recall that hydrogen has one valence electron in the first shell, but the shell's capacity is two electrons. When the two hydrogen atoms come close enough for their 1s orbitals to overlap, they share their electrons. Each hydrogen atom now has two electrons associated with it in what amounts to a completed valence shell. Two or more atoms held together by covalent bonds constitute a **molecule**. In this case, we have formed a hydrogen molecule (FIGURE 2.10a). We can abbreviate the structure of this molecule as H—H, where the line represents a covalent bond—that is, a pair of shared electrons. This notation, which represents both atoms and bonding, is called a **structural formula**. We can abbreviate even further by writing H_2, a **molecular formula** indicating simply that the molecule consists of two atoms of hydrogen.

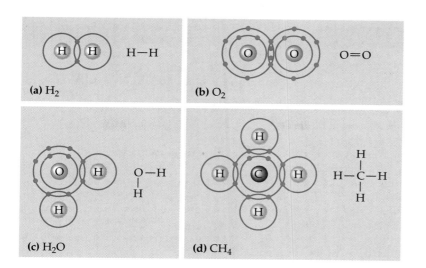

⮕ 2.3 **FIGURE 2.10** · **Covalent bonding in four molecules.** Each covalent bond consists of a pair of shared electrons. The number of electrons required to complete an atom's valence shell determines how many bonds that atom will form. **(a)** If two unattached hydrogen atoms meet, they can form a single covalent bond. **(b)** Two oxygen atoms form a molecule by sharing two pairs of valence electrons; the atoms are joined by a double covalent bond. **(c)** Two hydrogen atoms can be joined to one oxygen atom by covalent bonds to produce a molecule of water. **(d)** Four hydrogen atoms can satisfy the valence of one carbon atom, forming methane.

With six electrons in its second electron shell, oxygen needs *two* more electrons to complete its valence shell. Two oxygen atoms form a molecule by sharing *two* pairs of valence electrons (FIGURE 2.10b). The atoms are thus joined by what is called a **double covalent bond**.

Each atom that can share valence electrons has a bonding capacity corresponding to the number of covalent bonds the atom can form. When the bonds form, they give the atom a full complement of valence electrons. This bonding capacity is called the atom's **valence** and equals the number of unpaired electrons in the atom's outermost (valence) shell. You can readily determine the valences of life's most abundant elements from the electron configurations in FIGURE 2.9: The valence of hydrogen is 1; oxygen, 2; nitrogen, 3; and carbon, 4. One slightly more complicated case is phosphorus (P), another element important to life. Phosphorus can have a valence of 3, as we would predict. In biologically important molecules, however, it generally has a valence of 5, forming three single bonds and one double bond.

The molecules H_2 and O_2 are pure elements, not compounds. (Recall that a compound is a combination of two or more *different* elements.) An example of a molecule that is a compound is water, with the molecular formula H_2O. It takes two atoms of hydrogen to satisfy the valence of one oxygen atom. FIGURE 2.10c shows the structure of a water molecule. This molecule is so important to life that the next chapter is devoted entirely to its structure and behavior.

Another molecule that is a compound is methane, the main component of natural gas, with the molecular formula CH_4 (FIGURE 2.10d). It takes four hydrogen atoms, each with a valence of 1, to complement one atom of carbon, with its valence of 4. We will look at many other compounds of carbon in Chapter 4.

Nonpolar and Polar Covalent Bonds. The attraction of an atom for the electrons of a covalent bond is called its **electronegativity**. The more electronegative an atom, the more strongly it pulls shared electrons toward itself. In a covalent bond between two atoms of the same element, the outcome of the tug-of-war for common electrons is a standoff; the two atoms are equally electronegative. Such a bond is a **nonpolar covalent bond**; the electrons are shared equally. The covalent bond of H_2 is nonpolar, as is the double bond of O_2. The bonds of methane (CH_4) are also nonpolar; although the partners are different elements, carbon and hydrogen do not differ substantially in electronegativity. This is not always the case in a compound where covalent bonds join atoms of different elements. If one atom is more electronegative than the other, electrons of the bond will not be shared equally. In such cases, the bond is called a **polar covalent bond**. In a water molecule, the bonds between oxygen and hydrogen are polar (FIGURE 2.11). Oxygen is one of the most electronegative of the 92 elements, attracting shared electrons much more strongly than hydrogen does. In a covalent bond between oxygen and hydrogen, the electrons spend more time near the oxygen atom than

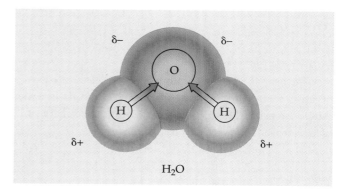

FIGURE 2.11 · **Polar covalent bonds in a water molecule.** Oxygen, being much more electronegative than hydrogen, pulls the shared electrons of the bond toward itself, as indicated by the arrows. This unequal sharing of electrons gives the oxygen a slight negative charge and the hydrogens a small positive charge. The Greek symbol delta (δ) indicates that the charges are less than full units. This "space-filling" model approximates the true shape of H_2O.

Radioactive isotopes are among the most versatile tools in biological research. Because organisms process radioactive and stable isotopes of the same element in exactly the same way, radioactive isotopes can serve as "spies" within an organism. Scientists use them to label certain chemical substances in order to follow a metabolic process or to locate the substance within an organism.

Here you see an experiment designed to determine how temperature affects the rate at which a population of dividing animal cells makes new copies of its DNA, the substance that functions as genetic information, and to locate the new DNA within the cells. First, the cells are grown in a medium that includes the ingredients for making DNA. One ingredient, thymidine, is labeled with ^3H, a radioactive isotope of hydrogen. Any new DNA the cells make will incorporate radioactive thymidine.

Cells are grown at various temperatures. After a certain amount of time, samples are taken from each culture, the cells are killed, and their DNA is bound to pieces of filter paper. The papers are then placed in vials containing scintillation fluid, which emits flashes of light whenever radiation from the decay of the tracer in the DNA excites certain chemicals in the fluid. The frequency of flashes, proportional to the amount of radioactive material present, is measured in counts per minute by placing the vials in a scintillation counter (FIGURE a). The higher the counts per minute, the more DNA the cells have made. When the counts for the various DNA samples are plotted against

the temperature at which the cells were grown (FIGURE b), it is apparent that temperature dramatically affects the rate of DNA synthesis. This result might be useful to researchers studying the details of DNA synthesis.

A technique known as autoradiography can be used to locate the radioactively labeled DNA within the cells. Thin slices of the cells are placed on glass slides and kept for some time in the dark covered by a layer of photographic emulsion. Radiation from the radioactive tracer present in any new DNA exposes the photographic emulsion, creating a pattern of black dots. IN FIGURE c, radioactive DNA in the cell on the left is clearly located in the nucleus.

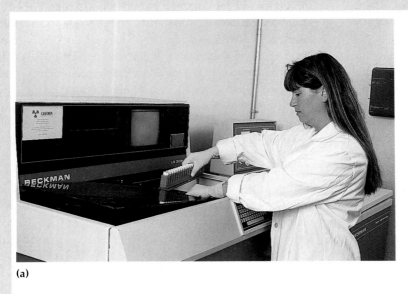

(a)

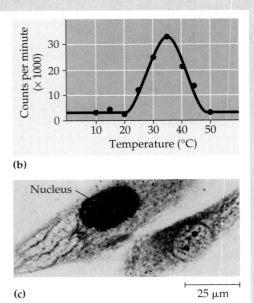

(b)

(c)

Nucleus

25 μm

they do near the hydrogen atom. Because electrons have a negative charge, the unequal sharing of electrons in water causes the oxygen atom to have a slight negative charge and each hydrogen atom a slight positive charge.

Ionic Bonds

In some cases, two atoms are so unequal in their attraction for valence electrons that the more electronegative atom strips an electron completely away from its partner. This is what happens when an atom of sodium ($_{11}Na$) encounters an atom of chlorine ($_{17}Cl$) (FIGURE 2.12). A sodium atom has a total of 11 electrons, with its single valence electron in the third electron

shell. A chlorine atom has a total of 17 electrons, with 7 electrons in its valence shell. When these two atoms meet, the lone valence electron of sodium is transferred to the chlorine atom, and both atoms end up with their valence shells complete. (Because sodium no longer has an electron in the third shell, the second shell is now outermost.)

The electron transfer between the two atoms moves one unit of negative charge from sodium to chlorine. Sodium, now with 11 protons but only 10 electrons, has a net electrical charge of $+1$. A charged atom (or molecule) is called an **ion**. When the charge is positive, the ion is specifically called a **cation**. Conversely, the chlorine atom, having gained an extra electron, now has 17 protons and 18 electrons, giving it a net

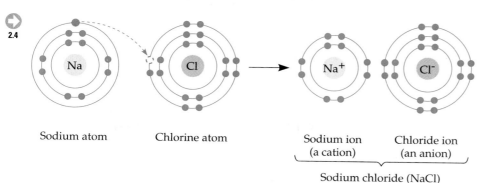

FIGURE 2.12 · **Electron transfer and ionic bonding.** A valence electron can be transferred from sodium (Na) to chlorine (Cl), giving both atoms completed valence shells. The electron transfer leaves the sodium atom with a net charge of +1 (cation) and the chlorine atom with a net charge of −1 (anion). The attraction between the oppositely charged atoms, or ions, is an ionic bond. Ions can bond not only to atoms with which they have reacted, but to any other ions of opposite charge.

Sodium atom · Chlorine atom · Sodium ion (a cation) · Chloride ion (an anion)

Sodium chloride (NaCl)

electrical charge of −1. It has become a chloride ion—an **anion**, or negatively charged ion. Because of their opposite charges, cations and anions attract each other in what is called an **ionic bond.** *Any* two ions of opposite charge can form an ionic bond. The ions need not have acquired their charge by an electron transfer with each other.

Ionic compounds are called salts. We know the compound sodium chloride (NaCl) as table salt (FIGURE 2.13). Salts are often found in nature as crystals of various sizes and shapes, each an aggregate of vast numbers of cations and anions bonded by their electrical attraction and arranged in a three-dimensional lattice. A salt crystal does not consist of molecules in the same sense that a covalent compound does, because a covalently bonded molecule has a definite size and number of atoms. The formula for an ionic compound, such as NaCl, indicates only the ratio of elements in a crystal of the salt.

Not all salts have equal numbers of cations and anions. For example, the ionic compound magnesium chloride ($MgCl_2$) has two chloride ions for each magnesium ion. Magnesium ($_{12}Mg$) must lose two outer electrons if the atom is to have a complete valence shell, so it tends to form a cation with a net charge of +2 (Mg^{2+}). One magnesium cation can then form ionic bonds with two chloride anions.

FIGURE 2.13 · **A sodium chloride crystal.** The sodium ions (Na^+) and chloride ions (Cl^-) are held together by ionic bonds.

The term *ion* also applies to entire molecules that are electrically charged. In the salt ammonium chloride (NH_4Cl), for instance, the anion is a single chloride ion (Cl^-), but the cation is ammonium (NH_4^+), a nitrogen atom with four covalently bonded hydrogen atoms. The whole ammonium ion has an electrical charge of +1 because it is one electron short.

Environment affects the strength of ionic bonds. In a dry salt crystal, the bonds are so strong that it takes a hammer and chisel to break enough of them to crack the crystal in two. Place the same salt crystal in water, however, and the salt dissolves as the attractions between its ions decrease. In the next chapter you will learn how water dissolves salts.

Weak chemical bonds play important roles in the chemistry of life

Covalent bonds are essential to life because they link atoms to form a cell's molecules. But bonding *between* molecules is also indispensable in the cell, where the properties of life emerge from molecular interactions. When two molecules in the cell make contact, they may adhere temporarily by types of chemical bonds that are much weaker than covalent bonds. The advantage of weak bonding is that the contact between the molecules can be brief; the molecules come together, respond to one another in some way, and then separate.

The importance of weak bonding can be seen in the example of chemical signaling in the brain. One brain cell signals another by releasing molecules that use weak bonds to dock onto receptor molecules on the nearby surface of a receiving cell. The bonds last just long enough to trigger a momentary response by the receiving cell. If the signal molecules attached by stronger bonds, the receiving cell would continue to respond long after the transmitting cell ceased dispatching the message, with perhaps disastrous consequences. (Imagine what it would be like, for instance, if your brain continued to perceive the ringing sound of a bell for hours after nerve cells transmitted the information from the ears to the brain.)

Several types of weak chemical bonds are important in living organisms. One is the ionic bond, which is relatively weak in the presence of water. Another type of weak bond, crucial to life, is known as a hydrogen bond.

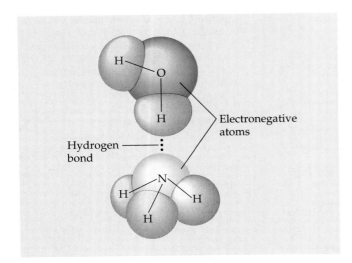

FIGURE 2.14 · **A hydrogen bond.** Through a weak electrical attraction, one electronegative atom shares a hydrogen atom with another electronegative atom. In this diagram, a hydrogen bond joins a hydrogen atom of a water molecule (H_2O) with the nitrogen atom of an ammonia molecule (NH_3).

Hydrogen Bonds

Among the various kinds of weak chemical bonds, hydrogen bonds are so important in the chemistry of life that they deserve special attention. A **hydrogen bond** occurs when a hydrogen atom covalently bonded to one electronegative atom is also attracted to another electronegative atom. In living cells, the electronegative partners involved are usually oxygen or nitrogen atoms.

Let's examine the simple case of hydrogen bonding between water (H_2O) and ammonia (NH_3) (FIGURE 2.14). You have seen how the polar covalent bonds of water result in the oxygen atom having a slight negative charge and the hydrogen atoms having a slight positive charge. A similar situation arises in the ammonia molecule, where an electronegative nitrogen atom has a small amount of negative charge because of its pull on the electrons it shares covalently with hydrogen. If a water molecule and an ammonia molecule are close together, a weak attraction will occur between the negatively charged nitrogen atom and a positively charged hydrogen atom of the adjacent water molecule. This attraction is a hydrogen bond.

Van der Waals Interactions

Even a molecule with nonpolar covalent bonds may have positively and negatively charged regions. Because electrons are in constant motion, they are not always symmetrically distributed in the molecule; at any instant, they may accumulate by chance in one part of the molecule or another. The results are ever-changing "hot spots" of positive and negative charge that enable all atoms and molecules to stick to one another. These

van der Waals interactions are weak and occur only when atoms and molecules are very close together.

Van der Waals interactions, hydrogen bonds, ionic bonds, and other weak bonds may form not only between molecules but also between different regions of a single large molecule, such as a protein. Although these bonds are individually weak, their cumulative effect is to reinforce the three-dimensional shape of a large molecule. You will learn more about the biological roles of weak bonds in Chapter 5.

A molecule's biological function is related to its shape

A molecule has a characteristic size and shape. The precise shape of a molecule is usually very important to its function in the living cell.

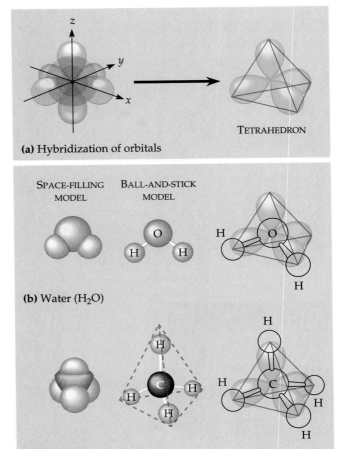

FIGURE 2.15 · **Molecular shapes due to hybrid orbitals. (a)** The four teardrop-shaped orbitals of a valence shell involved in covalent bonding form by hybridization of the single *s* and three *p* orbitals. The orbitals extend to the four corners of an imaginary tetrahedron (outlined in magenta). **(b)** Because of the positions of the hybrid orbitals, the two covalent bonds of water are angled at 104.5°. This is seen most clearly in the ball-and-stick model. The space-filling model comes closer to the actual shape of the molecule. **(c)** The hydrogens of methane occupy all four corners of the tetrahedron, giving methane a tetrahedral shape.

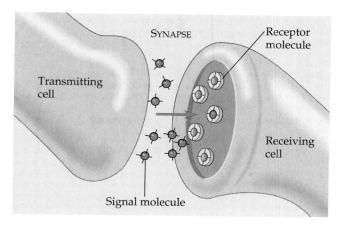

FIGURE 2.16 · **Molecular shape and brain chemistry.** One nerve cell in the brain signals another by releasing molecules with a shape that is complementary to the shape of receptor molecules located on the surface of the receiving cell. The signal molecules pass across the tiny gap (called the synapse) between the two nerve cells and attach to the receptors by weak bonds, stimulating the receiving cell in the process. The actual molecules have much more complex shapes than represented here. The role of molecular shape in brain chemistry is an example of the correlation between structure and function, one of biology's unifying themes.

A molecule consisting of two atoms, such as H_2 or O_2, is always linear, but molecules with more than two atoms have more complicated shapes. These shapes are determined by the positions of the atoms' orbitals. When an atom forms covalent bonds, the orbitals in its valence shell rearrange. For atoms with valence electrons in both *s* and *p* orbitals (see FIGURE 2.8), the single *s* and three *p* orbitals hybridize to form four new orbitals shaped like identical teardrops extending from the region of the atomic nucleus (FIGURE 2.15a). If we connect the larger ends of the teardrops with lines, we have the outline of a pyramidal shape called a tetrahedron.

For the water molecule (H_2O), two of the hybrid orbitals in the oxygen atom's valence shell are shared with hydrogen atoms. The result is a molecule shaped roughly like a V, its two covalent bonds spread apart at an angle of 104.5° (FIGURE 2.15b).

The methane molecule (CH_4) has the shape of a completed tetrahedron, because all four hybrid orbitals are shared (FIGURE 2.15c). The nucleus of the carbon atom is at the center, with its four covalent bonds radiating to the hydrogen nuclei at the corners of the tetrahedron. Larger molecules containing multiple carbon atoms, including many of the molecules that make up living matter, have more complex overall shapes. However, the tetrahedral shape of a carbon atom bonded to four other atoms is often a repeating motif within such molecules.

Molecular shape is crucial in biology because it determines how most molecules of life recognize and respond to one another. For instance, in the brain-cell signaling example mentioned earlier, the signal molecules released by the transmitting cell have a unique shape that specifically fits together with the shape of the receptor molecules on the surface of the receiving cell, much as a key fits into a lock (FIGURE 2.16). (This complementarity of shape aids the formation of weak bonds.) Molecules that have shapes similar to the brain's signal molecules can affect mood and pain perception. Morphine, heroin, and other opiate drugs, for example, mimic natural signal molecules called endorphins (FIGURE 2.17). These drugs artificially produce euphoria and relieve pain by binding to endorphin receptors in the brain.

Chemical reactions make and break chemical bonds

The making and breaking of chemical bonds, leading to changes in the composition of matter, are called **chemical**

FIGURE 2.17 · **A molecular mimic.** An endorphin is a natural brain signal molecule that helps us feel good. The boxed portion of the endorphin molecule is the shape that is recognized by receptor molecules on appropriate target cells in the brain. The boxed portion of the morphine molecule, an opiate drug, is a close match. Morphine, a chemical imposter, affects emotional state by mimicking the brain's natural endorphins. The discovery that opiates bind to receptors in the brain that normally recognize the brain's own endorphins was a major milestone in neurochemistry.

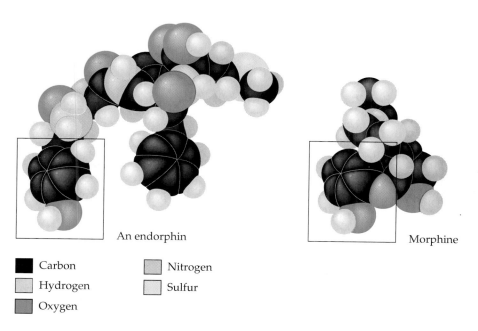

An endorphin   Morphine

■ Carbon	▢ Nitrogen
▢ Hydrogen	▢ Sulfur
▨ Oxygen	

FIGURE 2.18 ▪ **Photosynthesis: a solar-powered rearrangement of matter.** This *Elodea*, a freshwater plant, produces sugars and other food by rearranging the atoms of carbon dioxide and water in the chemical process known as photosynthesis. Sunlight powers this chemical transformation. The oxygen bubbles escaping from the leaves are by-products of photosynthesis. Humans and other animals ultimately depend on photosynthesis for food and oxygen, and this process is at the foundation of almost all ecosystems. Photosynthesis is an important example of how chemistry applies to the study of life.

reactions. An example is the reaction between hydrogen and oxygen to form water:

$$2\,H_2 \;+\; O_2 \longrightarrow 2\,H_2O$$

Reactants → Products

This reaction breaks the covalent bonds of H_2 and O_2 and forms the new bonds of H_2O. When we write a chemical reaction, we use an arrow to indicate the conversion of the starting materials, called **reactants**, to the **products**. The coefficients indicate the number of molecules involved; for example, the 2 in front of the H_2 means that the reaction starts with two molecules of hydrogen. Notice that all atoms of the reactants must be accounted for in the products. Matter is conserved in a chemical reaction: Reactions cannot create or destroy matter but can only rearrange it.

Following is the chemical shorthand that summarizes the process of photosynthesis, a particularly important example of chemical reactions rearranging matter:

$$6\,CO_2 + 6\,H_2O \longrightarrow C_6H_{12}O_6 + 6\,O_2$$

Photosynthesis takes place within the cells of green plant tissues. The raw materials are carbon dioxide (CO_2), which is taken from the air, and water (H_2O), which is absorbed from the soil. Within the plant cells, sunlight powers the conversion of these ingredients to a sugar called glucose ($C_6H_{12}O_6$) and oxygen (O_2), which the plant releases into the surroundings (FIGURE 2.18). Although photosynthesis is actually a sequence of many chemical reactions, we still end up with the same number and kinds of atoms we had when we started. Matter has simply been rearranged.

Some chemical reactions go to completion; that is, all the reactants are converted to products. But most reactions are reversible, the products of the forward reaction becoming the reactants for the reverse reaction. For example, hydrogen and nitrogen molecules can combine to form ammonia, but ammonia can also decompose to regenerate hydrogen and nitrogen:

$$3\,H_2 + N_2 \rightleftharpoons 2\,NH_3$$

The opposite-headed arrows indicate that the reaction is reversible.

One of the factors affecting the rate of a reaction is the concentration of reactants. The greater the concentration of reactant molecules, the more frequently they collide with one another and have an opportunity to react to form products. The same holds true for the products. As products accumulate, collisions resulting in the reverse reaction become increasingly frequent. Eventually, the forward and reverse reactions occur at the same rate, and the relative concentrations of products and reactants stop changing. The point at which the reactions offset one another exactly is called **chemical equilibrium**. This is a dynamic equilibrium; reactions are still going on, but with no net effect on the concentrations of reactants and products. Equilibrium does *not* mean that the reactants and products are equal in concentration, but only that their concentrations have stabilized. For the reaction involving ammonia, equilibrium is reached when ammonia decomposes as rapidly as it forms. In this case, at equilibrium there is far more ammonia than hydrogen and nitrogen.

We will return to the subject of chemical reactions after more detailed study of the various types of molecules that are important to life. In the next chapter we focus on water, the substance in which all the chemical processes of living organisms occur.

REVIEW OF KEY CONCEPTS

(with page numbers and key figures)

CHEMICAL ELEMENTS AND COMPOUNDS

- Matter consists of chemical elements in pure form and in combinations called compounds (pp. 22–23, FIGURE 2.2) Elements cannot be broken down to other substances. A compound contains two or more elements in a fixed ratio.

- Life requires about 25 chemical elements (pp. 23–24, TABLE 2.1) Carbon, oxygen, hydrogen, and nitrogen make up approximately 96% of living matter.

ATOMS AND MOLECULES

➡ **Atomic structure determines the behavior of an element (pp. 24–28, FIGURE 2.9)** An atom is the smallest unit of an element. An atom has a nucleus made up of positively charged protons and uncharged neutrons, and a surrounding cloud of negatively charged electrons. The number of electrons in an electrically neutral atom equals the number of protons. Most elements have two or more isotopes, different in neutron number and therefore mass. Some isotopes are unstable and give off particles and energy as radioactivity.

2.1
2.2

Electron configuration determines the chemical behavior of an atom—the way it reacts with other atoms. Electrons move within orbitals, three-dimensional spaces located within successive electron shells (energy levels). Chemical properties depend on the number of valence electrons, those in the outermost shell. An atom with an incomplete valence shell is reactive.

➡ **Atoms combine by chemical bonding to form molecules (pp. 28–31, FIGURES 2.10 and 2.12)** Chemical bonds form when atoms interact and complete their valence shells. A covalent bond is the sharing of a pair of valence electrons by two atoms. Molecules consist of two or more covalently bonded atoms. Electrons of a polar covalent bond are pulled closer to the more electronegative atom. A covalent bond is nonpolar if both atoms are equally electronegative.

2.3

➡ Two atoms may differ so much in electronegativity that one or more electrons are actually transferred from one atom to the other. The result is a negatively charged ion (anion) and a positively charged ion (cation). The attraction between two ions of opposite charge is called an ionic bond.

2.4

➡ **Weak chemical bonds play important roles in the chemistry of life (pp. 31–32, FIGURE 2.14)** Hydrogen bonds are relatively weak interactions between a partially positive hydrogen atom of one polar molecule and a partially negative atom of another polar molecule. Van der Waals interactions occur when transiently positive and negative regions of very close molecules are attracted to each other. Weak bonds reinforce the shapes of large biological molecules and also help molecules adhere to each other.

2.5

- **A molecule's biological function is related to its shape (pp. 32–33, FIGURE 2.15)** A molecule's shape is determined by the positions of its atoms' valence orbitals. When covalent bonds form, the *s* and *p* orbitals in the valence shell of an atom may combine to form four hybrid orbitals that extend to the corners of a tetrahedron; such orbitals are responsible for the shapes of H_2O, CH_4, and many more complex biological molecules. Shape is often the basis of the recognition of one biological molecule by another.

- **Chemical reactions make and break chemical bonds (pp. 33–34)** Chemical reactions change reactants into products while conserving matter. Most chemical reactions are reversible. Chemical equilibrium is reached when the forward and reverse reaction rates are equal.

SELF-QUIZ

1. An element is to a (an) _____ as a tissue is to a (an) _____.

    a. atom; organism
    b. compound; organ
    c. molecule; cell
    d. atom; organ
    e. compound; organelle

2. In the term *trace element,* the modifier *trace* means

    a. the element is required in very small amounts
    b. the element can be used as a label to trace atoms through an organism's metabolism
    c. the element is very rare on Earth
    d. the element enhances health but is not essential for the organism's long-term survival
    e. the element passes rapidly through the organism

3. Compared to ^{31}P, the radioactive isotope ^{32}P has

    a. a different atomic number
    b. one more neutron
    c. one more proton
    d. one more electron
    e. a different charge

4. Atoms can be represented by simply listing the number of protons, neutrons, and electrons—for example, $2p^+$; $2n^0$; $2e^-$ for helium. Which atom represents the ^{18}O isotope of oxygen?

    a. $6p^+$; $8n^0$; $6e^-$
    b. $8p^+$; $10n^0$; $8e^-$
    c. $9p^+$; $9n^0$; $9e^-$
    d. $7p^+$; $2n^0$; $9e^-$
    e. $10p^+$; $8n^0$; $10e^-$

5. The atomic number of sulfur is 16. Sulfur combines with hydrogen by covalent bonding to form a compound, hydrogen sulfide. Based on the electron configuration of sulfur, we can predict that the molecular formula of the compound will be (explain your answer)

    a. HS b. HS_2 c. H_2S d. H_3S_2 e. H_4S

6. Review the valences of carbon, oxygen, hydrogen, and nitrogen, and then determine which of the following molecules is most likely to exist.

    a. O═C─H

    b.
    ```
         H   H
         |   |
    H─O─C─C═O
         |
         H
    ```

    c.
    ```
        H       H
        |       |
    H─C─H─C═O
        |
        H
    ```

    d.
    ```
        O
        ‖
    H─N═H
    ```

7. The reactivity of an atom arises from

    a. the average distance of the outermost electron shell from the nucleus
    b. the existence of unpaired electrons in the valence shell
    c. the sum of the potential energies of all the electron shells
    d. the potential energy of the valence shell
    e. the energy difference between the *s* and *p* orbitals

8. Which of these statements is true of all anionic atoms?
    a. The atom has more electrons than protons.
    b. The atom has more protons than electrons.
    c. The atom has fewer protons than does a neutral atom of the same element.
    d. The atom has more neutrons than protons.
    e. The net charge is -1.

9. What coefficients must be placed in the blanks to balance this chemical reaction?

$$C_6H_{12}O_6 \longrightarrow \underline{\quad} C_2H_6O + \underline{\quad} CO_2$$

    a. 1; 2   b. 2; 2   c. 1; 3   d. 1; 1   e. 3; 1

10. Which of the following statements correctly describes any chemical reaction that has reached equilibrium?
    a. The concentration of products equals the concentration of reactants.
    b. The rate of the forward reaction equals the rate of the reverse reaction.
    c. Both forward and reverse reactions have halted.
    d. The reaction is now irreversible.
    e. No reactants remain.

CHALLENGE QUESTIONS

1. Female silkworm moths (*Bombyx mori*) attract males by emitting chemical signals that spread through the air. A male hundreds of meters away can detect these molecules and fly toward their source. The sensory organs responsible for this behavior are the comblike antennae visible in the photograph below. Each filament of an antenna is equipped with thousands of receptor cells that detect the sex attractant. Based on what you learned in this chapter, propose a hypothesis to account for the ability of the male moth to detect a specific molecule in the presence of many other molecules in the air. What predictions does your hypothesis make? Design an experiment to test one of these predictions.

2. Vitalism is the belief that life possesses supernatural forces that cannot be explained by physical and chemical principles. Explain why the concept of emergent properties does not lend credibility to vitalism.

SCIENCE, TECHNOLOGY, AND SOCIETY

1. The use of radioactive isotopes as tracers in biochemical research is based on cells using the tracers in place of nonradioactive isotopes. Explain why this ability of radioactive isotopes to infiltrate the chemical processes of the cell also compounds the threat posed by radioactive contaminants in air, soil, and water.

2. While waiting at an airport, Neil Campbell once overhead this claim: "It's paranoid and ignorant to worry about industry or agriculture contaminating the environment with their chemical wastes. After all, this stuff is just made of the same atoms that were already present in our environment." How would you counter this argument?

FURTHER READING

Atkins, P. W. *Molecules.* New York: Scientific American Library, 1987. Beautifully illustrated tour of the world of molecules.
Kahn, P. "A Grisly Archive of Key Cancer Data." *Science*, January 22, 1993. Alarming health problems among uranium workers in Germany.
Pennisi, E. "Natureworks." *Science News*, May 16, 1992. How organisms make minerals.
Sackheim, G. *Introduction to Chemistry for Biology Students*, 5th ed. Menlo Park, CA: Benjamin/Cummings, 1996. A programmed review of the fundamentals of chemistry.
Shcherbak, Yuri M. "Ten Years of the Chernobyl Era." *Scientific American*, April 1996.
Thornton, R. M. *The Chemistry of Life.* Menlo Park, CA: Benjamin/Cummings, 1998. A CD-ROM that uses interactive exercises to help bridge the gap between chemistry and biology.

WEB LINKS

Visit the special edition of *The Biology Place* for BIOLOGY, Fifth Edition, at http://www.biology.com/campbell. Go to Chapter 2 for online resources, including learning activities, practice exams, and links to the following web sites:

"BioChemNet"
The main page of an excellent site that links chemistry and the life sciences. It contains links to sites ranging from general chemistry to biotechnology and has a good weekly news and review section.

"CHEMystery: An Interactive Guide to Chemistry"
Written by high school seniors for the ThinkQuest contest, this is a good review and reference site for students at all levels.

"ChemiCool"
Interactive periodic table. Click on any element in the table and a full page of information about that element is displayed.

"The American Chemical Society"
The education page of the ACS that provides links to many aspects of chemistry.

*A*s astronomers study newly discovered planets orbiting distant stars, they hope to find evidence for water on these far-off worlds, for water is the substance that makes possible life as we know it here on Earth. All organisms familiar to us are made mostly of water and live in an environment dominated by water. Water is the biological medium here on Earth, and possibly on other planets as well.

Life on Earth began in water and evolved there for three billion years before spreading onto land. Modern life, even terrestrial (land-dwelling) life, remains tied to water. Most cells are surrounded by water, and cells themselves are about 70% to 95% water. Three-quarters of Earth's surface is submerged in water. Although most of this water is in liquid form, water is also present on Earth as ice and vapor. Water is the only common substance to exist in the natural environment in all three physical states of matter: solid, liquid, and gas. These three states of water are visible in the photograph on this page, a view of Earth from space.

The abundance of water is a major reason Earth is habitable. In a classic book called The Fitness of the Environment, Lawrence Henderson highlights the importance of water to life. While acknowledging that life adapts to its environment through natural selection, Henderson emphasizes that for life to exist at all in a particular location, the environment must first be a suitable abode. Your objective in this chapter is to develop a conceptual understanding of how water contributes to the fitness of Earth for life.

WATER AND THE FITNESS OF THE ENVIRONMENT

Effects of Water's Polarity
- The polarity of water molecules results in hydrogen bonding
- Organisms depend on the cohesion of water molecules
- Water moderates temperatures on Earth
- Oceans and lakes don't freeze solid because ice floats
- Water is the solvent of life

Dissociation of Water Molecules
- Organisms are sensitive to changes in pH
- Acid precipitation threatens the fitness of the environment

EFFECTS OF WATER'S POLARITY

Water is so common that it is easy to overlook the fact that it is an exceptional substance with many extraordinary qualities. Following the theme of emergent properties, we can trace water's unique behavior to the structure and interactions of its molecules.

The polarity of water molecules results in hydrogen bonding

3.1 Studied in isolation, the water molecule is deceptively simple. Its two hydrogen atoms are joined to the oxygen atom by single covalent bonds. Because oxygen is more electronegative than hydrogen, the electrons of the polar bonds spend more time closer to the oxygen atom. This results in the oxygen region of the molecule having a slight negative charge and the hydrogens having a slight positive charge. The water molecule, shaped something like a wide V, is a **polar molecule**, meaning that opposite ends of the molecule have opposite charges.

The anomalous properties of water arise from attractions among these polar molecules. The attraction is electrical; a slightly positive hydrogen of one molecule is attracted to the slightly negative oxygen of a nearby molecule. The two molecules are thus held together by a hydrogen bond (FIGURE 3.1). Each water molecule can form hydrogen bonds to a maximum of four neighbors. The extraordinary qualities of water are emergent properties resulting from the hydrogen bonding that orders molecules into a higher level of structural organization.

We will examine four of water's properties that contribute to the fitness of Earth as an environment for life: water's cohesive behavior, its ability to stabilize temperature, its expansion upon freezing, and its versatility as a solvent.

Organisms depend on the cohesion of water molecules

Water molecules stick together as a result of hydrogen bonding. When water is in its liquid form, its hydrogen bonds are very fragile, about one-twentieth as strong as covalent bonds. They form, break, and re-form with great frequency. Each hydrogen bond lasts only a few trillionths of a second, but the molecules are constantly forming new bonds with a succession of partners. Thus, at any instant, a substantial percentage of all the water molecules are bonded to their neighbors, making water more structured than most other liquids. Collectively, the hydrogen bonds hold the substance together, a phenomenon called **cohesion**.

Cohesion due to hydrogen bonding contributes to the transport of water against gravity in plants (FIGURE 3.2). Water reaches the leaves through microscopic vessels that extend upward from the roots. Water that evaporates from a leaf is replaced by water from the vessels in the veins of the leaf. Hydrogen bonds cause water molecules leaving the veins to tug on molecules farther down in the vessel, and the

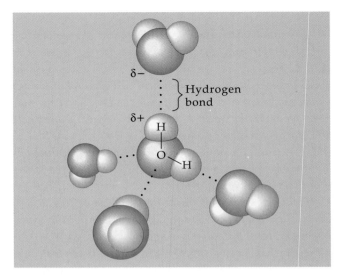

upward pull is transmitted along the vessel all the way down to the roots. **Adhesion**, the clinging of one substance to another, also plays a role. Adhesion of water to the walls of the vessels helps counter the downward pull of gravity.

Related to cohesion is **surface tension**, a measure of how difficult it is to stretch or break the surface of a liquid. Water has a greater surface tension than most other liquids. At the interface between water and air is an ordered arrangement of water molecules, hydrogen-bonded to one another and to the water below. This makes the water behave as though coated with an invisible film. We can observe the surface tension of water by slightly overfilling a drinking glass; the water will stand above the rim. Water's surface tension also allows us to

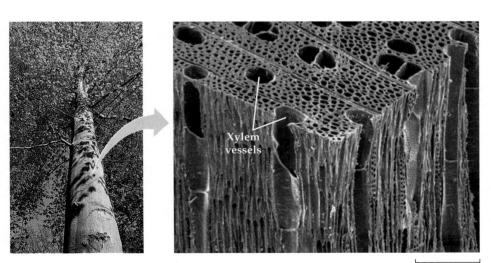

FIGURE 3.2 · **Water transport in plants.** Evaporation from leaves pulls water upward from the roots through microscopic tubes called xylem vessels, in this case located in the trunk of a tree. Cohesion due to hydrogen bonding helps hold together the column of water within a vessel. Adhesion of the water to the vessel wall also helps in resisting the downward pull of gravity.

Xylem vessels

100 μm

skip rocks on a pond. In a more biological example, some animals can stand, walk, or run on water without breaking the surface (FIGURE 3.3).

Water moderates temperatures on Earth

Water stabilizes air temperatures by absorbing heat from air that is warmer and releasing the stored heat to air that is cooler. Water is effective as a heat bank because it can absorb or release a relatively large amount of heat with only a slight change in its own temperature. To understand this quality of water, we must first look briefly at heat and temperature.

Heat and Temperature

Anything that moves has **kinetic energy**, the energy of motion. Atoms and molecules have kinetic energy because they are always moving, although not necessarily in any particular direction. The faster a molecule moves, the greater its kinetic energy. **Heat** is a measure of the *total* quantity of kinetic energy due to molecular motion in a body of matter. **Temperature** measures the intensity of heat due to the *average* kinetic energy of the molecules. When the average speed of the molecules increases, a thermometer records this as a rise in temperature. Heat and temperature are related, but they are not the same. A swimmer crossing the English Channel has a higher temperature than the water, but the ocean contains far more heat because of its volume.

Whenever two objects of different temperature are brought together, heat passes from the warmer to the cooler body until the two are the same temperature. Molecules in the cooler object speed up at the expense of the kinetic energy of the warmer object. An ice cube cools a drink not by adding coldness to the liquid, but by absorbing heat as the ice melts.

Throughout this book, we will use the **Celsius scale** to indicate temperature (Celsius degrees are abbreviated as °C). At sea level, water freezes at 0°C and boils at 100°C. The temperature of the human body averages 37°C, and comfortable room temperature is about 20–25°C.

One convenient unit of heat used in this book is the **calorie (cal)**. A calorie is the amount of heat energy it takes to raise the temperature of 1 g of water by 1°C. Conversely, a calorie is also the amount of heat that 1 g of water releases when it cools by 1°C. A **kilocalorie (kcal)**, 1000 cal, is the quantity of heat required to raise the temperature of 1 kilogram (kg) of water by 1°C. (The "calories" on food packages are actually kilocalories.) Another energy unit used in this book is the **joule (J)**. One joule equals 0.239 cal; a calorie equals 4.184 J.

Water's High Specific Heat

The ability of water to stabilize temperature depends on its relatively high specific heat. The **specific heat** of a substance is defined as the amount of heat that must be absorbed or lost for 1 g of that substance to change its temperature by 1°C. We already know water's specific heat because we have defined a calorie as the amount of heat that causes 1 g of water to change its temperature by 1°C. Therefore, the specific heat of water is 1 calorie per gram per degree Celsius, abbreviated as 1 cal/g/°C. Compared with most other substances, water has an unusually high specific heat. For example, ethyl alcohol, the type of alcohol in alcoholic beverages, has a specific heat of 0.6 cal/g/°C.

Because of the high specific heat of water relative to other materials, water will change its temperature less when it absorbs or loses a given amount of heat. The reason you can burn your fingers by touching the metal handle of a pot on the stove when the water in the pot is still lukewarm is that the

FIGURE 3.3 · Walking on water. The high surface tension of water, resulting from the collective strength of its hydrogen bonds, allows the water strider to walk on a pond without breaking the surface.

specific heat of water is ten times greater than that of iron. In other words, it will take only 0.1 cal to raise the temperature of 1 g of iron 1°C. Specific heat can be thought of as a measure of how well a substance resists changing its temperature when it absorbs or releases heat. Water resists changing its temperature; when it does change its temperature, it absorbs or loses a relatively large quantity of heat for each degree of change.

We can trace water's high specific heat, like many of its other properties, to hydrogen bonding. Heat must be absorbed in order to break hydrogen bonds, and heat is released when hydrogen bonds form. A calorie of heat causes a relatively small change in the temperature of water because much of the heat energy is used to disrupt hydrogen bonds before the water molecules can begin moving faster. And when the temperature of water drops slightly, many additional hydrogen bonds form, releasing a considerable amount of energy in the form of heat.

What is the relevance of water's high specific heat to life on Earth? A large body of water can absorb and store a huge amount of heat from the sun in the daytime and during summer, while warming up only a few degrees. At night and during winter, the gradually cooling water can warm the air. This is the reason coastal areas generally have milder climates than inland regions. The high specific heat of water also tends to stabilize ocean temperatures, creating a favorable environment for marine life. Thus, because of its high specific heat, the water that covers most of Earth keeps temperature fluctuations on land and in water within limits that permit life. Also, because organisms are made primarily of water, they are more able to resist changes in their own temperatures than if they were made of a liquid with a lower specific heat.

Evaporative Cooling

Molecules of any liquid stay close together because they are attracted to one another. Molecules moving fast enough to overcome these attractions can depart the liquid and enter the air as gas. This transformation from a liquid to a gas is called vaporization, or evaporation. Recall that the speed of molecular movement varies, and that temperature is the *average* kinetic energy of molecules. Even at low temperatures, the speediest molecules can escape into the air. Some evaporation occurs at any temperature; a glass of water, for example, will eventually evaporate at room temperature. If a liquid is heated, the average kinetic energy of molecules increases and the liquid evaporates more rapidly.

Heat of vaporization is the quantity of heat a liquid must absorb for 1 g of it to be converted from the liquid to the gaseous state. Compared with most other liquids, water has a high heat of vaporization. To evaporate each gram of water at room temperature, about 580 cal of heat are needed—nearly double the amount needed to vaporize a gram of alcohol or ammonia. Water's high heat of vaporization is another emer-

FIGURE 3.4 ▪ Evaporative cooling. Because of water's high heat of vaporization, evaporation of sweat significantly cools the body surface.

gent property caused by hydrogen bonds, which must be broken before the molecules can make their exodus from the liquid.

Water's high heat of vaporization helps moderate Earth's climate. A considerable amount of solar heat absorbed by tropical seas is consumed during the evaporation of surface water. Then, as moist tropical air circulates poleward, it releases heat as it condenses to form rain.

As a liquid evaporates, the surface of the liquid that remains behind cools down. This **evaporative cooling** occurs because the "hottest" molecules, those with the greatest kinetic energy, are the most likely to leave as gas. It is as if the 100 fastest runners at a college transferred to another school; the average speed of the remaining students would decline.

Evaporative cooling of water contributes to the stability of temperature in lakes and ponds and also provides a mechanism that prevents terrestrial organisms from overheating. For example, evaporation of water from the leaves of a plant helps keep the tissues in the leaves from becoming too warm in the sunlight. Evaporation of sweat from human skin dissipates body heat and helps prevent overheating on a hot day or when excess heat is generated by strenuous activity (FIGURE 3.4). High humidity on a hot day increases discomfort because the high concentration of water vapor in the air inhibits the evaporation of sweat from the body.

Oceans and lakes don't freeze solid because ice floats

Water is one of the few substances that are less dense as a solid than as a liquid. In other words, ice floats. While other materials contract when they solidify, water expands. The cause of this exotic behavior is, once again, hydrogen bonding. At temperatures above 4°C, water behaves like other liquids, expand-

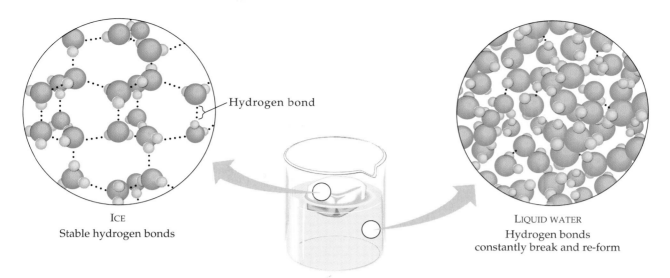

Hydrogen bond

ICE
Stable hydrogen bonds

LIQUID WATER
Hydrogen bonds
constantly break and re-form

FIGURE 3.5 ▪ **The structure of ice.** Each molecule is hydrogen-bonded to four neighbors in a three-dimensional crystal with open channels. Because the hydrogen bonds make the crystal spacious, ice contains fewer molecules than an equal volume of liquid water. In other words, ice is less dense than liquid water.

ing as it warms and contracting as it cools. Water begins to freeze when its molecules are no longer moving vigorously enough to break their hydrogen bonds. As the temperature reaches 0°C, the water becomes locked into a crystalline lattice, each water molecule bonded to the maximum of four partners (FIGURE 3.5). The hydrogen bonds keep the molecules at "arm's length," far enough apart to make ice about 10% less dense (10% fewer molecules for the same volume) than liquid water at 4°C. When ice absorbs enough heat for its temperature to rise above 0°C, hydrogen bonds between molecules are disrupted. As the crystal collapses, the ice melts, and molecules are free to slip closer together. Water reaches its greatest density at 4°C and then begins to expand as the molecules move faster. Keep in mind, however, that even liquid water is semistructured because of transient hydrogen bonds.

The ability of ice to float because of the expansion of water as it solidifies is an important factor in the fitness of the environment. If ice sank, then eventually all ponds, lakes, and even

FIGURE 3.6 ▪ **Floating ice and the fitness of the environment.** Floating ice becomes a barrier that protects the liquid water below from the colder air. These are invertebrates called krill, photographed beneath Antarctic ice.

oceans would freeze solid, making life as we know it impossible on Earth. During summer, only the upper few inches of the ocean would thaw. Instead, when a deep body of water cools, the floating ice insulates the liquid water below, preventing it from freezing and allowing life to exist under the frozen surface (FIGURE 3.6).

Water is the solvent of life

A sugar cube placed in a glass of water will dissolve. The glass will then contain a uniform mixture of sugar and water; the concentration of dissolved sugar will be the same everywhere in the mixture. A liquid that is a completely homogeneous mixture of two or more substances is called a **solution**. The dissolving agent of a solution is the **solvent**, and the substance that is dissolved is the **solute**. In this case, water is the solvent and sugar is the solute. An **aqueous solution** is one in which water is the solvent.

The medieval alchemists tried to find a universal solvent, one that would dissolve anything. They learned that nothing works better than water. However, water is not a universal solvent; if it were, it could not be stored in any container, including our cells. But water is a very versatile solvent, a quality we can trace to the polarity of the water molecule.

Suppose, for example, that a crystal of the ionic compound sodium chloride is placed in water (FIGURE 3.7, p. 42). At the surface of the crystal, the sodium and chloride ions are exposed to the solvent. The ions and water molecules have a mutual affinity through electrical attraction. The oxygen regions of the water molecules are negatively charged and cling to sodium cations. The hydrogen regions of the water molecules are positively charged and are attracted to chloride anions. Water surrounds the individual ions, separating the

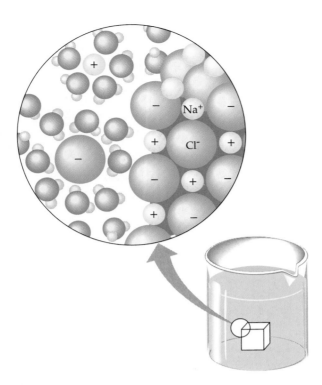

FIGURE 3.7 ▪ **A crystal of table salt dissolving in water.** The positive hydrogen regions of the polar water molecules are attracted to the chloride anions (green), whereas the negative oxygen regions cling to the sodium cations (yellow). The sphere of water molecules surrounding a solute ion (or molecule) is called a hydration shell.

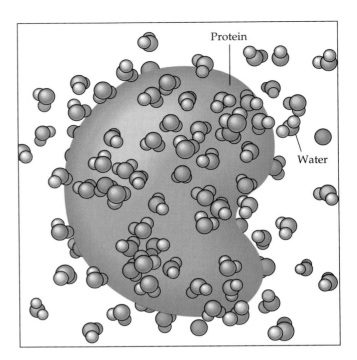

FIGURE 3.8 ▪ **A water-soluble protein.** Even a molecule as large as a protein can dissolve in water if it has enough ionic and polar regions on its surface. The mass of purple here represents a single such protein molecule, which water molecules are surrounding.

sodium from the chloride and shielding the ions from one another. Working inward from the surface of the salt crystal, water eventually dissolves all the ions. The result is a solution of two solutes, sodium and chloride, homogeneously mixed with water, the solvent. Other ionic compounds also dissolve in water. Seawater, for instance, contains a great variety of dissolved ions, as do living cells.

A compound does not need to be ionic in order to dissolve in water; polar compounds are also water-soluble. For example, sugars are soluble because water molecules can coat the polar sugar molecules. Even molecules as large as proteins can dissolve in water if they have ionic and polar regions on their surface (FIGURE 3.8). Many different kinds of polar compounds are dissolved (along with ions) in the water of such biological fluids as blood, the sap of plants, and the liquid within all cells. Water is the solvent of life.

Hydrophilic and Hydrophobic Substances

Whether ionic or polar, any substance that has an affinity for water is said to be **hydrophilic** (from the Greek *hydro,* "water," and *philios,* "loving"). This term is used even if the substance does not dissolve—because the molecules are too large, for instance. Cotton, a plant product, is an example of a hydrophilic substance that absorbs water without dissolving. Cotton consists of giant molecules of cellulose, a compound with numerous regions of partial positive and partial negative charges associated with polar bonds. Water adheres to the cellulose fibers. Thus, a cotton towel does a great job of drying the body, yet does not dissolve in the washing machine. Cellulose is also present in the walls of water-conducting vessels in a plant; you read earlier how the adhesion of water to these hydrophilic walls functions in water transport.

There are, of course, substances that do not have an affinity for water. Substances that are non-ionic and nonpolar actually seem to repel water; these substances are termed **hydrophobic** (Gr. *phobos,* "fearing"). An example from the kitchen is vegetable oil, which, as you know, does not mix stably with watery substances such as vinegar. The hydrophobic behavior of the oil molecules results from a prevalence of nonpolar bonds, in this case bonds between carbon and hydrogen, which share electrons almost equally. Hydrophobic molecules related to oils are major ingredients of cell membranes. (Imagine what would happen to a cell if its membrane dissolved.)

Solute Concentration in Aqueous Solutions

Biological chemistry is "wet" chemistry. Most of the chemical reactions that occur in organisms involve solutes dissolved in water. To understand the chemistry of life, it is important to learn how to calculate the concentrations of solutes dissolved in aqueous solutions.

Suppose we wanted to prepare an aqueous solution of table sugar having a specified concentration of sugar molecules (a certain number of solute molecules in a certain volume of solution). Because counting or weighing individual molecules is not practical, we instead usually measure substances in units called moles. A **mole (mol)** is equal in number to the molecular weight of a substance, but upscaled from daltons to units of grams. Imagine weighing out 1 mol of table sugar (sucrose), which has the molecular formula $C_{12}H_{22}O_{11}$. In round numbers, a carbon atom weighs 12 daltons, a hydrogen atom weighs 1 dalton, and an oxygen atom weighs 16 daltons. **Molecular weight** is the sum of the weights of all the atoms in a molecule; thus, the molecular weight of sucrose is 342 daltons. To obtain 1 mol of sucrose, we weigh out 342 g, the molecular weight of sucrose expressed in grams.

The practical advantage of measuring a quantity of chemicals in moles is that a mole of one substance has exactly the same number of molecules as a mole of any other substance. If substance A has a molecular weight of 10 daltons and substance B has a molecular weight of 100 daltons, then 10 g of A will have the same number of molecules as 100 g of B. The number of molecules in a mole, called Avogadro's number, is 6.02×10^{23}. A mole of table sugar contains 6.02×10^{23} sucrose molecules and weighs 342 g. A mole of ethyl alcohol (C_2H_6O) also contains 6.02×10^{23} molecules, but it weighs only 46 g because the molecules are smaller than those of sucrose. Measuring in moles makes it convenient for scientists working in the laboratory to combine substances in fixed ratios of molecules.

How would we make a liter (L) of solution consisting of 1 mol of sucrose dissolved in water? To obtain this concentration, we would weigh out 342 g of sucrose and then gradually add water, while stirring, until the sugar was completely dissolved. We would then add enough water to bring the total volume of the solution up to 1 L. At that point, we would have a one-molar (1 M) solution of sucrose. **Molarity**—the number of moles of solute per liter of solution—is the unit of concentration most often used by biologists for aqueous solutions.

DISSOCIATION OF WATER MOLECULES

3.2 Occasionally, a hydrogen atom shared between two water molecules in a hydrogen bond shifts from one molecule to the other. When this happens, the hydrogen atom leaves its electron behind, and what is actually transferred is a **hydrogen ion**, a single proton with a charge of $+1$. The water molecule that lost a proton is now a **hydroxide ion** (OH^-), which has a charge of -1. The proton binds to the other water molecule, making that molecule a hydronium ion (H_3O^+). We can picture the chemical reaction this way:

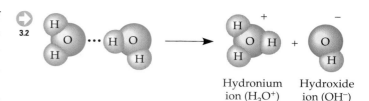

Hydronium ion (H_3O^+)   Hydroxide ion (OH^-)

Although this is technically what happens, we will think of the process in a simplified way, as the dissociation (separation) of a water molecule into a hydrogen ion and a hydroxide ion:

$$H_2O \rightleftharpoons H^+ + OH^-$$

Hydrogen ion   Hydroxide ion

As the double arrows indicate, this is a reversible reaction that will reach a state of dynamic equilibrium when water dissociates at the same rate that it is being re-formed from H^+ and OH^-. At this equilibrium point, the concentration of water molecules greatly exceeds the concentrations of H^+ and OH^-. In fact, in pure water, only one water molecule in every 554 million is dissociated. The concentration of each ion in pure water is $10^{-7} M$ (at 25°C). This means that there is only one ten-millionth of a mole of hydrogen ions per liter of pure water, and an equal number of hydroxide ions.

Although the dissociation of water is reversible and statistically rare, it is exceedingly important in the chemistry of life. Hydrogen and hydroxide ions are very reactive. Changes in their concentrations can drastically affect a cell's proteins and other complex molecules. As we have seen, the concentrations of H^+ and OH^- are equal in pure water, but adding certain kinds of solutes, called acids and bases, disrupts this balance. Biologists use something called the pH scale to describe how acidic or basic (the opposite of acidic) a solution is. In the remainder of the chapter you will learn about acids, bases, and pH, and why changes in pH can adversely affect organisms.

Organisms are sensitive to changes in pH

3.3 Before discussing the pH scale, let's see how acids and bases actually work.

Acids and Bases

What would cause an aqueous solution to have an imbalance in its H^+ and OH^- concentrations? When the substances called acids dissolve in water, they donate additional hydrogen ions to the solution. An **acid**, according to the definition most often used by biologists, is a substance that increases the H^+ concentration of a solution. For example, when hydrochloric acid (HCl) is added to water, hydrogen ions dissociate from chloride ions:

$$HCl \longrightarrow H^+ + Cl^-$$

This additional source of H^+ in the solution (dissociation of water is the other source) results in more H^+ than OH^-. Such a solution is known as an acidic solution.

A substance that reduces the hydrogen ion concentration in a solution is called a **base**. Some bases reduce the H^+ concentration indirectly by dissociating to form hydroxide ions, which then combine with hydrogen ions to form water. One base that acts this way is sodium hydroxide (NaOH), which in water dissociates into its ions:

$$NaOH \longrightarrow Na^+ + OH^-$$

Other bases reduce H^+ concentration directly by accepting hydrogen ions. Ammonia (NH_3), for instance, acts as a base when the unshared electron pair in nitrogen's valence shell attracts a hydrogen ion from the solution, resulting in an ammonium ion (NH_4^+):

$$NH_3 + H^+ \rightleftharpoons NH_4^+$$

In either case, the base reduces the H^+ concentration. Solutions with a higher concentration of OH^- than H^+ are known as basic solutions. A solution in which the H^+ and OH^- concentrations are equal is said to be neutral.

Notice that single arrows were used in the reactions for HCl and NaOH. These compounds dissociate completely when mixed with water. Hydrochloric acid is called a strong acid and sodium hydroxide a strong base because they dissociate completely. In contrast, ammonia is a relatively weak base. The double arrows in the reaction for ammonia indicate that the binding and release of the hydrogen ion are reversible, although at equilibrium there will be a fixed ratio of NH_4^+ to NH_3.

There are also weak acids, which reversibly release and reaccept hydrogen ions. An example is carbonic acid:

$$H_2CO_3 \quad \rightleftharpoons \quad HCO_3^- \quad + \quad H^+$$

Carbonic   Bicarbonate   Hydrogen
acid   ion   ion

Here the equilibrium so favors the reaction in the left direction that when carbonic acid is added to water, only 1% of the molecules are dissociated at any particular time. Still, that is enough to shift the balance of H^+ and OH^- from neutrality.

The pH Scale

In any solution, the *product* of the H^+ and the OH^- concentrations is constant at 10^{-14} M. This can be written

$$[H^+][OH^-] = 10^{-14} M^2$$

In such an equation, brackets indicate molar concentration for the substance enclosed within them. In a neutral solution at room temperature (25°C), $[H^+] = 10^{-7}$ and $[OH^-] = 10^{-7}$, so the product is $10^{-14} M^2$ ($10^{-7} \times 10^{-7}$). If enough acid

is added to a solution to increase $[H^+]$ to $10^{-5} M$, then $[OH^-]$ will decline by an equivalent amount to $10^{-9} M$ ($10^{-5} \times 10^{-9} = 10^{-14}$). An acid not only adds hydrogen ions to a solution, but also removes hydroxide ions because of the tendency for H^+ to combine with OH^- to form water. A base has the opposite effect, increasing OH^- concentration but also reducing H^+ concentration by the formation of water. If enough of a base is added to raise the OH^- concentration to $10^{-4} M$, the H^+ concentration will drop to $10^{-10} M$. Whenever we know the concentration of either H^+ or OH^- in a solution, we can deduce the concentration of the other ion.

Because the H^+ and OH^- concentrations of solutions can vary by a factor of 100 trillion or more, scientists have developed a way to express this variation more conveniently, by use of the **pH scale**, which ranges from 0 to 14 (FIGURE 3.9). The pH scale compresses the range of H^+ and OH^- concentra-

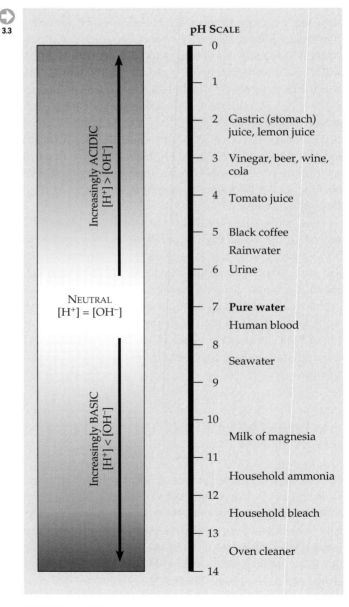

FIGURE 3.9 · **The pH of some aqueous solutions.**

tions by employing a common mathematical device: logarithms. The pH of a solution is defined as the negative logarithm (base 10) of the hydrogen ion concentration:

$$pH = -\log [H^+]$$

For a neutral solution, $[H^+]$ is $10^{-7}\ M$, giving us

$$-\log 10^{-7} = -(-7) = 7$$

Notice that pH *declines* as H^+ concentration *increases*. Notice, too, that although the pH scale is based on H^+ concentration, it also implies OH^- concentration. A solution of pH 10 has a hydrogen ion concentration of $10^{-10}\ M$ and a hydroxide ion concentration of $10^{-4}\ M$.

The pH of a neutral solution is 7, the midpoint of the scale. A pH value less than 7 denotes an acidic solution; the lower the number, the more acidic the solution. The pH for basic solutions is above 7. Most biological fluids are within the range pH 6 to pH 8. There are a few exceptions, however, including the strongly acidic digestive juice of the human stomach, which has a pH of about 2.

It is important to remember that each pH unit represents a tenfold difference in H^+ and OH^- concentrations. It is this mathematical feature that makes the pH scale so compact. A solution of pH 3 is not twice as acidic as a solution of pH 6, but a thousand times more acidic. When the pH of a solution changes slightly, the actual concentrations of H^+ and OH^- in the solution change substantially.

Buffers

The internal pH of most living cells is close to 7. Even a slight change in pH can be harmful, because the chemical processes of the cell are very sensitive to the concentrations of hydrogen and hydroxide ions.

Biological fluids resist changes to their own pH when acids or bases are introduced because of the presence of **buffers**, substances that minimize changes in the concentrations of H^+ and OH^- in a solution. Buffers in human blood, for example, normally maintain the blood pH very close to 7.4. A person cannot survive for more than a few minutes if the blood pH drops to 7 or rises to 7.8. Under normal circumstances, the buffering capacity of the blood prevents such swings in pH.

A buffer works by accepting hydrogen ions from the solution when they are in excess and donating hydrogen ions to the solution when they have been depleted. Most buffers are weak acids or weak bases that combine reversibly with hydrogen ions. One of the buffers that contributes to pH stability in human blood and many other biological solutions is carbonic acid (H_2CO_3), which, as already mentioned, dissociates to yield a bicarbonate ion (HCO_3^-) and a hydrogen ion (H^+):

Response to
a rise in pH

$$H_2CO_3 \rightleftharpoons HCO_3^- + H^+$$

| H^+ donor (acid) | Response to a drop in pH | H^+ acceptor (base) | Hydrogen ion |

The chemical equilibrium between carbonic acid and bicarbonate acts as a pH regulator, the reaction shifting left or right as other processes in the solution add or remove hydrogen ions. If the H^+ concentration in blood begins to fall (that is, if pH rises), more carbonic acid dissociates, replenishing hydrogen ions. But when H^+ concentration in blood begins to rise (pH drops), the bicarbonate ion acts as a base and removes the excess hydrogen ions from the solution. Thus, the carbonic acid–bicarbonate buffering system actually consists of an acid *and* a base in equilibrium with each other. Most other buffers are also acid-base pairs.

Acid precipitation threatens the fitness of the environment

Considering the dependence of all life on water, contamination of rivers, lakes, and seas is a dire environmental problem. One of the most serious assaults on water quality is acid precipitation.

Uncontaminated rain has a pH of about 5.6, slightly acidic, owing to the formation of carbonic acid from carbon dioxide and water. **Acid precipitation** refers to rain, snow, or fog more acidic than pH 5.6. What causes acid precipitation, and what are its effects on the fitness of the environment?

Acid precipitation is caused primarily by the presence in the atmosphere of sulfur oxides and nitrogen oxides, gaseous compounds that react with water in the air to form strong acids, which fall to earth with rain or snow. A major source of these oxides is the burning of fossil fuels (coal, oil, and gas) in factories and automobiles. Electrical power plants that burn coal produce more of these pollutants than any other single source. Ironically, the tall smokestacks built to reduce local pollution by dispersing factory exhaust help spread airborne pollutants. Winds carry the pollutants away, and acid rain may fall thousands of miles away from industrial centers. In the Adirondack Mountains of upstate New York, the pH of rainfall averages 4.2, about 25 times more acidic than normal rain. Acid precipitation falls on many other regions, including the Cascade Mountains of the Pacific Northwest and certain parts of Europe and Asia. One West Virginia storm dropped rain having a pH of 1.5, as acidic as the digestive juices in our stomachs!

The effect of acids in lakes and streams is most pronounced in the spring, as snow begins to melt. The surface snow melts first, drains down, and sends much of the acid that has accumulated over the winter into lakes and streams all at once. Early meltwater often has a pH as low as 3, and this

acid surge hits when fish and other forms of aquatic life are producing eggs and young, which are especially vulnerable to acidic conditions. Strong acidity can alter the structure of biological molecules and prevent them from carrying out the essential chemical processes of life.

Although acid precipitation can clearly damage life in lakes and streams, its direct effects on forests and other terrestrial life are controversial. However, recent research indicates that acid rain and snow can bring about profound changes in soils by affecting the solubility of soil minerals. Acid precipitation falling on land washes away certain mineral ions, such as calcium and magnesium ions, that ordinarily help buffer the soil solution and are essential nutrients for plant growth. At the same time, other minerals, such as aluminum, reach toxic concentrations when acidification increases their solubility. The effects of acid precipitation on soil chemistry have contributed to the decline of European forests and are taking a toll on some North American forests (FIGURE 3.10). Nevertheless, recent studies indicate that currently the majority of North American forests are not suffering substantially from acid precipitation.

If there is reason for optimism about the future quality of water resources, it is our progress in reducing certain kinds of

FIGURE 3.10 ▪ **The effects of acid precipitation on a forest.** Acid fog and acid rain are thought to be responsible for killing many of the spruce and fir trees on Mount Mitchell in North Carolina.

pollution. For example, in the United States, Canada, and Europe, emissions of sulfur oxides have declined markedly in recent decades, causing a decrease in acid precipitation. Continued progress can come only from the actions of individuals who are concerned about environmental quality. An essential part of their education is to understand the crucial role that water plays in the environmental fitness for continued life on Earth.

CHAPTER REVIEW

REVIEW OF KEY CONCEPTS

(with page numbers and key figures)

EFFECTS OF WATER'S POLARITY

3.1 ▸ **The polarity of water molecules results in hydrogen bonding (pp. 37–38, FIGURE 3.1)** A hydrogen bond forms when the oxygen of one water molecule is electrically attracted to the hydrogen of a nearby molecule. Hydrogen bonding between water molecules is the basis for water's unusual properties.

- **Organisms depend on the cohesion of water molecules (pp. 38–39)** Hydrogen bonding makes water molecules stick together, and this cohesion helps pull water upward in the microscopic vessels of plants. Hydrogen bonding is also responsible for water's surface tension.

- **Water moderates temperatures on Earth (pp. 39–40)** Hydrogen bonding gives water a high specific heat. Heat is absorbed when hydrogen bonds break and is released when hydrogen bonds form, minimizing temperature fluctuations to within limits that permit life. Evaporative cooling is based on water's high heat of vaporization. Water molecules must have a relatively high kinetic energy to break hydrogen bonds. The evaporative loss of these energetic water molecules cools a surface.

- **Oceans and lakes don't freeze solid because ice floats (pp. 40–41, FIGURE 3.6)** Ice is less dense than liquid water because its more organized hydrogen bonding causes expansion into a crystal formation. Floating ice allows life to exist under the frozen surfaces of lakes and polar seas.

- **Water is the solvent of life (pp. 41–43, FIGURE 3.7)** Water is an unusually versatile solvent because its polarity attracts it to charged and polar substances. When ions or polar substances are surrounded by water molecules, they dissolve and are called solutes. Hydrophilic substances have an affinity for water. Hydrophobic

substances do not; they seem to repel water. Biologists usually use molarity, the number of moles of solute per liter of solution, as a measure of solute concentration in solutions. A mole is the number of grams of a substance equal to its molecular weight.

DISSOCIATION OF WATER MOLECULES

3.2
3.3 ▸ **Organisms are sensitive to changes in pH (pp. 43–45, FIGURE 3.9)** Water can dissociate into H^+ and OH^-. The concentration of H^+ is expressed as pH, where $pH = -\log [H^+]$. Acids donate additional H^+ in aqueous solutions; bases donate OH^- or accept H^+. In a neutral solution, $[H^+] = [OH^-] = 10^{-7}$, and $pH = 7$. In an acidic solution, $[H^+]$ is greater than $[OH^-]$, and the pH is less than 7. In a basic solution, $[H^+]$ is less than $[OH^-]$, and the pH is greater than 7. Buffers in biological fluids resist changes in pH. A buffer consists of an acid-base pair that combines reversibly with hydrogen ions.

- **Acid precipitation threatens the fitness of the environment (pp. 45–46)** Acid precipitation is rain, snow, or fog with a pH below 5.6. It often results from a reaction in the air between water vapor and sulfur oxides and nitrogen oxides produced by the combustion of fossil fuels.

SELF-QUIZ

1. The main thesis of Lawrence Henderson's *The Fitness of the Environment* is
   a. Earth's environment is constant
   b. it is the physical environment, not life, that has evolved
   c. the environment of Earth has adapted to life
   d. life as we know it depends on certain environmental qualities on Earth
   e. water and other aspects of Earth's environment exist because they make the planet more suitable for life

2. Air temperature often increases slightly as clouds begin to drop rain or snow. Which behavior of water is *most directly* responsible for this phenomenon?
   a. water's change in density when it condenses
   b. water's reactions with other atmospheric compounds
   c. release of heat by the formation of hydrogen bonds
   d. release of heat by the breaking of hydrogen bonds
   e. water's high surface tension

3. For two bodies of matter in contact, heat always flows from
   a. the body with greater heat to the one with less heat
   b. the body of higher temperature to the one of lower temperature
   c. the denser body to the less dense body
   d. the body with more water to the one with less water
   e. the larger body to the smaller body

4. A slice of pizza has 500 kcal. If we could burn the pizza and use all the heat to warm a 50-L container of cold water, what would be the approximate increase in the temperature of the water? (*Note:* A liter of cold water weighs about 1 kg.)
   a. 50°C   d. 100°C
   b. 5°C   e. 1°C
   c. 10°C

5. The bonds that are broken when water vaporizes are
   a. ionic bonds
   b. bonds between water molecules
   c. bonds between atoms of individual water molecules
   d. polar covalent bonds
   e. nonpolar covalent bonds

6. Which of the following is an example of a hydrophobic material?
   a. paper   d. sugar
   b. table salt   e. pasta
   c. wax

7. We can be sure that a mole of table sugar and a mole of vitamin C are equal in their
   a. weight in daltons   d. number of atoms
   b. weight in grams   e. volume
   c. number of molecules

8. How many grams of acetic acid ($C_2H_4O_2$) would you use to make 10 L of a 0.1 M aqueous solution of acetic acid? (*Note:* The atomic weights, in daltons, are approximately 12 for carbon, 1 for hydrogen, and 16 for oxygen.)
   a. 10 g   d. 60 g
   b. 0.1 g   e. 0.6 g
   c. 6 g

9. Acid precipitation has lowered the pH of a particular lake to 4.0. What is the hydrogen ion concentration of the lake?
   a. 4.0 M d. 10^4 M
   b. 10^{-10} M e. 4%
   c. 10^{-4} M

10. What is the *hydroxide* ion concentration of the lake described in question 9?
   a. 10^{-7} M d. 10^{-14} M
   b. 10^{-4} M e. 10 M
   c. 10^{-10} M

CHALLENGE QUESTIONS

1. Explain how panting helps regulate a dog's body temperature.

2. Design a controlled experiment to test the hypothesis that acid precipitation inhibits the growth of *Elodea*, a common freshwater plant.

SCIENCE, TECHNOLOGY, AND SOCIETY

1. Agriculture, industry, and the growing populations of cities all compete, through political influence, for water. If you were in charge of water resources in an arid region, what would your priorities be for allocating the limited water supply for various uses? How would you try to build consensus among the different special interest groups?

2. Discuss the special political obstacles to reducing acid precipitation. (Compare this issue with environmental issues confined to a more localized region.)

FURTHER READING

Henderson, L. J. *The Fitness of the Environment.* New York: Macmillan, 1913. A classic book highlighting the importance of water and carbon to life.

Kaiser, J. "Acid Rain's Dirty Business: Stealing Minerals from Soil." *Science,* April 12, 1996. The surprisingly long-term effects of soil acidification.

Lehninger, A. L., D. L. Nelson, and M. M. Cox. *Principles of Biochemistry,* 2nd ed. New York: Worth, 1993. A readable biochemistry text with an excellent discussion of water in Chapter 4.

Mohner, V. A. "The Challenge of Acid Rain." *Scientific American,* August 1988. Analysis of a complex environmental problem.

Matthews, R. "Wacky Water." *New Scientist,* June 21, 1997. More about hydrogen bonding in water.

Pennisi, E. "Water, Water Everywhere." *Science News,* February 20, 1993. How water stabilizes the structure of proteins and other large biological molecules.

Pennisi, E. "Water: The Power, Promise, and Turmoil of North America's Fresh Water." *National Geographic.* A special 1993 issue examining how we use and abuse our water resources.

WEB LINKS

Visit the special edition of *The Biology Place* for BIOLOGY, Fifth Edition, at http://www.biology.com/campbell. Go to Chapter 3 for online resources, including learning activities, practice exams, and links to the following web sites:

"The pH Playground"
An interactive site that allows you to see the relationship between pH and H^+ ion concentration at different levels of precision.

"Acid Rain: A Student's First Sourcebook"
All you need to know about acid rain and its effect on society and the environment from the Environmental Protection Agency.

"Water Resources of the United States"
Water is one of humanity's most precious resources. This link will take you to the water resources page of the United States Geological Survey, one of the government bodies that look after the nation's water resources.

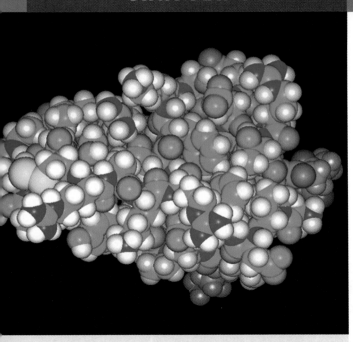

CHAPTER 4

*A*lthough water is the universal medium for life on Earth, most of the chemicals that make up living organisms are based on the element carbon. Of all chemical elements, carbon is unparalleled in its ability to form molecules that are large, complex, and diverse, and this molecular diversity has made possible the diversity of organisms that have evolved on Earth. The protein shown in the adjacent computer graphic model is an example of a large, complex molecule based on carbon (the green atoms). Proteins are a major topic of Chapter 5. In this chapter we focus on smaller molecules, using them to illustrate a few concepts of molecular architecture that highlight carbon's importance to life and the theme that emergent properties arise from the organization of life's matter.

CARBON AND THE MOLECULAR DIVERSITY OF LIFE

THE IMPORTANCE OF CARBON

Although a cell is composed of 70% to 95% water, most of the rest consists of carbon-based compounds. Proteins, DNA, carbohydrates, and other molecules that distinguish living matter from inanimate material are all composed of carbon atoms bonded to one another and to atoms of other elements. Hydrogen (H), oxygen (O), nitrogen (N), sulfur (S), and phosphorus (P) are other common ingredients of these compounds, but it is carbon (C) that accounts for the endless diversity of biological molecules.

Organic chemistry is the study of carbon compounds

Compounds containing carbon are said to be organic, and the branch of chemistry that specializes in the study of carbon compounds is called **organic chemistry**. Once thought to come only from living things, organic compounds range from simple molecules such as methane (CH_4) to colossal ones such as proteins with thousands of atoms and molecular weights in excess of 100,000 daltons. The percentages of the major elements of life—C, H, O, N, S, and P—are quite uniform from one organism to another. Because of carbon's versatility, however, this limited assortment of atomic building blocks, taken in roughly the same proportions, can be used to build an inexhaustible variety of organic molecules. Different species of organisms, and different individuals within a species, are distinguished by variations among their organic molecules.

Since the dawn of human history, people have used other organisms as sources of valued substances—from foods to medicines and fabrics. Organic chemistry originated in attempts to purify and improve the yield of such products. By the early nineteenth century, chemists had learned to make many simple compounds in the laboratory by combining elements under the right conditions. Artificial synthesis of the

complex molecules extracted from living matter seemed impossible, however. It was at that time that the Swedish chemist Jöns Jakob Berzelius first made the distinction between organic compounds, those that seemingly could arise only within living organisms, and inorganic compounds, those that were found in the nonliving world. The new discipline of organic chemistry was first built on a foundation of vitalism, the belief in a life force outside the jurisdiction of physical and chemical laws.

Chemists began to chip away at the foundation of vitalism when they learned to synthesize organic compounds in their laboratories. In 1828, Friedrich Wöhler, a German chemist who had studied with Berzelius, attempted to make an inorganic salt, ammonium cyanate, by mixing solutions of ammonium (NH_4^+) and cyanate (CNO^-) ions. Wöhler was astonished to find that instead of the expected product, he had made urea, an organic compound present in the urine of animals. Wöhler challenged the vitalists when he wrote, "I must tell you that I can prepare urea without requiring a kidney or an animal, either man or dog." However, one of the ingredients used in the synthesis, the cyanate, had been extracted from animal blood, and the vitalists were not swayed by Wöhler's discovery. But then, a few years later, Hermann Kolbe, a student of Wöhler's, made the organic compound acetic acid from inorganic substances that could themselves be prepared directly from pure elements.

The foundation of vitalism finally crumbled after several more decades of laboratory synthesis of increasingly complex organic compounds. In 1953, Stanley Miller, a graduate student at the University of Chicago, helped bring this abiotic (nonliving) synthesis of organic compounds into the context of evolution. Miller used a laboratory simulation of chemical conditions on the primitive Earth to demonstrate that the spontaneous synthesis of organic compounds could have been an early stage in the origin of life (FIGURE 4.1).

The pioneers of organic chemistry helped shift the mainstream of biological thought from vitalism to mechanism, the belief that all natural phenomena, including the processes of life, are governed by physical and chemical laws. Organic chemistry was redefined as the study of carbon compounds, regardless of their origin. Most naturally occurring organic compounds are produced by organisms, and these molecules represent a diversity and range of complexity unrivaled by inorganic compounds. However, the same rules of chemistry apply to inorganic and organic molecules alike. The foundation of organic chemistry is not some intangible life force, but the unique chemical versatility of the element carbon.

Carbon atoms are the most versatile building blocks of molecules

The key to the chemical characteristics of an atom, as you learned in Chapter 2, is in its configuration of electrons; electron configuration determines the kinds and number of bonds an atom will form with other atoms. Carbon has a total of six electrons, with two in the first electron shell and four in the second shell. Having four valence electrons in a shell that holds eight, carbon has little tendency to gain or lose electrons and form ionic bonds; it would have to donate or accept four electrons to do so. Instead, a carbon atom usually completes its valence shell by sharing electrons with other atoms in four covalent bonds. Each carbon atom thus acts as an intersection point from which a molecule can branch off in up to four directions. This *tetravalence* is one facet of carbon's versatility that makes large, complex molecules possible.

In Chapter 2 you also learned that when a carbon atom forms single covalent bonds, the arrangement of its four hybrid orbitals causes the bonds to angle toward the corners of an imaginary tetrahedron (see FIGURE 2.15c). The bond angles in methane (CH_4) are 109°, and they would be approximately the same in any molecule where carbon has four single bonds. For example, ethane (C_2H_6) is shaped like two tetrahedrons joined at their apexes (FIGURE 4.2, p. 50). In molecules with more carbons, every grouping of a carbon bonded to four other atoms has a tetrahedral shape. It is convenient to write structural formulas as though molecules were flat, but it is important to remember that molecules are three-dimensional and that the shape of a molecule often determines its function.

FIGURE 4.1 ▪ Abiotic synthesis of organic compounds under "early Earth" conditions. Stanley Miller re-creates his 1953 experiment, a laboratory simulation demonstrating that environmental conditions on the lifeless, primordial Earth favored the spontaneous synthesis of some organic molecules. Miller used electrical discharges (simulated lightning) to trigger reactions in a primitive "atmosphere" of H_2O, H_2, NH_3 (ammonia), and CH_4 (methane)—some of the gases released by volcanoes. From these ingredients, Miller's apparatus made a variety of organic compounds that play key roles in living cells. Similar chemical reactions may have set the stage for the origin of life on Earth, a hypothesis we will explore in more detail in Chapter 26.

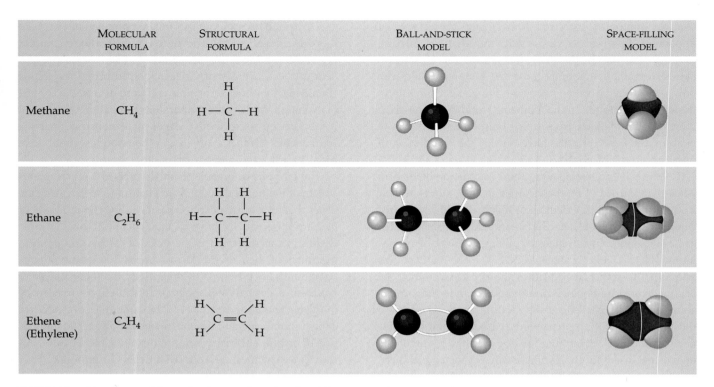

	MOLECULAR FORMULA	STRUCTURAL FORMULA	BALL-AND-STICK MODEL	SPACE-FILLING MODEL
Methane	CH_4			
Ethane	C_2H_6			
Ethene (Ethylene)	C_2H_4			

FIGURE 4.2 · The shapes of three simple organic molecules. Whenever a carbon atom has four single bonds, the bonds angle toward the corners of an imaginary tetrahedron. When two carbons are joined by a double bond, all bonds around those atoms are in the same plane. (Notice, for example, that ethene is a flat molecule; its atoms all lie in the same plane.)

The electron configuration of carbon gives it covalent compatibility with many different elements. FIGURE 4.3 reviews the valences of the four major atomic components of organic molecules: carbon and its most frequent partners, oxygen, hydrogen, and nitrogen. We can think of these valences as the rules of covalent bonding in organic chemistry—the building code that governs the architecture of organic molecules.

A couple of additional examples will show how the rules of covalent bonding apply to carbon atoms with partners other than hydrogen. In the carbon dioxide molecule (CO_2), a single carbon atom is joined to two atoms of oxygen by double covalent bonds. The structural formula for CO_2 is O=C=O. Each line (bond) in a structural formula represents a pair of shared electrons. Notice that the carbon atom in CO_2 is involved in four covalent bonds, two with each oxygen atom. The arrangement completes the valence shells of all atoms in the molecule. Carbon dioxide is such a simple molecule that it is often considered inorganic, even though it contains carbon.

Whether we call CO_2 organic or inorganic is an arbitrary distinction, but there is no ambiguity about its importance to the living world. Taken from the air by plants and incorporated into sugar and other foods during photosynthesis, CO_2 is the source of carbon for all the organic molecules found in organisms.

Another relatively simple molecule is urea, $CO(NH_2)_2$. This is the organic compound found in urine that Wöhler learned to synthesize in the early nineteenth century. The structural formula for urea is:

Again, each atom has the required number of covalent bonds. In this case, one carbon atom is involved in both single and double bonds.

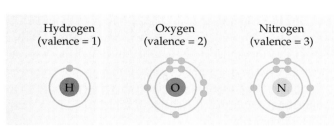

Hydrogen (valence = 1)	Oxygen (valence = 2)	Nitrogen (valence = 3)	Carbon (valence = 4)

FIGURE 4.3 · Valences for the major elements of organic molecules. Valence is the number of covalent bonds an atom will usually form. It is equal to the number of electrons required to complete the atom's outermost (valence) electron shell. Forming bonds with other atoms gives each valence-shell orbital a pair of electrons.

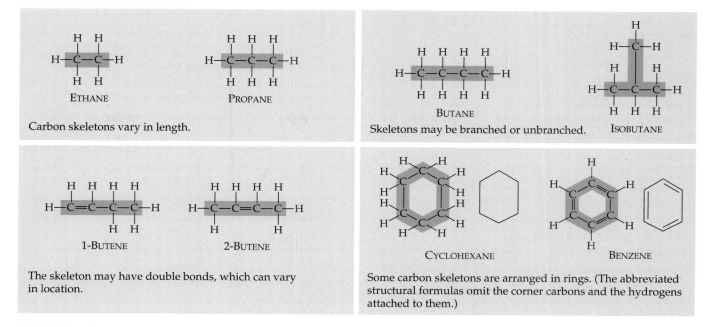

FIGURE 4.4 ▪ **Variations in carbon skeletons.** Hydrocarbons, organic molecules consisting only of carbon and hydrogen, illustrate the diversity of the carbon skeletons of organic molecules.

Both urea and carbon dioxide are molecules with only one carbon atom. But as FIGURE 4.2 shows, a carbon atom can also use one or more of its valence electrons to form covalent bonds to other carbon atoms, making it possible to link the atoms into chains of seemingly infinite variety.

Variation in carbon skeletons contributes to the diversity of organic molecules

Carbon chains form the skeletons of most organic molecules. The skeletons vary in length and may be straight, branched, or arranged in closed rings (FIGURE 4.4). Some carbon skeletons have double bonds, which vary in number and location. Such variation in carbon skeletons is one important source of the molecular complexity and diversity that characterize living matter. In addition, atoms of other elements can be bonded to the skeletons at available sites.

All the molecules shown in FIGURES 4.2 and 4.4 are **hydrocarbons**, organic molecules consisting only of carbon and hydrogen. Atoms of hydrogen are attached to the carbon skeleton wherever electrons are available for covalent bonding. Hydrocarbons are the major components of petroleum, which is called a fossil fuel because it consists of the partially decomposed remains of organisms that lived millions of years ago. Although hydrocarbons are not prevalent in living organisms, many of a cell's organic molecules have regions consisting of only carbon and hydrogen. For example, the molecules known as fats have long hydrocarbon tails attached to a non-hydrocarbon component (FIGURE 4.5). Neither petroleum nor fat mixes with water; both are hydrophobic compounds

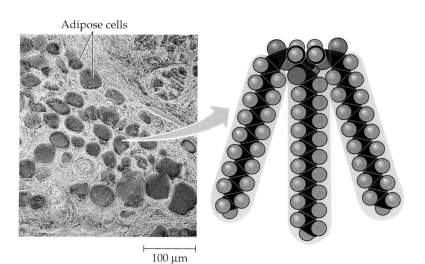

Adipose cells

100 µm

FIGURE 4.5 ▪ **The role of hydrocarbons in the characteristics of fats.** Humans and other mammals store fats in specialized cells called adipose cells. Each cell is almost completely filled with a large fat droplet (stained red in this light micrograph), which stockpiles an enormous number of fat molecules. The drawing is a space-filling model of one fat molecule (black = carbon; gray = hydrogen; red = oxygen). Three hydrocarbon tails are attached to a headpiece containing oxygen as well as carbon and hydrogen. Hydrocarbon bonds are nonpolar, which accounts for the hydrophobic behavior of fats. Another characteristic of hydrocarbons is that they store a relatively large amount of energy. The gasoline that fuels a car consists of hydrocarbons, and the hydrocarbon tails of fat molecules serve as stored fuel for your body.

because the bonds between the carbon and hydrogen atoms are nonpolar.

Isomers

Variation in the architecture of organic molecules can be seen in **isomers**, compounds that have the same molecular formula but different structures and hence different properties. Compare, for example, the two butanes in FIGURE 4.4. Both have the molecular formula C_4H_{10}, but they differ in the covalent arrangement of their carbon skeletons. The skeleton is straight in butane, but branched in isobutane. We will examine three types of isomers: structural isomers, geometric isomers, and enantiomers (FIGURE 4.6).

Structural isomers differ in the covalent arrangements of their atoms. The number of possible isomers increases tremendously as carbon skeletons increase in size. There are only two butanes, but there are 18 variations of C_8H_{18} and 366,319 possible structural isomers of $C_{20}H_{42}$. Structural isomers may also differ in the location of double bonds.

Geometric isomers of a molecule have all the same covalent partnerships, but they differ in their spatial arrangements. Geometric isomers arise from the inflexibility of double bonds, which, unlike single bonds, will not allow the atoms they join to rotate freely about the bond axis. The subtle difference in shape between geometric isomers can dramatically affect the biological activities of organic molecules. For example, the biochemistry of vision involves a light-induced change of rhodopsin, a chemical compound in the eye, from one geometric isomer to another.

Enantiomers are molecules that are mirror images of each other. In the ball-and-stick models shown in FIGURE 4.6c, the middle carbon is called an *asymmetric carbon* because it is attached to four different atoms or groups of atoms. The four groups can be arranged in space about the asymmetric carbon in two different ways that are mirror images. They are, in a way, left-handed and right-handed versions of the molecule. A cell can distinguish these isomers based on their different shapes. Usually, one isomer is biologically active and the other is inactive.

The concept of enantiomers is important in the pharmaceutical industry, because the two enantiomers of a drug may not be equally effective (FIGURE 4.7). In some cases, one of the isomers may even produce harmful effects. This was the case with thalidomide, a drug prescribed for thousands of pregnant women in the early 1960s. The drug was a mixture of two enantiomers. One enantiomer produced the desired effect by acting as a sedative, but the other caused birth defects. Scientists are developing new techniques for synthesizing such drugs in pure isomeric form rather than as mixtures of enantiomers. The differing effects of enantiomers in the body demonstrate that organisms are sensitive to even the

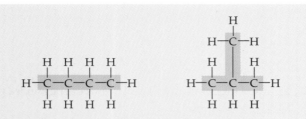

(a) Structural isomers: variation in covalent partners, as shown in the example of butane and isobutane.

(b) Geometric isomers: variation in arrangement about a double bond. (In these diagrams, "X" represents an atom or group of atoms attached to a double–bonded carbon.)

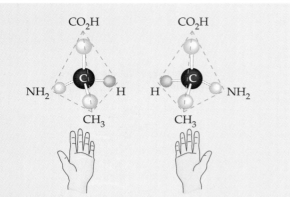

(c) Enantiomers: variation in spatial arrangement around an asymmetric carbon, resulting in molecules that are mirror images, like left and right hands. Enantiomers cannot be superimposed on each other.

FIGURE 4.6 ▪ **Three types of isomers.** Compounds with the same molecular formula but different structures, isomers are a source of diversity in organic molecules.

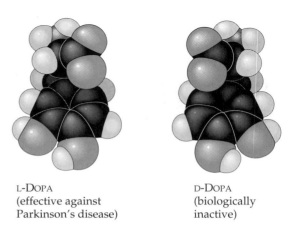

L-DOPA
(effective against Parkinson's disease)

D-DOPA
(biologically inactive)

FIGURE 4.7 ▪ **The pharmacological importance of enantiomers.** L-dopa is a drug used to treat Parkinson's disease, a disorder of the central nervous system. The drug's enantiomer, the mirror-image molecule designated D-dopa, has no effect on patients.

most subtle variations in molecular architecture. Once again, we see that molecules have emergent properties that depend on the specific arrangement of their atoms.

FUNCTIONAL GROUPS

The distinctive properties of an organic molecule depend not only on the arrangement of its carbon skeleton, but also on the molecular components attached to that skeleton. We will now examine certain groups of atoms that are frequently attached to the skeletons of organic molecules.

Functional groups also contribute to the molecular diversity of life

4.2 The components of organic molecules that are most commonly involved in chemical reactions are known as **functional groups**. If we think of hydrocarbons as the simplest organic molecules, we can, in general, view functional groups as attachments that replace one or more of the hydrogens bonded to the carbon skeleton of the hydrocarbon. (However, some functional groups include atoms of the carbon skeleton, as we will see.)

Each functional group behaves consistently from one organic molecule to another, and the number and arrangement of the groups help give each molecule its unique properties. Consider the differences between estrone and testosterone, female and male sex hormones, respectively, in humans and other vertebrates (FIGURE 4.8). Both are steroids, organic molecules with a common carbon skeleton in the form of four fused rings. These sex hormones differ only in the presence of certain functional groups on the four rings. The different actions of these two molecules on many targets throughout the body help produce the contrasting features of females and males. Thus, even our sexuality has its biological basis in variations of molecular architecture.

The six functional groups most important in the chemistry of life are the hydroxyl, carbonyl, carboxyl, amino, sulfhydryl, and phosphate groups (TABLE 4.1, p. 54). All are hydrophilic and thus increase the solubility of organic compounds in water.

The Hydroxyl Group

In a **hydroxyl group**, a hydrogen atom is bonded to an oxygen atom, which in turn is bonded to the carbon skeleton of the organic molecule. Organic compounds containing hydroxyl groups are called **alcohols**, and their specific names usually end in *-ol*, as in ethanol, the drug present in alcoholic beverages. In a structural formula, the hydroxyl group is usually abbreviated by omission of the covalent bond between the oxygen and hydrogen, and is written as —OH or HO—. (Do not confuse this functional group with the hydroxide ion, OH^-, formed by the dissociation of bases such as sodium hydroxide.) The hydroxyl group is polar as a result of the electronegative oxygen atom drawing electrons toward itself. Consequently, water molecules are attracted to the hydroxyl group, and this helps dissolve organic compounds containing such groups. Sugars, for example, owe their solubility in water to the presence of hydroxyl groups.

The Carbonyl Group

The **carbonyl group** ($>CO$) consists of a carbon atom joined to an oxygen atom by a double bond. If the carbonyl group is on the end of a carbon skeleton, the organic compound is called an **aldehyde**; otherwise the compound is called a

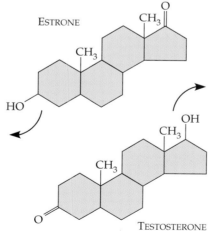

FIGURE 4.8 · A comparison of functional groups of female (estrone) and male (testosterone) sex hormones. The two molecules differ in the attachment of functional groups to a common carbon skeleton of four fused rings. The carbon skeleton has been simplified here by omitting the carbons in the rings, as well as their double bonds and hydrogens. The subtle variations in the molecular architecture of the molecules influence the development of the anatomical and physiological differences between female and male vertebrates. Compare, for example, the plumage of the female (left) and male (right) wood ducks.

Table 4.1 ■ **Functional Groups of Organic Compounds**

FUNCTIONAL GROUP	FORMULA	NAME OF COMPOUNDS	EXAMPLE
Hydroxyl	—OH	Alcohols	Ethanol (the drug of alcoholic beverages)
Carbonyl		Aldehydes	Propanal
		Ketones	Acetone
Carboxyl	(non-ionized) (ionized)	Carboxylic acids	Acetic acid* (the acid of vinegar)
Amino	(non-ionized) (ionized)	Amines	Glycine* (an amino acid)
Sulfhydryl	—SH	Thiols	Ethanethiol
Phosphate		Organic phosphates	Glycerol phosphate

*The ionized forms of the carboxyl and amino groups prevail in cells. However, acetic acid and glycine are represented here in their non-ionized forms.

ketone. The simplest ketone is acetone, which is three carbons long (see TABLE 4.1). Acetone has different properties from propanal, a three-carbon aldehyde (acetone and propanal are structural isomers). Thus, variation in locations of functional groups along carbon skeletons is a major source of molecular diversity.

The Carboxyl Group

When an oxygen atom is double-bonded to a carbon atom that is also bonded to a hydroxyl group, the entire assembly of atoms is called a **carboxyl group** (—COOH). Compounds containing carboxyl groups are known as **carboxylic acids**, or

organic acids. The simplest is the one-carbon compound called formic acid (HCOOH), the substance some ants inject when they sting. Acetic acid, which has two carbons, gives vinegar its sour taste. (In general, acids, including carboxylic acids, taste sour.)

Why does a carboxyl group have acidic properties? A carboxyl group is a source of hydrogen ions. The covalent bond between the oxygen and the hydrogen is so polar that the hydrogen tends to dissociate reversibly from the molecule as an ion (H^+). In the case of acetic acid, we have:

Acetic acid   Acetate ion   Hydrogen ion

Dissociation occurs as a result of the two electronegative oxygen atoms of the carboxyl group pulling shared electrons away from hydrogen. If the double-bonded oxygen and the hydroxyl group were attached to *separate* carbon atoms, there would be less tendency for the —OH group to dissociate because the second oxygen would be farther away. Here is another example of how emergent properties result from a specific arrangement of building components.

The Amino Group

The **amino group** (—NH_2) consists of a nitrogen atom bonded to two hydrogen atoms and to the carbon skeleton. Organic compounds with this functional group are called **amines**. An example is glycine, illustrated in TABLE 4.1. Because glycine *also* has a carboxyl group, it is both an amine and a carboxylic acid. Most of the cell's organic compounds have two or more different functional groups. Glycine belongs to a group of organic compounds named amino acids, which are the molecular building blocks of proteins.

The amino group acts as a base. You learned in Chapter 3 that ammonia (NH_3) can pick up a proton from the surrounding solution. Amino groups of organic compounds can do the same:

This process gives the amino group a charge of $+1$, its most common state within the cell.

The Sulfhydryl Group

Sulfur is directly below oxygen in the periodic table; both have six valence electrons and form two covalent bonds. The organic functional group known as the **sulfhydryl group** (—SH), which consists of a sulfur atom bonded to an atom of hydrogen, resembles a hydroxyl group in shape (see TABLE 4.1). Organic compounds containing sulfhydryls are called **thiols**. In Chapter 5 you will learn how sulfhydryl groups can interact to help stabilize the intricate structure of many proteins.

The Phosphate Group

Phosphate is an anion formed by dissociation of an inorganic acid called phosphoric acid (H_3PO_4). The loss of hydrogen ions by dissociation leaves the phosphate with a negative charge. Organic compounds containing **phosphate groups** have a phosphate ion covalently attached by one of its oxygen atoms to the carbon skeleton (see TABLE 4.1). One function of phosphate groups is the transfer of energy between organic molecules. In Chapter 6 you will learn how cells harness the transfer of phosphate groups to perform work, such as the contraction of muscle cells.

The chemical elements of life: *a review*

Living matter, as you have learned, consists mainly of carbon, oxygen, hydrogen, and nitrogen, with smaller amounts of sulfur and phosphorus. These elements share the characteristic of forming strong covalent bonds, a quality that is essential in the architecture of complex organic molecules. Of all these elements, carbon is the virtuoso of the covalent bond. The chemical behavior of carbon makes it exceptionally versatile as a building block in molecular architecture: It can form four covalent bonds, link together into intricate molecular skeletons, and join with several other elements. The versatility of carbon makes possible the great diversity of organic molecules, each with special properties that emerge from the unique arrangement of its carbon skeleton and the functional groups appended to that skeleton. At the foundation of all biological diversity lies this variation at the molecular level.

Now that we have examined the basic architectural principles of organic compounds, we can move on to the next chapter, where we will explore the specific structures and functions of the large and complex molecules made by living cells: carbohydrates, lipids, proteins, and nucleic acids.

(with page numbers and key figures)

THE IMPORTANT OF CARBON

■ **Organic chemistry is the study of carbon compounds (pp. 48–49)** Organic compounds were once thought to arise only within living organisms, but this idea (vitalism) was disproved when chemists were able to synthesize organic compounds from inorganic ones.

■ **Carbon atoms are the most versatile building blocks of molecules (pp. 49–51, FIGURE 4.2)** A covalent bonding capacity of four contributes to carbon's ability to form diverse molecules. Carbon can bond to a variety of atoms, including O, H, N, and S. Carbon atoms can also bond to other carbons, forming the carbon skeletons of organic compounds.

4.1 **Variation in carbon skeletons contributes to the diversity of organic molecules (pp. 51–53, FIGURE 4.4)** The carbon skeletons of organic molecules vary in length and shape and have bonding sites for atoms of other elements. Hydrocarbons consist only of carbon and hydrogen. Carbon's versatile bonding is the basis for isomers, molecules with the same molecular formula but different structures and thus different properties. Three types of isomers are structural isomers, geometric isomers, and enantiomers.

FUNCTIONAL GROUPS

4.2 **Functional groups also contribute to the molecular diversity of life (pp. 53–55, TABLE 4.1)** Functional groups are specific, chemically reactive groups of atoms within organic molecules that give the overall molecule distinctive chemical properties. The hydroxyl group (—OH), found in alcohols, has a polar covalent bond, which helps alcohols dissolve in water. The carbonyl group ($>$CO) can be either at the end of a carbon skeleton (aldehyde) or within the skeleton (ketone). The carboxyl group (—COOH) is found in carboxylic acids. The hydrogen of this group can dissociate, making the molecule a weak acid. The amino group (—NH$_2$) can accept an H$^+$, thereby acting as a base. The sulfhydryl group (—SH) helps stabilize the structure of some proteins. The phosphate group can bond to a carbon skeleton by one of its oxygen atoms and has an important role in the transfer of cellular energy.

■ **The chemical elements of life:** *a review* **(p. 55)** Living matter is made mostly of carbon, oxygen, hydrogen, and nitrogen, with some sulfur and phosphorus. Biological diversity has its molecular basis in carbon's ability to form a huge number of molecules with particular shapes and chemical properties.

1. Organic chemistry is currently defined as
   a. the study of compounds that can be made only by living cells
   b. the study of carbon compounds
   c. the study of vital forces
   d. the study of natural (as opposed to synthetic) compounds
   e. the study of hydrocarbons

2. Choose the pair of terms that correctly completes this sentence: Hydroxyl is to _____ as _____ is to aldehyde.
   a. carbonyl; ketone
   b. oxygen; carbon
   c. alcohol; carbonyl
   d. amine; carboxyl
   e. alcohol; ketone

3. Which of the following hydrocarbons has a double bond in its carbon skeleton?
   a. C_3H_8
   b. C_2H_6
   c. CH_4
   d. C_2H_4
   e. C_2H_2

4. The gasoline consumed by an automobile is a fossil fuel consisting mostly of
   a. aldehydes
   b. amino acids
   c. alcohols
   d. hydrocarbons
   e. thiols

5. Choose the term that correctly describes the relationship between these two sugar molecules:

   a. structural isomers
   b. geometric isomers
   c. enantiomers
   d. isotopes

6. Identify the asymmetric carbon in this molecule:

7. Which functional group is *not* present on this molecule?

   a. carboxyl
   b. sulfhydryl
   c. hydroxyl
   d. amino

8. Which action could produce a carbonyl group?
   a. the removal of the hydroxyl from a carboxyl
   b. the addition of a thiol to a hydroxyl
   c. the addition of a hydroxyl to a phosphate
   d. the replacement of the nitrogen of an amine with oxygen
   e. the addition of a sulfhydryl to a carboxyl

9. Which functional group is most responsible for some organic molecules behaving as bases?
   a. hydroxyl   d. amino
   b. carbonyl   e. phosphate
   c. carboxyl

10. Which of the following molecules would be the strongest acid? Explain your answer.

a.
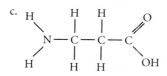
c.
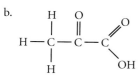

b.
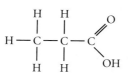
d.

CHALLENGE QUESTIONS

1. Draw an organic molecule having all six functional groups described in this chapter.

2. Draw three structural isomers of the hydrocarbon pentane (C_5H_{12}).

3. Alice, in Lewis Carroll's classic *Alice in Wonderland,* poses this question: "Is looking-glass milk good to drink?" Respond, and justify your answer based on what you have learned about the structure of organic molecules, the importance of isomers, and the biological relevance of molecular shape.

SCIENCE, TECHNOLOGY, AND SOCIETY

1. The role of the Food and Drug Administration (FDA) in monitoring the testing of new drugs continues to be controversial. The thalidomide tragedy (p. 52) is often cited by those who argue that the FDA should not approve any drug until no doubt remains that the drug can be safely prescribed. Others would like to see FDA standards less rigid for drugs that may help people suffering from terminal diseases, such as AIDS. Where do you stand on this issue? Defend your position.

2. Each year, industrial chemists synthesize and test thousands of new organic compounds for use as insecticides and weed killers. In what ways are these chemicals useful and important to us? In what ways can they be harmful? What influences have shaped your opinions about these chemicals?

FURTHER READING

Asimov, I. *The World of Carbon,* 2nd ed. New York: Macmillan, 1962. A primer on the basics of organic chemistry by one of America's most popular science writers.
Bada, J. L. "Extraterrestrial Handedness?" *Science,* February 14, 1997. A possible explanation for why cells use certain enantiomers exclusively.
Bradley, D. "Frog Venom Cocktail Yields a One-Handed Painkiller." *Science,* August 27, 1993. Organic chemists synthesize a new drug based on the toxic compound secreted by the "poison arrow frog."
Bradley, D. "A New Twist in the Tale of Nature's Asymmetry." *Science,* May 13, 1994. The pharmaceutical importance of isomers.
Kessler, D. A., and K. L. Feiden. "Faster Evaluation of Vital Drugs." *Scientific American,* March 1995. When is it ethical to trade safety for speed in order to make new drugs available?
Ourisson, G., P. Albrecht, and M. Rohmer. "The Microbial Origin of Fossil Fuels." *Scientific American,* August 1984. The biology behind our important energy resources.

WEB LINKS

Visit the special edition of *The Biology Place* for BIOLOGY, Fifth Edition, at http://www.biology.com/campbell. Go to Chapter 4 for online resources, including learning activities, practice exams, and links to the following web sites:

"IUPAC Nomenclature of Organic Chemistry"
Exhaustive lists, descriptions, and explanations of correct IUPAC nomenclature for chemical compounds.

"Organic Chemistry from BioChemNet"
Comprehensive list of tutorial, reference, and other organic chemistry educational resources. Some sites offer free downloadable demo software.

"Basic Reactions in Organic Chemistry—Interactive"
An interesting virtual reality site that features a number of three-dimensional, animated, basic organic chemistry reactions.

"MathMol"
Good introductory site for those interested in molecular modeling. Numerous links to freely downloadable public domain software.

THE STRUCTURE AND FUNCTION OF MACROMOLECULES

*W*e have applied the concept of emergent properties to our study of water and relatively simple organic molecules. These substances are central to life, each one having unique behavior arising from the orderly arrangement of its atoms. Another level in the hierarchy of biological organization is attained when cells join together small organic molecules to form larger molecules that belong to four classes: carbohydrates, lipids, proteins, and nucleic acids. Many of these cellular molecules are, on the molecular scale, huge. For example, a protein may consist of thousands of covalently connected atoms that form a molecular colossus weighing over 100,000 daltons. Biologists use the term **macromolecule** for such giant molecules.

Considering the size and complexity of macromolecules, it is remarkable that biochemists have determined the detailed structures of so many of them (FIGURE 5.1). The architecture of a macromolecule helps explain how that molecule works. For example, the structure of the silk protein from which the orb spider in the photo on this page weaves its web gives the fibers their strength and springiness. Proteins and the other large molecules of life are the main subject of this chapter. For these molecules, as at all levels in the biological hierarchy, form and function are inseparable.

POLYMER PRINCIPLES

In examining the relationship between the structure and function of life's macromolecules, we begin with a key generalization about how cells build these large molecules from smaller ones.

Most macromolecules are polymers

The large molecules in three of the four classes of life's organic compounds—carbohydrates, proteins, and nucleic acids—are chainlike molecules called polymers (from the Greek *polys*, "many," and *meris*, "part"). A **polymer** is a long molecule consisting of many identical or similar building blocks linked by covalent bonds, much as a train consists of a chain of cars. The repeating units that serve as the building blocks of a polymer are small molecules called **monomers**. Some of the molecules that serve as monomers also have other functions of their own.

The classes of polymeric macromolecules differ in the nature of their monomers, but the chemical mechanisms that cells use to make and break polymers are basically the same in all cases (FIGURE 5.2). Monomers are connected by a reaction in which two molecules are covalently bonded to each other through loss of a water molecule; this is called a **condensation reaction**, specifically a **dehydration reaction**, because the molecule lost is water (FIGURE 5.2a). When a bond forms between two monomers, each monomer contributes part of the water molecule that is lost: One molecule provides a

(a)

(b)

FIGURE 5.1 · **Building models to study the structure and function of macromolecules.** **(a)** Linus Pauling (1901–1994), here with a model of part of a protein. In the 1950s, Pauling discovered several of the basic structural features of proteins. **(b)** Today, scientists use computers to help build molecular models. Though methods have improved, the goal remains to correlate the structure of macromolecules with their functions.

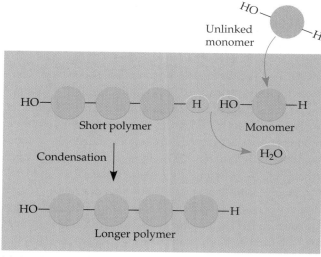

(a) Condensation (dehydration) synthesis of a polymer

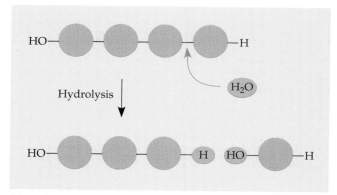

(b) Hydrolysis of a polymer

FIGURE 5.2 · **The synthesis and breakdown of polymers.** **(a)** Monomers are joined by condensation reactions (dehydration reactions). The net effect is the removal of a water molecule. **(b)** The reverse of this process, hydrolysis, breaks bonds between monomers by adding water molecules.

hydroxyl group (—OH), while the other provides a hydrogen (—H). To make a polymer, this reaction is repeated as monomers are added to the chain one by one. The cell must expend energy to carry out these condensation reactions, and the process occurs only with the help of enzymes, specialized proteins that speed up chemical reactions in cells.

Polymers are disassembled to monomers by **hydrolysis,** a process that is essentially the reverse of the dehydration reaction (FIGURE 5.2b). Hydrolysis means to break with water (from the Greek *hydro,* "water," and *lysis,* "break"). Bonds between monomers are broken by the addition of water molecules, a hydrogen from the water attaching to one monomer, and a hydroxyl attaching to the adjacent monomer. An exam-

ple of hydrolysis working in our bodies is the process of digestion. The bulk of the organic material in our food is in the form of polymers that are much too large to enter our cells. Within the digestive tract, various enzymes attack the polymers, speeding up hydrolysis. The released monomers are then absorbed into the bloodstream for distribution to all body cells. Those cells can then use dehydration reactions to assemble the monomers into new polymers that differ from the ones that were digested.

An immense variety of polymers can be built from a small set of monomers

Each cell has thousands of different kinds of macromolecules; the collection varies from one type of cell to another in the same organism. The inherent differences between human siblings reflect variations in polymers, particularly DNA and

proteins. Molecular differences between unrelated individuals are more extensive, and between species greater still. The diversity of macromolecules in the living world is vast—and the potential variety is effectively limitless.

What is the basis for such diversity in life's polymers? These molecules are constructed from only 40 to 50 common monomers and some others that occur rarely. Building an enormous variety of polymers from such a limited list of monomers is analogous to constructing hundreds of thousands of words from only 26 letters of the alphabet. The key is arrangement—variation in the linear sequence the units follow. However, this analogy falls far short of describing the great diversity of macromolecules, because most biological polymers are much longer than the longest word. Proteins, for example, are built from 20 kinds of amino acids arranged in chains that are typically hundreds of amino acids long. The molecular logic of life is simple but elegant: Small molecules common to all organisms are ordered into unique macromolecules.

We are now ready to investigate the specific structures and functions of the four major classes of organic compounds found in cells. For each class, we will see that the large molecules have emergent properties not found in their individual building blocks.

CARBOHYDRATES—FUEL AND BUILDING MATERIAL

The term **carbohydrates** includes both sugars and their polymers. The simplest carbohydrates are the monosaccharides, single sugars also known as simple sugars (FIGURE 5.3). Disaccharides are double sugars, consisting of two monosaccharides joined by condensation. The carbohydrates that are macromolecules are polysaccharides, polymers of many sugars.

Sugars, the smallest carbohydrates, serve as fuel and carbon sources

Monosaccharides (from the Greek *monos,* "single," and *sacchar,* "sugar") generally have molecular formulas that are some multiple of CH_2O (see FIGURE 5.3). Glucose ($C_6H_{12}O_6$), the most common monosaccharide, is of central importance in the chemistry of life. In the structure of glucose, we can see all the trademarks of a sugar. A hydroxyl group is attached to each carbon except one, which is double-bonded to an oxygen to form a carbonyl group. Depending on the location of the carbonyl group, a sugar is either an aldose (aldehyde sugar) or a ketose (ketone sugar). Glucose, for example, is an aldose;

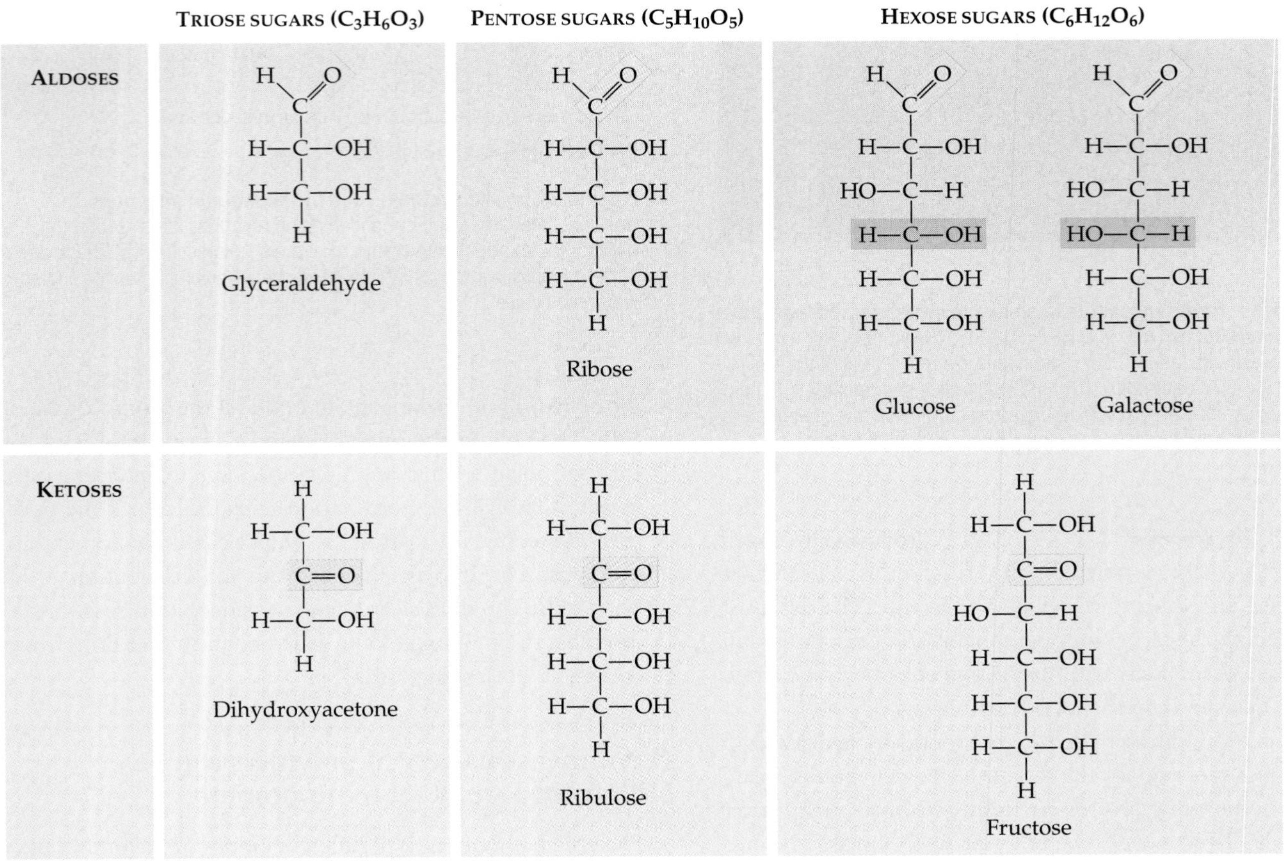

| | TRIOSE SUGARS ($C_3H_6O_3$) | PENTOSE SUGARS ($C_5H_{10}O_5$) | HEXOSE SUGARS ($C_6H_{12}O_6$) | |

ALDOSES: Glyceraldehyde, Ribose, Glucose, Galactose

KETOSES: Dihydroxyacetone, Ribulose, Fructose

FIGURE 5.3 ▪ The structure and classification of some monosaccharides. Sugars may be aldoses (aldehyde sugars) or ketoses (ketone sugars), depending on the location of the carbonyl group (pink). Sugars are also classified according to the length of their carbon skeletons. A third point of variation is in the spatial arrangement around asymmetric carbons (compare, for example, the gray portions of glucose and galactose).

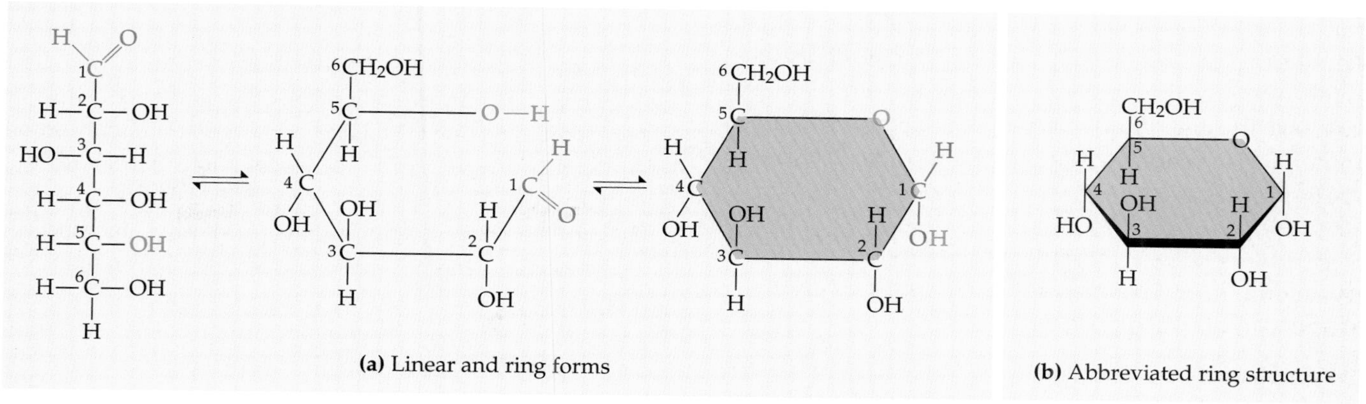

(a) Linear and ring forms

(b) Abbreviated ring structure

FIGURE 5.4 ▪ **Linear and ring forms of glucose.** **(a)** Chemical equilibrium between the linear and ring structures greatly favors the formation of rings. To form the glucose ring, carbon 1 bonds to the oxygen attached to carbon 5. **(b)** In this abbreviated ring formula, the carbons in the ring are omitted. The ring's thicker edge indicates that you are looking at the ring edge-on; the components attached to the ring lie above or below the plane of the ring.

fructose, a structural isomer of glucose, is a ketose. (Most names for sugars end in -*ose.*) Another criterion for classifying sugars is the size of the carbon skeleton, which ranges from three to seven carbons long. Glucose, fructose, and other sugars that have six carbons are called hexoses. Trioses and pentoses are also common.

Still another source of diversity for simple sugars is in the spatial arrangement of their parts around asymmetric carbons. (Recall from Chapter 4 that an asymmetric carbon is one attached to four different kinds of covalent partners.) Glucose and galactose, for example, differ only in the placement of parts around one asymmetric carbon (see the gray boxes in FIGURE 5.3). What may seem at first a small difference is significant enough to give the two sugars distinctive shapes and behaviors.

Although it is convenient to draw glucose with a linear carbon skeleton, this representation is not accurate. In aqueous solutions, glucose molecules, as well as most other sugars, form rings (FIGURE 5.4).

Monosaccharides, particularly glucose, are major nutrients for cells. In the process known as cellular respiration, cells extract the energy stored in glucose molecules. Not only are simple sugar molecules a major fuel for cellular work, but their carbon skeletons serve as raw material for the synthesis of other types of small organic molecules, including amino acids and fatty acids. Sugar molecules that are not immediately used in these ways are generally incorporated as monomers into disaccharides or polysaccharides.

A **disaccharide** (FIGURE 5.5) consists of two monosaccharides joined by a **glycosidic linkage**, a covalent bond formed between two monosaccharides by a dehydration reaction. For example, maltose is a disaccharide formed by linking two molecules of glucose. Also known as malt sugar, maltose is an ingredient for brewing beer. Lactose, the sugar present in

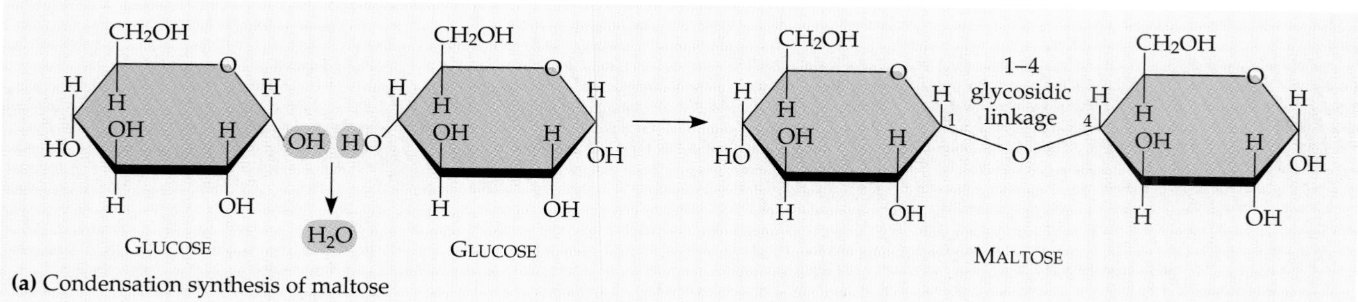

(a) Condensation synthesis of maltose

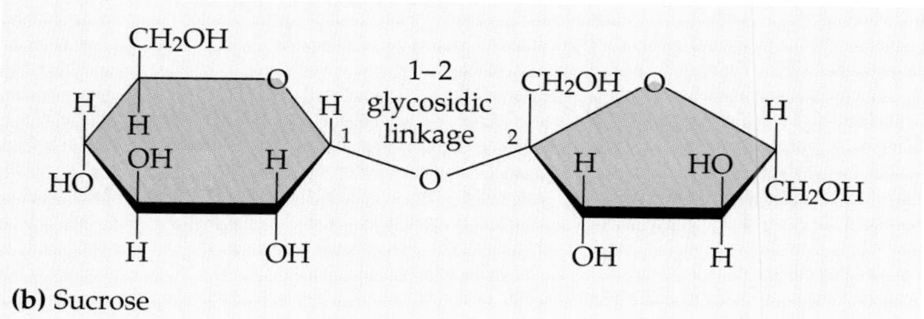

(b) Sucrose

FIGURE 5.5 ▪ **Examples of disaccharides. (a)** The bonding of two glucose units forms maltose. The glycosidic link joins the number 1 carbon of one glucose to the number 4 carbon of the second glucose. Joining the glucose monomers in a different way would result in a different disaccharide. **(b)** Sucrose is a disaccharide formed from glucose and fructose. Notice that fructose, though a hexose like glucose, forms a five-sided ring.

milk, is another disaccharide, consisting of a glucose molecule joined to a galactose molecule. The most prevalent disaccharide is sucrose, which is table sugar. Its two monomers are glucose and fructose. Plants generally transport carbohydrates from leaves to roots and other nonphotosynthetic organs in the form of sucrose.

Polysaccharides, the polymers of sugars, have storage and structural roles

Polysaccharides are macromolecules, polymers with a few hundred to a few thousand monosaccharides joined by glycosidic linkages. Some polysaccharides serve as storage material, hydrolyzed as needed to provide sugar for cells. Other polysaccharides serve as building material for structures that protect the cell or the whole organism. The architecture and function of a polysaccharide are determined by its sugar monomers and by the positions of its glycosidic linkages.

Storage Polysaccharides

Starch, a storage polysaccharide of plants (FIGURE 5.6a), is a polymer consisting entirely of glucose monomers. Most of these monomers are joined by 1–4 linkages (number 1 carbon to number 4 carbon), like the glucose units in maltose (see FIGURE 5.5a). The angle of these bonds makes the polymer helical. The simplest form of starch, amylose, is unbranched. Amylopectin, a more complex form of starch, is a branched polymer with 1–6 linkages at the branch points.

Plants store starch as granules within cellular structures called plastids, including chloroplasts (see FIGURE 5.6a). By synthesizing starch, the plant can stockpile surplus sugar. Because glucose is a major cellular fuel, starch represents stored energy. The sugar can later be withdrawn from this carbohydrate bank by hydrolysis, which breaks the bonds between the glucose monomers. Most animals, including humans, also have enzymes that can hydrolyze plant starch, making glucose available as a nutrient for cells. Potato tubers

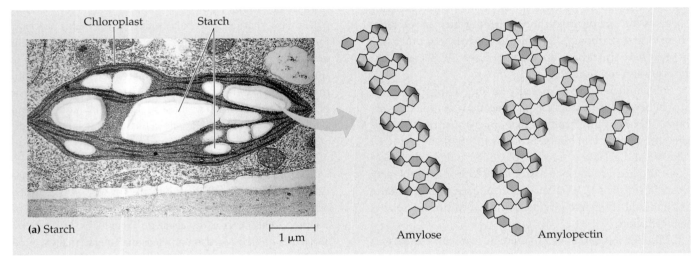

(a) Starch   1 µm

Amylose   Amylopectin

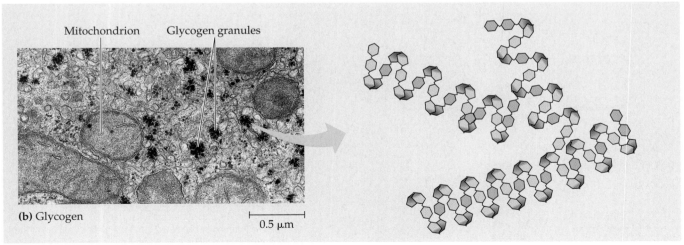

(b) Glycogen   0.5 µm

FIGURE 5.6 ▪ **Storage polysaccharides.** These examples, starch and glycogen, are composed entirely of glucose monomers, abbreviated here as hexagons. The polymer chains spiral to form helices. **(a)** Two forms of starch are amylose (unbranched) and amylopectin (branched). The light ovals in the micrograph are granules of starch within a chloroplast of a plant cell (TEM). **(b)** Glycogen is more extensively branched than amylopectin. Animal cells stockpile glycogen as dense clusters of granules within liver and muscle cells. Hydrolysis frees the glucose from storage (TEM, portion of a liver cell).

and grains—the fruits of wheat, corn, rice, and other grasses—are the major sources of starch in the human diet.

Animals store a polysaccharide called **glycogen**, a polymer of glucose that is like amylopectin but more extensively branched (FIGURE 5.6b). Humans and other vertebrates store glycogen mainly in liver and muscle cells. Hydrolysis of glycogen in these cells releases glucose when the demand for sugar increases. This stored fuel cannot sustain an animal for long, however. In humans, for example, the glycogen bank is depleted in about a day unless it is replenished by consumption of food.

Structural Polysaccharides

Organisms build strong materials from structural polysaccharides. For example, the polysaccharide called **cellulose** is a major component of the tough walls that enclose plant cells. On a global scale, plants produce almost 10^{11} (100 billion) tons of cellulose per year; it is the most abundant organic compound on Earth. Like starch, cellulose is a polymer of glucose, but the glycosidic linkages in these two polymers differ. The difference is based on the fact that there are actually two, slightly different ring structures for glucose. When glucose forms a ring, the hydroxyl group attached to the number 1 carbon is locked into one of two alternative positions: lying either below or above the plane of the ring. These two ring forms for glucose are called alpha (α) and beta (β), respec-

tively (FIGURE 5.7a). In starch, all the glucose monomers are in the α configuration (FIGURE 5.7b), the arrangement we saw in FIGURES 5.4 and 5.5. In contrast, the glucose monomers of cellulose are all in the β configuration, making every other glucose monomer upside down with respect to the others (FIGURE 5.7c).

The differing glycosidic links in starch and cellulose give the two molecules distinct three-dimensional shapes. Whereas a starch molecule is helical, a cellulose molecule is straight (and never branched), and its hydroxyl groups are free to hydrogen-bond with the hydroxyls of other cellulose molecules lying parallel to it. In plant cell walls, many parallel cellulose molecules, held together in this way, are grouped into units called microfibrils (FIGURE 5.8, p. 64). These cables are a strong building material for plants—as well as for humans, who use wood, which is rich in cellulose, for lumber.

Enzymes that digest starch by hydrolyzing its α linkages are unable to hydrolyze the β linkages of cellulose. In fact, few organisms possess enzymes that can digest cellulose. Humans do not; the cellulose fibrils in our food pass through the digestive tract and are eliminated with the feces. Along the way, the fibrils abrade the wall of the digestive tract and stimulate the lining to secrete mucus, which aids in the smooth passage of food through the tract. Thus, although cellulose is not a nutrient for humans, it is an important part of a healthful diet. Most fresh fruits, vegetables, and grains are rich in cellulose, or fiber.

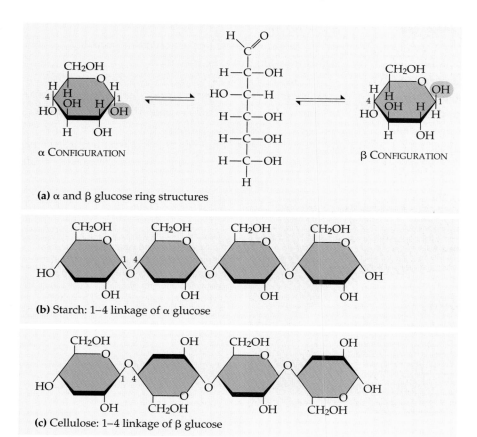

FIGURE 5.7 · Starch and cellulose structures compared. (a) Glucose forms two interconvertible ring structures, designated α and β. These two forms differ in the placement of the hydroxyl group attached to the number 1 carbon. **(b)** The α ring form is the monomer for starch. **(c)** Cellulose consists of glucose monomers in the β configuration. The angles of the bonds that link the rings make every other glucose monomer "upside down."

(a) α and β glucose ring structures

(b) Starch: 1–4 linkage of α glucose

(c) Cellulose: 1–4 linkage of β glucose

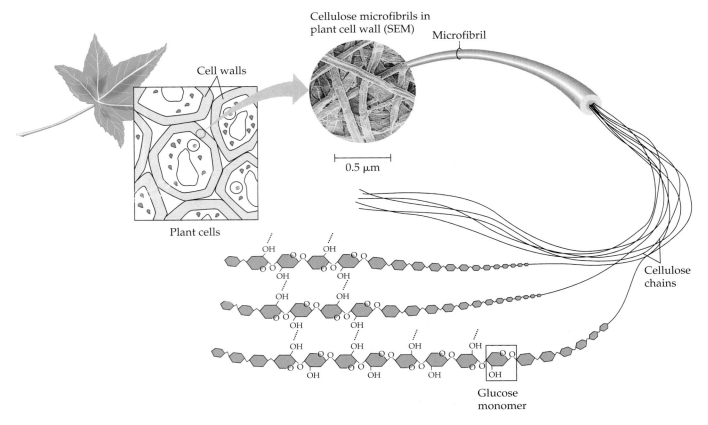

Cellulose microfibrils in plant cell wall (SEM)

Microfibril

Cell walls

Plant cells

0.5 μm

Cellulose chains

OH

Glucose monomer

FIGURE 5.8 ▪ The arrangement of cellulose in plant cell walls. Cellulose is an unbranched polysaccharide. Parallel cellulose molecules are held together by hydrogen bonds (dotted lines) between hydroxyl groups projecting from both sides. About 80 cellulose molecules associate to form a microfibril, the main architectural unit of the plant cell wall.

Some bacteria and other microbes can digest cellulose, breaking it down to glucose monomers. A cow harbors cellulose-digesting bacteria in the rumen, the first compartment in its stomach. The bacteria hydrolyze the cellulose of hay and grass and convert the glucose to other nutrients that nourish the cow. Similarly, a termite, which is unable to digest cellulose for itself, has microbes living in its gut that can make a meal of wood. Some molds (fungi) can also digest cellulose, thereby serving as decomposers that are crucial in recycling chemical elements within Earth's ecosystems.

Another important structural polysaccharide is **chitin**, the carbohydrate used by arthropods (insects, spiders, crustaceans, and related animals) to build their exoskeletons (FIGURE 5.9). An exoskeleton is a hard case that surrounds the soft parts of the animal. Pure chitin is leathery, but it becomes hardened when encrusted with calcium carbonate, a salt.

(a)

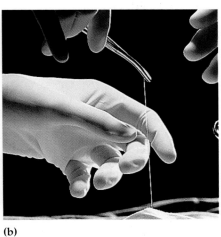

(b)

FIGURE 5.9 ▪ Chitin. A structural polysaccharide, chitin forms the exoskeleton of arthropods. **(a)** This cicada is molting, shedding its old exoskeleton and emerging in adult form. Chitin is similar to cellulose, except that the glucose monomer of chitin has a nitrogen-containing addition. **(b)** Chitin is used to make a strong and flexible surgical thread that decomposes after the wound or incision heals.

Chitin is also found in many fungi, which use this polysaccharide rather than cellulose as the building material for their cell walls. The monomer of chitin is a glucose molecule with a nitrogen-containing appendage:

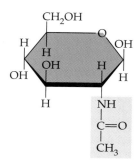

LIPIDS—DIVERSE HYDROPHOBIC MOLECULES

Lipids are the one class of large biological molecules that does not include polymers. The compounds called **lipids** are grouped together because they share one important trait: They have little or no affinity for water. The hydrophobic behavior of lipids is based on their molecular structure.

Although they may have some polar bonds associated with oxygen, lipids consist mostly of hydrocarbons. Smaller than true (polymeric) macromolecules, lipids are a highly varied group in both form and function. Lipids include waxes and certain pigments, but we will focus on the most important families of lipids: the fats, phospholipids, and steroids.

Fats store large amounts of energy

Although fats are not polymers, they are large molecules, and they are assembled from smaller molecules by dehydration reactions. A **fat** is constructed from two kinds of smaller molecules: glycerol and fatty acids (FIGURE 5.10). Glycerol is an alcohol with three carbons, each bearing a hydroxyl group. A **fatty acid** has a long carbon skeleton, usually 16 or 18 carbon atoms in length. At one end of the fatty acid is a "head" consisting of a carboxyl group, the functional group that gives these molecules the name fatty *acids*. Attached to the carboxyl group is a long hydrocarbon "tail." The nonpolar C—H bonds in the tails of fatty acids are the reason fats are hydrophobic. Fats separate from water because the water molecules hydrogen-bond to one another and exclude the fats. A common example of this phenomenon is the separation of

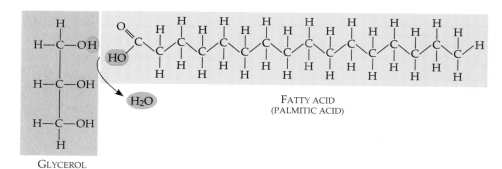

(a) Dehydration synthesis

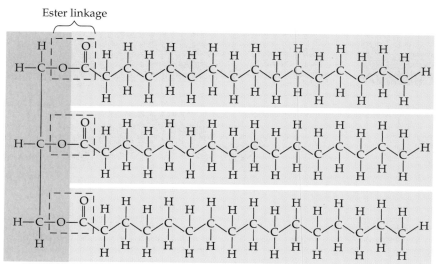

(b) Fat molecule

FIGURE 5.10 ▪ **The synthesis and structure of a fat, or triacylglycerol.** The molecular building blocks of a fat are one molecule of glycerol and three molecules of fatty acids. **(a)** One water molecule is removed for each fatty acid joined to the glycerol. **(b)** The result is a fat. Although the fat shown here has three identical fatty acid units, other fats have two or even three different kinds of fatty acids.

vegetable oil (a liquid fat) from the aqueous vinegar solution in a bottle of salad dressing.

In making a fat, three fatty acids each join to glycerol by an ester linkage, a bond between a hydroxyl group and a carboxyl group. The resulting fat, also called a **triacylglycerol**, thus consists of three fatty acids linked to one glycerol molecule. (Still another name for a fat is triglyceride, a word often found in the list of ingredients on packaged foods.) The fatty acids in a fat can be the same (see FIGURE 5.10b), or they can be of two or three different kinds.

Fatty acids vary in length and in the number and locations of double bonds. The terms *saturated fats* and *unsaturated fats* are commonly used in the context of nutrition. These terms refer to the structure of the hydrocarbon tails of the fatty acids. If there are no double bonds between the carbon atoms composing the tail, then as many hydrogen atoms as possible are bonded to the carbon skeleton, creating a **saturated fatty acid** (FIGURE 5.11a). An **unsaturated fatty acid** has one or more double bonds, formed by the removal of hydrogen atoms from the carbon skeleton. The fatty acid will have a kink in its shape wherever a double bond occurs (FIGURE 5.11b).

Most animal fats are saturated: The tails of their fatty acids lack double bonds. Saturated animal fats—such as lard and butter—are solid at room temperature. In contrast, the fats of plants and fishes are generally unsaturated. Usually liquid at room temperature, plant and fish fats are referred to as oils—for instance, corn oil and cod liver oil. The kinks where the double bonds are located prevent the molecules from packing together closely enough to solidify at room temperature. The phrase "hydrogenated vegetable oils," often found on food labels, means that unsaturated fats have been synthetically converted to saturated fats by adding hydrogen. Peanut butter, margarine, and many other products are hydrogenated to prevent lipids from separating out in liquid (oil) form.

A diet rich in saturated fats is one of several factors that may contribute to the human cardiovascular disease known as atherosclerosis. In this condition, deposits called plaques develop on the internal lining of blood vessels, impeding blood flow and reducing the resilience of the vessels.

Fat has come to have such a negative connotation in our culture that you might wonder whether fats serve any useful purpose. The major function of fats is energy storage. The hydrocarbon chains of fats are similar to gasoline molecules and are just as rich in energy. A gram of fat stores more than twice as much energy as a gram of a polysaccharide, such as starch. Because plants are relatively immobile, they can function with bulky energy storage in the form of starch. (Vegetable oils are generally obtained from seeds, where more compact storage is an asset to the plant.) Animals, on the other hand, must carry their energy stores with them, so there is an advantage to having a more compact reservoir of fuel—fat. Humans and other mammals stock their long-term food reserves in adipose cells (see FIGURE 4.5), which swell and shrink as fat is deposited and withdrawn from storage. In addition to storing energy, adipose tissue also cushions such vital organs as the kidneys, and a layer of fat beneath the skin insulates the body. This subcutaneous layer is especially thick in whales, seals, and most other marine mammals.

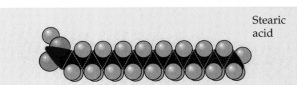

(a) Saturated fat and fatty acid

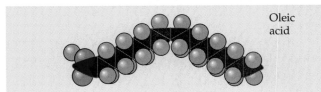

(b) Unsaturated fat and fatty acid

FIGURE 5.11 ▪ Saturated and unsaturated fats and fatty acids. (a) If its fatty acids are saturated (with hydrogen), a fat is also said to be saturated. Most animal fats, such as those in butter, are saturated. They are solids at room temperature. **(b)** Unsaturated fatty acids, such as oleic acid, have one or more double bonds between carbons. The fatty acid bends where double bonds are located. Unsaturated fats have one or more unsaturated fatty acids. Most vegetable fats are unsaturated and are called oils because they are liquids at room temperature. The kinks in the fatty acids prevent the fat molecules from packing together closely enough to solidify.

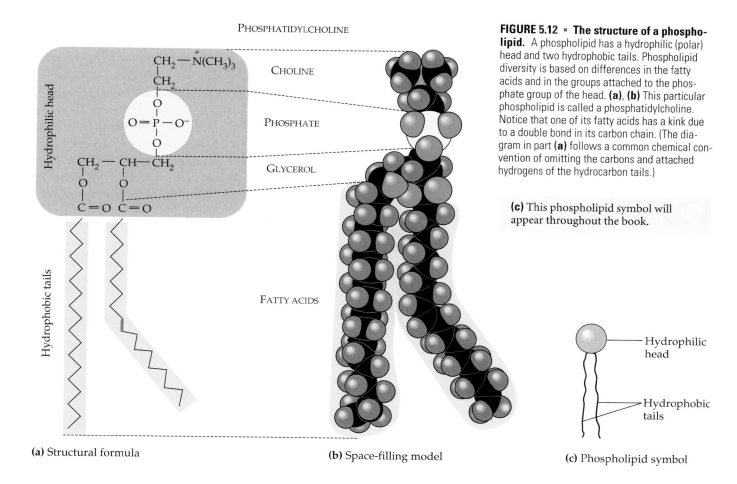

PHOSPHATIDYLCHOLINE

Hydrophilic head

$CH_2 - \overset{+}{N}(CH_3)_3$

CH_2

O

$O = P - O^-$

O

$CH_2 - CH - CH_2$

$O \quad O$

$C = O \quad C = O$

CHOLINE

PHOSPHATE

GLYCEROL

FATTY ACIDS

Hydrophobic tails

FIGURE 5.12 ▪ **The structure of a phospholipid.** A phospholipid has a hydrophilic (polar) head and two hydrophobic tails. Phospholipid diversity is based on differences in the fatty acids and in the groups attached to the phosphate group of the head. **(a)**, **(b)** This particular phospholipid is called a phosphatidylcholine. Notice that one of its fatty acids has a kink due to a double bond in its carbon chain. (The diagram in part **(a)** follows a common chemical convention of omitting the carbons and attached hydrogens of the hydrocarbon tails.)

(c) This phospholipid symbol will appear throughout the book.

Hydrophilic head

Hydrophobic tails

(a) Structural formula

(b) Space-filling model

(c) Phospholipid symbol

Phospholipids are major components of cell membranes

Phospholipids are similar to fats, but they have only two fatty acids rather than three. The third hydroxyl group of glycerol is joined to a phosphate group, which is negative in electrical charge. Additional small molecules, usually charged or polar, can be linked to the phosphate group to form a variety of phospholipids (FIGURE 5.12).

Phospholipids show ambivalent behavior toward water. Their tails, which consist of hydrocarbons, are hydrophobic and are excluded from water. However, the phosphate group and its attachments form a hydrophilic head that has an affinity for water.

When phospholipids are added to water, they self-assemble into aggregates that shield their hydrophobic portions from water. One such cluster is a micelle, a phospholipid droplet with the phosphate heads on the outside, in contact with water. The hydrocarbon tails are restricted to the water-free interior of the micelle (FIGURE 5.13a).

At the surface of a cell, phospholipids are arranged in a bilayer, or double layer (FIGURE 5.13b). The hydrophilic heads of the molecules are on the outside of the bilayer, in contact with the aqueous solutions inside and outside the cell. The

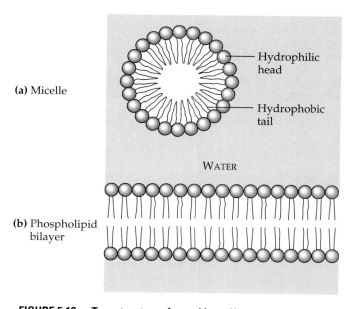

(a) Micelle

Hydrophilic head

Hydrophobic tail

WATER

(b) Phospholipid bilayer

FIGURE 5.13 ▪ **Two structures formed by self-assembly of phospholipids in aqueous environments.** **(a)** A micelle, in cross section. **(b)** A cross section of a phospholipid bilayer between two aqueous compartments. Such bilayers are the main fabric of biological membranes. The hydrophilic heads (spheres) of the phospholipids are in contact with water, whereas the hydrophobic tails are in contact with each other and remote from water.

hydrophobic tails point toward the interior of the membrane, away from the water. The phospholipid bilayer forms a boundary between the cell and its external environment; in fact, phospholipids are major components of cell membranes. This behavior provides another example of how form fits function at the molecular level.

Steroids include cholesterol and certain hormones

Steroids are lipids characterized by a carbon skeleton consisting of four fused rings (FIGURE 5.14). Different steroids vary in the functional groups attached to this ensemble of rings. One steroid, **cholesterol**, is a common component of animal cell membranes and is also the precursor from which other steroids are synthesized. Many hormones, including vertebrate sex hormones, are steroids produced from cholesterol (see FIGURE 4.8). Thus, cholesterol is a crucial molecule in animals, although a high level of it in the blood may contribute to atherosclerosis.

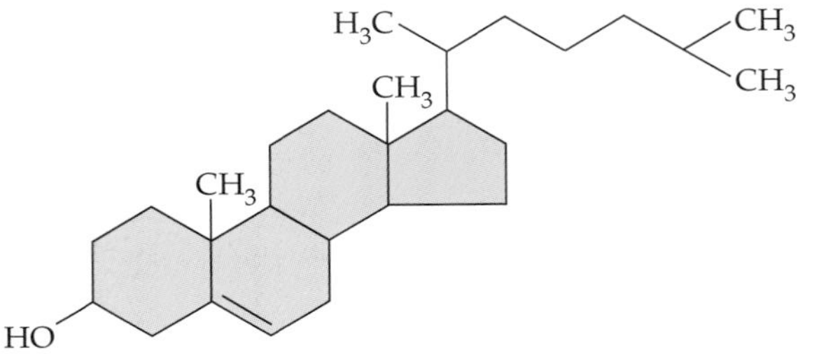

FIGURE 5.14 · Cholesterol: a steroid. Cholesterol is the molecule from which other steroids, including the sex hormones, are synthesized. Steroids vary in the functional groups attached to their four interconnected rings (shown in gold).

PROTEINS—THE MOLECULAR TOOLS OF THE CELL

5.3 The importance of proteins is implied by their name, which comes from the Greek word *proteios,* meaning "first place." **Proteins** account for more than 50% of the dry weight of most cells, and they are instrumental in almost everything organisms do (TABLE 5.1). Proteins are used for structural support, storage, transport of other substances, signaling from one part of the organism to another, movement, and defense against foreign substances. In addition, as enzymes, proteins regulate metabolism by selectively accelerating chemical reactions in the cell. A human has tens of thousands of different proteins, each with a specific structure and function.

Proteins are the most structurally sophisticated molecules known. Consistent with their diverse functions, they vary extensively in structure, each type of protein having a unique three-dimensional shape, or **conformation**. Diverse though proteins may be, they are all polymers constructed from the same set of 20 amino acids. Polymers of amino acids are called **polypeptides**. A protein consists of one or more polypeptides folded and coiled into specific conformations.

A polypeptide is a polymer of amino acids connected in a specific sequence

As mentioned in Chapter 4, **amino acids** are organic molecules possessing both carboxyl and amino groups. The figure at the right shows the general formula for an amino acid:

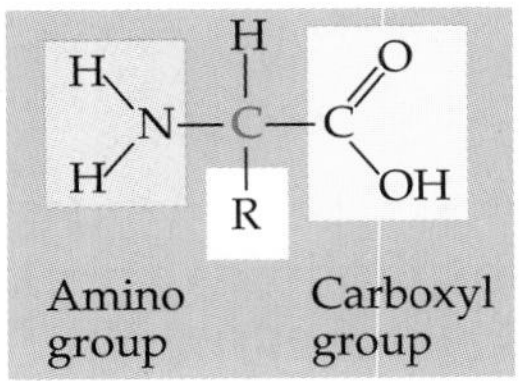

Amino group   Carboxyl group

Table 5.1 ■ An Overview of Protein Functions

TYPE OF PROTEIN	FUNCTION	EXAMPLES
Structural proteins	Support	Insects and spiders use silk fibers to make their cocoons and webs, respectively. Collagen and elastin provide a fibrous framework in animal connective tissues, such as tendons and ligaments. Keratin is the protein of hair, horns, feathers, and other skin appendages.
Storage proteins	Storage of amino acids	Ovalbumin is the protein of egg white, used as an amino acid source for the developing embryo. Casein, the protein of milk, is the major source of amino acids for baby mammals. Plants have storage proteins in their seeds.
Transport proteins	Transport of other substances	Hemoglobin, the iron-containing protein of vertebrate blood, transports oxygen from the lungs to other parts of the body. Other proteins transport molecules across cell membranes.
Hormonal proteins	Coordination of an organism's activities	Insulin, a hormone secreted by the pancreas, helps regulate the concentration of sugar in the blood of vertebrates.
Receptor proteins	Response of cell to chemical stimuli	Receptors built into the membrane of a nerve cell detect chemical signals released by other nerve cells.
Contractile proteins	Movement	Actin and myosin are responsible for the movement of muscles. Contractile proteins are responsible for the undulations of cilia and flagella, which propel many cells.
Defensive proteins	Protection against disease	Antibodies combat bacteria and viruses.
Enzymatic proteins	Selective acceleration of chemical reactions	Digestive enzymes hydrolyze the polymers in food.

At the center of the amino acid is an asymmetric carbon atom. Its four different partners are an amino group, a carboxyl group, a hydrogen atom, and a variable group symbolized by R. The R group, also called the side chain, differs with the amino acid. FIGURE 5.15 shows the 20 amino acids that cells use to build their thousands of proteins. (Here the amino and carboxyl groups are all depicted in ionized form.) The R group may be as simple as a hydrogen atom, as in the amino acid glycine (the one amino acid lacking an asymmetric carbon), or it may be a carbon skeleton with various functional

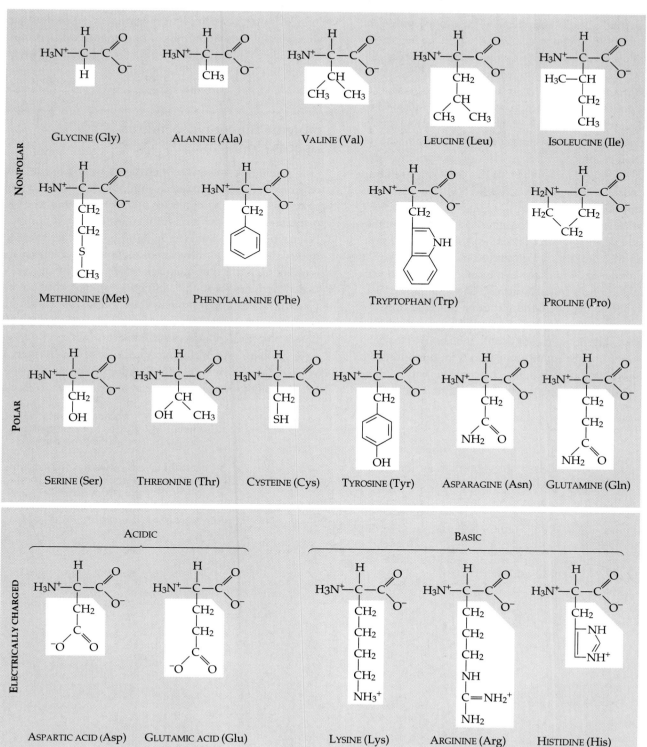

FIGURE 5.15 · The 20 amino acids of proteins. The amino acids are grouped here according to the properties of their side chains (R groups), highlighted in white. The amino acids are shown in their prevailing ionic forms at pH 7, the approximate pH within a cell. In parentheses are the three-letter abbreviations for the amino acids.

groups attached, as in glutamine. (Other amino acids, not shown in FIGURE 5.15, have important functions in organisms, but these amino acids are not incorporated into proteins.)

The physical and chemical properties of the side chain determine the unique characteristics of a particular amino acid. In FIGURE 5.15 the amino acids are grouped according to the properties of their side chains. One group consists of amino acids with nonpolar side chains, which are hydrophobic. Another group consists of amino acids with polar side chains, which are hydrophilic. Acidic amino acids are those with side chains that are generally negative in charge owing to the presence of a carboxyl group, which is usually dissociated (ionized) at cellular pH. Basic amino acids have amino groups in their side chains that are generally positive in charge. (Notice that *all* amino acids have carboxyl groups and amino groups; the terms *acidic* and *basic* in this context refer only to the side chains.) Because they are ionic, acidic and basic side chains are also hydrophilic.

Now that we have examined amino acids, let's see how they are linked to form polymers. When two amino acids are positioned so that the carboxyl group of one is adjacent to the amino group of the other, an enzyme can join the amino acids by means of a dehydration reaction. The resulting covalent bond is called a **peptide bond**. Repeated over and over, this process yields a polypeptide, a polymer of many amino acids linked by peptide bonds (FIGURE 5.16). At one end of the polypeptide chain is a free amino group, and at the opposite end is a free carboxyl group. Thus, the chain has polarity, with an amino end (or N-terminus) and a carboxyl end (C-terminus).

The repeating sequence of atoms highlighted in purple in FIGURE 5.16b is called the polypeptide backbone. Attached to this repetitive backbone are different kinds of appendages, the side chains of the amino acids. Polypeptides range in length from a few monomers to a thousand or more. Each specific polypeptide has a unique linear sequence of amino acids. The immense variety of polypeptides existing in nature illustrates an important concept introduced earlier—that cells can make many different polymers by linking a limited set of monomers into diverse sequences.

A protein's function depends on its specific conformation

"Polypeptide" is not quite synonymous with "protein." The relationship is somewhat analogous to that between a long strand of yarn and a sweater of particular size and shape that one can knit from the yarn. A functional protein is not *just* a polypeptide chain, but one or more polypeptides precisely twisted, folded, and coiled into a molecule of unique shape (FIGURE 5.17). It is the amino acid sequence of a polypeptide that determines what three-dimensional conformation the protein will take. Many proteins are globular (roughly spherical), while others are fibrous in shape. However, within these broad categories, countless variations are possible.

A protein's specific conformation determines how it works. In almost every case, the function of a protein depends on its ability to recognize and bind to some other molecule.

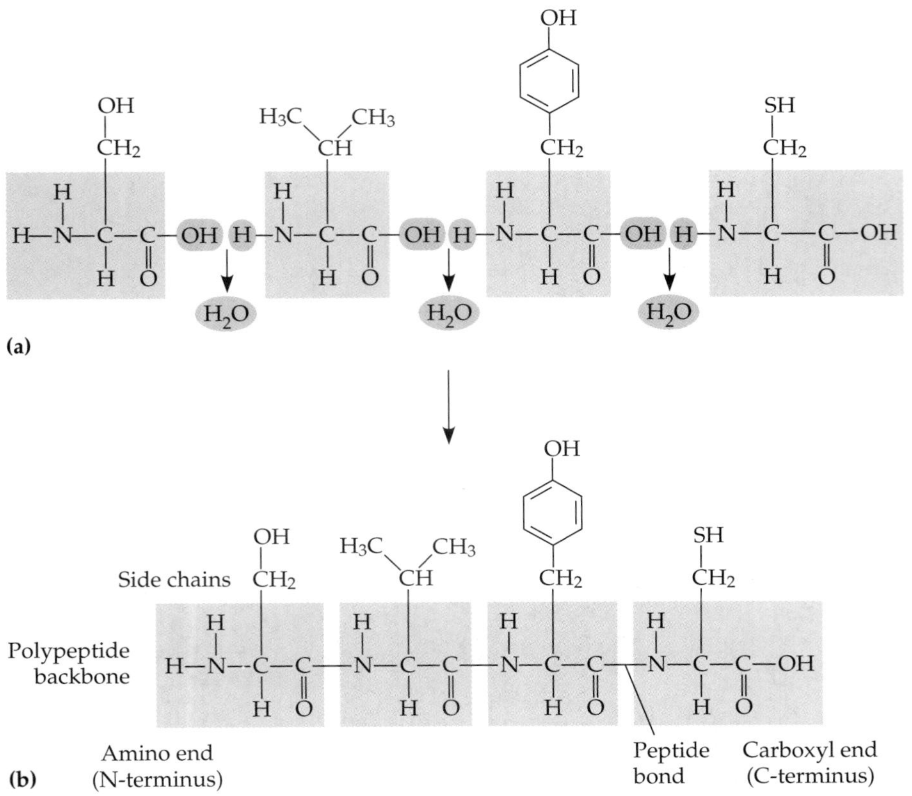

FIGURE 5.16 · **Making a polypeptide chain. (a)** Peptide bonds formed by dehydration reactions link the carboxyl group of one amino acid to the amino group of the next. **(b)** The polypeptide has a repetitive backbone (purple) to which the amino acid side chains are attached. The peptide bonds are formed one at a time, starting with the amino acid at the amino end (N-terminus).

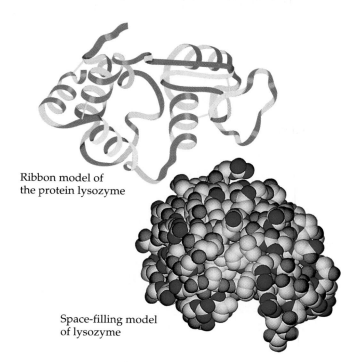

Ribbon model of
the protein lysozyme

Space-filling model
of lysozyme

FIGURE 5.17 ▪ **Functional conformation of a protein, the enzyme lysozyme.** Present in our sweat, tears, and saliva, lysozyme is an enzyme that helps prevent infection by binding to and destroying specific molecules on the surface of many kinds of bacteria. In the ribbon model of lysozyme, you can see how the single polypeptide chain, represented by the ribbon, folds and coils to form the functional protein. (In this simplification, the yellow lines symbolize one type of chemical bond that stabilizes the protein's shape.) The space-filling model shows more clearly that lysozyme's overall shape is roughly spherical (globular), as are many other proteins. This *exact* conformation, however, is unique to lysozyme, and the protein's specialized function emerges from this shape. A groove on the surface of lysozyme is the part of the protein that recognizes and binds to the target molecules on bacterial walls.

For instance, an antibody binds to a particular foreign substance that has invaded the body, and an enzyme recognizes and binds to its substrate, the substance the enzyme works on. In Chapter 2 you learned that one nerve cell in the brain signals another by dispatching specific molecules that have a unique shape. The receptor molecules on the surface of the receiving cell are proteins that fit the signal molecules something like a lock and key (see FIGURE 2.16).

Four Levels of Protein Structure

5.4 When a cell synthesizes a polypeptide, the chain generally folds spontaneously to assume the functional conformation for that protein. This folding is driven and reinforced by the formation of a variety of bonds between parts of the chain. Thus, the function of a protein—the ability of a receptor protein to identify and associate with a particular chemical messenger, for instance—is an emergent property resulting from exquisite molecular order. In the complex architecture of a protein, we can recognize three superimposed levels of structure, known as primary, secondary, and tertiary structure. A

fourth level, quaternary structure, occurs when a protein consists of two or more polypeptide chains.

Primary Structure. The **primary structure** of a protein is its unique sequence of amino acids. As an example, we will examine the primary structure of lysozyme, the antibacterial enzyme illustrated in its three-dimensional form in FIGURE 5.17. Lysozyme is a relatively small protein, its single polypeptide chain only 129 amino acids long. In FIGURE 5.18 the polypeptide chain is unraveled for a closer look at its primary structure. A specific one of the 20 amino acids occupies each of the 129 positions along the chain. The primary structure is

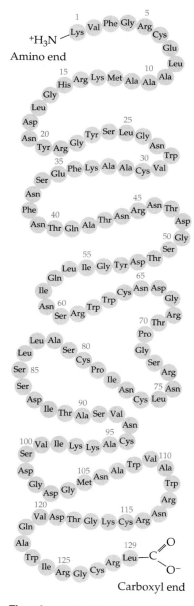

FIGURE 5.18 ▪ **The primary structure of a protein.** This is the unique amino acid sequence, or primary structure, of the enzyme lysozyme. The names of the amino acids are given as their three-letter abbreviations. (The chain was drawn in this serpentine fashion to make the entire sequence readily visible. The actual shape of lysozyme is shown in Figure 5.17.)

like the order of letters in a very long word. If left to chance, there would be 20^{129} different ways of arranging amino acids into a polypeptide chain of this length. However, the precise primary structure of a protein is determined not by the random linking of amino acids, but by inherited genetic information.

Even a slight change in primary structure can affect a protein's conformation and ability to function. For instance, the substitution of one amino acid for another at a particular position in the primary structure of hemoglobin, the protein that carries oxygen in red blood cells, causes sickle-cell anemia, an inherited blood disorder (FIGURE 5.19).

The pioneer in determining the primary structure of proteins was Frederick Sanger, who, with his colleagues at Cambridge University in England, worked out the amino acid sequence of the hormone insulin in the late 1940s and early 1950s. His approach was to use protein-digesting enzymes and other catalysts that break polypeptides at specific places rather than completely hydrolyzing the chain. Treatment with one of these agents would cleave the polypeptide into fragments that could be separated by a technique called chromatography. Hydrolysis with another agent would break the polypeptide at different sites, yielding a second group of fragments. Sanger used chemical methods to determine the sequence of amino acids in these small fragments. Then he searched for overlapping regions among the pieces obtained by hydrolyzing with the different agents. Consider, for instance, two fragments with the following sequences:

Cys-Ser-Leu-Tyr-Gln-Leu

Tyr-Gln-Leu-Glu-Asn

We can deduce from the overlapping regions that the intact polypeptide contains in its primary structure the following segment:

Cys-Ser-Leu-Tyr-Gln-Leu-Glu-Asn

Just as we could reconstruct this sentence from a collection of fragments with overlapping sequences of letters, Sanger and his co-workers were able, after years of effort, to reconstruct the complete primary structure of insulin. Since then, most of the steps involved in sequencing a polypeptide have been automated. However, it was Sanger's analysis of insulin that first demonstrated what is now a fundamental axiom of molecular biology: Each type of protein has a unique primary structure, a precise sequence of amino acids.

Secondary Structure. Most proteins have segments of their polypeptide chain repeatedly coiled or folded in patterns that contribute to the protein's overall conformation. These coils and folds, collectively referred to as **secondary structure**, are the result of hydrogen bonds at regular intervals along the polypeptide backbone (FIGURE 5.20). Because they are electronegative, both the oxygen and the nitrogen atoms of the backbone have weak negative charges (see Chapter 2). The weakly positive hydrogen atom attached to the nitrogen atom has an affinity for the oxygen atom of a nearby peptide bond. Individually, these hydrogen bonds are weak, but because they are repeated many times over a relatively long region of the polypeptide chain, they can support a particular shape for that part of the protein. One such secondary structure is the **alpha (α) helix,** a delicate coil held together by hydrogen bonding between every fourth amino acid. The regions of α

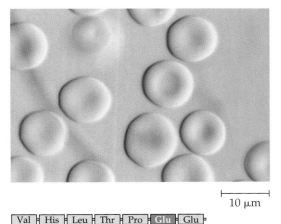

|--- 10 μm ---|

Val	His	Leu	Thr	Pro	Glu	Glu
1	2	3	4	5	6	7 . . . 146

(a) Normal red blood cells and normal hemoglobin

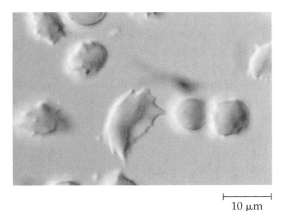

|--- 10 μm ---|

Val	His	Leu	Thr	Pro	Val	Glu
1	2	3	4	5	6	7 . . . 146

(b) Sickled red blood cells and sickle-cell hemoglobin

FIGURE 5.19 · A single amino acid substitution in a protein causes sickle-cell disease. **(a)** Normal human red blood cells are disk-shaped, as seen in this light micrograph. Each cell contains millions of molecules of the protein hemoglobin, which transports oxygen molecules from the lungs to the other organs of the body. The first seven amino acids of one of the polypeptides of normal hemoglobin are shown below the micrograph; this polypeptide has a total of 146 amino acids. **(b)** A slight change in the primary structure of hemoglobin—an inherited substitution of one amino acid—causes sickle-cell disease. The substitution occurs in the number 6 position of the polypeptide. The abnormal hemoglobin molecules tend to crystallize, deforming some of the cells into a "sickle" shape. The life of someone with the disease is punctuated by "sickle-cell crises," which occur when the angular cells clog tiny blood vessels, impeding blood flow.

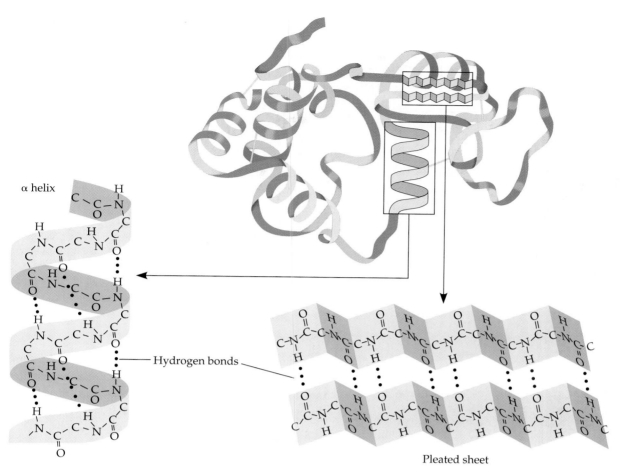

FIGURE 5.20 ▪ **The secondary structure of a protein.** Two types of secondary structure, the α helix and the pleated sheet, can both be found in the protein lysozyme. Both patterns depend on hydrogen bonding between ⊃CO and ⊃NH groups along the polypeptide backbone. The R groups of the amino acids are omitted in these diagrams, as are some H atoms.

helix in the enzyme lysozyme are evident in FIGURE 5.20, where one α helix is enlarged to show the hydrogen bonds. Lysozyme is fairly typical of a globular protein in that it has a few stretches of α helix separated by nonhelical regions. In contrast, some fibrous proteins, such as α-keratin, the structural protein of hair, have the α-helix formation over most of their length.

The other main type of secondary structure is the **pleated sheet**, in which two regions of the polypeptide chain lie parallel to each other. Hydrogen bonds between the parts of the backbone in the parallel regions hold the structure together. Pleated sheets make up the core of many globular proteins, and we can see one such region in lysozyme in FIGURE 5.20. Also, pleated sheets dominate some fibrous proteins, including the silk produced by many insects and spiders (FIGURE 5.21, p. 74).

Tertiary Structure. Superimposed on the patterns of secondary structure is a protein's **tertiary structure**, consisting of irregular contortions from bonding between side chains (R groups) of the various amino acids. One of the types of bond-

ing that contributes to tertiary structure is called a **hydrophobic interaction**. As a polypeptide folds into its functional conformation, amino acids with hydrophobic (nonpolar) side chains usually congregate in clusters at the core of the protein, out of contact with water. Thus, what we call a hydrophobic interaction is actually initiated by the behavior of water molecules, which exclude nonpolar substances as the water molecules hydrogen-bond to one another and to hydrophilic parts of the protein. Once nonpolar amino acid side chains are close together, van der Waals attractions reinforce the hydrophobic interactions. Meanwhile, hydrogen bonds between polar side chains and ionic bonds between positively and negatively charged side chains also help stabilize tertiary structure. These are all weak interactions, but their cumulative effect helps give the protein a specific shape.

The conformation of a protein may be reinforced further by strong, covalent bonds called **disulfide bridges**. Disulfide bridges form where two cysteine monomers, amino acids with sulfhydryl groups (—SH) on their side chains, are brought close together by the folding of the protein. The

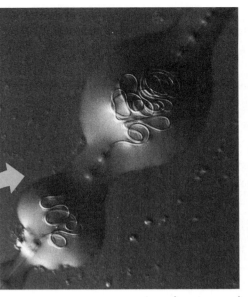

FIGURE 5.21 · Spider silk: a structural protein. Abdominal glands of this spider secrete silk fibers in liquid form; the protein solidifies upon contact with air. The silk protein owes its strength to its secondary structure, consisting of many pleated sheets. The teamwork of so many hydrogen bonds makes each silk fiber stronger than steel. The strands that radiate out from the web's center, made of dry silk protein, maintain the basic shape of the web. The strands forming the spiral, called capture strands, are elastic; they stretch and coil in response to wind, rain, and insects that are unfortunate enough to fly into the web. The light micrograph, right, helps us understand this resilience. A capture strand consists of a coiled silk fiber coated by a sticky fluid. Force on the strand unwinds the silk fiber, absorbing the shock. Then the fluid's surface tension—the tendency for the aqueous solution to "bead"—rewinds the fiber.

├─────────┤
100 μm

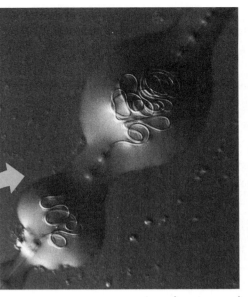

FIGURE 5.22 · Examples of bonds contributing to the tertiary structure of a protein. Hydrogen bonds, ionic bonds, hydrophobic interactions, and van der Waals interactions are weak bonds between side chains that collectively hold the protein in a specific conformation. Much stronger are the disulfide bridges, covalent bonds between the side chains of cysteine pairs.

sulfur of one cysteine bonds to the sulfur of the second, and the disulfide bridge (—S—S—) rivets parts of the protein together. (The yellow lines in FIGURES 5.17 and 5.20 represent disulfide bridges.) All of these different kinds of bonds can occur in one protein, as shown diagrammatically in FIGURE 5.22.

Quaternary Structure. As mentioned previously, some proteins consist of two or more polypeptide chains aggregated into one functional macromolecule. **Quaternary structure** is the overall protein structure that results from the aggregation of these polypeptide subunits. For example, collagen is a fibrous protein that has helical subunits supercoiled into a larger triple helix (FIGURE 5.23a). This supercoiled organization of collagen, which is similar to the construction of a rope, gives the long fibers great strength. This suits collagen fibers to their function as the girders of connective tissue, such as tendons and ligaments. Hemoglobin, the oxygen-binding protein of red blood cells, is an example of a globular protein with quaternary structure (FIGURE 5.23b). It consists of two kinds of polypeptide chains, with two of each kind per hemoglobin molecule.

We have taken the reductionist approach in dissecting proteins to their four levels of structural organization. However, it is the overall product, a macromolecule with a unique shape, that works in a cell. The specific function of a protein is an emergent property that arises from the architecture of the molecule (FIGURE 5.24).

What Determines Protein Conformation?

You've learned that unique conformation endows each protein with a specific function, but what are the key factors determining conformation? You already know most of the answer: A polypeptide chain of a given amino acid sequence can spontaneously arrange itself into a three-dimensional shape maintained by the interactions responsible for secondary and tertiary structure. This normally occurs as the protein is being synthesized within the cell. However, protein conformation also depends on the physical and chemical con-

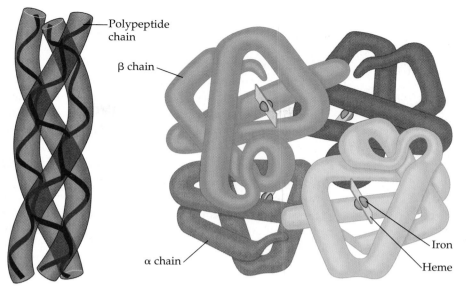

-Polypeptide chain

β chain

α chain

Iron

Heme

(a) Collagen

(b) Hemoglobin

FIGURE 5.23 ▪ **The quaternary structure of proteins.** At this level of structure, two or more polypeptide subunits associate to form a functional protein. **(a)** Collagen is a fibrous protein consisting of three helical polypeptides that are supercoiled to form a ropelike structure of great strength. Accounting for 40% of the protein in the human body, collagen strengthens connective tissue in our skin, bones, ligaments, tendons, and other body parts. **(b)** Hemoglobin is a globular protein with four polypeptide subunits, two of one kind (α chains) and two of another kind (β chains). Both α and β subunits consist primarily of α-helical secondary structure, represented by the thicker cylindrical sections of the polypeptides in this model. (Each subunit has a nonpolypeptide component, called heme, with an iron atom that binds oxygen.)

ditions of the protein's environment. If the pH, salt concentration, temperature, or other aspects of its environment are altered, the protein may unravel and lose its native conformation, a change called **denaturation** (FIGURE 5.25, p. 76). Misshapen, the denatured protein is biologically inactive. Most proteins become denatured if they are transferred from an aqueous environment to an organic solvent, such as ether or chloroform; the protein turns inside out, its hydrophobic regions changing places with its hydrophilic portions. Other agents of denaturation include chemicals that disrupt the hydrogen bonds, ionic bonds, and disulfide bridges that maintain a protein's shape. Denaturation can also result from

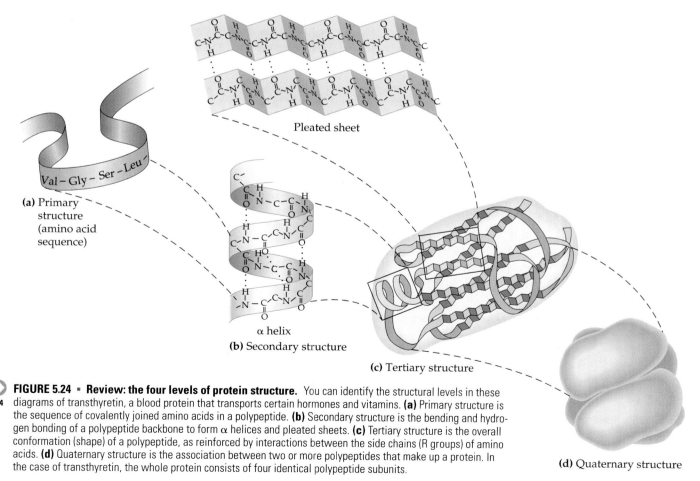

Pleated sheet

Val – Gly – Ser – Leu

(a) Primary structure (amino acid sequence)

α helix
(b) Secondary structure

(c) Tertiary structure

(d) Quaternary structure

FIGURE 5.24 ▪ **Review: the four levels of protein structure.** You can identify the structural levels in these diagrams of transthyretin, a blood protein that transports certain hormones and vitamins. **(a)** Primary structure is the sequence of covalently joined amino acids in a polypeptide. **(b)** Secondary structure is the bending and hydrogen bonding of a polypeptide backbone to form α helices and pleated sheets. **(c)** Tertiary structure is the overall conformation (shape) of a polypeptide, as reinforced by interactions between the side chains (R groups) of amino acids. **(d)** Quaternary structure is the association between two or more polypeptides that make up a protein. In the case of transthyretin, the whole protein consists of four identical polypeptide subunits.

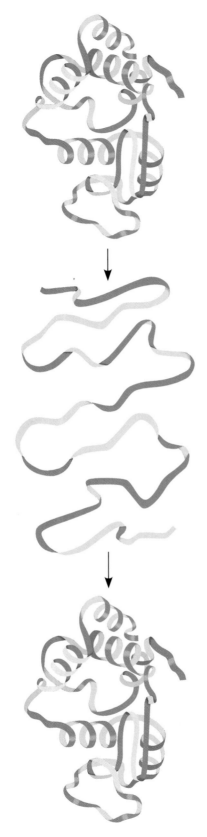

FIGURE 5.25 · Denaturation and renaturation of a protein. High temperatures or various chemical treatments will denature a protein, causing it to lose its conformation and hence its ability to function. If the denatured protein remains dissolved, it can often renature when the chemical and physical aspects of its environment are restored to normal.

excessive heat, which agitates the polypeptide chain enough to overpower the weak interactions that stabilize conformation. The white of an egg becomes opaque during cooking because the denatured proteins are insoluble and solidify.

When a protein in a test-tube solution is denatured by heat or chemicals, it will often return to its functional shape when the denaturing agent is removed. We can conclude that the information for building specific shape is intrinsic in the protein's primary structure. The sequence of amino acids determines conformation—where an α helix can form, where pleated sheets can occur, where disulfide bridges are located, where ionic bonds can form, and so on. However, in the crowded environment inside a cell, correct refolding of a denatured protein—and even correct folding during protein synthesis—may be more of a problem.

The Protein-Folding Problem

Biochemists now know the amino acid sequences of more than 100,000 proteins and the three-dimensional shapes of about 10,000 (see the Methods Box on p. 80). One would think that by correlating the primary structures of many proteins with their conformations, it would be possible to discover the rules of protein folding, especially with the help of computers. Unfortunately, the protein-folding problem is not that simple. Most proteins probably go through several intermediate states on their way to a stable conformation, and looking at the "mature" conformation does not reveal the stages of folding that are required to achieve that form. However, biochemists have developed methods for tracking a protein through its intermediate stages of folding. Researchers have also discovered **chaperone proteins**, molecules that function as temporary braces in assisting the folding of other proteins. These breakthroughs will accelerate our understanding of protein folding.

The protein-folding problem is as important as it is challenging. Once the rules of protein folding are known, it should be possible to design proteins that will carry out specific tasks by making polypeptide chains with appropriate amino acid sequences.

NUCLEIC ACIDS— INFORMATIONAL POLYMERS

5.5 If the primary structure of polypeptides determines the conformation of a protein, what determines primary structure? The amino acid sequence of a polypeptide is programmed by a unit of inheritance known as a **gene**. Genes consist of DNA, which is a polymer belonging to the class of compounds known as **nucleic acids**.

Nucleic acids store and transmit hereditary information

There are two types of nucleic acids: **deoxyribonucleic acid (DNA)** and **ribonucleic acid (RNA)**. These are the molecules that enable living organisms to reproduce their complex components from one generation to the next. Unique among molecules, DNA provides directions for its own replication. DNA also directs RNA synthesis and, through RNA, controls protein synthesis.

DNA is the genetic material that organisms inherit from their parents. A DNA molecule is very long and usually consists of hundreds or thousands of genes. When a cell reproduces itself by dividing, its DNA is copied and passed along from one generation of cells to the next. Encoded in the structure of DNA is the information that programs all the cell's activities. The DNA, however, is not directly involved in running the operations of the cell, any more than computer software by itself can print a bank statement or read the bar code on a box of cereal. Just as a printer is needed to print out a statement and a scanner is needed to read a bar code, proteins are required to implement genetic programs. Proteins are the molecular hardware of the cell—the tools for most biological functions. For example, it is the protein hemoglobin that carries oxygen in the blood, not the DNA that specifies the structure of hemoglobin.

How does RNA, the other type of nucleic acid, fit into the flow of genetic information from DNA to proteins? Each gene along the length of the DNA molecule directs the synthesis of a type of RNA called messenger RNA (mRNA). The mRNA molecule then interacts with the cell's protein-synthesizing machinery to direct the production of a polypeptide. We can summarize the flow of genetic information as DNA→RNA→protein (FIGURE 5.26). The actual sites of protein synthesis are cellular structures called ribosomes. In a eukaryotic cell, ribosomes are located in the cytoplasm, but DNA resides in the nucleus. Messenger RNA conveys the genetic instructions for building proteins from the nucleus to the cytoplasm. Prokaryotic cells lack nuclei, but they still use RNA to send a message from the DNA to the ribosomes and other equipment of the cell that translate the coded information into amino acid sequences.

A nucleic acid strand is a polymer of nucleotides

Nucleic acids are polymers of monomers called **nucleotides**. Each nucleotide is itself composed of three parts: an organic molecule called a nitrogenous base, a pentose (five-carbon sugar), and a phosphate group (FIGURE 5.27, p. 78).

There are two families of nitrogenous bases: pyrimidines and purines. A **pyrimidine** has a six-membered ring of carbon and nitrogen atoms. (The nitrogen atoms tend to take up H^+ from solution, which explains the term *nitrogenous base*.) The members of the pyrimidine family are cytosine (C), thymine (T), and uracil (U). **Purines** are larger, with the six-membered ring fused to a five-membered ring. The purines are adenine (A) and guanine (G). The specific pyrimidines and purines differ in the functional groups attached to the rings. Adenine, guanine, and cytosine are found in both types of nucleic acid. Thymine is found only in DNA and uracil only in RNA.

The pentose connected to the nitrogenous base is **ribose** in the nucleotides of RNA and **deoxyribose** in DNA. The only difference between these two sugars is that deoxyribose lacks an oxygen atom on its number 2 carbon—hence its name. So far, we have built a nucleoside, which is a nitrogenous base joined to a sugar. To complete the construction of a nucleotide, we attach a phosphate group to the number 5 carbon of the sugar (FIGURE 5.27b). The molecule is now a nucleoside monophosphate, better known as a nucleotide.

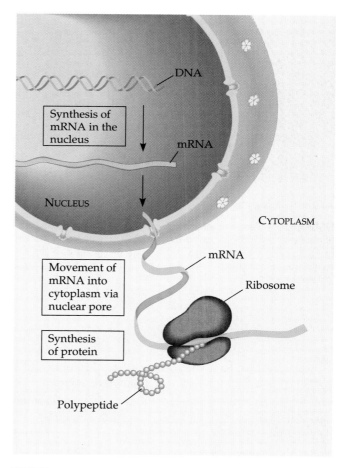

FIGURE 5.26 · DNA→RNA→protein: a diagrammatic overview of information flow in a cell. In a eukaryotic cell, DNA in the nucleus programs protein production in the cytoplasm by dictating the synthesis of messenger RNA (mRNA), which travels to the cytoplasm and binds to ribosomes. As a ribosome (greatly enlarged in this drawing) moves along the mRNA, the genetic message is translated into a polypeptide of specific amino acid sequence.

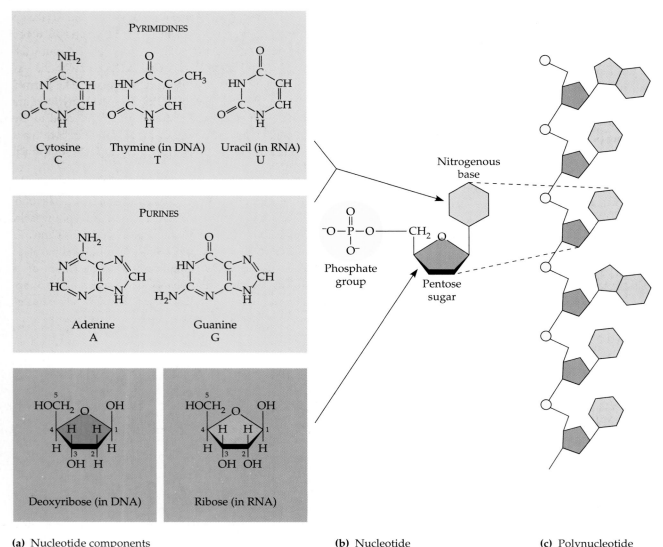

(a) Nucleotide components

(b) Nucleotide

(c) Polynucleotide

⬇ **FIGURE 5.27** · **The structures of**
5.5 **nucleotides and polynucleotides.**
(a) Nucleotides, the monomers of nucleic acids, are themselves composed of three smaller molecular building blocks: a nitrogenous base

(either a purine or a pyrimidine), a pentose sugar, (either deoxyribose or ribose), and a phosphate group. RNA has ribose as its sugar, and DNA has deoxyribose. Also, RNA has uracil, and DNA has thymine. **(b)** In polynucleotides, each nucleotide

monomer has its phosphate group bonded to the sugar of the next nucleotide. The polymer has a regular sugar-phosphate backbone with variable appendages, the four kinds of nitrogenous bases.

In a nucleic acid polymer, or **polynucleotide**, nucleotides are joined by covalent bonds called phosphodiester linkages between the phosphate of one nucleotide and the sugar of the next. This bonding results in a backbone with a repeating pattern of sugar-phosphate-sugar-phosphate (FIGURE 5.27c). All along this sugar-phosphate backbone are appendages consisting of the nitrogenous bases. Unlike the backbone, the sequence of bases along a DNA polymer is unique for each gene. Because genes are hundreds to thousands of nucleotides long, the number of possible base sequences is effectively limitless. A gene's meaning to the cell is encoded in its specific sequence of the four DNA bases. For example, the sequence

AGGTAACTT means one thing, whereas the sequence CGCTTTAAC has a different translation. (Real genes, of course, are much longer.) The linear order of bases in a gene specifies the amino acid sequence—the primary structure—of a protein, which in turn specifies that protein's three-dimensional conformation and function in the cell.

Inheritance is based on replication of the DNA double helix

The DNA molecules of cells actually consist of two polynucleotides that spiral around an imaginary axis to form a **dou-**

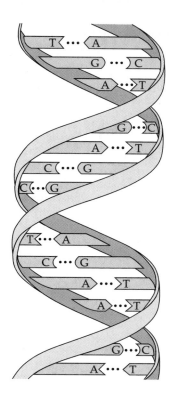

FIGURE 5.28 · The double helix. The DNA molecule is usually double-stranded, with the sugar-phosphate backbone of the polynucleotides (abbreviated here by blue ribbons) on the outside of the helix. In the interior are pairs of nitrogenous bases, holding the two strands together by hydrogen bonds. Hydrogen bonding between the bases is specific. As illustrated here with symbolic shapes for the bases, adenine (A) can pair only with thymine (T), and guanine (G) can pair only with cytosine (C). As a cell prepares to divide, the two strands of the double helix separate, and each serves as a template for the precise ordering of nucleotides into new complementary strands.

Table 5.2 ■ Polypeptide Sequence as Evidence for Evolutionary Relationships	
SPECIES	**NUMBER OF AMINO ACID DIFFERENCES IN THE β CHAIN OF HEMOGLOBIN, COMPARED TO HUMAN HEMOGLOBIN (TOTAL CHAIN LENGTH = 146 AMINO ACIDS)**
Human	0
Gorilla	1
Gibbon	2
Rhesus monkey	8
Mouse	27
Frog	67

Thus, the structure of DNA accounts for its function in transmitting genetic information whenever a cell reproduces.

We can use DNA and proteins as tape measures of evolution

Genes (DNA) and their products (proteins) document the hereditary background of an organism. The linear sequences of nucleotides in DNA molecules are passed from parents to offspring, and these DNA sequences determine the amino acid sequences of proteins. Siblings have greater similarity in their DNA and proteins than do unrelated individuals of the same species. If the evolutionary view of life is valid, we should be able to extend this concept of "molecular genealogy" to relationships *between* species: We should expect two species that appear to be closely related based on fossil and anatomical evidence to also share a greater proportion of their DNA and protein sequences than do more distantly related species. That is the case. For example, TABLE 5.2 compares a polypeptide chain of human hemoglobin with the corresponding hemoglobin polypeptide in five other vertebrates. In this chain of 146 amino acids, humans and gorillas differ in just one amino acid. More distantly related species have chains that are less similar. Molecular biology has added a new tape measure to the toolkit biologists use to assess evolutionary kinship.

■   ■   ■

We have concluded our survey of macromolecules, but not our study of the chemistry of life. Applying the reductionist strategy, we have examined the architecture of molecules, but we have yet to explore the dynamic interactions between molecules that result in the biochemical changes collectively called cellular metabolism. Chapter 6, the final chapter of this unit, will take us another step up the hierarchy of biological order by introducing the fundamental principles of metabolism.

ble helix. James Watson and Francis Crick, working at Cambridge University, first proposed the double helix as the three-dimensional structure of DNA in 1953 (FIGURE 5.28). The two sugar-phosphate backbones are on the outside of the helix, and the nitrogenous bases are paired in the interior of the helix. The two polynucleotides, or strands, as they are called, are held together by hydrogen bonds between the paired bases and by van der Waals attractions between the stacked bases. Most DNA molecules are very long, with thousands or even millions of base pairs connecting the two chains. One long DNA double helix includes many genes, each one a particular segment of the molecule.

Only certain bases in the double helix are compatible with each other. Adenine (A) always pairs with thymine (T), and guanine (G) always pairs with cytosine (C). If we were to read the sequence of bases along one strand as we traveled the length of the double helix, we would know the sequence of bases along the other strand. If a stretch of one strand has the base sequence AGGTCCG, then the base-pairing rules tell us that the same stretch of the other strand must have the sequence TCCAGGC. The two strands of the double helix are *complementary*, each the predictable counterpart of the other. It is this feature of DNA that makes possible the precise copying of genes that is responsible for inheritance. In preparation for cell division, the two strands of each DNA molecule separate, and each strand serves as a template to order nucleotides into a new complementary strand. The identical copies of the DNA molecule are then distributed to the two daughter cells.

Three-dimensional structures of biological macromolecules provide important insights into molecular function. Determining the structures of macromolecules as complex as proteins, each made up of thousands of atoms, is a formidable task. Pauling, Watson and Crick, and the other pioneers of molecular biology built models from wood, wire, and plastic model sets. Computers have made it possible to build models much more quickly.

In the illustrations in this box (from the Department of Biochemistry at the University of California, Riverside), we follow the development of a computer model for the structure of an enzymatic protein called ribonuclease, whose function involves binding to a nucleic acid molecule. The first step is to crystallize the protein. (In this case, the protein is combined with a short strand of nucleic acid.) Then, using a method called X-ray crystallography, an instrument aims an X-ray beam through the crystal. ① The regularly spaced atoms of the crystal diffract (deflect) the X-rays into an orderly array. ② The diffracted X-rays expose photographic film, producing a pattern of spots. ③ From such diffraction patterns, computers generate electron density maps of successive, cross-sectional slices through the protein.

By combining the information from electron density maps with the primary structure of the protein, as determined by chemical methods, it is possible to plot the three-dimensional (x, y, z) coordinates of each atom. ④ Finally, graphics software enables the computer to create a picture showing the position of each atom in the molecule. The scientist can use the software to view the molecule's appearance from various angles—even from *inside* the molecule. Thus, computers have expanded the ways we can view a molecule.

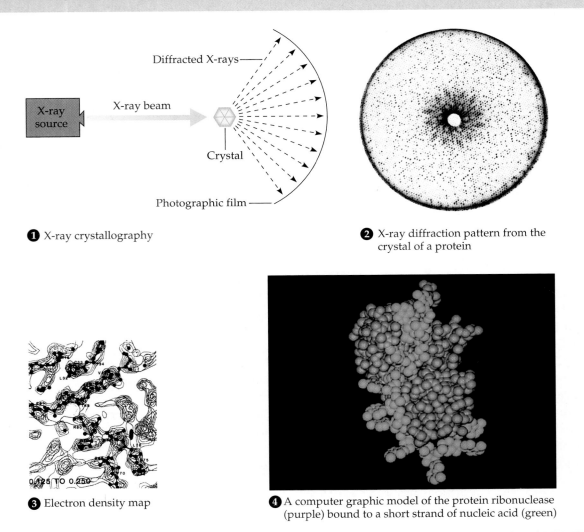

❶ X-ray crystallography

❷ X-ray diffraction pattern from the crystal of a protein

❸ Electron density map

❹ A computer graphic model of the protein ribonuclease (purple) bound to a short strand of nucleic acid (green)

(with page numbers and key figures)

POLYMER PRINCIPLES

■ **Most macromolecules are polymers (pp. 58–59, FIGURE 5.2)**
Carbohydrates, lipids, proteins, and nucleic acids are the four
major classes of organic compounds in cells. Some of these compounds are *very* large and are called macromolecules. Most macromolecules are polymers, chains of identical or similar building
blocks called monomers. Monomers form larger molecules by condensation reactions in which water molecules are released (dehydration). Polymers can disassemble by the reverse process,
hydrolysis.

■ **An immense variety of polymers can be built from a small set of
monomers (pp. 59–60)** Each class of polymer is formed from a
specific set of monomers. Although organisms share the same limited number of monomer types, each organism is unique because
of the specific arrangement of monomers into polymers.

CARBOHYDRATES—FUEL AND BUILDING MATERIAL

5.1 **Sugars, the smallest carbohydrates, serve as fuel and carbon
sources (pp. 60–61, FIGURES 5.3–5.5)** Monosaccharides are the
simplest carbohydrates. They are used directly for fuel, converted
to other types of organic molecules, or used as monomers for
polymers. Disaccharides consist of two monosaccharides connected by a glycosidic linkage.

■ **Polysaccharides, the polymers of sugars, have storage and structural roles (pp. 62–65, FIGURES 5.6–5.8)** The monosaccharide
monomers of polysaccharides are connected by glycosidic linkages.
Starch in plants and glycogen in animals are both storage polymers
of glucose. Cellulose is an important structural polymer of glucose
in plant cell walls. Starch, glycogen, and cellulose differ in the positions and orientations of their glycosidic linkages.

LIPIDS—DIVERSE HYDROPHOBIC MOLECULES

5.2 **Fats store large amounts of energy (p. 66, FIGURE 5.10)** Fats, also
known as triacylglycerols, are constructed by joining a glycerol
molecule to three fatty acids by dehydration reactions. Saturated
fatty acids have the maximum number of hydrogen atoms. Unsaturated fatty acids (present in oils) have one or more double bonds
between their carbons.

■ **Phospholipids are major components of cell membranes (pp.
67–68, FIGURE 5.12)** Where fats have a third fatty acid linked to
glycerol, phospholipids have a negatively charged phosphate
group, which may be joined, in turn, to another small hydrophilic
molecule. Thus, the "head" of a phospholipid is hydrophilic.

■ **Steroids include cholesterol and certain hormones (p. 68, FIGURE
5.14)** Steroids have a basic structure of four fused rings of carbon
atoms.

PROTEINS—THE MOLECULAR TOOLS OF THE CELL

5.3 A protein consists of one or more polypeptide chains folded into a
specific three-dimensional conformation.

■ **A polypeptide is a polymer of amino acids connected in a specific
sequence (pp. 68–70, FIGURE 5.16)** Proteins are constructed from
20 different amino acids, each with a characteristic side chain (R
group). The carboxyl and amino groups of adjacent amino acids
link together in peptide bonds.

5.4 **A protein's function depends on its specific conformation (pp.
70–76, FIGURE 5.24)** The primary structure of a protein is its
unique sequence of amino acids. Secondary structure is the folding
or coiling of the polypeptide into repeating configurations, such as
the α helix and the pleated sheet, which result from hydrogen

bonding between parts of the polypeptide backbone. Tertiary
structure is the overall three-dimensional shape of a polypeptide
and results from interactions between amino acid side chains. Proteins made of more than one polypeptide chain (subunits) have a
quaternary level of structure. The structure and function of a protein are sensitive to physical and chemical conditions. Protein
shape is ultimately determined by its primary structure, but in the
cell chaperone proteins may help the folding process.

NUCLEIC ACIDS—INFORMATIONAL POLYMERS

5.5 **Nucleic acids store and transmit hereditary information (pp.
76–77, FIGURE 5.26)** DNA stores information for the synthesis of
specific proteins. RNA carries this genetic information to the protein-synthesizing machinery.

■ **A nucleic acid strand is a polymer of nucleotides (pp. 77–78, FIG-
URE 5.27)** Each nucleotide monomer consists of a pentose covalently bonded to a phosphate group and to one of four different
nitrogenous bases (A, G, C, and T or U). RNA has ribose as its pentose; DNA has deoxyribose. RNA has U and DNA T. In making a
polynucleotide, nucleotides join to form a sugar-phosphate backbone from which the nitrogenous bases project. The sequence of
bases along a gene specifies the amino acid sequence of a particular
protein.

■ **Inheritance is based on replication of the DNA double helix (pp.
78–79, FIGURE 5.28)** DNA is a helical, double-stranded macromolecule with bases projecting into the interior of the molecule.
Because A always hydrogen-bonds to T, and C to G, the nucleotide
sequences of the two strands are complementary. One strand can
serve as a template for the formation of the other. This unique feature of DNA provides a mechanism for the continuity of life.

■ **We can use DNA and proteins as tape measures of evolution (p. 79,
TABLE 5.2)** Molecular comparisons help biologists sort out the evolutionary connections among species.

1. Which of the following terms includes all others in the list?
   a. monosaccharide   d. carbohydrate
   b. disaccharide   e. polysaccharide
   c. starch

2. The molecular formula for glucose is $C_6H_{12}O_6$. What would be
   the molecular formula for a polymer made by linking ten glucose
   molecules together by condensation reactions? Explain your
   answer.
   a. $C_{60}H_{120}O_{60}$ d. $C_{60}H_{100}O_{50}$
   b. $C_6H_{12}O_6$ e. $C_{60}H_{111}O_{51}$
   c. $C_{60}H_{102}O_{51}$

3. The two ring forms of glucose (α and β)
   a. are made from different structural isomers of glucose
   b. arise from different linear (nonring) glucose molecules
   c. arise when different carbons of the linear structure join to
      form the rings
   d. arise because the hydroxyl group at the point of ring closure
      can be trapped in either one of two possible positions
   e. include an aldose and a ketose

4. Choose the pair of terms that correctly completes this sentence:
   Nucleotides are to _____ as _____ are to
   proteins.
   a. nucleic acids; amino acids
   b. amino acids; polypeptides

c. glycosidic linkages; polypeptide linkages
d. genes; enzymes
e. polymers; polypeptides

5. Which of the following statements concerning *unsaturated* fats is correct?
   a. They are more common in animals than in plants.
   b. They have double bonds in the carbon chains of their fatty acids.
   c. They generally solidify at room temperature.
   d. They contain more hydrogen than saturated fats having the same number of carbon atoms.
   e. They have fewer fatty acid molecules per fat molecule.

6. The structural level of a protein least affected by a disruption in hydrogen bonding is the:
   a. primary level
   b. secondary level
   c. tertiary level
   d. quaternary level
   e. all structural levels are equally affected

7. To convert a nucleoside to a nucleotide, it would be necessary to:
   a. combine two nucleosides using dehydration synthesis
   b. remove the pentose from the nucleoside
   c. replace the purine with a pyrimidine
   d. add phosphate to the nucleoside
   e. replace ribose with deoxyribose

CHALLENGE QUESTIONS

1. A particular small polypeptide is nine amino acids long. Using three different enzymes to hydrolyze the polypeptide at various sites, we obtain the following five fragments (N denotes the amino end of the chain): Ala-Leu-Asp-Tyr-Val-Leu; Tyr-Val-Leu; N-Gly-Pro-Leu; Asp-Tyr-Val-Leu; N-Gly-Pro-Leu-Ala-Leu. Determine the primary structure of this polypeptide.

2. Most amino acids can exist in two forms:

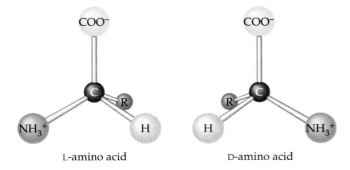

L-amino acid   D-amino acid

   a. Apply what you learned in Chapter 4 to explain the structural difference between these two molecules.
   b. When an organic chemist synthesizes amino acids, a mixture of these two forms is made; the result was probably the same when the first amino acids formed by abiotic synthesis in the "primordial soup" on the early Earth. However, with very few exceptions, only the L form of amino acids occurs in proteins. This is one example of molecular "handedness" in life. What are the possible advantages of life's becoming locked into the exclusive use of one of these two amino acid versions? Speculate on the possible evolutionary significance of this "handedness."

SCIENCE, TECHNOLOGY, AND SOCIETY

Some amateur and professional athletes take anabolic steroids to help them "bulk up" or build strength. The health risks of this practice are extensively documented. Apart from health considerations, how do you feel about the use of chemicals to enhance athletic performance? Is an athlete who takes anabolic steroids cheating, or is his or her use of such chemicals just part of the preparation required to succeed in a competitive sport? Defend your answer.

FURTHER READING

Dushesne, L. C., and D. W. Larson. "Cellulose and the Evolution of Plant Life." *Bioscience,* April 1989. The chemistry and natural history of the most abundant organic molecule in the biosphere.
Fackelmann, K. "Olestra: Too Good to Be True?" *Science News,* January 27, 1996. Researchers identify some health risks of fake fat.
Gibbons, A. "Geneticists Trace the DNA Trail of the First Americans." *Science,* January 15, 1993. Applying the "DNA tape measure" to a problem in anthropology.
Hoberman, J. M., and C. E. Yesalis. "The History of Synthetic Testosterone." *Scientific American,* February 1995. Anabolic steroids and sports.
Horgan, J. "Stubbornly Ahead of His Time." *Scientific American,* March 1993. A profile of Linus Pauling, a controversial giant of twentieth-century science.
Lewis, R. "Unraveling the Weave of Spider Silk." *BioScience,* October 1996. The structure of silk protein and its possible use in human inventions.
Mathews, C. K., and K. E. van Holde. *Biochemistry,* 2nd ed. Menlo Park, CA: Benjamin/Cummings, 1996. Excellent explanations and beautiful art.
Pennisi, E. "Twirling Ribbons, Billowing Bubbles." *Science News,* November 19, 1994. Computer visualization brings protein structure into view.
Strauss, E. "How Proteins Take Shape." *Science News,* September 6, 1997. How chaperone proteins help proteins fold correctly.
Taubes, G. "Misfolding the Way to Disease." *Science,* March 15, 1996. Alzheimer's disease and others may result from incorrect protein folding.

 WEB LINKS

Visit the special edition of *The Biology Place* for BIOLOGY, Fifth Edition, at http://www.biology.com/campbell. Go to Chapter 5 for online resources, including learning activities, practice exams, and links to the following web sites:

"ChemCenter"
ChemCenter is a one-stop web site for chemists and also provides resources for educators, students, and individuals who want reliable, accurate information about the chemistry-related sciences.

"US Food & Drug Administration"
Advances in applied biology and chemistry have given rise to many new consumable items. The FDA ensures that the food we eat is safe and wholesome and that medicines are safe and effective.

"BioChemNet"
This is the main page of an excellent site that links chemistry and the life sciences. Contains links to sites from general chemistry to biotechnology and has a good weekly news section.

"ChemEd: Chemistry Education Resources"
A comprehensive list of links to chemistry education-related sites.

CHAPTER 6

*T*he living cell is a chemical industry in miniature, where thousands of reactions occur within a microscopic space. Sugars are converted to amino acids, and vice versa. Small molecules are assembled into polymers, which may be hydrolyzed later as the needs of the cell change. In plants and animals, many cells export chemical products that are used in other parts of the organism. The chemical process known as cellular respiration drives the cellular economy by extracting the energy stored in sugars and other fuels. Cells apply this energy to perform various types of work, such as the synthesis of the macromolecules featured in Chapter 5. In a more exotic example, cells of the fungus from New Guinea in the photo at the right convert the energy stored in certain organic molecules to light, a process called bioluminescence. (The glow may attract insects that benefit the fungus by dispersing its spores.) Bioluminescence and all other metabolic activities carried out by a cell are precisely coordinated and controlled. In its complexity, its efficiency, its integration, and its responsiveness to subtle changes, the cell is peerless as a chemical institution. The concepts of metabolism you learn in this chapter will help you further understand the connections between chemistry and life.

AN INTRODUCTION TO METABOLISM

METABOLISM, ENERGY, AND LIFE

The totality of an organism's chemical processes is called **metabolism** (from the Greek *metabole*, "change"). Metabolism is an emergent property of life that arises from specific interactions between molecules within the orderly environment of the cell.

Metabolism, Energy, and Life
- The chemistry of life is organized into metabolic pathways
- Organisms transform energy
- The energy transformations of life are subject to two laws of thermodynamics
- Organisms live at the expense of free energy
- ATP powers cellular work by coupling exergonic reactions to endergonic reactions

Enzymes
- Enzymes speed up metabolic reactions by lowering energy barriers
- Enzymes are substrate-specific
- The active site is an enzyme's catalytic center
- A cell's physical and chemical environment affects enzyme activity

The Control of Metabolism
- Metabolic control often depends on allosteric regulation
- The localization of enzymes within a cell helps order metabolism
- The theme of emergent properties is manifest in the chemistry of life

The chemistry of life is organized into metabolic pathways

We can think of a cell's metabolism as an elaborate road map of the thousands of chemical reactions that occur in that cell (FIGURE 6.1, p. 84). These reactions are arranged in intricately branched metabolic pathways that alter molecules by a series of steps. Enzymes route matter through the metabolic pathways by selectively accelerating each step. Analogous to the red, yellow, and green lights that control the flow of traffic and prevent snarls, mechanisms that regulate enzymes balance metabolic supply and demand, averting deficits and surpluses of chemicals.

As a whole, metabolism is concerned with managing the material and energy resources of the cell. Some metabolic pathways release energy by breaking down complex molecules to simpler compounds. These degradative processes are called **catabolic pathways**. A major thoroughfare of catabolism is cellular respiration, in which the sugar glucose and other organic fuels are broken down to carbon dioxide and water. Energy that was stored in the organic molecules becomes available to do the work of the cell. **Anabolic pathways**, in contrast,

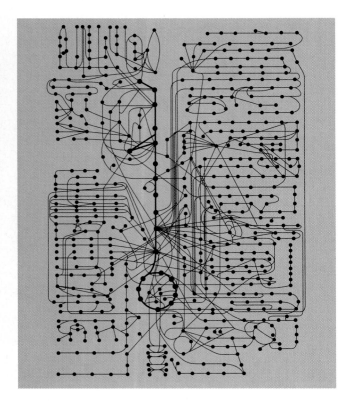

FIGURE 6.1 · The complexity of metabolism. This schematic diagram traces only a few hundred of the thousands of metabolic reactions that occur in a cell. The dots represent molecules, and the lines represent the chemical reactions that transform them. The reactions proceed in stepwise sequences called metabolic pathways, each step catalyzed by a specific enzyme.

consume energy to build complicated molecules from simpler ones. An example of anabolism is the synthesis of a protein from amino acids. Catabolic and anabolic pathways are the downhill and uphill avenues of the metabolic map. The metabolic pathways intersect in such a way that energy released from the "downhill" reactions of catabolism can be used to drive the "uphill" reactions of the anabolic pathways. This transfer of energy from catabolism to anabolism is called energy coupling.

In this chapter we will focus on the mechanisms common to metabolic pathways. Since energy is fundamental to all metabolic processes, a basic knowledge of energy is necessary to understand how the living cell works. Although we will use some nonliving examples to study energy, keep in mind that the same concepts demonstrated by these examples also apply to **bioenergetics**, the study of how organisms manage their energy resources. An understanding of energy is as important for students of biology as it is for students of physics, chemistry, and engineering.

Organisms transform energy

Energy is the capacity to do work—that is, to move matter against opposing forces, such as gravity and friction. Put

another way, energy is the ability to rearrange a collection of matter. For example, you expend energy to turn the pages of this book. Energy exists in various forms, and the work of life depends on the ability of cells to transform energy from one type into another.

Anything that moves possesses a form of energy called **kinetic energy**, the energy of motion. Moving objects perform work by imparting motion to other matter: A pool player uses the motion of the cue stick to push the cue ball, which in turn moves the other balls; water gushing through a dam turns turbines; electrons flowing along a wire run household appliances; the contraction of leg muscles pushes bicycle pedals. Light is also a type of kinetic energy that can be harnessed to perform work, such as powering photosynthesis in green plants. Heat, or thermal energy, is kinetic energy that results from the random movement of molecules.

A resting object not presently at work may still possess energy, which, remember, is the *capacity* to do work. Stored energy, or **potential energy**, is energy that matter possesses because of its location or structure. Water behind a dam, for instance, stores energy because of its altitude. Chemical energy, a form of potential energy especially important to biologists, is stored in molecules because of the structural arrangement of the atoms in those molecules.

How is energy converted from one form to another? Consider, for example, the playground scene in FIGURE 6.2. The girl at the bottom of the slide transformed kinetic energy to

FIGURE 6.2 · Transformations between kinetic and potential energy. The children in this playground scene have more potential energy at the top of the slide (because of the effect of gravity) than they do at the bottom. They convert kinetic energy to potential (stored) energy when they climb up the slide, and convert potential energy back to kinetic energy during their descent.

potential energy when she climbed to the top of the slide. This stored energy was converted back to kinetic energy as she slid down. It was another source of potential energy, the chemical energy in the food she ate for breakfast, that enabled the girl to climb to the top in the first place.

Chemical energy can be tapped when chemical reactions rearrange the atoms of molecules in such a way that potential energy stored in the molecules is converted to kinetic energy. This transformation occurs, for example, in the engine of an automobile when the hydrocarbons of gasoline react explosively with oxygen, releasing the energy that pushes the pistons. Similarly, chemical energy fuels organisms. Cellular respiration and other catabolic pathways unleash energy stored in sugar and other complex molecules and make that energy available for cellular work. Each child who climbed the hill in FIGURE 6.2 transformed some of the chemical energy that was stored in the organic molecules of food to the kinetic energy of movements. The chemical energy stored in these fuel molecules had itself been derived from light energy by plants during photosynthesis. Organisms are energy transformers.

The energy transformations of life are subject to two laws of thermodynamics

The study of the energy transformations that occur in a collection of matter is called **thermodynamics**. Scientists use the word *system* to denote the matter under study and refer to the rest of the universe—everything outside the system—as the *surroundings*. A *closed system,* such as that approximated by liquid in a thermos bottle, is isolated from its surroundings. In an *open system,* energy (and often matter) can be transferred between the system and its surroundings. Organisms are open systems. They absorb energy—for instance, chemical energy in the form of organic molecules, or light energy—and release heat and metabolic waste products, such as carbon dioxide, to the surroundings. Two laws of thermodynamics govern energy transformations in organisms and all other collections of matter.

According to the **first law of thermodynamics**, the energy of the universe is constant. *Energy can be transferred and transformed, but it can be neither created nor destroyed.* The first law is also known as *conservation of energy.* The electric company does not manufacture energy, but merely converts it to a form that is convenient to use. By converting light to chemical energy, a green plant acts as an energy transformer, not an energy producer. What happens to energy after it has performed work in a machine or an organism? If energy cannot be destroyed, what prevents organisms from behaving like closed systems and recycling their energy? The second law answers these questions.

The **second law of thermodynamics** can be stated many ways. Let's begin with the following interpretation: Every energy transfer or transformation makes the universe more

disordered. Scientists use a quantity called **entropy** as a measure of disorder, or randomness. The more random a collection of matter is, the greater its entropy. We can now restate the second law as follows: *Every energy transfer or transformation increases the entropy of the universe.* There is an unstoppable trend toward randomization. In many cases, increased entropy is evident in the physical disintegration of a system's organized structure. For example, you can observe this increasing entropy in the gradual decay of an unmaintained building. Much of the increasing entropy of the universe is less apparent, however, because it takes the form of an increasing amount of heat, which is the energy of random molecular motion.

In most energy transformations, ordered forms of energy are at least partly converted to heat. Only about 25% of the chemical energy stored in the fuel tank of an automobile is transformed into the motion of the car; the remaining 75% is lost from the engine as heat, which dissipates rapidly through the surroundings. Similarly, the children in FIGURE 6.2 convert only a fraction of the energy stored in their food to the kinetic energy of hill climbing and other play. In performing various kinds of work, living cells unavoidably convert organized forms of energy to heat. (This can make a room crowded with people uncomfortably warm.)

In machines and organisms, even energy that performs useful work is eventually converted to heat. The organized energy of an automobile's forward movement becomes heat when the friction of the brakes and tires stops the car. Conversion to heat is the fate of *all* the chemical energy a child uses to climb a slide: Metabolic breakdown of food generates heat during the climb, and the fraction of energy temporarily stored as gravitational potential energy is converted to heat on the way down, as friction between child and slide warms the surrounding air.

Conversion of other forms of energy to heat does not violate the first law of thermodynamics. Energy has been conserved, because heat is a form of energy, though energy in its most random state. By combining the first and second laws of thermodynamics, we can conclude that the *quantity* of energy in the universe is constant, but its *quality* is not. In a sense, heat is the lowest grade of energy. It is the uncoordinated movement of molecules, which many systems cannot harness in order to perform work. A system can only put heat to work when there is a temperature difference that results in the heat flowing from a warmer location to a cooler one. If temperature is uniform throughout a system, as it is in a living cell, then the only use for heat energy is to warm a body of matter, such as an organism.

Thus, an organism takes in organized forms of matter and energy from the surroundings and replaces them with less ordered forms. For example, an animal obtains starch, proteins, and other complex molecules from the food it eats. As catabolic pathways break these molecules down, the animal releases carbon dioxide and water, relatively small, simple

molecules that store less chemical energy than the food. The depletion of chemical energy is accounted for by heat generated during metabolism. On a larger scale, energy flows into an ecosystem in the form of light and leaves in the form of heat. Living systems increase the entropy of their surroundings, as predicted by thermodynamic law.

How can we reconcile the second law of thermodynamics—the unstoppable increase in the entropy of the universe—with the orderliness of life, which is one of this book's themes? The key is to remember another theme: Organisms are open systems that exchange energy and materials with their surroundings. It is true that cells create ordered structures from less organized starting materials. For example, amino acids are ordered into the specific sequences of polypeptide chains. And during the early history of life, complex organisms evolved from simpler ancestors (FIGURE 6.3). However, this increase in organization in no way violates the second law. The entropy of a particular system, such as an organism, may actually decrease, so long as the total entropy of the *universe*—the system plus its surroundings—increases. Thus, organisms are islands of low entropy in an increasingly random universe. The evolution of biological order is perfectly consistent with the laws of thermodynamics.

Organisms live at the expense of free energy

How can we predict what can and cannot occur in nature? How can we distinguish the possible from the impossible? We know from experience that certain events occur spontaneously and others do not. For instance, we know that water flows downhill, that objects of opposite charge move toward each other, that an ice cube melts at room temperature, and that a sugar cube dissolves in water. Explaining *why* these processes occur spontaneously is tricky.

Let's begin by defining a spontaneous process as a change that can occur without outside help. A spontaneous change can be harnessed in order to perform work. The downhill flow of water can be used to turn a turbine in a power plant, for example. A process that cannot occur on its own is said to be nonspontaneous; it will happen only if energy is added to the system. Water moves uphill only when a windmill or some other machine pumps the water against gravity, and a cell must expend energy to synthesize a protein from amino acids.

When a spontaneous process occurs in a system, the stability of that system increases. Unstable systems tend to change in such a way that they become more stable. A body of elevated water, such as a reservoir, is less stable than the same water at sea level. A system of charged particles is less stable when opposite charges are apart than when they are together. In situations less familiar to us, how can we predict which changes lead to greater stability in a system—that is, which changes are spontaneous? You have already learned that a process can occur spontaneously only if it increases the disorder (entropy) of the universe. This principle is helpful in theory, but it does not give us a practical criterion to apply to biological systems because it requires that we measure changes in the surroundings. We need some standard for spontaneity that is based on the system alone. That criterion is called free energy.

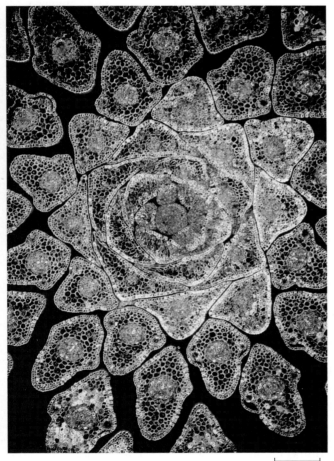

FIGURE 6.3 ▪ The evolution of biological order is consistent with thermodynamic law. Order is a characteristic of life. It is evident, for example, in the detailed anatomy of this bud from a spruce tree (TEM of a cross section). Organisms decrease their entropy when they order raw materials, such as organic monomers, into macromolecules and then organize these macromolecules into cellular structures. Biological order has, at times, also increased over the grander scale of geological time. For example, we can trace the ancestry of the plant kingdom to much simpler organisms called green algae. An evolutionary interpretation of biological history does not violate thermodynamic law. The second law requires only that processes increase the entropy of the universe. Open systems can increase their order at the expense of the order of their surroundings.

1 mm

Free Energy: A Criterion for Spontaneous Change

The concept of free energy is not easy to grasp, but the effort is worthwhile because we can apply the idea to many biological problems. ***Free energy*** *is the portion of a system's energy that can perform work when temperature is uniform throughout the system,* as in a living cell. It is called *free* energy because it is available for work, not because it can be spent without cost to

the universe. In fact, you will soon understand that organisms can live only at the expense of free energy acquired from the surroundings.

A system's quantity of free energy is symbolized by the letter G. There are two components to G: the system's total energy (symbolized by H) and its entropy (symbolized by S). Free energy is related to these factors in the following way:

$$G = H - TS$$

T stands for absolute temperature (in Kelvin units, K, equal to °C + 273; see Appendix Two). Notice that temperature amplifies the entropy term of the equation. This makes sense if you remember that temperature measures the intensity of random molecular motion (heat), which tends to disrupt order. What does this equation tell us about free energy? Not all the energy stored in a system (H) is available for work. The system's disorder, the entropy factor, is subtracted from total energy in computing the maximum capacity of the system to perform useful work. We are then left with free energy, which is somewhat less than the system's total energy. The relationships between free energy, equilibrium, and work are illustrated in FIGURE 6.4.

How does the concept of free energy help us determine whether a particular process can occur spontaneously? Think of free energy, G in the previous equation, as a measure of a system's instability—its tendency to change to a more stable state. Systems that are rich in energy, such as stretched springs or separated charges, are unstable; so are highly ordered systems, such as complex molecules. Thus, those systems that tend to change spontaneously to a more stable state are those that have high energy, low entropy, or both. The free-energy equation weighs these two factors, which are consolidated in the system's G content. Now we can state a versatile criterion for spontaneous change: *In any spontaneous process, the free energy of a system decreases.*

The change in free energy as a system goes from a starting state to a different state is represented by ΔG:

$$\Delta G = G_{final\ state} - G_{starting\ state}$$

Or, put another way:

$$\Delta G = \Delta H - T\Delta S$$

For a process to occur spontaneously, the system must either give up energy (a decrease in H), give up order (an increase in S), or both. When these changes in H and S are tallied, ΔG must have a negative value. The greater this decrease in free energy, the greater the maximum amount of work the spontaneous process can perform. This is a formal, mathematical way of stating the obvious: Nature runs "downhill"—downhill in the metaphorical sense of a loss in useful energy, the capacity to perform work.

More free energy
Less stable
Greater work capacity

 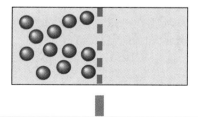 

Free energy decreases; direction of spontaneous change; ΔG < 0; change in the direction of equilibrium; change can be harnessed to perform work

Less free energy
More stable
Less work capacity

 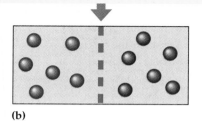 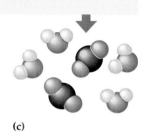

(a) (b) (c)

FIGURE 6.4 · The relationship of free energy to stability, spontaneous change, equilibrium, and work. An unstable system is rich in free energy. It has a tendency to change spontaneously to a more stable state, and it is possible to harness this "downhill" change in order to perform work. **(a)** In this case, free energy is proportional to the girl's altitude. **(b)** The free-energy concept also applies on the molecular scale, in this case to the physical movement of molecules known as diffusion. Here, molecules of a particular solute are distributed unequally across a membrane separating two aqueous compartments. This ordered state is unstable; it is rich in free energy. If the solute molecules can cross the membrane, there will be a net movement (diffusion) of the molecules until they are equally concentrated in both compartments. **(c)** Chemical reactions also involve free energy. The sugar molecule on top is less stable than the simpler molecules below. When catabolic pathways break down complex organic molecules, a cell can harness the free energy stored in the molecules to perform work.

Free Energy and Equilibrium

There is an important relationship between free energy and equilibrium, including chemical equilibrium. Recall from Chapter 2 that most chemical reactions are reversible and proceed until the forward and backward reactions occur at the same rate. The reaction is then said to be at chemical equilibrium, and there is no further change in the concentration of products or reactants. As a reaction proceeds toward equilibrium, the free energy of the mixture of reactants and products decreases. Free energy increases when a reaction is somehow pushed away from equilibrium. For a reaction at equilibrium, $\Delta G = 0$, because there is no net change in the system. We can think of equilibrium as an energy valley. A chemical reaction or physical process at equilibrium performs no work. A process is spontaneous and can perform work when sliding toward equilibrium. Movement away from equilibrium is nonspontaneous; it can occur only with the help of an outside energy source. We can now apply the free-energy concept more specifically to the chemistry of life.

Free Energy and Metabolism

Exergonic and Endergonic Reactions in Metabolism. Based on their free-energy changes, chemical reactions can be classified as either exergonic (meaning "energy outward") or endergonic ("energy inward"). An **exergonic reaction** proceeds with a net release of free energy. Since the chemical mixture loses free energy, ΔG is negative for an exergonic reaction. In other words, exergonic reactions are those that occur spontaneously. The magnitude of ΔG for an exergonic reaction is the maximum amount of work the reaction can perform. We can use the overall reaction for cellular respiration as an example:

$$C_6H_{12}O_6 + 6\,O_2 \longrightarrow 6\,CO_2 + 6\,H_2O$$

$$\Delta G = -686 \text{ kcal/mol} \, (-2870 \text{ kJ/mol})$$

For each mole (180 g) of glucose broken down by respiration, 686 kilocalories (or 2870 kilojoules) of energy are made available for work (under what scientists call standard conditions). Because energy must be conserved, the chemical products of respiration store 686 kcal less free energy than the reactants. The products are, in a sense, the spent exhaust of a process that tapped most of the free energy stored in the sugar molecules.

An **endergonic reaction** is one that absorbs free energy from its surroundings. Because this kind of reaction stores free energy in molecules, ΔG is positive. Such reactions are nonspontaneous, and the magnitude of ΔG is the quantity of energy required to drive the reaction. If a chemical process is exergonic (downhill) in one direction, then the reverse process must be endergonic (uphill). A reversible process cannot be downhill in both directions. If $\Delta G = -686$ kcal/mol for respiration, then in order for photosynthesis to produce sugar from

carbon dioxide and water, $\Delta G = +686$ kcal/mol. Sugar production in the leaf cells of a plant is steeply endergonic, an uphill process powered by the absorption of light energy from the sun.

Metabolic Disequilibrium. The chemical reactions of metabolism are reversible and would reach equilibrium if they occurred in the isolation of a test tube. Because chemical systems at equilibrium have a ΔG of zero and can do no work, a cell that has reached equilibrium is dead! In fact, metabolic disequilibrium is one of the defining features of life. We'll use the catabolic pathway of respiration as an example. Some of the reversible reactions of respiration are pulled in one direction and kept out of equilibrium. The key to sustaining this disequilibrium is that the product of one reaction does not accumulate, but instead becomes a reactant in the next step along the metabolic pathway; FIGURE 6.5 shows an analogy. The overall sequence of reactions is pulled by the huge free-energy difference between glucose at the uphill end of respiration and carbon dioxide and water at the downhill end of the pathway. As long as the cell has a steady supply of glucose or other fuels and is able to expel the CO_2 waste to the surroundings, the cell does not reach equilibrium and continues to do the work of life.

We see once again how important it is to think of organisms as open systems. Sunlight provides a daily source of free energy for an ecosystem's plants and other photosynthetic organisms. Animals and other nonphotosynthetic organisms in an ecosystem depend on free-energy transfusions in the form of the organic products of photosynthesis.

Now that we have applied the free-energy concept to metabolism, we are ready to see how a cell actually performs the work of life. A key strategy in bioenergetics is **energy coupling**, the use of an exergonic process to drive an endergonic one. A molecule called ATP is responsible for mediating most energy coupling in cells.

ATP powers cellular work by coupling exergonic reactions to endergonic reactions

A cell does three main kinds of work:

1. *Mechanical work*, such as the beating of cilia, the contraction of muscle cells, and the movement of chromosomes during cellular reproduction.
2. *Transport work*, the pumping of substances across membranes against the direction of spontaneous movement.
3. *Chemical work*, the pushing of endergonic reactions that would not occur spontaneously, such as the synthesis of polymers from monomers.

In most cases, the immediate source of energy that powers cellular work is ATP.

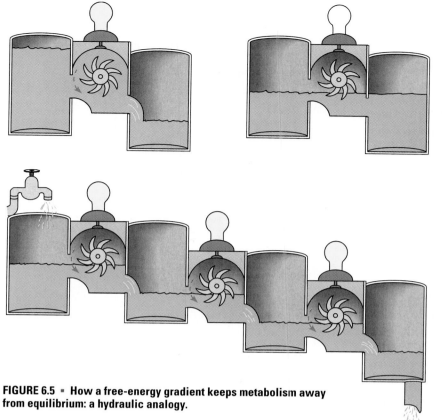

(a) This diagram portrays a system in which water generates electric energy only while it is falling. Once the levels in the two containers are equal, the turbine ceases to turn and the light goes out. The individual steps of respiration, in isolation, would also come to equilibrium, and cellular work would cease.

(b) If there is a series of drops in water level, electric energy can be generated at each drop. In respiration, there is a series of drops in free energy between glucose, the starting material, and the metabolic wastes at the end (carbon dioxide and water). The overall process never reaches equilibrium as long as the organism lives. A cell continues to acquire free energy in the form of glucose. The product of each reaction becomes the reactant for the next, and the metabolic wastes are expelled from the cell.

FIGURE 6.5 ▪ **How a free-energy gradient keeps metabolism away from equilibrium: a hydraulic analogy.**

The Structure and Hydrolysis of ATP

ATP (adenosine triphosphate) is closely related to one type of nucleotide found in nucleic acids. ATP has the nitrogenous base adenine bonded to ribose, as in an adenine nucleotide of RNA. However, in RNA, *one* phosphate group is attached to the ribose

(see FIGURE 5.27a). Adenosine *tri*phosphate has a chain of *three* phosphate groups attached to the ribose (FIGURE 6.6a).

The bonds between the phosphate groups of ATP's tail can be broken by hydrolysis. When the terminal phosphate bond is broken, a molecule of inorganic phosphate (abbreviated P_i throughout this book) leaves the ATP, which becomes

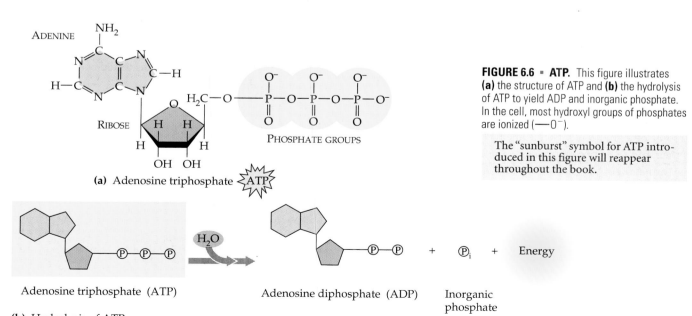

(a) Adenosine triphosphate

(b) Hydrolysis of ATP

Adenosine triphosphate (ATP)

Adenosine diphosphate (ADP)

Inorganic phosphate

FIGURE 6.6 ▪ **ATP.** This figure illustrates **(a)** the structure of ATP and **(b)** the hydrolysis of ATP to yield ADP and inorganic phosphate. In the cell, most hydroxyl groups of phosphates are ionized ($-O^-$).

The "sunburst" symbol for ATP introduced in this figure will reappear throughout the book.

adenosine diphosphate, or ADP (FIGURE 6.6b). The reaction is exergonic and, under laboratory conditions, releases 7.3 kcal of energy per mole of ATP hydrolyzed:

$$ATP + H_2O \longrightarrow ADP + \textcircled{P}_i$$

$$\Delta G = -7.3 \text{ kcal/mol} (-31 \text{ kJ/mol})$$

This is the free-energy change measured under what are called standard conditions. However, the chemical and physical conditions in the cell do not conform to standard conditions. When the reaction occurs in the cellular environment rather than in a test tube, the actual ΔG is about -13 kcal/mole, 78% greater than the energy released by ATP hydrolysis under standard conditions.

Because their hydrolysis releases energy, the phosphate bonds of ATP are sometimes referred to as high-energy phosphate bonds, but the term is misleading. The phosphate bonds of ATP are not unusually strong bonds, as the words "high-energy" imply. In fact, compared to most bonds in organic molecules, these bonds are relatively weak, and it is *because* they are somewhat unstable that their hydrolysis yields energy. The products of hydrolysis (ADP and $\textcircled{P}_i$) are more stable than ATP. When a system changes in the direction of greater stability—as when a compressed spring relaxes, for instance—the change is exergonic. Thus, the release of energy during the hydrolysis of ATP comes from the chemical change to a more stable condition, not from the phosphate bonds themselves. Why are the phosphate bonds so fragile? If we reexamine the ATP molecule in FIGURE 6.6a, we can see that all three phosphate groups are negatively charged. These like charges are crowded together, and their repulsion contributes to the instability of this region of the ATP molecule. The triphosphate tail of ATP is the chemical equivalent of a loaded spring.

How ATP Performs Work

When ATP is hydrolyzed in a test tube, the release of free energy merely heats the surrounding water. In the cell, that would be an inefficient and dangerous use of a valuable energy resource. With the help of specific enzymes, the cell is able to couple the energy of ATP hydrolysis directly to endergonic processes by transferring a phosphate group from ATP to some other molecule. The recipient of the phosphate group is then said to be phosphorylated. The key to the coupling is the formation of this **phosphorylated intermediate**, which is more reactive (less stable) than the original molecule (FIGURE 6.7). Nearly all cellular work depends on ATP's energizing of other molecules by transferring phosphate groups. For instance, ATP powers the movement of muscles by transferring phosphate to contractile proteins.

The Regeneration of ATP

An organism at work uses ATP continuously, but ATP is a renewable resource that can be regenerated by the addition of

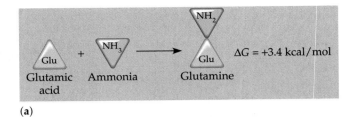

(a)

(b)

$$Glu + NH_3 \longrightarrow Glu{-}NH_2 \qquad \Delta G = +3.4 \text{ kcal/mol}$$

$$ATP \longrightarrow ADP + \textcircled{P}_i \qquad \underline{\Delta G = -7.3 \text{ kcal/mol}}$$

$$\text{Net } \Delta G = -3.9 \text{ kcal/mol}$$

(c)

FIGURE 6.7 · Energy coupling by phosphate transfer. In this example, ATP hydrolysis is used to drive an endergonic reaction, the conversion of the amino acid glutamic acid (Glu) to another amino acid, glutamine (Glu—NH₂). **(a)** Without the help of ATP, the conversion is nonspontaneous. **(b)** As it actually occurs in the cell, the synthesis of glutamine is a two-step reaction driven by ATP. The formation of a phosphorylated intermediate couples the two steps. ① ATP phosphorylates glutamic acid, making the amino acid less stable. ② Ammonia displaces the phosphate group, forming glutamine. **(c)** Adding the ΔG for the amino acid conversion to the ΔG for the ATP hydrolysis gives the free-energy change for the overall reaction. Because the overall process is exergonic (has a negative ΔG), it occurs spontaneously.

phosphate to ADP (FIGURE 6.8). The ATP cycle moves at an astonishing pace. For example, a working muscle cell recycles its entire pool of ATP about once each minute. That turnover represents 10 million molecules of ATP consumed and regenerated per second per cell. If ATP could not be regenerated by the phosphorylation of ADP, humans would consume nearly their body weight in ATP each day.

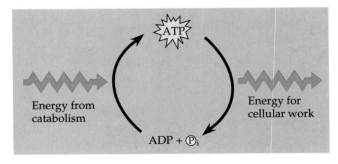

FIGURE 6.8 · The ATP cycle. Energy released by breakdown reactions (catabolism) in the cell is used to phosphorylate ADP, regenerating ATP. Energy stored in ATP drives most cellular work. Thus ATP couples the cell's energy-yielding processes to the energy-consuming ones.

Because a reversible process cannot go downhill both ways, the regeneration of ATP from ADP is necessarily endergonic:

$$ADP + \text{P}_i \longrightarrow ATP + H_2O$$

$$\Delta G = +7.3 \text{ kcal/mol (standard conditions)}$$

Catabolic (exergonic) pathways, especially cellular respiration, provide the energy for the endergonic process of making ATP. Plants also use light energy to produce ATP.

Thus the ATP cycle is a turnstile through which energy passes during its transfer from catabolic to anabolic pathways.

ENZYMES

The laws of thermodynamics tell us what can and cannot happen but say nothing about the speed of these processes. A spontaneous chemical reaction may occur so slowly that it is imperceptible. For example, the hydrolysis of sucrose (table sugar) to glucose and fructose is exergonic, occurring spontaneously with a release of free energy ($\Delta G = -7$ kcal/mol). Yet a solution of sucrose dissolved in sterile water will sit for years at room temperature with no appreciable hydrolysis. However, if we add a small amount of the enzyme sucrase to the solution, then all the sucrose may be hydrolyzed within seconds. How does an enzyme do this?

Enzymes speed up metabolic reactions by lowering energy barriers

Enzymes are catalytic proteins. (Another class of biological catalysts, ribozymes, made of RNA, is discussed in Chapters 17 and 26.) A **catalyst** is a chemical agent that changes the rate of a reaction without being consumed by the reaction. In the absence of enzymes, chemical traffic through the pathways of metabolism would become hopelessly congested. What impedes a spontaneous reaction, and how does an enzyme change the situation?

Every chemical reaction involves both bond breaking and bond forming. For example, the hydrolysis of sucrose involves first breaking the bond between glucose and fructose and then forming new bonds with a hydrogen and a hydroxyl group from water. Whenever a reaction rearranges the atoms of molecules, existing bonds in the reactants must be broken and the new bonds of the products formed. The reactant molecules must absorb energy from their surroundings for their bonds to break, and energy is released when the new bonds of the product molecules are formed.

The initial investment of energy for starting a reaction—the energy required to break bonds in the reactant molecules—is known as the **free energy of activation**, or **activation energy**, abbreviated E_A in this book. It is usually provided in the form of heat that the reactant molecules absorb from the surroundings. If the reaction is exergonic, E_A will be repaid with dividends, as the formation of new bonds releases more energy

than was invested in the breaking of old bonds. FIGURE 6.9 graphs these energy changes for a hypothetical reaction that swaps portions of two reactant molecules:

$$AB + CD \longrightarrow AC + BD$$

The bonds of the reactants break only when the molecules have absorbed enough energy to become unstable. (Recall that systems rich in free energy are intrinsically unstable, and unstable systems are reactive.) The activation energy is represented by the uphill portion of the graph, with the free-energy content of the reactants increasing. The absorption of thermal energy increases the speed of the reactants, so they are colliding more often and more forcefully. Also, thermal agitation of the atoms in the molecules makes the bonds more likely to break. At the summit, the reactants are in an unstable condition known as the *transition state;* they are primed, and the reaction can occur. As the molecules settle into their new bonding arrangements, energy is released to the surroundings. This phase of the reaction corresponds to the downhill part of the curve, which indicates a loss of free energy by the molecules. The difference in the free energy of the products and reactants is ΔG for the overall reaction, which is negative for an exergonic reaction.

As FIGURE 6.9 shows, even for an exergonic reaction, which is energetically downhill overall, the barrier of activation energy must be scaled before the reaction can occur. For some reactions, E_A is modest enough that even at room temperature there is sufficient thermal energy for many of the reactants to

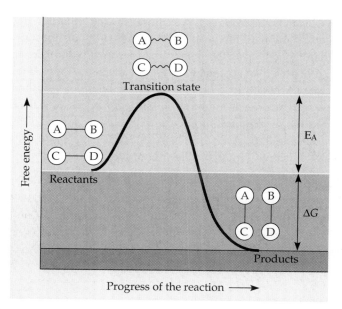

FIGURE 6.9 ▪ **An energy profile of a reaction.** In this hypothetical reaction, the reactants AB and CD must absorb enough energy from the surroundings to surmount the hill of activation energy (E_A) and reach the unstable transition state. The bonds can then break, and as the reaction proceeds, energy is released to the surroundings during the formation of new bonds. This particular graph profiles the energy inputs and outputs of an exergonic reaction, which has a negative ΔG; the products have less free energy than the reactants.

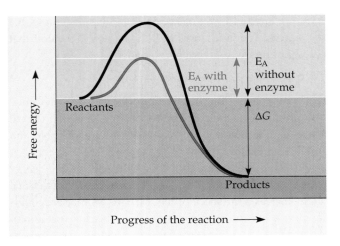

FIGURE 6.10 · Enzymes lower the barrier of activation energy.
Without affecting the free-energy change (ΔG) for the reaction, an enzyme speeds the reaction by reducing the uphill climb to the transition state. The black curve shows the course of the reaction without an enzyme; the red curve shows the course of the reaction with an enzyme.

reach the transition state. In most cases, however, the E_A barrier is loftier, and the reaction will occur at a noticeable rate only if the reactants are heated. The spark plugs in an automobile engine energize the gasoline-oxygen mixture so that the molecules reach the transition state and react; only then can there be the explosive release of energy that pushes the pistons. Without a spark, the hydrocarbons of gasoline are too stable to react with oxygen.

The barrier of activation energy is essential to life. Proteins, DNA, and other complex molecules of the cell are rich in free energy and have the potential to decompose spontaneously; that is, the laws of thermodynamics favor their breakdown. These molecules exist only because at temperatures typical for cells, few molecules can make it over the hump of activation energy. Occasionally, however, the barrier for selected reactions must be surmounted, or else the cell would be metabolically stagnant. Heat speeds a reaction, but high temperature kills cells. Organisms must therefore use an alternative: a catalyst.

An enzyme speeds a reaction by lowering the E_A barrier (FIGURE 6.10), so that the precipice of the transition state is within reach even at moderate temperatures. An enzyme cannot change the ΔG for a reaction; it cannot make an endergonic reaction exergonic. Enzymes can only hasten reactions that would occur eventually anyway, but this function makes it possible for the cell to have a dynamic metabolism. Further, because enzymes are very selective in the reactions they catalyze, they determine which chemical processes will be going on in the cell at any particular time.

Enzymes are substrate-specific

The reactant an enzyme acts on is referred to as the enzyme's **substrate**. The enzyme binds to its substrate (or substrates, when there are two or more reactants). While enzyme and substrate are joined, the catalytic action of the enzyme converts the substrate to the product (or products) of the reaction. The overall process can be summarized as follows, with the name of the enzyme written above the reaction arrow:

$$\text{Substrate(s)} \xrightarrow{\text{Enzyme}} \text{Product(s)}$$

For example, the enzyme sucrase (most enzyme names end in *-ase*) breaks the disaccharide sucrose into its two monosaccharides, glucose and fructose:

$$\text{Sucrose} + \text{H}_2\text{O} \xrightarrow{\text{Sucrase}} \text{Glucose} + \text{Fructose}$$

An enzyme can distinguish its substrate from even closely related compounds, such as isomers, so that each type of enzyme catalyzes a particular reaction. For instance, sucrase will act only on sucrose and will reject other disaccharides, such as maltose. What accounts for this molecular recognition? Recall that enzymes are proteins, and proteins are macromolecules with unique three-dimensional conformations. The specificity of an enzyme results from its shape.

Only a restricted region of the enzyme molecule actually binds to the substrate. This region, called the **active site**, is

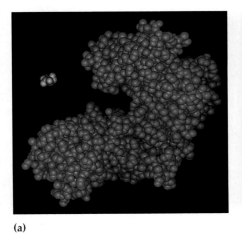

(a)

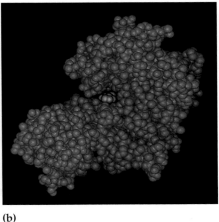

(b)

FIGURE 6.11 · The induced fit between an enzyme's active site and its substrate.
(a) The active site of this enzyme, called hexokinase, can be seen in this computer graphic model as a groove on the surface of the blue protein. **(b)** On entering the active site, the substrate, which is glucose (red), induces a slight change in the shape of the protein, causing the active site to embrace the substrate.

typically a pocket or groove on the surface of the protein (FIGURE 6.11). Usually, the active site is formed by only a few of the enzyme's amino acids, with the rest of the protein molecule providing a framework that reinforces the configuration of the active site.

The specificity of an enzyme is attributed to a compatible fit between the shape of its active site and the shape of the substrate. The active site, however, is not a rigid receptacle for the substrate. As the substrate enters the active site, it induces the enzyme to change its shape slightly so that the active site fits even more snugly around the substrate. This **induced fit** is like a clasping handshake. Induced fit brings chemical groups of the active site into positions that enhance their ability to catalyze the chemical reaction.

The active site is an enzyme's catalytic center

In an enzymatic reaction, the substrate binds to the active site to form an enzyme-substrate complex (FIGURE 6.12). In most cases, the substrate is held in the active site by weak interactions, such as hydrogen bonds and ionic bonds. Side chains (R groups) of a few of the amino acids that make up the active site catalyze the conversion of substrate to product, and the product departs from the active site. The enzyme is then free to take another substrate molecule into its active site. The entire cycle happens so fast that a single enzyme molecule typically acts on about a thousand substrate molecules per second. Some enzymes are much faster. Enzymes, like other catalysts, emerge from the reaction in their original form.

Therefore, very small amounts of enzyme can have a huge metabolic impact by functioning over and over again in catalytic cycles.

Enzymes use a variety of mechanisms that lower activation energy and speed up a reaction. In reactions involving two or more reactants, the active site provides a template for the substrates to come together in the proper orientation for a reaction to occur between them. As the active site clutches the substrates with an induced fit, the enzyme may stress the substrate molecules, stretching and bending critical chemical bonds that must be broken during the reaction. Since E_A is proportional to the difficulty of breaking bonds, distorting the substrate reduces the amount of thermal energy that must be absorbed to achieve a transition state.

The active site may also provide a microenvironment that is conducive to a particular type of reaction. For example, if the active site has amino acids with acidic side chains (R groups), the active site may be a pocket of low pH in an otherwise neutral cell. In such cases, an acidic amino acid may facilitate H^+ transfer to the substrate as a key step in catalyzing the reaction. Still another mechanism of catalysis is the direct participation of the active site in the chemical reaction. Sometimes this process even involves brief covalent bonding between the substrate and a side chain of an amino acid of the enzyme. Subsequent steps of the reaction restore the side chains to their original states, so the active site is the same after the reaction as it was before.

The rate at which a given amount of enzyme converts substrate to product is partly a function of the initial concentration

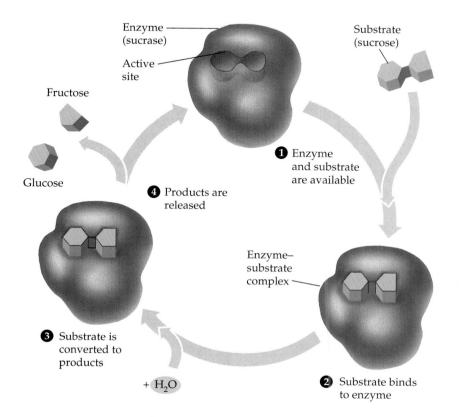

Fructose

Glucose

❶ Enzyme and substrate are available

❹ Products are released

Enzyme (sucrase)

Active site

Substrate (sucrose)

Enzyme–substrate complex

❸ Substrate is converted to products

+ H_2O

❷ Substrate binds to enzyme

FIGURE 6.12 ▪ **The catalytic cycle of an enzyme.** In this example, the enzyme sucrase catalyzes the hydrolysis of sucrose to glucose and fructose. ① When the active site of an enzyme is unoccupied and its substrate is available, the cycle begins. ② An enzyme-substrate complex forms when the substrate enters the active site and attaches by weak bonds. The active site changes shape to fit snugly around the substrate (induced fit). ③ The substrate is converted to products while in the active site. ④ The enzyme releases the products, and its active site is then available for another molecule of substrate. Most metabolic reactions are reversible, and an enzyme can catalyze both the forward and the reverse reactions. Which reaction prevails depends mainly on the relative concentrations of reactants and products; that is, the enzyme catalyzes the reaction in the direction of equilibrium.

6.1

of substrate: The more substrate molecules available, the more frequently they access the active sites of the enzyme molecules. However, there is a limit to how fast the reaction can be pushed by adding more substrate to a fixed concentration of enzyme. At some point, the concentration of substrate will be high enough that all enzyme molecules have their active sites engaged. As soon as the product exits an active site, another substrate molecule enters. At this substrate concentration, the enzyme is said to be saturated, and the rate of the reaction is determined by the speed at which the active site can convert substrate to product. When an enzyme population is saturated, the only way to increase productivity is to add more enzyme. Cells sometimes do this by making more enzyme molecules.

A cell's physical and chemical environment affects enzyme activity

The activity of an enzyme is affected by general environmental factors, such as temperature and pH, and also by particular chemicals that specifically influence that enzyme.

Effects of Temperature and pH

Recall from Chapter 5 that the three-dimensional structures of proteins are sensitive to their environment. As a protein, an enzyme has conditions under which it works optimally, because that environment favors the most active conformation for the enzyme molecule.

Temperature is one environmental factor important in the activity of an enzyme (FIGURE 6.13a). Up to a point, the velocity of an enzymatic reaction increases with increasing temperature, partly because substrates collide with active sites more frequently when the molecules move rapidly. Beyond that temperature, however, the speed of the enzymatic reaction drops sharply. The thermal agitation of the enzyme molecule disrupts the hydrogen bonds, ionic bonds, and other weak interactions that stabilize the active conformation, and the protein molecule denatures. Each enzyme has an optimal temperature at which its reaction rate is fastest. This temperature allows the greatest number of molecular collisions without denaturing the enzyme. Most human enzymes have optimal temperatures of about 35°C to 40°C (close to human body temperature). Bacteria that live in hot springs contain enzymes with optimal temperatures of 70°C or higher.

Just as each enzyme has an optimal temperature, it also has a pH at which it is most active (FIGURE 6.13b). The optimal pH values for most enzymes fall in the range of 6 to 8, but there are exceptions. For example, pepsin, a digestive enzyme in the stomach, works best at pH 2. Such an acidic environment denatures most enzymes, but the active conformation of pepsin is adapted to the acidic environment of the stomach.

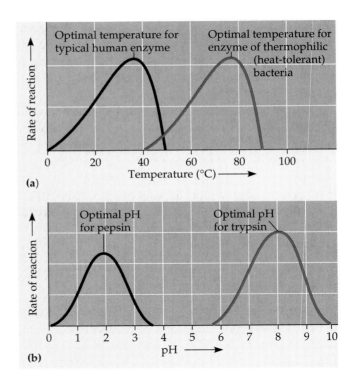

FIGURE 6.13 · **Environmental factors affecting enzymes.** Each enzyme has an optimal **(a)** temperature and **(b)** pH that favor the active conformation of the protein molecule.

In contrast, trypsin, a digestive enzyme residing in the alkaline environment of the intestine, has an optimal pH of 8.

Cofactors

Many enzymes require nonprotein helpers for catalytic activity. These adjuncts, called **cofactors**, may be bound tightly to the active site as permanent residents, or they may bind loosely and reversibly along with the substrate. The cofactors of some enzymes are inorganic, such as the metal atoms zinc, iron, and copper. If the cofactor is an organic molecule, it is more specifically called a **coenzyme**. Most vitamins are coenzymes or raw materials from which coenzymes are made. Cofactors function in various ways, but in all cases they are necessary for catalysis to take place.

Enzyme Inhibitors

Certain chemicals selectively inhibit the action of specific enzymes (FIGURE 6.14). If the inhibitor attaches to the enzyme by covalent bonds, inhibition is usually irreversible. It is reversible, however, if the inhibitor binds by weak bonds.

Some inhibitors resemble the normal substrate molecule and compete for admission into the active site. These mimics, called **competitive inhibitors**, reduce the productivity of enzymes by blocking the substrate from entering active sites. This kind of inhibition is reversible. It can be overcome by

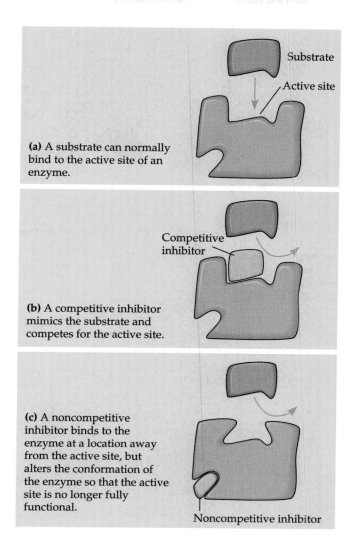

(a) A substrate can normally bind to the active site of an enzyme.

(b) A competitive inhibitor mimics the substrate and competes for the active site.

(c) A noncompetitive inhibitor binds to the enzyme at a location away from the active site, but alters the conformation of the enzyme so that the active site is no longer fully functional.

FIGURE 6.14 ▪ **Enzyme inhibition.**

increasing the concentration of substrate so that as active sites become available, more substrate molecules than inhibitor molecules are around to gain entry to the sites.

So-called **noncompetitive inhibitors** do not directly compete with the substrate at the active site. Instead, they impede enzymatic reactions by binding to another part of the enzyme. This interaction causes the enzyme molecule to change its shape, rendering the active site unreceptive to substrate, or leaving the enzyme less effective at catalyzing the conversion of substrate to product.

Some poisons absorbed from an organism's environment act by inhibiting enzymes. For example, the pesticides DDT and parathion are inhibitors of key enzymes in the nervous system. Many antibiotics are inhibitors of specific enzymes in bacteria. For instance, penicillin blocks the active site of an enzyme that many bacteria use to make their cell walls.

Mentioning enzyme inhibitors that are metabolic poisons may give the impression that enzyme inhibition is generally abnormal and harmful. In fact, selective inhibition and activation of enzymes by molecules naturally present in the cell are essential mechanisms in metabolic control, as we discuss next.

THE CONTROL OF METABOLISM

Chemical chaos would result if all of a cell's metabolic pathways were open simultaneously. Imagine, for example, a substance synthesized by one pathway being immediately broken down by another—the cell would be spinning its metabolic wheels. Actually, a cell tightly regulates its metabolic pathways by controlling when and where its various enzymes are active. Pathways are controlled either by switching on and off the genes that encode specific enzymes (as we will discuss in Unit Three) or, as we discuss here, by regulating the activity of enzymes once they are made.

Metabolic control often depends on allosteric regulation

In many cases, the molecules that naturally regulate enzyme activity in a cell behave something like reversible noncompetitive inhibitors (see FIGURE 6.14c): These regulatory molecules change an enzyme's shape and function by binding to an **allosteric site**, a specific receptor site on some part of the enzyme molecule remote from the active site. The effect may be either inhibition or stimulation of the enzyme's activity.

Allosteric Regulation

Most allosterically regulated enzymes are constructed from two or more polypeptide chains, or subunits. Each subunit has its own active site, and allosteric sites are usually located where subunits are joined (FIGURE 6.15a, p. 96). The entire complex oscillates between two conformational states, one catalytically active and the other inactive. The binding of an activator to an allosteric site stabilizes the conformation that has a functional active site, whereas the binding of an allosteric inhibitor stabilizes the inactive form of the enzyme (FIGURE 6.15b). The areas of contact between the subunits of an allosteric enzyme articulate in such a way that a conformational change in one subunit is transmitted to all others. Through this interaction of subunits, a single activator or inhibitor molecule that binds to one allosteric site will affect the active sites of all subunits.

Because allosteric regulators attach to an enzyme by weak bonds, the activity of the enzyme changes in response to fluctuating concentrations of the regulators. In some cases, an inhibitor and an activator are similar enough in shape to compete for the same allosteric site. For example, some enzymes of catabolic pathways, may have an allosteric site that fits both ATP and AMP (adenosine monophosphate), which the cell routinely derives from ADP. Such enzymes are inhibited by ATP and activated by AMP. This is logical because a major function of catabolism is to regenerate ATP. If ATP production lags behind its use, AMP accumulates and activates key enzymes that speed up catabolism. If the supply of ATP

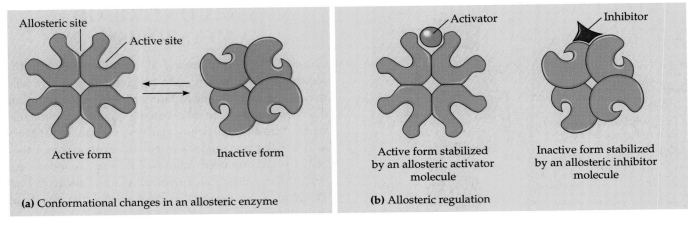

(a) Conformational changes in an allosteric enzyme

(b) Allosteric regulation

FIGURE 6.15 ▪ **Allosteric regulation.** **(a)** Most allosteric enzymes are constructed from two or more polypeptide subunits, each having its own active site. The enzyme oscillates between two conformational states, one active and the other inactive. Remote from the active sites are allosteric sites, specific receptors for regulators of the enzyme, which may be activators or inhibitors. **(b)** Here we see the opposing effects of an allosteric inhibitor and an allosteric activator on the conformation of all four subunits of an enzyme.

exceeds demand, then catabolism slows down as ATP molecules accumulate and compete for allosteric sites. In this way, allosteric enzymes control the rates of key reactions in metabolic pathways.

Feedback Inhibition

The inhibition of an ATP-generating catabolic pathway by the allosteric binding of ATP to an enzyme in the pathway is an example of feedback inhibition, one of the most common methods of metabolic control. **Feedback inhibition** is the switching off of a metabolic pathway by its end-product, which acts as an inhibitor of an enzyme within the pathway. FIGURE 6.16 shows an example of this control mechanism operating on an anabolic pathway. Some cells use this pathway of five steps to synthesize the amino acid isoleucine from threonine, another amino acid. As isoleucine, the end-product of the pathway, accumulates, it slows down its own synthesis by allosterically inhibiting the enzyme for the very first step of the pathway. Feedback inhibition thereby prevents the cell from wasting chemical resources to synthesize more isoleucine than is necessary.

Cooperativity

By a mechanism that resembles allosteric activation, substrate molecules may stimulate the catalytic powers of an enzyme (FIGURE 6.17). Recall that the binding of a substrate to an enzyme induces a favorable change in the shape of the active site (induced fit). If an enzyme has two or more subunits, this interaction with one substrate molecule triggers the same favorable conformational change in all other subunits of the enzyme. Called **cooperativity**, this mechanism amplifies the response of enzymes to substrates: One substrate molecule primes an enzyme to accept additional substrate molecules.

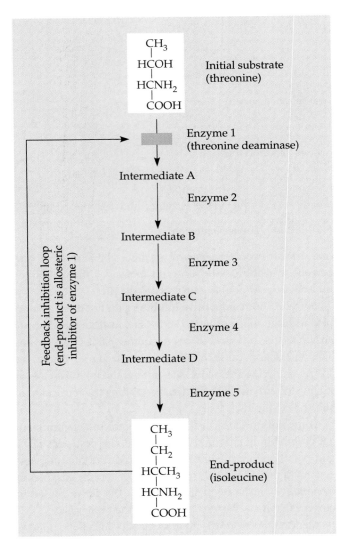

FIGURE 6.16 ▪ **Feedback inhibition.** Many metabolic pathways are switched off by an end-product, which acts as an allosteric inhibitor of an enzyme earlier in the pathway. This example is the pathway for synthesizing the amino acid isoleucine.

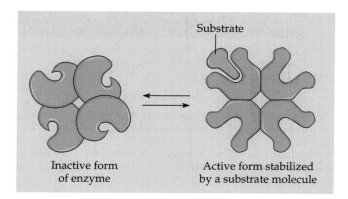

FIGURE 6.17 ▪ **Cooperativity.** In an enzyme molecule with multiple subunits, the binding of one substrate molecule to the active site of one subunit causes all the subunits to assume their active conformation, via the mechanism of induced fit.

The localization of enzymes within a cell helps order metabolism

The cell is not just a bag of chemicals with thousands of different kinds of enzymes and substrates wandering about randomly. Structures within the cell help bring order to metabolic pathways. In some cases, a team of enzymes for several steps of a metabolic pathway is assembled together as a multienzyme complex. The arrangement controls the sequence of reactions, as the product from the first enzyme becomes substrate for the adjacent enzyme in the complex, and so on, until the end-product is released. Some enzymes and enzyme complexes have fixed locations within the cell as structural components of particular membranes. Others are in solution within specific membrane-enclosed eukaryotic organelles, each with its own internal chemical environment. For example, in eukaryotic cells the enzymes for cellular respiration reside within mitochondria (FIGURE 6.18). If the cell had the same number of enzyme molecules for respiration but they were diluted throughout the entire volume of the cell, respiration would be very inefficient.

The structural basis of metabolic order brings us back to the theme with which this unit of chapters began.

The theme of emergent properties is manifest in the chemistry of life: *a review*

Recall that life is organized along a hierarchy of structural levels. With each increase in the level of order, new properties emerge in addition to those of the component parts. In Chapters 2–6 we have dissected the chemistry of life using the strategy of the reductionist. But we have also begun to develop a more integrated view of life as we have seen how properties emerge with increasing order.

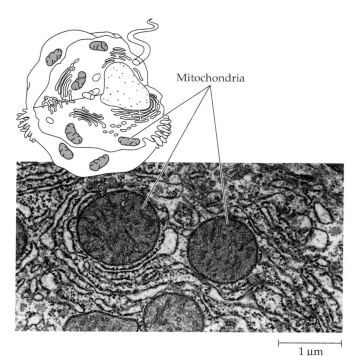

1 μm

FIGURE 6.18 ▪ **Organelles and structural order in metabolism.** Membranes partition a eukaryotic cell into various metabolic compartments, or organelles, each with a corps of enzymes that carry out specific functions. The organelles shown here, called mitochondria, are the sites of cellular respiration (TEM).

We have seen that the peculiar behavior of water, so essential to life on Earth, results from interactions of the water molecules, themselves an ordered arrangement of hydrogen and oxygen atoms. We reduced the great complexity and diversity of organic compounds to the chemical characteristics of carbon, but we also saw that the unique properties of organic compounds are related to the specific structural arrangements of carbon skeletons and their appended functional groups. We learned that small organic molecules are often assembled into giant molecules, but we also discovered that a macromolecule does not behave like a simple composite of its monomers. For example, the unique form and function of a protein are consequences of a hierarchy of primary, secondary, and tertiary structures. And in this chapter we have seen that metabolism, that orderly chemistry that characterizes life, is a concerted interplay of thousands of different kinds of molecules in an organized cell.

By completing our overview of metabolism with an introduction to its structural basis in the compartmentalized cell, we have built a bridge to Unit Two, where we will study the cell's structure and function in more depth. We will maintain our balance between the need to reduce life to a conglomerate of simpler processes and the ultimate satisfaction of viewing those processes in their integrated context.

(with page numbers and key figures)

METABOLISM, ENERGY, AND LIFE

- **The chemistry of life is organized into metabolic pathways (pp. 83–84)** Metabolism is the collection of chemical reactions that occur in an organism. Aided by enzymes, it follows intersecting pathways, which may be catabolic (breaking down complex molecules, releasing energy) or anabolic (building complex molecules, consuming energy).

- **Organisms transform energy (pp. 84–85)** Energy is the capacity to do work by moving matter. A moving object has kinetic energy. Potential energy is stored in the location or structure of matter and includes chemical energy stored in molecular structure. Energy can change form, governed by the laws of thermodynamics.

- **The energy transformations of life are subject to two laws of thermodynamics (pp. 85–86, FIGURE 6.4)** The first, conservation of energy, states that energy cannot be created or destroyed. The second states that when energy changes form, entropy (S), or the disorder of the universe, increases. Matter can become more ordered only if the surroundings become more disordered.

- **Organisms live at the expense of free energy (pp. 86–88, FIGURE 6.5)** A living system's free energy is energy that can do work under cellular conditions. Free energy (G) is related directly to total energy (H) and to entropy (S): $\Delta G = \Delta H - T\Delta S$. Spontaneous changes involve a decrease in free energy ($-\Delta G$). In an exergonic (spontaneous) chemical reaction, the products have less free energy than the reactants ($-\Delta G$). Endergonic (nonspontaneous) reactions require an input of energy ($+\Delta G$). In cellular metabolism, exergonic reactions power endergonic reactions (energy coupling). The addition of starting materials and the removal of end-products prevent metabolism from reaching equilibrium.

- **ATP powers cellular work by coupling exergonic reactions to endergonic reactions (pp. 88–91, FIGURE 6.6)** ATP is the cell's energy shuttle. Hydrolysis of one of its phosphate bonds releases ADP, inorganic phosphate, and free energy. ATP drives endergonic reactions by transfer of the phosphate group to specific reactants, making them more reactive. In this way, cells can carry out work, such as movement and anabolism. Catabolic pathways, such as cellular respiration, drive the regeneration of ATP from ADP and phosphate.

ENZYMES

6.1 **Enzymes speed up metabolic reactions by lowering energy barriers (pp. 91–92, FIGURE 6.10)** Enzymes, which are proteins, are biological catalysts. They speed reactions by lowering activation energy (E_A), so bonds can break at the moderate temperatures of most organisms.

- **Enzymes are substrate-specific (pp. 92–93, FIGURE 6.11)** Each type of enzyme has a unique active site that combines specifically with its substrate, the reactant molecule on which it acts. The enzyme changes shape slightly when it binds the substrate (induced fit).

- **The active site is an enzyme's catalytic center (pp. 93–94, FIGURE 6.12)** The active site can lower activation energy by orienting substrates correctly, straining their bonds, and providing a suitable microenvironment.

- **A cell's physical and chemical environment affects enzyme activity (pp. 94–95, FIGURES 6.13–6.14)** As proteins, enzymes are sensitive to conditions that influence their three-dimensional structure. Each has an optimal temperature and pH. Cofactors are ions or molecules required for some enzymes to function. Coenzymes are organic cofactors. Inhibitors reduce enzyme function. A competitive inhibitor binds to the active site, while a noncompetitive inhibitor binds to a different site.

THE CONTROL OF METABOLISM

- **Metabolic control often depends on allosteric regulation (pp. 95–96, FIGURES 6.15–6.17)** Some enzymes change shape when regulatory molecules, either activators or inhibitors, bind to specific allosteric sites. In feedback inhibition, the end-product of a metabolic pathway allosterically inhibits the enzyme for an early step in the pathway. In cooperativity, a substrate molecule binding to one active site of a multi-subunit enzyme activates the other subunits.

- **The localization of enzymes within a cell helps order metabolism (p. 97, FIGURE 6.18)** Some enzymes are grouped into complexes, some are incorporated into membranes, and others are contained in organelles.

- **The theme of emergent properties is manifest in the chemistry of life: *a review* (p. 97)** Increasing levels of organization result in the emergence of new properties. Organization is the key to the chemistry of life.

1. Choose the pair of terms that correctly completes this sentence: Catabolism is to anabolism as _____ is to _____.
   a. exergonic; spontaneous
   b. exergonic; endergonic
   c. free energy; entropy
   d. work; energy
   e. entropy; order

2. Most cells cannot harness heat in order to perform work because
   a. heat is not a form of energy
   b. cells do not have much heat; they are relatively cool
   c. temperature is usually uniform throughout a cell
   d. there are no mechanisms in nature that can use heat to do work
   e. heat denatures enzymes

3. According to the first law of thermodynamics,
   a. matter can be neither created nor destroyed
   b. energy is conserved in all processes
   c. all processes increase the order of the universe
   d. systems rich in energy are intrinsically stable
   e. the universe constantly loses energy because of friction

4. Which of the following metabolic processes can occur without a net influx of energy from some other process?
   a. $ADP + \textcircled{P}_i \longrightarrow ATP + H_2O$
   b. $C_6H_{12}O_6 + 6\,O_2 \longrightarrow 6\,CO_2 + 6\,H_2O$
   c. $6\,CO_2 + 6\,H_2O \longrightarrow C_6H_{12}O_6 + 6\,O_2$
   d. amino acids $\longrightarrow$ protein
   e. glucose + fructose $\longrightarrow$ sucrose

5. If an enzyme has been noncompetitively inhibited
   a. the ΔG for the reaction it catalyzes will always be negative
   b. the active site will be occupied by the inhibitor molecule
   c. increasing the substrate concentration will increase the inhibition

d. a higher activation energy will be necessary to initiate the reaction

e. the inhibitor molecule may be chemically unrelated to the substrate

6. If an enzyme solution is saturated with substrate, the most effective way to obtain an even faster yield of products would be to

a. add more of the enzyme

b. heat the solution to 90°C

c. add more substrate

d. add an allosteric inhibitor

e. add a noncompetitive inhibitor

7. An enzyme accelerates a metabolic reaction by

a. altering the overall free-energy change for the reaction

b. making an endergonic reaction occur spontaneously

c. lowering the activation energy

d. pushing the reaction away from equilibrium

e. making the substrate molecule more stable

8. Some bacteria are metabolically active in hot springs because

a. they are able to maintain an internal temperature much cooler than that of the surrounding water

b. the high temperatures facilitate active metabolism without the need of catalysis

c. their enzymes have high optimal temperatures

d. their enzymes are insensitive to temperature

e. they use molecules other than proteins as their main catalysts

9. Which of the following characteristics is not associated with allosteric regulation of an enzyme's activity?

a. A molecule mimics the substrate and competes for the active site.

b. A naturally occurring molecule stabilizes a catalytically active conformation.

c. Regulatory molecules bind to a site remote from the active site.

d. Inhibitor and activator molecules may compete with one another.

e. The enzyme usually has a quaternary structure.

10. In the following branched metabolic pathway, a dotted arrow with a minus sign symbolizes inhibition of a metabolic step by an end-product:

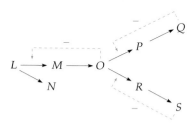

Which reaction would prevail if both Q and S are present in the cell in high concentrations?

a. $L \longrightarrow M$

b. $M \longrightarrow O$

c. $L \longrightarrow N$

d. $O \longrightarrow P$

e. $R \longrightarrow S$

CHALLENGE QUESTION

A particular enzyme has an optimal temperature of 37°C and begins to denature at 45°C. During denaturation, entropy increases (the protein loses much of its organization). The protein also increases its energy content (energy must be absorbed from the surroundings to break the numerous weak bonds that reinforce the native conformation). Thus, for denaturation, ΔS and ΔH are both positive. Using the free-energy equation ($\Delta G = \Delta H - T\Delta S$), explain why denaturation becomes spontaneous at a certain temperature.

SCIENCE, TECHNOLOGY, AND SOCIETY

As mandated by the 1996 Food Quality Protection Act, the EPA has announced its intention to evaluate the safety of the most commonly used organophosphate insecticides. In agriculture, the most frequently used organophosphates account for half of the 58 million pounds applied annually nationwide. Organophosphates typically interfere with nerve transmission by inhibiting the enzymes that degrade the transmitter molecules that diffuse from one neuron to another. Noxious insects are not uniquely susceptible; humans and other vertebrates can be affected as well. Thus the use of pesticides creates some health risks. As a consumer, what levels of risk are you willing to accept in exchange for an abundant and affordable food supply? Is it prudent to expect "a reasonable certainty that no harm will result from pesticide exposure"? What other facts would you like to know about this situation before you could defend your opinion?

FURTHER READING

Adams, S. "No Way Back." *New Scientist,* October 22, 1994. An entertaining article about the second law of thermodynamics.

Becker, W. M., J. B. Reece, and M. F. Poenie. *The World of the Cell,* 3rd ed. Menlo Park, CA: Benjamin/Cummings, 1996. Provides a lucid explanation of cellular energetics and enzymes in Chapters 5 and 6.

Deeth, R. "Chemical Choreography." *New Scientist,* July 5, 1997. Computer modeling is being used to study how enzymes work in the cell.

Harold, F. M. *The Vital Force: A Study of Bioenergetics.* New York: W. H. Freeman, 1986. A challenging but clear introduction to energy and life in Chapters 1–3.

Kauffman, S. A. *The Origins of Order.* New York: Oxford University Press, 1993. An influential book applying thermodynamics and chaos theory to life.

Lewin, R. "A Simple Matter of Complexity." *New Scientist,* February 5, 1994. Our interpretation of life's history depends in part on how we define complexity.

Mathews, C. K., and K. E. van Holde. *Biochemistry,* 2nd ed. Menlo Park, CA: Benjamin/Cummings, 1996. An introduction to enzymes and metabolism in Chapters 10 and 12.

WEB LINKS

Visit the special edition of *The Biology Place* for BIOLOGY, Fifth Edition, at http://www.biology.com/campbell. Go to Chapter 6 for online resources, including learning activities, practice exams, and links to the following web sites:

"About Temperature"
This site clearly explains temperature and heat in an interesting manner.

"Elementary Thermodynamics and Biochemical Systems"
Helpful lecture notes from the University of Illinois.

"The Food Zone"
A lively site that students will find useful for reviewing macromolecules, energy transformations, enzymes, ATP, and related topics.

"Activation Energy and Enzymes"
Graphic explanation of the role of enzymes in lowering the activation energy of reactions.

THE CELL

Bruce Alberts first experienced scientific research by volunteering to work in a lab as an undergraduate. He went on to build a successful career investigating DNA chemistry, first at Princeton and then at the University of California, San Francisco, where he is a professor of biochemistry. Currently on leave from UCSF, Dr. Alberts is serving as president of the National Academy of Sciences in Washington, D.C. Under his leadership, the Academy has made the improvement of science education a top priority. Many biology students will have a chance to meet Bruce Alberts again if they use his classic text, Molecular Biology of the Cell.

How did you start in science?

I went to a large public high school in Illinois and really enjoyed my chemistry class. That's probably how I got so interested in science, but I don't think I really knew what science was. I do remember going to a career night at the high school where they invited parents and others working in various careers to come and talk about their occupations. I looked at all the occupations on the list that might use chemistry or science and there were two. One was medicine and one was chemical engineering, so I went to those two talks and decided I didn't want to be a chemical engineer, but thought maybe I would become a doctor. From my perspective as a 17-year-old, I didn't have any conception that there was an occupation of "scientist" for which you could get paid. I subsequently went to college at Harvard, where I took a lot of science courses because I was pre-med. But I still didn't get any hint from these courses about what doing science might be like.

So when did you begin to see that you could become a scientist?

During my junior year, Jacques Fresco, a postdoctoral researcher who was my tutor, asked me if I wanted to work in his lab during the summer. Since my girlfriend, now my wife, was going to Europe that summer, I had nothing else to do. I worked very hard all summer in his laboratory. The lab group worked on nucleic acids, and my project involved deciphering how errors in pairing between bases in DNA affect the helical structure of the DNA. I actually made a discovery that people were excited about, and the experience was completely different from the laboratory work that I had done in courses. We also used this discovery to analyze RNA— specifically, how helical structure forms due to base-pairing

between certain regions of an RNA strand. So my research as an undergraduate that summer led to two papers, one published in *Nature*, the other in *Proceedings of the National Academy of Sciences*. Given the success of that one summer of work, and since it was so exciting to do this stuff, why go to medical school? I didn't even apply. I stayed at Harvard and did graduate work for a PhD degree.

How did your parents react to that?

I think parents like their children to choose safe careers. Being a doctor had a good, solid image with my father, while it seemed like

INTERVIEW

BRUCE ALBERTS

being a scientist had a shakier future. But although my parents were a little surprised, they were supportive.

Did your graduate work go as well as your undergraduate research projects?

Actually, my research career has been a series of ups and downs. My success as an undergraduate researcher gave me a false view of science—that it is easy. So I was extremely naive when I went to graduate school. My major professor, Paul Doty, told me I could pick my own research project. Overconfident, I thought I might as well tackle something very important, so I decided that I would solve the genetic code, which had not been deciphered at that point. I got the idea when I took a discussion course in molecular biology and we had to write a term paper proposing experiments. My experiments were my idea of how you might solve the genetic code using a

method that turned out to be very cumbersome and would never have worked. But I got an A on the term paper, and I got excited about my idea. This is a very dangerous thing in science, when you get too excited about your own ideas! So when I started my research for the PhD, I tried to solve the genetic code using my term paper as the outline for my experimental plan. I spent three years on experiments that really didn't have a prayer of working.

What was wrong with your plan?

Basically, the problem was that I did this long series of experiments to solve the genetic code without first doing the control experiment that would have told me that the plan couldn't work. About the time I realized the problem, Francis Crick visited our group at Harvard and I explained to him what I had been trying to do. I'm sure Francis Crick doesn't remember this at all, but it is burned in my memory. As soon as I started telling him what my plan was, before I even got to the punch line that it didn't work, Crick asked if I had done the very control experiment that I had left out! I was really impressed that he saw the problem immediately, when it had taken me three or four years to see it. So, I had a lot of trouble with my thesis research, but I was able to shift to a different project to complete my PhD. And, most importantly, I didn't make the same type of mistake again.

In the medical center environment of UCSF, you and your colleagues are at an intersection of basic research in cell biology and biotechnology. How do you see the science-technology relationship?

I've actually lived through the explosive revolution that led to the biotech industry. When I first arrived at UCSF in 1976, Herbert Boyer invited my wife and me over for dinner, and during a walk he told me how he was going to start this company, Genentech. He asked if I would like to be involved, and I said no. I was too busy, and like most academics at the time, I wasn't interested in starting companies. Herb was unusual in that he was comfortable with the idea of applying what we knew in commercial ventures. But most of us also had not seen the potential benefits from technology based on gene cloning and other methods in molecular biology—how the different techniques could be combined to produce useful things for society. But here it was, this ability to make commercial quantities of rare proteins, such as human growth factors. The technology has revolutionized the pharma-

ceutical industry and has improved human health on a scale that I think even surprises Herb Boyer and the other pioneers of biotechnology. All that knowledge came from the basic research of scientists trying to figure out how cells work. In turn, basic biological research is benefiting from new knowledge in chemistry combined with engineering breakthroughs, such as machines that can sequence DNA very rapidly. As this illustrates, the whole enterprise of science builds up units of knowledge that can be combined in many ways. The progress of science and technology is ever accelerating; the more things you know, the more ways you can combine that knowledge.

Can you give an example of how such a synthesis of existing knowledge could give us a new breakthrough in cell biology?

We know a lot of facts about what is called cell signaling. We know that various growth factors and hormones bind to the outside of a cell and send signals inside. Right now, all the steps and variations make cell signaling look incredibly complicated, like a complete jumble that doesn't make sense. There seem to be too many signal pathways, with the complexity compounded by cross-talk between the pathways. We have lots of facts, but we don't yet understand the network properties of cell signaling. We can understand every piece of the puzzle of cell signaling, but until we understand how it all fits together in a network of communication and control, the whole picture won't come together and seem simpler. Solving the problem demands different ways of thinking about cells as complex networks, and I think this provides a role for new kinds of people in this field—perhaps people who would otherwise have gone into physics. I'm sure when we understand these cellular networks, we'll say, "How were we so stupid not to see that this is what the cell is doing?"

Sometimes these signaling and response systems run amok, with cancer being an important example. What are some of your thoughts about the cell biology of cancer?

I think this is another case where we already have a lot of knowledge but need to start putting the facts together in new ways. We now know that for a normal cell to become a cancerous cell, it has to be disturbed in a large number of different ways. A lot of check points have evolved in our cells, safety mechanisms that allow large multicellular organisms to grow and develop without the individual cells being selfish and growing out of control. Cancer therefore requires that several different defects occur in the same line of cells. For that to happen, there must be some breakdown in the cell's DNA metabolism—in its ability to repair DNA damage, for example. Different tumors can be caused by different defects in DNA metabolism. And yet the chemotherapy used to treat cancer is usually a kitchen-sink

approach, a mixture of drugs. As we learn more about these defects in DNA metabolism, we'll be able to screen a particular tumor cell for the type of defect that it contains, and then take a much more tailored approach to chemotherapy. We will soon see some major breakthroughs in both our understanding and treatment of cancer. If I wasn't in my present job, that's exactly what I'd be working on right now.

Speaking of your present job, tell us a little about the National Academy of Sciences.

The National Academy of Sciences was chartered by Abraham Lincoln in 1863 to be an honorary society of scientists. The charter we received is unusual, because it requires the members elected to this honorary society to advise the government, without compensation, on matters involving science and technology. For example, committees set up by the Academy now do a lot of work on environmental questions, such as, "What is a wetland, and why should we protect wetlands?" "What is the best strategy for cleaning up radioactive waste that has accumulated around the nuclear weapons sites that are now being dismantled all over the world?" As another example, in 1991 the federal government asked us, in response to an earlier request by the governors of all 50 states, to facilitate the development of the first-ever national standards for science education in our nation's elementary and secondary schools.

What advice do you have for students with aspirations for research or other careers that involve science?

First, I think it's important for science students to get a strong background in the fundamentals of chemistry, physics, and biology. But there is much more to being a successful scientist than that. Enthusiasm and persistence are so important. There are a lot of times when you're doing science that things go wrong, as you've heard from my failures. Of the 30 or so graduate students I've had

during my career, the most successful were the ones who persevered and worked even harder when their research wasn't going well. Otherwise, you never get past the rough spots. To succeed in science, you also have to get satisfaction from making progress in small steps. We don't make big discoveries every day. Sometimes it's a victory just to get a particular technique to work a little better. The only way to find out if you're good at science and enjoy it is to work at it for a while. And I don't think we're very good at predicting who will succeed in science. It depends a lot more on creativity, imagination, and persistence than on how many facts you can recall on an exam.

What if a student likes biology or some other science as an undergraduate major, but doesn't want to go to medical school or become a research scientist?

I think far too many science professors still have the idea that their most important teaching goal is to produce more scientists. That's one reason to teach science, but a much bigger reason is that we need more people with science backgrounds in many fields, not just in research careers. For instance, we need more people with science backgrounds in industry, in journalism, in government, and certainly as teachers in elementary and secondary schools. There are so many ways to use a science background successfully without being a research scientist or professor. I encourage students to keep an open mind about how they can put their science abilities to work in different careers. And I urge science professors to become much more inclusive in how they define the science community—to welcome not just academic scientists and researchers as part of their world, but the many others who are using their science education to improve schools, businesses, government, and other institutions.

Spreading both science and its values throughout our society has become the central mission of the Academy. Please visit us at www.nas.edu

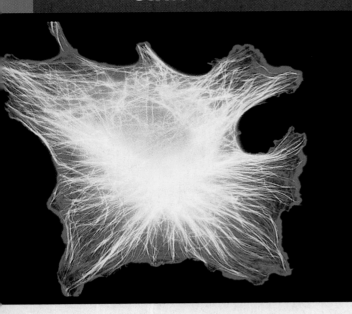

CHAPTER 7

A TOUR OF THE CELL

How We Study Cells
- Microscopes provide windows to the world of the cell
- Cell biologists can isolate organelles to study their functions

A Panoramic View of the Cell
- Prokaryotic and eukaryotic cells differ in size and complexity
- Internal membranes compartmentalize the functions of a eukaryotic cell

The Nucleus and Ribosomes
- The nucleus contains a eukaryotic cell's genetic library
- Ribosomes build a cell's proteins

The Endomembrane System
- The endoplasmic reticulum manufactures membranes and performs many other biosynthetic functions
- The Golgi apparatus finishes, sorts, and ships cell products
- Lysosomes are digestive compartments
- Vacuoles have diverse functions in cell maintenance

Other Membranous Organelles
- Peroxisomes consume oxygen in various metabolic functions
- Mitochondria and chloroplasts are the main energy transformers of cells

The Cytoskeleton
- Providing structural support to the cell, the cytoskeleton also functions in cell motility and regulation

Cell Surfaces and Junctions
- Plant cells are encased by cell walls
- The extracellular matrix (ECM) of animal cells functions in support, adhesion, movement, and development
- Intercellular junctions help integrate cells into higher levels of structure and function

The cell is as fundamental to biology as the atom is to chemistry: All organisms are made of cells. In the hierarchy of biological organization, the cell is the simplest collection of matter that can live. Indeed, there are diverse forms of life existing as single-celled organisms. More complex organisms, including plants and animals, are multicellular; their bodies are cooperatives of many kinds of specialized cells that could not survive for long on their own. However, even when they are arranged into higher levels of organization, such as tissues and organs, cells can be singled out as the organism's basic units of structure and function. The contraction of muscle cells moves your eyes as you read this sentence; when you decide to turn this page, nerve cells will transmit that decision from your brain to the muscle cells of your hand. Everything an organism does occurs fundamentally at the cellular level. This chapter introduces the microscopic world of the cell.

This book takes a thematic approach to the study of life, and the cell is a microcosmic model of many of the themes introduced in Chapter 1. We will see that life at the cellular level arises from structural order, reinforcing the themes of emergent properties and the correlation between structure and function. For example, the movement of an animal cell depends on an intricate interplay of structures that make up a cellular skeleton (visible in the light micrograph on this page of a cell called a fibroblast). Another recurring theme in biology is the interaction of organisms with their environment. Cells sense and respond to environmental fluctuations. As open systems, they continuously exchange both materials and energy with their surroundings. And keep in mind the one biological theme that unifies all others: evolution. All cells are related by their descent from earlier cells, but they have been modified in various ways during the long evolutionary history of life on Earth. For example, if one unicellular organism lives in fresh water and another inhabits the sea, we can expect these cells to be somewhat differently equipped as a result of their divergent adaptations to disparate environments.

HOW WE STUDY CELLS

Perhaps the greatest obstacle to becoming acquainted with the cell is imagining how something too small to be seen by the unaided eye can be so complex. How can cell biologists possibly dissect so small a package to investigate its inner workings? Before we actually tour the cell, it will be helpful to learn how cells are studied.

Microscopes provide windows to the world of the cell

The evolution of a science often parallels the invention of instruments that extend human senses to new limits. The discovery and early study of cells progressed with the invention and improvement of microscopes in the seventeenth century.

Microscopes of various types are still indispensable tools for the study of cells.

The microscopes first used by Renaissance scientists, as well as the microscopes you are likely to use in the laboratory, are all **light microscopes (LMs)**. Visible light is passed through the specimen and then through glass lenses. The lenses refract (bend) the light in such a way that the image of the specimen is magnified as it is projected into the eye. (See Appendix Four at the back of the book, which diagrams microscope structure.)

Two important values in microscopy are magnification and resolving power, or resolution. Magnification is how much larger the object appears compared to its real size. **Resolving power** is a measure of the clarity of the image; it is the minimum distance two points can be separated and still be distinguished as two separate points. For example, what appears to the unaided eye as one star in the sky may be resolved as twin stars with a telescope.

Just as the resolving power of the human eye is limited, the resolving power of telescopes and microscopes is limited. Microscopes can be designed to magnify objects as much as desired, but the light microscope can never resolve detail finer than about 0.2 μm, the size of a small bacterium (FIGURE 7.1). This resolution is limited by the wavelength of the visible light used to illuminate the specimen. Light microscopes can magnify effectively to about 1000 times the size of the actual specimen; greater magnifications increase blurriness. Most of the improvements in light microscopy since the beginning of the twentieth century have involved new methods for enhancing contrast, which makes the details that can be resolved stand out better to the eye (TABLE 7.1, p. 104).

Although cells were discovered by Robert Hooke in 1665, the geography of the cell was largely uncharted until the past few decades. Most subcellular structures, or **organelles**, are too small to be resolved by the light microscope. Cell biology advanced rapidly in the 1950s with the introduction of the electron microscope. Instead of using visible light, the **electron microscope (EM)** focuses a beam of electrons through the specimen. Resolving power is inversely related to the wavelength of radiation a microscope uses, and electron beams have wavelengths much shorter than the wavelengths of visible light. Modern electron microscopes can theoretically achieve a resolution of about 0.1 nanometer (nm), but the practical limit for biological structures is generally only about 2 nm—still a hundredfold improvement over the light microscope. Biologists use the term *cell ultrastructure* to refer to a cell's anatomy as resolved by an electron microscope.

There are two basic types of electron microscopes: the **transmission electron microscope (TEM)** and the **scanning electron microscope (SEM)**. The TEM aims an electron beam through a thin section of the specimen, similar to the way a light microscope transmits light through a slide. However, instead of using glass lenses, which are opaque to electrons, the TEM uses electromagnets as lenses to focus and magnify

the image by bending the paths of the electrons. The image is ultimately focused onto a screen for viewing or onto photographic film. To enhance contrast in the image, very thin

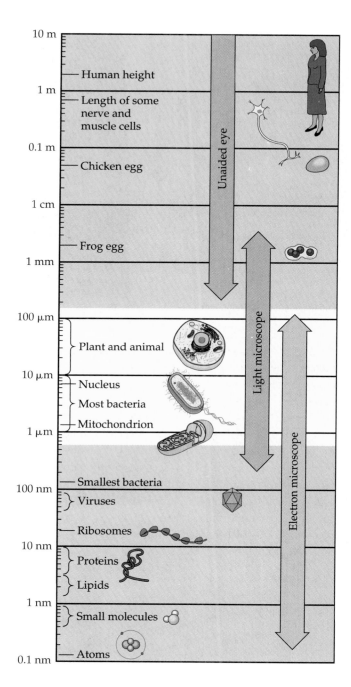

MEASUREMENTS
1 centimeter (cm) = 10^{-2} meter (m) = 0.4 inch
1 millimeter (mm) = 10^{-3} m
1 micrometer (μm) = 10^{-3} mm = 10^{-6} m
1 nanometer (nm) = 10^{-3} μm = 10^{-9} m

FIGURE 7.1 ▪ The size range of cells. Most cells are between 1 and 100 μm in diameter and are therefore visible only under a microscope. Notice that the scale is logarithmic to accommodate the range of sizes shown. Starting at the top of the scale with 10 meters and going down, each reference measurement along the left side marks a *tenfold* decrease in size.

Table 7.1 ■ Different Types of Light Microscopy: A Comparison

TYPE OF MICROSCOPY	LIGHT MICROGRAPHS OF HUMAN CHEEK EPITHELIAL CELLS		TYPE OF MICROSCOPY
Brightfield (unstained specimen): Passes light directly through specimen; unless cell is naturally pigmented or artificially stained, image has little contrast.	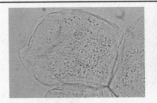	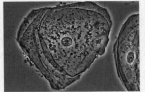	**Phase-contrast:** Enhances contrast in unstained cells by amplifying variations in density within specimen; especially useful for examining living, unpigmented cells.
Brightfield (stained specimen): Staining with various dyes enhances contrast, but most staining procedures require that cells be fixed (preserved).	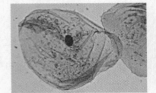		**Differential-interference-contrast (Nomarski):** Like phase-contrast microscopy, it uses optical modifications to exaggerate differences in density.
Fluorescence: Shows the locations of specific molecules in the cell. Fluorescent substances absorb short wavelength, ultraviolet radiation and emit longer wavelength, visible light. The fluorescing molecules may occur naturally in the specimen but more often are made by tagging the molecules of interest with fluorescent dyes or antibodies.		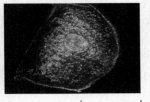 50 μm	**Confocal:** Uses lasers and special optics for "optical sectioning." Only those regions within a narrow depth of focus are imaged. Light at regions above and below the selected plane of view appear black rather than blurry.

sections of preserved cells are stained with atoms of heavy metals, which attach at certain places in the cells. Cell biologists use the TEM mainly to study the internal ultrastructure of cells (FIGURE 7.2a).

The SEM is especially useful for detailed study of the surface of the specimen (FIGURE 7.2b). The electron beam scans the surface of the sample, which is usually coated with a thin film of gold. The beam excites electrons on the sample's surface, and these secondary electrons are collected and focused onto a screen. The result is an image of the topography of the specimen. An important attribute of the SEM is its great depth of field, which results in an image that appears three-dimensional.

Electron microscopes reveal many organelles that are impossible to resolve with the light microscope. But the light microscope offers advantages, especially for the study of live cells. A disadvantage of electron microscopy is that the methods used to prepare the specimen kill cells. Also, they may introduce artifacts, structural features seen in micrographs that do not exist in the living cell. (Artifacts can occur in light microscopy, too.)

Microscopes are the most important tools of cytology, the study of cell structure. But simply describing the diverse organelles within the cell reveals little about their function. Modern cell biology developed from an integration of cytology with biochemistry, the study of the molecules and chemical

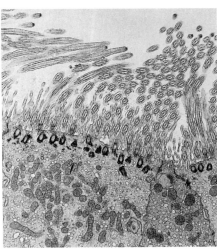

(a) TEM ⊢ 1 μm

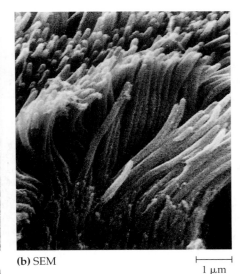

(b) SEM ⊢ 1 μm

FIGURE 7.2 ■ Electron micrographs: photographs taken with electron microscopes. (a) This micrograph, taken with a transmission electron microscope (TEM), profiles a thin section of part of a cell from a rabbit trachea (windpipe), revealing its ultrastructure. **(b)** The scanning electron microscope (SEM) produces a three-dimensional image of the surface of the same type of cell. Both micrographs show motile organelles called cilia. Beating of the cilia that line the windpipe helps move inhaled debris upward toward the pharynx (throat).

Throughout this book, micrographs are identified by the type of microscopy: LM for a light micrograph, TEM for a transmission electron micrograph, and SEM for a scanning electron micrograph.

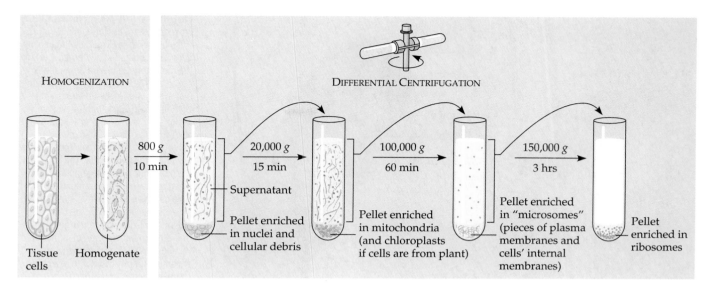

HOMOGENIZATION

DIFFERENTIAL CENTRIFUGATION

800 g
10 min

20,000 g
15 min

100,000 g
60 min

150,000 g
3 hrs

Tissue cells

Homogenate

Supernatant

Pellet enriched in nuclei and cellular debris

Pellet enriched in mitochondria (and chloroplasts if cells are from plant)

Pellet enriched in "microsomes" (pieces of plasma membranes and cells' internal membranes)

Pellet enriched in ribosomes

FIGURE 7.3 ▪ **Cell fractionation.** Disrupted cells are centrifuged at various speeds and durations to isolate components of different sizes. The process begins with homogenization, the disruption of a tissue and its cells with the help of such instruments as kitchen blenders or ultrasound devices. The homogenate, a soupy mixture of organelles, bits of membrane, and molecules from the broken cells, is then fractionated by a series of spins in a centrifuge. After each centrifugation, the unpelleted portion, or supernatant, is decanted and centrifuged again, at a higher speed. By determining which cell fractions are associated with particular metabolic processes, those functions can be tied to certain organelles.

processes of metabolism. A biochemical approach called cell fractionation has been particularly important in cell biology.

Cell biologists can isolate organelles to study their functions

The goal of **cell fractionation** is to take cells apart, separating the major organelles so that their individual functions can be studied (FIGURE 7.3). The instrument used to fractionate cells is the centrifuge, a merry-go-round for test tubes capable of spinning at various speeds. The most powerful machines, called **ultracentrifuges**, can spin as fast as 80,000 revolutions per minute (rpm) and apply forces on particles of up to 500,000 times the force of gravity (500,000 g).

Fractionation begins with homogenization, the disruption of cells. The objective is to break the cells apart without severely damaging their organelles. Spinning the soupy homogenate in a centrifuge separates the parts of the cell into two fractions: the pellet, consisting of the larger structures that become packed at the bottom of the test tube; and the supernatant, consisting of smaller parts of the cell suspended in the liquid above the pellet. The supernatant is decanted into another tube and centrifuged again. The process is repeated, increasing the speed with each step, collecting smaller and smaller components of the homogenized cells in successive pellets.

Cell fractionation enables the researcher to prepare specific components of cells in bulk quantity in order to study their composition and functions. By following this approach, biologists have been able to assign various functions of the cell to the different organelles, a task that would be far more difficult with intact cells. For example, one cellular fraction collected by centrifugation has enzymes that function in the metabolic process known as cellular respiration. The electron microscope reveals this fraction to be very rich in the organelles called mitochondria. This evidence helped cell biologists determine that mitochondria are the sites of cellular respiration. Cytology and biochemistry complement each other in correlating cellular structure and function.

A PANORAMIC VIEW OF THE CELL

Every organism is composed of one of two structurally different types of cells: prokaryotic cells or eukaryotic cells. Only the bacteria and archaea have prokaryotic cells. Protists, plants, fungi, and animals are all eukaryotes.

Prokaryotic and eukaryotic cells differ in size and complexity

A major difference between prokaryotic and eukaryotic cells is indicated by their names. The word *prokaryote* is from the Greek *pro,* "before," and *karyon,* "kernel," referring here to the nucleus. The **prokaryotic cell** has no nucleus (FIGURE 7.4, p. 106). Its genetic material (DNA) is concentrated in a region called the **nucleoid,** but no membrane separates this region from the rest of the cell. In contrast, the eukaryotic cell (Gr. *eu,*

7.1

This symbol links topics in the text to interactive exercises in the CD-ROM that accompanies the book. The number indicates the appropriate activity in the CD.

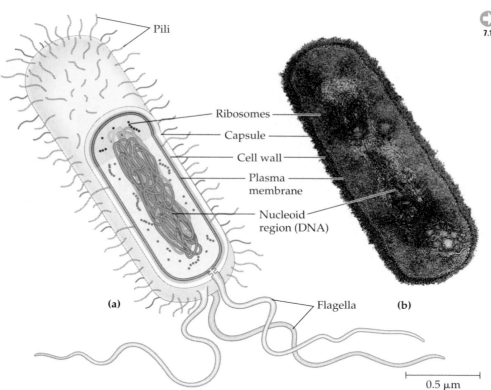

Pili

Ribosomes

Capsule

Cell wall

Plasma membrane

Nucleoid region (DNA)

(a)

Flagella

(b)

0.5 μm

FIGURE 7.4 · A prokaryotic cell. Prokaryotes are bacteria, including cyanobacteria. **(a)** The drawing depicts a typical rod-shaped bacterium. Lacking the membrane-enclosed organelles of a eukaryote, the prokaryote is much simpler in structure. The area where the DNA is located is called the nucleoid region, and no membrane separates the DNA from the rest of the cell. A prokaryote has many ribosomes, where proteins are synthesized. The border of the cell is the plasma membrane. Outside the plasma membrane are a fairly rigid cell wall and often an outer capsule, usually jellylike. Some bacteria have flagella (locomotion organelles), pili (attachment structures), or both projecting from their surface. **(b)** This electron micrograph shows a thin section through the bacterium *Bacillus coagulans* (TEM).

"true," and *karyon*) has a true nucleus enclosed by a membranous nuclear envelope. The entire region between the nucleus and the membrane bounding the cell is called the **cytoplasm**. It consists of a semifluid medium called the **cytosol**, in which are located organelles of specialized form and function, most of them absent in prokaryotic cells. Thus the presence or absence of a true nucleus is just one example of the disparity in struc-

tural complexity between the two types of cells. Prokaryotic cells will be described in detail in Chapters 18 and 27, and the possible evolutionary relationships between the two types of cells will be discussed in Chapter 28. Most of the discussion of cell structure that follows in this chapter applies to eukaryotes.

Size is a general feature of cell structure that relates to function. The logistics of carrying out metabolism set limits

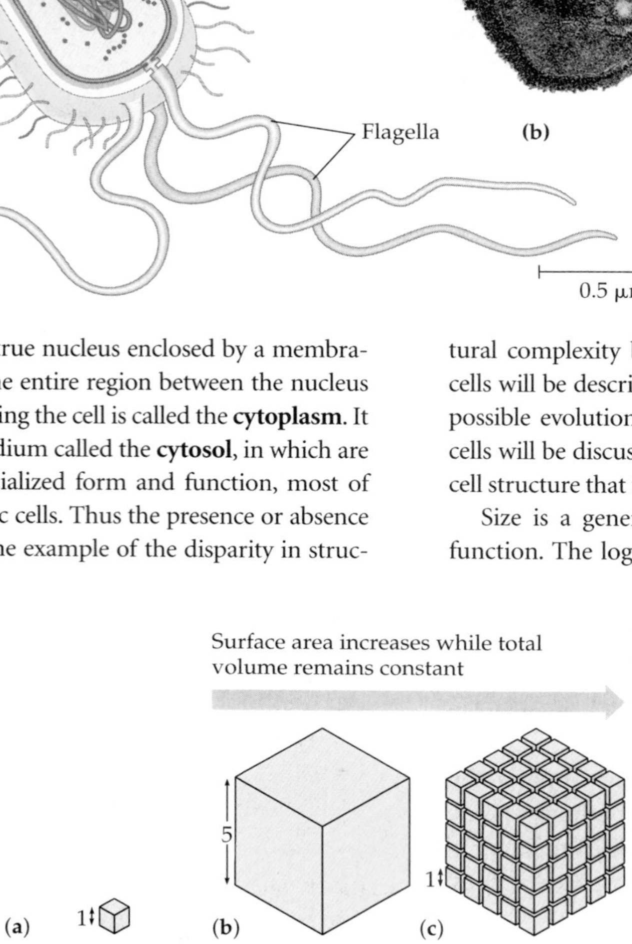

Surface area increases while total volume remains constant

5

1

1

(a)   (b)   (c)

	(a)	(b)	(c)
Total surface area (height × width × number of sides × number of boxes)	6	150	750
Total volume (height × width × length × number of boxes)	1	125	125
Surface-area-to-volume ratio (area ÷ volume)	6	1.2	6

FIGURE 7.5 · Why are most cells microscopic? In this diagram, cells are represented as boxes. **(a)** In arbitrary units of length, this small cell measures 1 on each side. We can calculate the cell's surface area (in square units), volume (in cubic units), and surface-area-to-volume ratio. **(b)** As the size of the cell increases to 5 units of length per side, the ratio of surface area to volume decreases compared to the smaller cell. Rates of chemical exchange with the extracellular environment might be inadequate to maintain the cell because most of its cytoplasm is relatively far from the outer membrane. **(c)** By dividing the large cell into many smaller cells, we can restore a surface-area-to-volume ratio that can serve each cell's need for acquiring nutrients and expelling waste products. These geometric relationships explain why most cells are microscopic, and why larger organisms do not generally have *larger* cells than smaller organisms, but *more* cells.

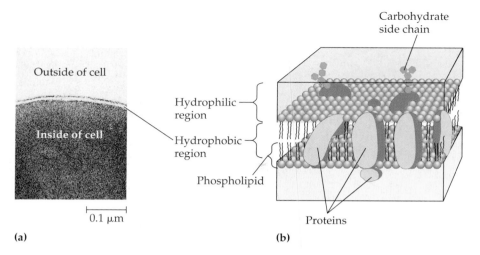

Outside of cell

Inside of cell

0.1 μm

(a)

Carbohydrate
side chain

Hydrophilic
region

Hydrophobic
region

Phospholipid

Proteins

(b)

FIGURE 7.6 ▪ The plasma membrane. **(a)** In electron micrographs of sufficient magnification, the plasma membrane appears as a pair of dark bands separated by a light band. Shown here is the membrane of a red blood cell (TEM). **(b)** The plasma membrane and the various internal membranes of cells consist of a double layer (bilayer) of phospholipids with proteins of diverse functions attached to or embedded in it. (See Chapter 5 to review the dual hydrophilic/hydrophobic behavior of phospholipids.) The specific functions of the plasma membrane and of the various types of membranes within the cell depend on the kinds of phospholipids and proteins present. The plasma membrane also has carbohydrates attached to its outer surface.

on the size range of cells. The smallest cells known are bacteria called mycoplasmas, which have diameters between 0.1 and 1.0 micrometer (μm). These are perhaps the smallest packages with enough DNA to program metabolism and enough enzymes and other cellular equipment to carry out the activities necessary for a cell to sustain itself and reproduce. Most bacteria are 1 to 10 μm in diameter, about ten times larger than mycoplasmas (see FIGURE 7.1). Eukaryotic cells are typically 10 to 100 μm in diameter, ten times larger than bacteria.

Metabolic requirements also impose upper limits on the size that is practical for a single cell. As an object of a particular shape increases in size, its volume grows proportionately more than its surface area. (Area is proportional to a linear dimension squared, whereas volume is proportional to the linear dimension cubed.) Thus for objects of the same shape, the smaller the object, the greater its ratio of surface area to volume (FIGURE 7.5).

At the boundary of every cell, the **plasma membrane** functions as a selective barrier that allows sufficient passage of oxygen, nutrients, and wastes to service the entire volume of the cell (FIGURE 7.6). For each square micrometer of membrane, only so much of a particular substance can cross per second. The need for a surface sufficiently large to accommodate the volume helps explain the microscopic size of most cells.

Internal membranes compartmentalize the functions of a eukaryotic cell

In addition to the plasma membrane at its outer surface, a eukaryotic cell has extensive and elaborately arranged internal membranes, which partition the cell into compartments. These membranes also participate directly in the cell's metabolism; many enzymes are built right into the membranes. Because the cell's compartments provide different local environments that facilitate specific metabolic functions, incompatible processes can go on simultaneously inside the same cell.

Membranes of various kinds are fundamental to the organization of the cell. In general, biological membranes consist

of a double layer of phospholipids and other lipids. Embedded in this lipid bilayer or attached to its surfaces are diverse proteins (see FIGURE 7.6). However, each membrane has a unique composition of lipids and proteins suited to that membrane's specific functions. For example, enzymes that function in cellular respiration are embedded in the membranes of the organelles called mitochondria.

Before continuing with this chapter, examine the overviews of eukaryotic cells in FIGURES 7.7 and 7.8 on pages 108 and 109. These figures and their legends introduce the various organelles and provide a map of the cell for the detailed tour upon which we will soon embark. FIGURES 7.7 and 7.8 also contrast animal and plant cells. As eukaryotic cells, they have much more in common than either has with any prokaryote. As you will see, however, there are important differences between plant and animal cells.

The first stop on our detailed tour of the cell are two organelles involved in the genetic control of the cell.

THE NUCLEUS AND RIBOSOMES

The nucleus contains a eukaryotic cell's genetic library

The **nucleus** contains most of the genes that control the eukaryotic cell (some genes are located in mitochondria and chloroplasts). It is generally the most conspicuous organelle in a eukaryotic cell, averaging about 5 μm in diameter. The nuclear envelope encloses the nucleus (FIGURE 7.9 on page 110), separating its contents from the cytoplasm.

The nuclear envelope is a double membrane. The two membranes, each a lipid bilayer with associated proteins, are separated by a space of about 20–40 nm. The envelope is perforated by pores that are about 100 nm in diameter. At the lip of each pore, the inner and outer membranes of the nuclear

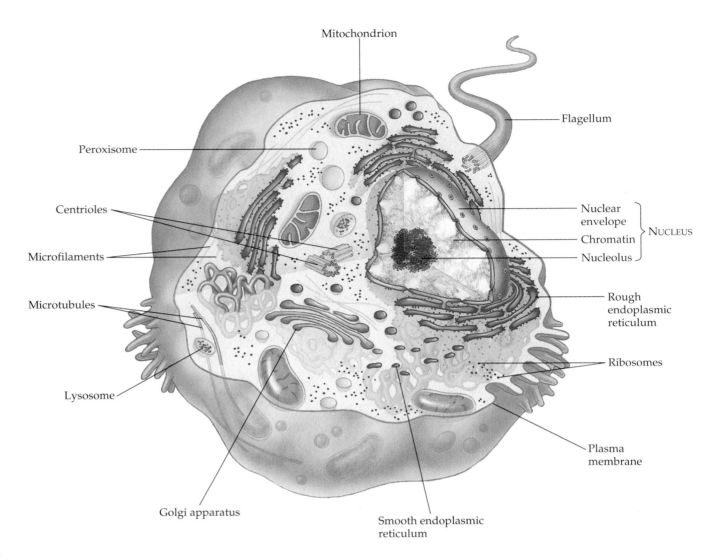

Mitochondrion

Flagellum

Peroxisome

Centrioles

Microfilaments

Microtubules

Lysosome

Golgi apparatus

Smooth endoplasmic
reticulum

Nuclear
envelope

Chromatin

Nucleolus

NUCLEUS

Rough
endoplasmic
reticulum

Ribosomes

Plasma
membrane

FIGURE 7.7 · Overview of an animal cell.

7.2 This drawing of a generalized animal cell combines all the most common structures found in animal cells (no cell actually looks just like this). Within the cell are a variety of components called organelles ("little organs"), many of which are bounded by membranes. The most prominent organelle in an animal cell is usually the nucleus. The chromatin in the nucleus consists of DNA, which carries genes, along with proteins. Chromatin is actually a collection of separate structures called chromosomes, visible as separate units only in a dividing cell. Adjoining part of the chromatin in the nucleus are one or more nucleoli (singular, nucleolus). Nucleoli are involved in the production of particles called ribosomes, which synthesize proteins. The nucleus is bordered by a porous envelope consisting of two membranes.

Most of the cell's metabolic activities occur in the cytoplasm, the entire region between the nucleus and the plasma membrane surrounding the cell. The cytoplasm is full of specialized organelles suspended in a semifluid medium called the cytosol. Pervading much of the cytoplasm is the endoplasmic reticulum (ER), a labyrinth of membranes forming flattened sacs and tubes that segregate the contents of the ER from the cytosol. The ER takes two forms: rough (studded with ribosomes) and smooth. Many types of proteins are made by ribosomes attached to ER membranes, and the ER also plays a major role in assembling the cell's other membranes. The Golgi apparatus, another type of membranous organelle, consists of stacks of flattened sacs active in the synthesis, refinement, storage, sorting, and secretion of a variety of chemical products.

Other membrane-enclosed organelles are: lysosomes, which contain mixtures of digestive enzymes that hydrolyze macromolecules; peroxisomes, a diverse group of organelles containing enzymes that perform specialized metabolic processes; and vacuoles, which have a variety of storage and metabolic functions. The mitochondria (singular, mitochondrion) carry out cellular respiration, which generates ATP from organic fuels such as sugar.

Nonmembranous organelles within the cells include microtubules and microfilaments. They help form a framework called the cytoskeleton, which reinforces the cell's shape and functions in cell movement. The cell in the drawing has a flagellum, an organelle of locomotion, which is an assembly of microtubules. Also made of microtubules are centrioles, located near the nucleus. These play a role in cell division.

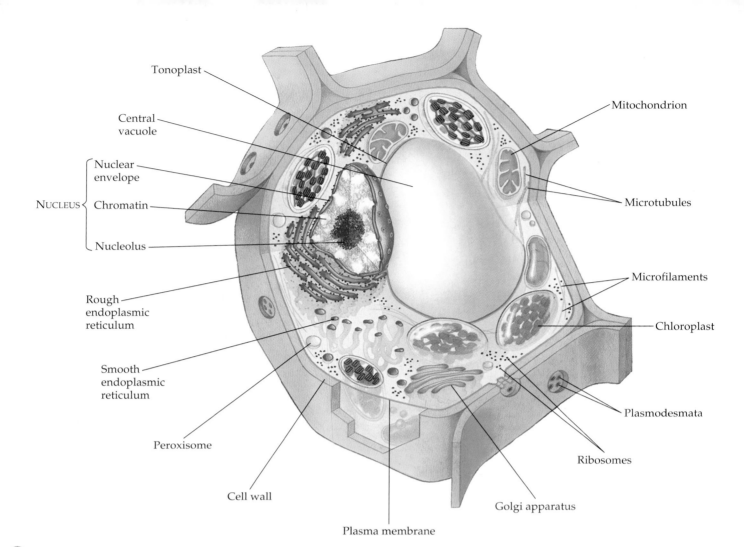

Tonoplast

Central vacuole

NUCLEUS {
Nuclear envelope
Chromatin
Nucleolus
}

Rough endoplasmic reticulum

Smooth endoplasmic reticulum

Peroxisome

Cell wall

Plasma membrane

Golgi apparatus

Ribosomes

Plasmodesmata

Chloroplast

Microfilaments

Microtubules

Mitochondrion

FIGURE 7.8 ▪ **Overview of a plant cell.** This
drawing of a generalized plant cell reveals the
similarities and differences between an animal
cell and a plant cell. Like the animal cell, the
plant cell is surrounded by a plasma membrane
and contains a nucleus, ribosomes, ER, Golgi
apparatus, mitochondria, peroxisomes, and
microfilaments and microtubules. However, a
plant cell also contains a family of membrane-
enclosed organelles called plastids. The most
important type of plastid is the chloroplast,
which carries out photosynthesis, converting
sunlight to chemical energy stored in sugar and
other organic molecules. Another prominent
organelle in many plant cells, especially older
ones, is a large central vacuole. The vacuole
stores chemicals, breaks down macromolecules,
and, by enlarging, plays a major role in plant
growth. The vacuole membrane is called the
tonoplast. Outside a plant cell's plasma membrane (and in fungi and some protists as well) is
a thick cell wall, which helps maintain the cell's
shape and protects the cell from mechanical
damage. The cytosol of adjacent cells connects
through trans-wall channels called plasmodesmata.

If you preview the rest of the chapter
now, you'll see Figures 7.7 and 7.8
repeated in miniature as orientation
diagrams. In each case, a particular
organelle is highlighted, color-coded
to its appearance in Figures 7.7 and 7.8.
As we take a closer look at individual
organelles, the orientation diagrams
will help you place those structures in
the context of the whole cell.

envelope are fused. An intricate protein structure called a pore
complex lines each pore and regulates the entry and exit of
certain large macromolecules and particles. Except at the
pores, the nuclear side of the envelope is lined by the **nuclear
lamina**, a netlike array of protein filaments that maintains the
shape of the nucleus. There is also much evidence for a
nuclear matrix, a framework of fibers extending throughout
the nuclear interior. (We will examine possible functions of
the nuclear lamina and matrix in Chapter 19.)

Within the nucleus, the DNA is organized along with proteins into material called **chromatin**. Stained chromatin

appears through both light microscopes and electron microscopes as a diffuse mass. As a cell prepares to divide (reproduce), the stringy, entangled chromatin coils up (condenses),
becoming thick enough to be discerned as separate structures
called **chromosomes**. Each eukaryotic species has a characteristic number of chromosomes. A human cell, for example, has
46 chromosomes in its nucleus; the exceptions are the sex
cells—eggs and sperm—which have only 23 chromosomes in
humans.

A prominent structure within the nondividing nucleus is
the **nucleolus**, where components of ribosomes are synthesized

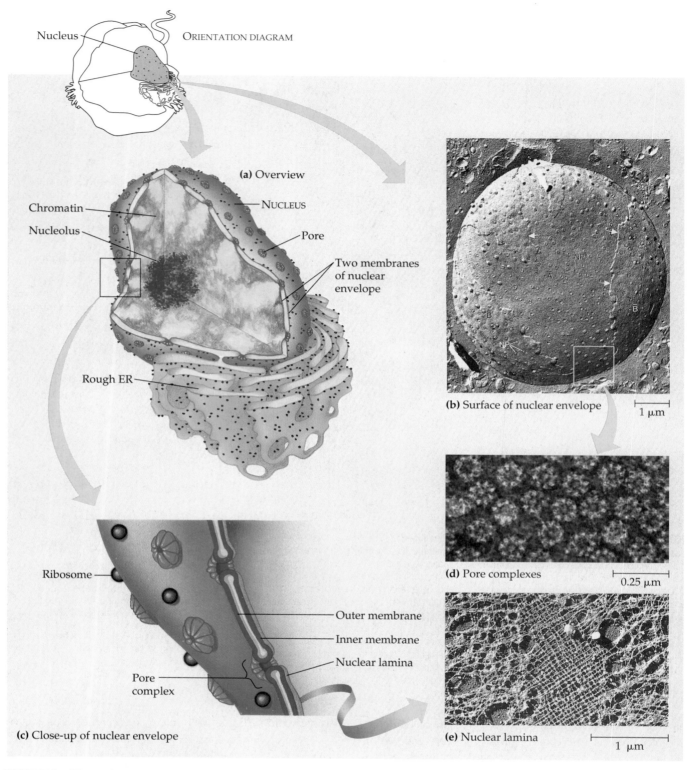

(a) Overview

Chromatin

Nucleolus

NUCLEUS

Pore

Two membranes of nuclear envelope

Rough ER

(b) Surface of nuclear envelope

1 μm

(c) Close-up of nuclear envelope

Ribosome

Outer membrane

Inner membrane

Nuclear lamina

Pore complex

(d) Pore complexes

0.25 μm

(e) Nuclear lamina

1 μm

FIGURE 7.9 ▪ The nucleus and its envelope.
(a) Within the nucleus is chromatin, consisting of DNA and proteins. When a cell prepares to divide, individual chromosomes become visible as the chromatin condenses. The nucleolus functions in ribosome synthesis. The nuclear envelope, which consists of two membranes separated by a narrow space, is perforated with

pores. **(b)** Numerous nuclear pores (NP) through the envelope are evident in this electron micrograph, prepared by a method called freeze-fracture (TEM). (The A and B labels distinguish the two membranes of the envelope.) **(c)** The nuclear envelope. **(d)** An electron micrograph of the outer surface of the envelope reveals that each pore is bordered by a ring of protein particles

(TEM). **(e)** The netlike nuclear lamina lines the inner surface of the envelope and reinforces the shape of the nucleus (TEM).

7.9b from L. Orci and A. Perrelet, *Freeze-Hetch Histology*, (Heidelberg: Springer-Verlag, 1975). ©1975 Springer-Verlag.

7.9d from A. C. Faberge, *Cell Tissue Res.* 151(1974):403. ©1974 Springer-Verlag.

and assembled. These components then pass through the nuclear pores to the cytoplasm, where they combine to form ribosomes. Sometimes there are two or more nucleoli; the number depends on the species and the stage in the cell's reproductive cycle. A nucleolus is roughly spherical, and through the electron microscope it appears as a mass of densely stained granules and fibers adjoining part of the chromatin.

The nucleus controls protein synthesis in the cytoplasm by sending molecular messengers in the form of RNA. As we saw in FIGURE 5.26, this messenger RNA (mRNA) is synthesized in the nucleus according to instructions provided by the DNA. The mRNA then conveys the genetic messages to the cytoplasm via the nuclear pores. Once in the cytoplasm, an mRNA molecule attaches to ribosomes, where the genetic message is translated into the primary structure of a specific protein. This process of translating genetic information is described in detail in Chapter 17.

Ribosomes build a cell's proteins

Ribosomes are the sites where the cell makes proteins. Cells that have high rates of protein synthesis have a particularly large number of ribosomes. For example, a human liver cell has a few million ribosomes. Not surprisingly, cells active in protein synthesis also have prominent nucleoli.

Ribosomes build proteins in two cytoplasmic locales (FIGURE 7.10). *Free* ribosomes are suspended in the cytosol, while *bound* ribosomes are attached to the outside of the membranous network called the endoplasmic reticulum. Most of the proteins made by free ribosomes will function within the cytosol; examples are enzymes that catalyze metabolic processes localized in the cytosol. Bound ribosomes generally make proteins that are destined either for inclusion into membranes, for packaging within certain organelles such as lysosomes, or for export from the cell. Cells that specialize in protein secretion—for instance, the cells of the pancreas and other glands that secrete digestive enzymes—frequently have a high proportion of bound ribosomes. Bound and free ribosomes are structurally identical and interchangeable, and the cell can adjust the relative numbers of each as its metabolism changes. You will learn more about ribosome structure and function in Chapter 17.

THE ENDOMEMBRANE SYSTEM

Many of the different membranes of the eukaryotic cell are part of an **endomembrane system**. These membranes are related either through direct physical continuity or by the transfer of membrane segments as tiny vesicles (membrane-enclosed sacs). These relationships, however, do not mean that the various membranes are alike in structure and function. The thickness, molecular composition, and metabolic behavior of a membrane are not fixed, but may be modified several times during the membrane's life. The endomembrane system includes the nuclear envelope, endoplasmic reticulum, Golgi apparatus, lysosomes, various kinds of vacuoles, and the plasma membrane (not actually an *endo*membrane in physical location, but nevertheless related to the endoplasmic reticulum and other internal membranes). We have already discussed the nuclear envelope and will now focus on the endoplasmic reticulum and the other endomembranes to which it gives rise.

The endoplasmic reticulum manufactures membranes and performs many other biosynthetic functions

The **endoplasmic reticulum (ER)** is a membranous labyrinth so extensive that it accounts for more than half the total membrane in many eukaryotic cells. (The word *endoplasmic* means "within the cytoplasm," and *reticulum* is derived from the Latin for "network.") The ER consists of a network of membranous tubules and sacs called cisternae (L. *cisterna*, "box" or "chest"). The ER membrane separates its internal compartment, the cisternal space, from the cytosol. And because the ER membrane is continuous with the nuclear envelope, the space between the two membranes of the envelope is continuous with the cisternal space of the ER.

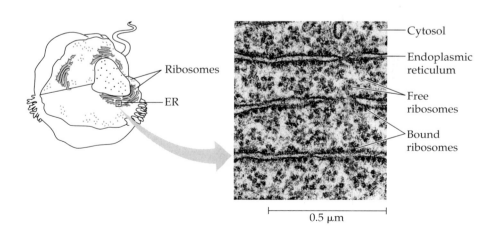

Cytosol

Endoplasmic reticulum

Free ribosomes

Bound ribosomes

Ribosomes

ER

0.5 μm

FIGURE 7.10 · Ribosomes. Both free and bound ribosomes are abundant in this electron micrograph of part of a pancreas cell (TEM). The pancreas is a gland specialized for the secretion of proteins. It secretes hormones, including the protein insulin, into the bloodstream, and secretes digestive enzymes, which are also proteins, into the intestine. Bound ribosomes, those presently attached to the endoplasmic reticulum (ER), produce secretory proteins. Free ribosomes mainly make proteins that will remain dissolved in the cytosol. Bound and free ribosomes are identical and can alternate between these two roles.

There are two distinct, though connected, regions of ER that differ in structure and function: smooth ER and rough ER. **Smooth ER** is so named because its cytoplasmic surface lacks ribosomes. **Rough ER** appears rough through the electron microscope because ribosomes stud the cytoplasmic surface of the membrane. Ribosomes are also attached to the cytoplasmic side of the nuclear envelope's outer membrane, which is confluent with rough ER (FIGURE 7.11).

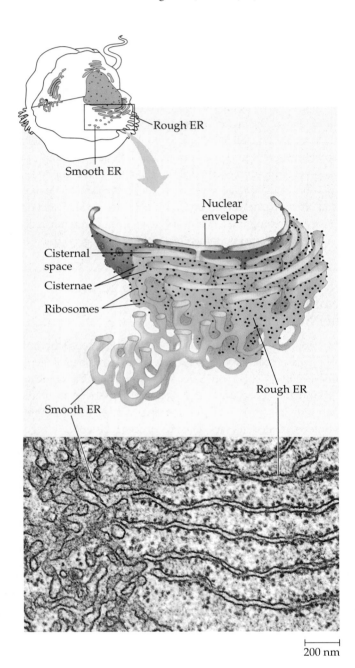

FIGURE 7.11 ▪ Endoplasmic reticulum (ER). A membranous system of interconnected tubules and flattened sacs called cisternae, the ER is also continuous with the nuclear envelope. (The drawing is a cutaway view.) The membrane of the ER encloses a compartment called the cisternal space. Rough ER, which is studded on its outer surface with ribosomes, can be distinguished from smooth ER in the electron micrograph (TEM).

Functions of Smooth ER

The smooth ER of various cell types functions in diverse metabolic processes, including synthesis of lipids, metabolism of carbohydrates, and detoxification of drugs and poisons.

Enzymes of the smooth ER are important to the synthesis of lipids, including phospholipids and steroids. Among the steroids produced by smooth ER are the sex hormones of vertebrates and the various steroid hormones secreted by the adrenal glands. The cells that actually synthesize and secrete these hormones—in the testes and ovaries, for example—are rich in smooth ER, a structural feature that fits the function of these cells.

Liver cells provide one example of the role of smooth ER in carbohydrate metabolism. Liver cells store carbohydrate in the form of glycogen, a polysaccharide. The hydrolysis of glycogen leads to the release of glucose from the liver cells, which is important in the regulation of sugar concentration in the blood. However, the first product of glycogen hydrolysis is glucose phosphate, an ionic form of the sugar that cannot exit the cell and enter the blood. An enzyme embedded in the membrane of the liver cell's smooth ER removes the phosphate from the glucose, which can then leave the cell.

Enzymes of the smooth ER help detoxify drugs and poisons, especially in liver cells. Detoxification usually involves adding hydroxyl groups to drugs, making them more soluble and easier to flush from the body. The sedative phenobarbital and other barbiturates are examples of drugs metabolized in this manner by smooth ER in liver cells. In fact, barbiturates, alcohol, and many other drugs induce the proliferation of smooth ER and its associated detoxification enzymes. This in turn increases tolerance to the drugs, meaning that higher doses are required to achieve a particular effect, such as sedation. Also, because some of the detoxification enzymes have relatively broad action, the proliferation of smooth ER in response to one drug can increase tolerance to other drugs as well. Barbiturate abuse, for example, may decrease the effectiveness of certain antibiotics and other useful drugs.

Muscle cells exhibit still another specialized function of smooth ER. The ER membrane pumps calcium ions from the cytosol into the cisternal space. When a muscle cell is stimulated by a nerve impulse, calcium rushes back across the ER membrane into the cytosol and triggers contraction of the muscle cell.

Rough ER and Synthesis of Secretory Proteins

Many types of specialized cells secrete proteins produced by ribosomes attached to rough ER. For example, certain cells in the pancreas secrete the protein insulin, a hormone, into the bloodstream. As a polypeptide chain grows from a bound ribosome, it is threaded into the cisternal space through a pore formed by a protein in the ER membrane. As it enters the cisternal space, the new protein folds into its native conforma-

tion. Most secretory proteins are **glycoproteins**, proteins that are covalently bonded to carbohydrates. The carbohydrate is attached to the protein in the ER by specialized molecules built into the ER membrane. The carbohydrate appendage of a glycoprotein is an oligosaccharide, the term for a relatively small polymer of sugar units.

Once secretory proteins are formed, the ER membrane keeps them separate from the proteins, produced by free ribosomes, that will remain in the cytosol. Secretory proteins depart from the ER wrapped in the membranes of vesicles that bud like bubbles from a specialized region called transitional ER. Such vesicles in transit from one part of the cell to another are called **transport vesicles**, and we will soon learn their fate.

Rough ER and Membrane Production

In addition to making secretory proteins, rough ER is a membrane factory that grows in place by adding proteins and phospholipids. As polypeptides destined to be membrane proteins grow from the ribosomes, they are inserted into the ER membrane itself and are anchored there by hydrophobic portions of the proteins. The rough ER also makes its own membrane phospholipids; enzymes built into the ER membrane assemble phospholipids from precursors in the cytosol. The ER membrane expands and can be transferred in the form of transport vesicles to other components of the endomembrane system.

The Golgi apparatus finishes, sorts, and ships cell products

After leaving the ER, many transport vesicles travel to the **Golgi apparatus**. We can think of the Golgi as a center of manufacturing, warehousing, sorting, and shipping. Here, products of the ER are modified and stored, and then sent to other destinations. Not surprisingly, the Golgi apparatus is especially extensive in cells specialized for secretion.

The Golgi apparatus consists of flattened membranous sacs—cisternae—looking like a stack of pita bread (FIGURE 7.12). A cell may have several of these stacks. The membrane of each cisterna in a stack separates its internal space from the cytosol. Vesicles concentrated in the vicinity of the Golgi apparatus are engaged in the transfer of material between the Golgi and other structures.

The Golgi apparatus has a distinct polarity, with the membranes of cisternae at opposite ends of a stack differing in thickness and molecular composition. The two poles of a

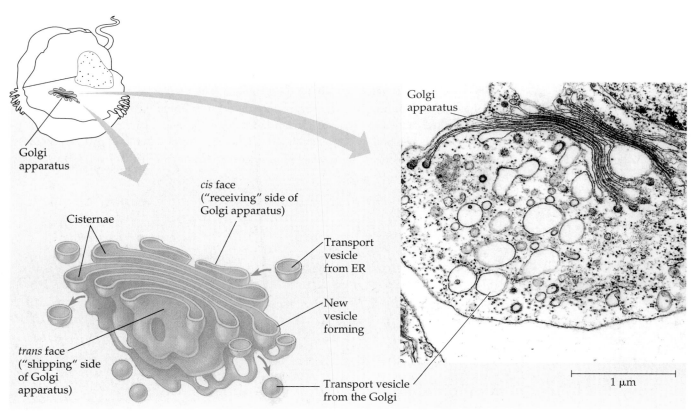

FIGURE 7.12 · The Golgi apparatus. A Golgi apparatus consists of stacks of flattened sacs, or cisternae, which unlike ER cisternae are not physically connected. (The drawing is a cutaway view.) The apparatus receives and dispatches transport vesicles and the products they contain. Materials received from the ER are modified and stored in the Golgi and eventually shipped to the cell surface or other destinations. Note the vesicles joining and leaving the cisternae. A stack has a structural and functional polarity, with a *cis* face that receives vesicles and a *trans* face that dispatches vesicles (at right, TEM).

Golgi stack are referred to as the *cis* face and the *trans* face; these act, respectively, as the receiving and shipping departments of the Golgi apparatus. The *cis* face is usually located near ER. Transport vesicles move material from the ER to the Golgi. A vesicle that buds from the ER will add its membrane and the contents of its lumen (cavity) to the *cis* face by fusing with a Golgi membrane. The *trans* face gives rise to vesicles, which pinch off and travel to other sites.

Products of the ER are usually modified during their transit from the *cis* pole to the *trans* pole of the Golgi. Proteins and phospholipids of membranes may be altered. For example, various Golgi enzymes modify the oligosaccharide portions of glycoproteins. When first added to proteins in the ER, the oligosaccharides of all glycoproteins are identical. The Golgi removes some sugar monomers and substitutes others, producing diverse oligosaccharides.

In addition to its finishing work, the Golgi apparatus manufactures certain macromolecules by itself. Many polysaccharides secreted by cells are Golgi products, including hyaluronic acid, a sticky substance that helps glue animal cells together. Golgi products that will be secreted depart from the *trans* faces of Golgi inside transport vesicles that eventually fuse with the plasma membrane.

The Golgi manufactures and refines its products in stages, with different cisternae between the *cis* and *trans* ends containing unique teams of enzymes. Products in various stages of processing appear to be transferred from one cisterna to the next by vesicles.

Before the Golgi apparatus dispatches its products by budding vesicles from the *trans* face, it sorts these products and targets them for various parts of the cell. Molecular identification tags, such as phosphate groups that have been added to the Golgi products, aid in sorting. And transport vesicles budded from the Golgi may have external molecules on their membranes that recognize "docking sites" on the surface of specific organelles.

Lysosomes are digestive compartments

A **lysosome** is a membrane-bounded sac of hydrolytic enzymes that the cell uses to digest macromolecules (FIGURE 7.13). There are lysosomal enzymes that can hydrolyze proteins, polysaccharides, fats, and nucleic acids—all the major classes of macromolecules. These enzymes work best in an acidic environment, at about pH 5. The lysosomal membrane maintains this low internal pH by pumping hydrogen ions from the cytosol into the lumen of the lysosome. If a lysosome breaks open or leaks its contents, the enzymes are not very active in the neutral environment of the cytosol. However, excessive leakage from a large number of lysosomes can destroy a cell by autodigestion. From this example we can see once again how important compartmental organization is to the functions of the cell: The lysosome provides a space where the cell can digest macromolecules safely, without the general destruction that would occur if hydrolytic enzymes roamed at large.

Hydrolytic enzymes and lysosomal membrane are made by rough ER and then transferred to a Golgi apparatus for further processing. At least some lysosomes probably arise by budding from the *trans* face of the Golgi apparatus (FIGURE 7.14). Proteins of the inner surface of the lysosomal membrane and the digestive enzymes themselves are probably spared from destruction by having three-dimensional conformations that protect vulnerable bonds from enzymatic attack.

Lysosomes function in intracellular digestion in a variety of circumstances. *Amoeba* and many other protists eat by engulfing smaller organisms or other food particles, a process called **phagocytosis** (Gr. *phagein*, "to eat," and *kytos*, "vessel,"

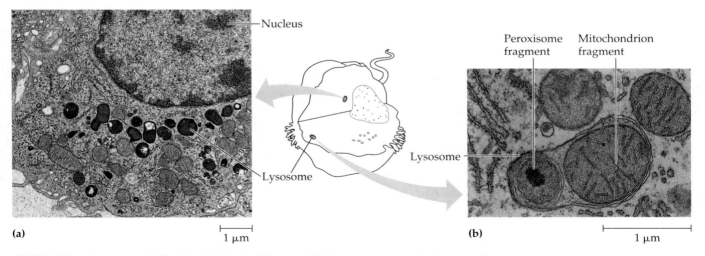

(a)   1 μm   (b)   1 μm

FIGURE 7.13 · Lysosomes. (a) In this white blood cell from a rat, the lysosomes are very dark because of a specific stain that reacts with one of the products of digestion within the lysosome. This type of white blood cell ingests bacteria and viruses and destroys them in the lysosomes (TEM). **(b)** In the cytoplasm of this rat liver cell, an autophagic lysosome has engulfed two disabled organelles, a mitochondrion and a peroxisome (TEM).

referring here to the cell). The food vacuole formed in this way then fuses with a lysosome, whose enzymes digest the food (see FIGURE 7.14). Some human cells also carry out phagocytosis. Among them are macrophages, cells that help defend the body by destroying bacteria and other invaders.

Lysosomes also use their hydrolytic enzymes to recycle the cell's own organic material, a process called autophagy. This occurs when a lysosome engulfs another organelle or a small parcel of cytosol (see FIGURE 7.13b). The lysosomal enzymes dismantle the ingested material, and the organic monomers are returned to the cytosol for reuse. With the help of lysosomes, the cell continually renews itself. A human liver cell, for example, recycles half of its macromolecules each week.

Programmed destruction of cells by their own lysosomal enzymes is important in the development of many organisms. During the transforming of a tadpole into a frog, for instance, lysosomes destroy the cells of the tail. And the hands of human embryos are webbed until lysosomes digest the tissue between the fingers.

A variety of inherited disorders called lysosomal storage diseases affects lysosomal metabolism. A person afflicted with a storage disease lacks one of the active hydrolytic enzymes normally present in lysosomes. The lysosomes become engorged with indigestible substrates, which begin to interfere with other cellular functions. In Pompe's disease, for example, the liver is damaged by an accumulation of glycogen due to the absence of a lysosomal enzyme needed to break down the polysaccharide. In Tay-Sachs disease, a lipid-digesting enzyme is missing or inactive, and the brain becomes impaired by an accumulation of lipids in the cells. Fortunately, storage diseases are rare in the general population. In the future, it might be possible to treat storage diseases by injecting the missing enzymes into the blood along with adaptor molecules that target the enzymes for engulfment by cells and fusion with lysosomes. It might also be possible someday to repair a disorder directly by inserting genes (DNA) for the missing enzyme into the appropriate cells (see Chapter 20).

Vacuoles have diverse functions in cell maintenance

Vacuoles and vesicles are both membrane-bounded sacs within the cell, but vacuoles are larger than vesicles. Vacuoles have various functions. **Food vacuoles**, formed by phagocytosis, have already been mentioned (see FIGURE 7.14). Many freshwater protists have **contractile vacuoles** that pump excess water out of the cell (see FIGURE 8.12). Mature plant cells generally contain a large **central vacuole** (FIGURE 7.15, p. 116) enclosed by a membrane called the **tonoplast**, which is part of their endomembrane system.

The plant cell vacuole is a versatile compartment. It is a place to store organic compounds, such as the proteins that are stockpiled in the vacuoles of storage cells in seeds. This vacuole is also the plant cell's main repository of inorganic ions, such as potassium and chloride. Many plant cells use their vacuoles as disposal sites for metabolic by-products that would endanger the cell if they accumulated in the cytosol. Some vacuoles are enriched in pigments that color the cells,

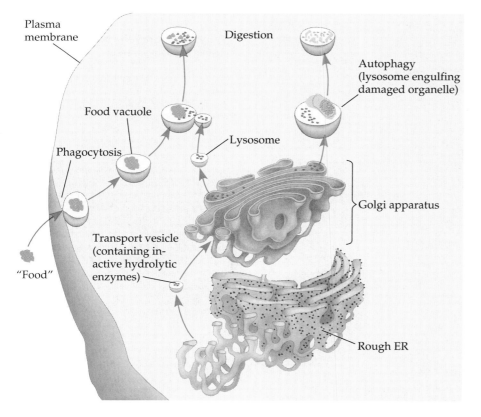

Plasma membrane

Digestion

Autophagy (lysosome engulfing damaged organelle)

Food vacuole

Phagocytosis

Lysosome

Golgi apparatus

Transport vesicle (containing inactive hydrolytic enzymes)

"Food"

Rough ER

FIGURE 7.14 · The formation and functions of lysosomes. Lysosomes digest materials taken into the cell and recycle materials from intracellular refuse. During phagocytosis, the cell encloses food in a vacuole with a membrane that pinches off internally from the plasma membrane. This food vacuole fuses with a lysosome, and hydrolytic enzymes digest the food. After hydrolysis, simple sugars, amino acids, and other monomers pass across the lysosomal membrane into the cytosol as nutrients for the cell. By the process of autophagy, lysosomes recycle the molecular ingredients of organelles. The ER and Golgi generally cooperate in the production of lysosomes containing active enzymes.

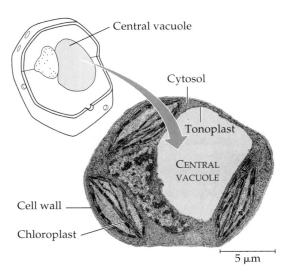

FIGURE 7.15 ▪ **The plant cell vacuole.** The central vacuole is usually the largest compartment in a plant cell, comprising 80% or more of a mature cell. The rest of the cytoplasm is generally confined to a narrow zone between the vacuole and the plasma membrane. The membrane of the vacuole, the tonoplast, separates the cytosol from the solution inside the vacuole, which is called cell sap. Like all cellular membranes, the tonoplast is selective in transporting solutes; therefore, cell sap differs in composition from the cytosol. Functions of the vacuole include storage, waste disposal, protection, and growth (TEM).

such as the red and blue pigments of petals that help attract pollinating insects to flowers. Vacuoles may also help protect the plant against predators by containing compounds that are poisonous or unpalatable to animals. The vacuole has a major role in the growth of plant cells, which elongate as their vacuoles absorb water, enabling the cell to become larger with a minimal investment in new cytoplasm. And because the cytosol often occupies only a thin layer between the plasma membrane and the tonoplast, the ratio of membrane surface to cytosolic volume is great, even for a large plant cell.

The large vacuole of a plant cell develops by the coalescence of smaller vacuoles, themselves derived from the endoplasmic reticulum and Golgi apparatus. Through these relationships, the vacuole is an integral part of the endomembrane system. FIGURE 7.16 reviews the endomembrane system. We'll continue our tour of the cell with some membranous organelles that are *not* closely related to the endomembrane system.

OTHER MEMBRANOUS ORGANELLES

Mitochondria and chloroplasts are the main energy transformers of cells

One of this book's themes is that organisms are open systems that transform energy they acquire from their surroundings. In eukaryotic cells, mitochondria and chloroplasts are the organelles that convert energy to forms that cells can use for work. **Mitochondria** (singular, **mitochondrion**) are the sites of cellular respiration, the catabolic process that generates ATP by extracting energy from sugars, fats, and other fuels with the help of oxygen. **Chloroplasts**, found only in plants and eukaryotic algae, are the sites of photosynthesis. They convert solar energy to chemical energy by absorbing sunlight

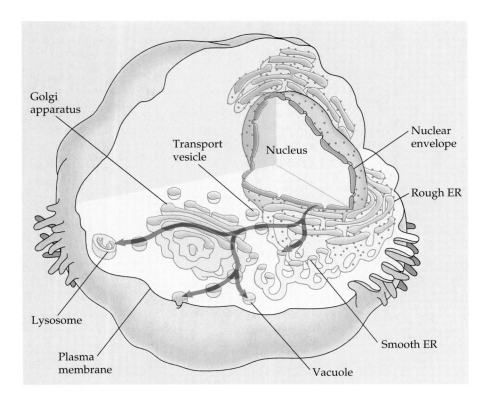

FIGURE 7.16 ▪ **Review: relationships among endomembranes.** The red arrows show some pathways of membrane migration through the various organelles of the endomembrane system. The nuclear envelope is connected to the rough ER, which is also confluent with smooth ER. Membrane produced by the ER flows in the form of transport vesicles to the Golgi. The Golgi, in turn, pinches off vesicles that give rise to lysosomes and vacuoles. Even the plasma membrane expands by the fusion of vesicles born in the ER and Golgi. (Coalescence of vesicles with the plasma membrane also releases secretory proteins and other products to the outside of the cell.) As membranes of the system flow from ER to the Golgi and then elsewhere, their molecular compositions and metabolic functions are modified. The endomembrane system is a complex and dynamic player in the cell's compartmental organization.

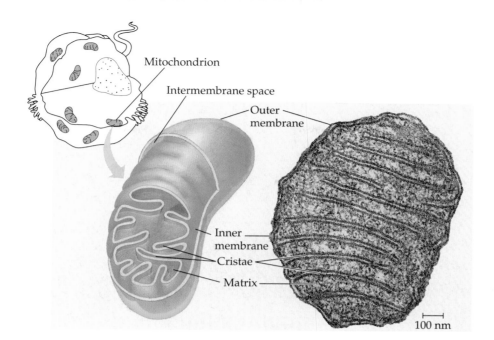

Mitochondrion

Intermembrane space

Outer membrane

Inner membrane

Cristae

Matrix

100 nm

and using it to drive the synthesis of organic compounds from carbon dioxide and water.

Although mitochondria and chloroplasts are enclosed by membranes, they are not part of the endomembrane system. Their membrane proteins are made not by the ER, but by free ribosomes in the cytosol and by ribosomes contained within the mitochondria and chloroplasts themselves. Not only do these organelles have ribosomes, but they also contain a small amount of DNA. It is this DNA that programs the synthesis of the proteins made on the organelle's own ribosomes. (Proteins imported from the cytosol—constituting most of the organelle's proteins—are programmed by nuclear DNA.) Mitochondria and chloroplasts are semiautonomous organelles that grow and reproduce within the cell. In Chapters 9 and 10 we will focus on how mitochondria and chloroplasts function. We will consider the evolution of these organelles in Chapter 28. Here we are concerned mainly with the structure of these energy transformers.

Mitochondria

Mitochondria are found in nearly all eukaryotic cells. In some cases, there is a single large mitochondrion, but more often a cell has hundreds or even thousands of mitochondria; the number is correlated with the cell's level of metabolic activity. Mitochondria are about 1 to 10 μm long. Time-lapse films of living cells reveal mitochondria moving around, changing their shapes, and dividing in two, unlike the static cylinders seen in electron micrographs of dead cells.

The mitochondrion is enclosed in an envelope of two membranes, each a phospholipid bilayer with a unique collection of embedded proteins (FIGURE 7.17). The outer membrane is smooth, but the inner membrane is convoluted, with

infoldings called **cristae**. The inner membrane divides the mitochondrion into two internal compartments. The first is the intermembrane space, the narrow region between the inner and outer membranes. The second compartment, the **mitochondrial matrix**, is enclosed by the inner membrane. Some of the metabolic steps of cellular respiration occur in the matrix, where many different enzymes are concentrated. Other proteins that function in respiration, including the enzyme that makes ATP, are built into the inner membrane. The cristae give the inner mitochondrial membrane a large surface area that enhances the productivity of cellular respiration, another example of the correlation between structure and function.

Chloroplasts

The chloroplast is a specialized member of a family of closely related plant organelles called **plastids**. Amyloplasts are colorless plastids that store starch (amylose), particularly in roots and tubers. Chromoplasts are enriched in pigments that give fruits and flowers their orange and yellow hues. Chloroplasts contain the green pigment chlorophyll along with enzymes and other molecules that function in the photosynthetic production of food. These lens-shaped organelles, measuring about 2 μm by 5 μm, are found in leaves and other green organs of plants and in eukaryotic algae (FIGURE 7.18, p. 118).

The contents of a chloroplast are partitioned from the cytosol by an envelope consisting of two membranes separated by a very narrow intermembrane space. Inside the chloroplast is another membranous system, arranged into flattened sacs called **thylakoids**. In some regions, thylakoids are stacked like poker chips, forming structures called **grana** (singular, **granum**). The fluid outside the thylakoids is called

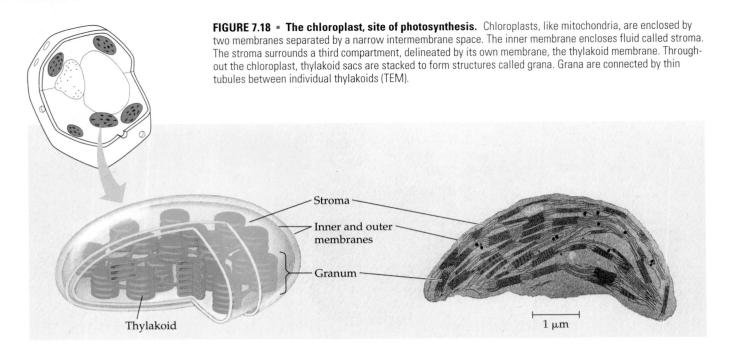

FIGURE 7.18 ▪ **The chloroplast, site of photosynthesis.** Chloroplasts, like mitochondria, are enclosed by two membranes separated by a narrow intermembrane space. The inner membrane encloses fluid called stroma. The stroma surrounds a third compartment, delineated by its own membrane, the thylakoid membrane. Throughout the chloroplast, thylakoid sacs are stacked to form structures called grana. Grana are connected by thin tubules between individual thylakoids (TEM).

Stroma

Inner and outer membranes

Granum

Thylakoid

1 μm

the **stroma**. Thus, the thylakoid membrane divides the interior of the chloroplast into two compartments: the thylakoid space and the stroma. In Chapter 10 you will learn how this compartmental organization enables the chloroplast to convert light energy to chemical energy during photosynthesis.

As with mitochondria, the static and rigid appearance of chloroplasts in electron micrographs is not true to their dynamic behavior in the living cell. Their shapes are plastic, and they occasionally pinch in two. They are mobile and move around the cell with mitochondria and other organelles along tracks of the cytoskeleton.

Peroxisomes consume oxygen in various metabolic functions

The **peroxisome** is a specialized metabolic compartment bounded by a single membrane (FIGURE 7.19). Peroxisomes contain enzymes that transfer hydrogen from various substrates to oxygen, producing hydrogen peroxide (H_2O_2) as a by-product, from which the organelle derives its name. These reactions may have many different functions. Some peroxisomes use oxygen to break fatty acids down into smaller molecules that can then be transported to mitochondria as fuel for cellular respiration. Peroxisomes in the liver detoxify alcohol and other harmful compounds by transferring hydrogen from the poisons to oxygen. The H_2O_2 formed by peroxisome metabolism is itself toxic, but the organelle contains an enzyme that converts the H_2O_2 to water. Enclosing in the same space both the enzymes that produce hydrogen peroxide and those that dispose of this toxic compound is another example of how the cell's compartmental structure is crucial to its functions.

Specialized peroxisomes called glyoxysomes are found in the fat-storing tissues of plant seeds. These organelles contain enzymes that initiate the conversion of fatty acids to sugar, which the emerging seedling can use as an energy and carbon source until it is able to produce its own sugar by photosynthesis.

Unlike lysosomes, peroxisomes do not bud from the endomembrane system. They grow by incorporating proteins and lipids made in the cytosol, and increase in number by splitting in two when they reach a certain size.

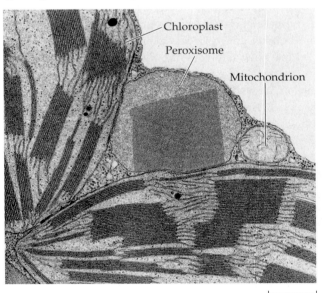

Chloroplast

Peroxisome

Mitochondrion

1 μm

FIGURE 7.19 ▪ **Peroxisomes.** Peroxisomes are roughly spherical and often have a granular or crystalline core that is probably a dense collection of enzymes. This peroxisome is in a leaf cell. Notice its proximity to two chloroplasts and a mitochondrion. These organelles cooperate with peroxisomes in certain metabolic functions (TEM).

THE CYTOSKELETON

In the early days of electron microscopy, biologists thought that the organelles of a eukaryotic cell floated freely in the cytosol. But improvements in both light microscopy and electron microscopy have revealed the **cytoskeleton**, a network of fibers extending throughout the cytoplasm (FIGURE 7.20). The cytoskeleton plays a major role in organizing the structures and activities of the cell.

Providing structural support to the cell, the cytoskeleton also functions in cell motility and regulation

The most obvious function of the cytoskeleton is to give mechanical support to the cell and maintain its shape. This is especially important for animal cells, which lack walls. The remarkable strength and resilience of the cytoskeleton as a whole is based on its architecture. Like a geodesic dome, the cytoskeleton is stabilized by a balance between opposing forces exerted by its elements. And, just as the skeleton of an animal helps fix the positions of other body parts, the cytoskeleton provides anchorage for many organelles and even cytosolic enzyme molecules. The cytoskeleton is more dynamic than an animal skeleton, however. It can be quickly dismantled in one part of the cell and reassembled in a new location, changing the shape of the cell.

The cytoskeleton is also involved in several types of cell motility (movement). The term *cell motility* encompasses both changes in cell location and more limited movements of parts of the cell. Cell motility generally requires the interaction of the cytoskeleton with proteins called motor molecules (FIGURE 7.21). Examples of such cell motility abound. Motor molecules of the cytoskeleton wiggle cilia and flagella. They also cause muscle cells to contract. Vesicles may travel to their destinations in the cell along "monorails" provided by the cytoskeleton, and the cytoskeleton manipulates the plasma membrane to form food vacuoles during phagocytosis. The streaming of cytoplasm that circulates materials within many large plant cells is yet another kind of cellular movement brought about by components of the cytoskeleton.

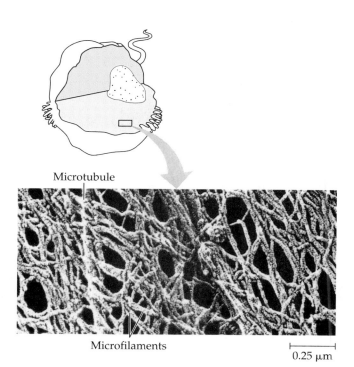

Microtubule

Microfilaments

0.25 μm

FIGURE 7.20 ▪ **The cytoskeleton.** The cytoskeleton gives the cell shape, anchors some organelles and directs the movement of others, and may enable the entire cell to change shape or move. It may even play a regulatory role, by mechanically transmitting signals from the cell's surface to its interior. In this electron micrograph, prepared by a method known as deep-etching, microtubules and microfilaments are visible. A third component of the cytoskeleton, intermediate filaments, is not evident here (TEM).

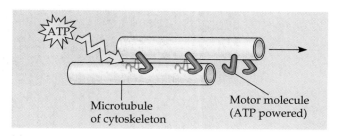

Microtubule of cytoskeleton

Motor molecule (ATP powered)

(a)

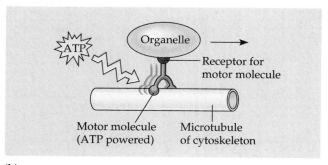

Organelle

Receptor for motor molecule

Motor molecule (ATP powered)

Microtubule of cytoskeleton

(b)

FIGURE 7.21 ▪ **Motor molecules and the cytoskeleton.** The microtubules and microfilaments of the cytoskeleton function in motility by interacting with proteins called motor molecules. Motor molecules work by changing their shapes, moving back and forth something like microscopic legs. ATP powers these conformational changes. With each cycle of shape change, the motor molecule releases at its free end and then grips at a site farther along a microtubule or microfilament. **(a)** In some types of cell motility, motor molecules attached to one element of the cytoskeleton cause it to slide past another cytoskeletal element. For example, a sliding of neighboring microtubules moves cilia and flagella. A similar mechanism causes muscle cells to contract, but in this case motor molecules slide microfilaments rather than microtubules. **(b)** Motor molecules can also attach to receptors on organelles such as vesicles and enable the organelles to "walk" along microtubules of the cytoskeleton. For example, this is how vesicles containing neurotransmitters migrate to the tips of axons, the long extensions of nerve cells that release transmitter molecules as chemical signals to adjacent nerve cells.

Table 7.2 ■ The Structure and Function of the Cytoskeleton

PROPERTY	MICROTUBULES	MICROFILAMENTS (ACTIN FILAMENTS)	INTERMEDIATE FILAMENTS
Structure	Hollow tubes; wall consists of 13 columns of tubulin molecules	Two intertwined strands of actin	Fibrous proteins supercoiled into thicker cables
Diameter	25 nm with 15-nm lumen	7 nm	8–12 nm
Protein subunits	Tubulin, consisting of α-tubulin and β-tubulin	Actin	One of several different proteins of the keratin family, depending on cell type
Functions	Maintenance of cell shape (compression-resisting "girders") Cell motility (as in cilia or flagella) Chromosome movements in cell division Organelle movements	Maintenance of cell shape (tension-bearing elements) Changes in cell shape Muscle contraction Cytoplasmic streaming Cell motility (as in pseudopodia) Cell division (cleavage furrow formation)	Maintenance of cell shape (tension-bearing elements) Anchorage of nucleus and certain other organelles Formation of nuclear lamina

SOURCE: Adapted from W. M. Becker, J .B. Reece, and M. F. Poenie, *The World of the Cell*, 3rd ed. Menlo Park, CA: Benjamin/Cummings, 1996, p. 555.

The most recent addition to the list of possible cytoskeletal functions is the regulation of biochemical activities in the cell. A growing body of evidence suggests that the cytoskeleton can transmit mechanical forces from the surface of the cell to its interior—and even, via other fibers, into the nucleus. In one experiment, investigators used a micromanipulation device to pull on certain plasma-membrane proteins attached to the cytoskeleton. A video microscope captured almost instantaneous rearrangements of nucleoli and other structures in the nucleus. It is easy to imagine that transmission of mechanical signals by the cytoskeleton may help regulate the functioning of the cell.

Let's now look more closely at the three main types of fibers that make up the cytoskeleton (TABLE 7.2). **Microtubules** are the thickest of the three types; **microfilaments** (also called actin filaments) are the thinnest. **Intermediate filaments** are fibers with diameters in a middle range.

Microtubules

Microtubules are found in the cytoplasm of all eukaryotic cells. They are straight, hollow rods measuring about 25 nm in diameter and from 200 nm to 25 μm in length. The wall of the hollow tube is constructed from a globular protein called tubulin. Each tubulin molecule consists of two similar polypeptide subunits, α-tubulin and β-tubulin. A microtubule elongates by adding tubulin molecules to its ends. Microtubules can be disassembled and their tubulin used to build microtubules elsewhere in the cell.

Microtubules shape and support the cell and also serve as tracks along which organelles equipped with motor molecules can move (see FIGURE 7.21). For example, microtubules seem to guide secretory vesicles from the Golgi apparatus to the plasma membrane. Microtubules are also involved in the separation of chromosomes during cell division, discussed in Chapter 12.

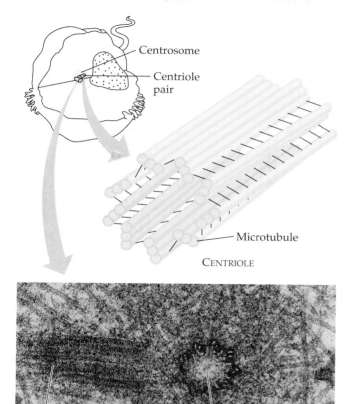

CENTRIOLE

Centrosome

Centriole pair

Microtubule

Longitudinal section of centriole

Microtubules

Cross section of centriole

0.25 μm

FIGURE 7.22 ▪ Centrosome containing a pair of centrioles. An animal cell has a pair of centrioles within its centrosome, the region near the nucleus where the cell's microtubules are initiated. The centrioles, each about 250 nm (0.25 μm) in diameter, are arranged at right angles to each other, and each is made up of nine sets of three microtubules (TEM).

Centrosomes and Centrioles. In many cells, microtubules grow out from a **centrosome**, a region located near the nucleus. These microtubules function as compression-resisting girders of the cytoskeleton. Within the centrosome of an animal cell are a pair of **centrioles**, each composed of nine sets of triplet microtubules arranged in a ring (FIGURE 7.22). When a cell divides, the centrioles replicate. Although centrioles may help organize microtubule assembly, they are not essential for this function in all eukaryotes; centrosomes of most plants lack centrioles altogether.

Cilia and Flagella. In eukaryotes, a specialized arrangement of microtubules is responsible for the beating of **flagella** and **cilia**, locomotive appendages that protrude from some cells. Many unicellular eukaryotic organisms are propelled through water by cilia or flagella, and the sperm of animals, algae, and some plants are flagellated. If cilia or flagella extend from cells that are held in place as part of a tissue layer, they function to move fluid over the surface of the tissue. For example, the ciliated lining of the windpipe sweeps mucus with trapped debris out of the lungs (see FIGURE 7.2).

Cilia usually occur in large numbers on the cell surface. They are about 0.25 μm in diameter and about 2 to 20 μm in length. Flagella are the same diameter but longer than cilia, measuring 10 to 200 μm in length. Also, flagella are usually limited to just one or a few per cell.

Flagella and cilia also differ in their beating patterns. A flagellum has an undulating motion that generates force in the same direction as the flagellum's axis. In contrast, cilia work more like oars, with alternating power and recovery strokes generating force in a direction perpendicular to the cilium's axis (FIGURE 7.23).

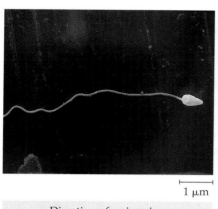

1 μm

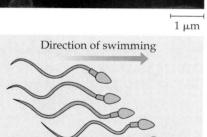

Direction of swimming

(a) Motion of flagella

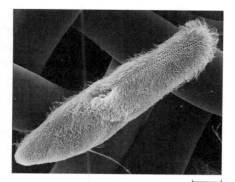

25 μm

Direction of organism's movement

Direction of active stroke

Direction of recovery stroke

(b) Motion of cilia

FIGURE 7.23 ▪ A comparison of the beating of flagella and cilia. (a) A flagellum usually undulates, its snakelike motion driving a cell in the same direction as the axis of the flagellum. Propulsion of a sperm cell is an example of flagellate locomotion (SEM). **(b)** A dense nap of beating cilia covers this *Paramecium*, a motile protist (SEM). The cilia beat at a rate of about 40 to 60 strokes per second. Cilia have a back-and-forth motion, alternating active strokes with recovery strokes. This moves the cell, or moves a fluid over the surface of a stationary cell, in a direction perpendicular to the axis of the cilium.

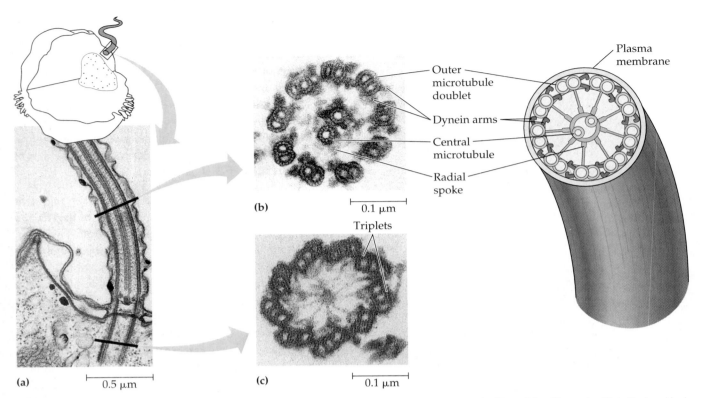

FIGURE 7.24 · Ultrastructure of a eukaryotic flagellum or cilium. **(a)** In this electron micrograph of a longitudinal section of a cilium, microtubules can be seen running the length of the structure (TEM). **(b)** A cross section through the cilium shows the "9 + 2" arrangement of microtubules (TEM). **(c)** The basal body anchoring the cilium or flagellum to the cell has a ring of nine microtubule triplets (the basal body is structurally identical to a centriole). The nine doublets of the cilium extend into the basal body, where each doublet joins another microtubule to form the ring of nine triplets. The two central microtubules of the cilium terminate above the basal body (TEM).

Though different in length, number per cell, and beating pattern, cilia and flagella actually share a common ultrastructure. A cilium or flagellum has a core of microtubules sheathed in an extension of the plasma membrane (FIGURE 7.24). Nine doublets of microtubules, the members of each pair sharing part of their walls, are arranged in a ring. In the center of the ring are two single microtubules. This arrangement, referred to as the "9 + 2" pattern, is found in nearly all eukaryotic flagella and cilia. (The flagella of motile prokaryotes, which will be discussed in Chapter 27, are entirely different.) The doublets of the outer ring are connected to the center of the cilium or flagellum by radial spokes that terminate near the central pair of microtubules. Each doublet of the outer ring also has pairs of arms evenly spaced along its length and reaching toward the neighboring doublet of microtubules. The microtubule assembly of a cilium or flagellum is anchored in the cell by a **basal body**, which is structurally identical to a centriole. In fact, in many animals (including humans), the basal body of the fertilizing sperm's flagellum enters the egg and becomes a centriole.

The arms extending from each microtubule doublet to the next are the motors responsible for the bending movements of cilia and flagella. The motor molecule that makes up these arms is a very large protein called **dynein**. A dynein arm performs a complex cycle of movements caused by changes in the conformation of the protein, with ATP providing the energy for these changes.

The mechanics of dynein "walking" are reminiscent of a cat climbing a tree by attaching its claws, moving its legs, releasing its claws, and grabbing again farther up the tree. Similarly, the dynein arms of one doublet attach to an adjacent doublet and pull so that the doublets slide past each other in opposite directions. The arms then release from the other doublet and reattach a little farther along its length. Without any restraints on the movement of the microtubule doublets, one doublet would continue to "walk" along the surface of the other, elongating the cilium or flagellum rather than bending it. For lateral movement of a cilium or flagellum, the dynein "walking" must have something to pull against, as when the muscles in your leg pull against your bones to move your knee. In cilia and flagella, the microtubule doublets are held in place, presumably by the radial spokes or other structural elements. Thus neighboring doublets cannot slide past each other very far. Instead, the forces exerted by the dynein arms cause the doublets to curve, bending the cilium or flagellum (FIGURE 7.25).

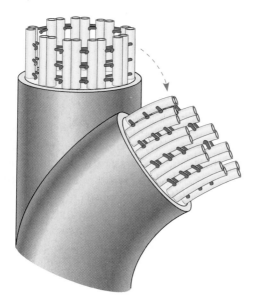

FIGURE 7.25 ▪ How dynein "walking" moves cilia and flagella.
The dynein arms of one microtubule doublet grip the adjacent doublet, pull, release, and then grip again. This cycle of the dynein motors is powered by ATP. The doublets cannot slide far because they are physically restrained within the cilium. Instead, the action of the dynein arms causes the doublets to bend.

Microfilaments (Actin Filaments)

Microfilaments are solid rods about 7 nm in diameter. They are also called actin filaments, because they are built from molecules of **actin**, a globular protein. A microfilament is a twisted double chain of actin subunits (see TABLE 7.2). Microfilaments seem to be present in all eukaryotic cells.

In contrast to the compression-resisting role of microtubules, the structural role of microfilaments in the ctyoskeleton is to bear tension (pulling forces). In combination with other proteins, they often form a three-dimensional network just inside the plasma membrane, helping support the cell's shape. This network gives the cortex (outer cytoplasmic layer) of such a cell the semisolid consistency of a gel, in contrast with the more fluid (sol) state of the interior cytoplasm. In animal cells specialized for transporting materials across the plasma membrane, bundles of microfilaments make up the core of microvilli, delicate projections that increase the cell surface area (FIGURE 7.26).

Microfilaments are well known for their roles in cell motility, in particular as part of the contractile apparatus of muscle cells. Thousands of actin filaments are arranged parallel to one another along the length of a muscle cell, interdigitated with thicker filaments made of a protein called **myosin** (FIGURE 7.27a, p. 124). Contraction of the muscle cell results from the actin and myosin filaments sliding past one another, shortening the cell. In other kinds of cells, actin filaments are associated with myosin in miniature and less elaborate versions of the arrangement in muscle cells. These actin–myosin

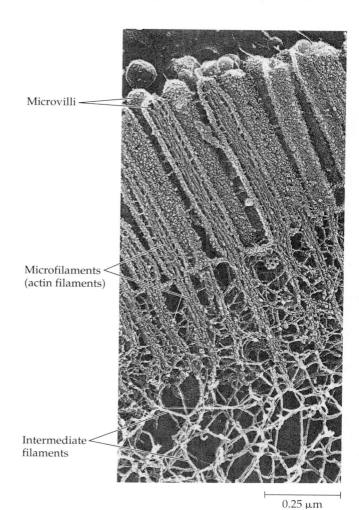

0.25 μm

FIGURE 7.26 ▪ A structural role of microfilaments. The surface area of this nutrient-absorbing intestinal cell is increased by its many microvilli, cellular extensions reinforced by bundles of microfilaments. These actin filaments are anchored to a network of intermediate filaments (TEM, Hirokawa et al. 1982. *J. Cell Biol.* 94, pp. 425–443, Fig. 1).

aggregates are responsible for localized contractions of cells. For example, a contracting belt of microfilaments forms a cleavage furrow that pinches a dividing animal cell into two daughter cells.

Localized contraction brought about by actin and myosin also plays a role in ameboid movement (FIGURE 7.27b), in which a cell crawls along a surface by extending and flowing into cellular extensions called **pseudopodia** (Gr. *pseudes*, "false," and *pod*, "foot"). Pseudopodia extend and contract through the *reversible* assembly of actin subunits into microfilaments and of microfilaments into networks that convert cytoplasm from sol to gel. Not only do amoebas move by crawling, but so do many cells in the animal body, such as white blood cells.

In plant cells, both actin–myosin interactions and sol-gel transformations brought about by actin may be involved in **cytoplasmic streaming**, a circular flow of cytoplasm within

cells (FIGURE 7.27c). This movement, which is especially common in large plant cells, speeds the distribution of materials within the cell.

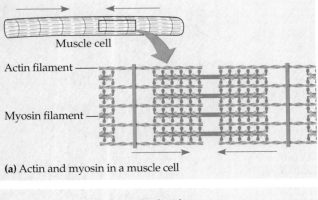

(a) Actin and myosin in a muscle cell

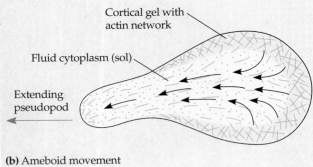

(b) Ameboid movement

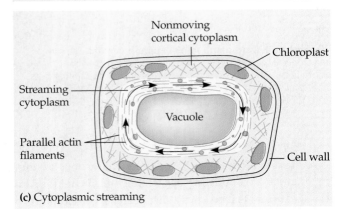

(c) Cytoplasmic streaming

FIGURE 7.27 ▪ Microfilaments and motility. (a) In muscle cells, actin filaments (orange) lie parallel to thick myosin filaments (purple). Myosin acts as a motor molecule by means of arms that "walk" the two types of filaments past each other. The teamwork of many such sliding filaments enables the entire muscle cell to shorten. **(b)** In a crawling cell (ameboid movement), actin is organized into a network in the gel-like cortex (outer layer) but exists as subunits and linear filaments in the more fluid (sol) interior. According to one hypothesis, filaments at the cell's trailing end interact with myosin, causing contraction. Like squeezing on a toothpaste tube, this contraction forces the interior fluid into the pseudopod, where the actin network has been weakened. The pseudopod extends until the actin reassembles into a network. **(c)** In cytoplasmic streaming, a layer of cytoplasm cycles around the cell, moving over a carpet of parallel actin filaments. Myosin motors attached to organelles in the fluid cytosol may drive the streaming by interacting with the actin. Also, rapid changes between the gel and sol states may occur locally. (In this figure, cell nuclei and most other organelles have been omitted.)

Intermediate Filaments

Intermediate filaments are named for their diameter, which, at 8 to 12 nm, is larger than the diameter of microfilaments but smaller than that of microtubules (see TABLE 7.2 and FIGURE 7.26). Specialized for bearing tension (like microtubules), intermediate filaments are a diverse class of cytoskeletal elements. Each type is constructed from a different molecular subunit belonging to a diverse family of proteins called keratins. Microtubules and microfilaments, in contrast, are consistent in diameter and composition in all eukaryotic cells.

Intermediate filaments are more permanent fixtures of cells than are microfilaments and microtubules, which are often disassembled and reassembled in various parts of a cell. Chemical treatments that remove microfilaments and microtubules from the cytoplasm leave a web of intermediate filaments that retains its original shape. Such experiments suggest that intermediate filaments are especially important in reinforcing the shape of a cell and fixing the position of certain organelles. For example, the nucleus commonly sits within a cage made of intermediate filaments, fixed in location by branches of the filaments that extend into the cytoplasm. Other intermediate filaments make up the nuclear lamina that lines the interior of the nuclear envelope (see FIGURE 7.9c). In cases where the shape of the entire cell is correlated with function, intermediate filaments support that shape. For instance, the long extensions (axons) of nerve cells that transmit impulses are strengthened by one class of intermediate filament. The various kinds of intermediate filaments may function as the framework of the entire cytoskeleton.

CELL SURFACES AND JUNCTIONS

Having crisscrossed the interior of the cell to explore various organelles, we complete our tour of the cell by returning to the surface of this microscopic world, where there are additional structures with important functions. Although the plasma membrane is usually regarded as the boundary of the living cell, most cells synthesize and secrete coats of one kind or another that are external to the plasma membrane.

Plant cells are encased by cell walls

The **cell wall** is one of the features of plant cells that distinguishes them from animal cells. The wall protects the plant cell, maintains its shape, and prevents excessive uptake of water. On the level of the whole plant, the strong walls of specialized cells hold the plant up against the force of gravity. Prokaryotes, fungi, and some protists also have cell walls, but we will postpone discussion of them until Unit Five.

Plant cell walls are much thicker than the plasma membrane, ranging from 0.1 μm to several micrometers. The exact

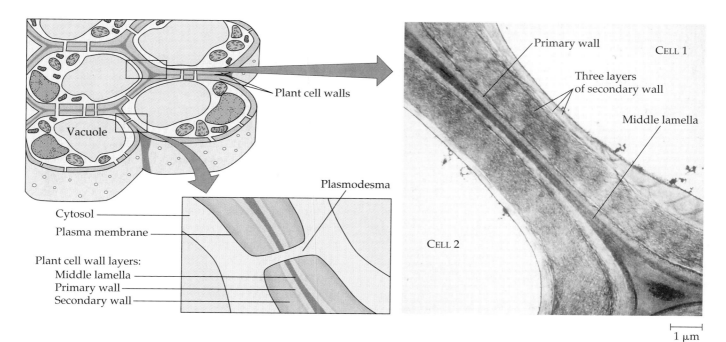

FIGURE 7.28 ▪ **Plant cell walls.** Young cells first construct thin primary walls, often adding stronger secondary walls to the inside of the primary wall when growth ceases. A sticky middle lamella cements adjacent cells together. Thus, the multilayered partition between these cells consists of adjoining walls individually secreted by the cells. The walls do not isolate the cells: The cytoplasm of one cell is continuous with the cytoplasm of its neighbors via plasmodesmata, channels through the walls (TEM).

chemical composition of the wall varies from species to species and from one cell type to another in the same plant, but the basic design of the wall is consistent (see FIGURE 5.8). Microfibrils made of the polysaccharide cellulose are embedded in a matrix of other polysaccharides and protein. This combination of materials, strong fibers in a "ground substance" (matrix), is the same basic architectural design found in steel-reinforced concrete and in fiberglass.

A young plant cell first secretes a relatively thin and flexible wall called the **primary cell wall** (FIGURE 7.28). Between primary walls of adjacent cells is the **middle lamella**, a thin layer rich in sticky polysaccharides called pectins. The middle lamella glues the cells together (pectin is used as a thickening agent in jams and jellies). When the cell matures and stops growing, it strengthens its wall. Some plant cells do this simply by secreting hardening substances into the primary wall. Other cells add a **secondary cell wall** between the plasma membrane and the primary wall. The secondary wall, often deposited in several laminated layers, has a strong and durable matrix that affords the cell protection and support. Wood, for example, consists mainly of secondary walls.

The extracellular matrix (ECM) of animal cells functions in support, adhesion, movement, and regulation

Although animal cells lack walls akin to those of plant cells, they do have an elaborate **extracellular matrix (ECM)** (FIGURE 7.29). The main ingredients of the ECM are glycoproteins

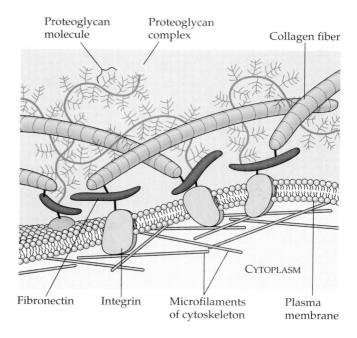

FIGURE 7.29 ▪ **Extracellular matrix (ECM) of an animal cell.** The molecular composition and structure of the ECM varies from one cell type to another. In this example, three different types of glycoproteins are present. Fibers made of the glycoprotein collagen are embedded in a web of proteoglycans, which can be as much as 95% carbohydrate; the proteoglycan molecules have formed complexes by noncovalently attaching to long polysaccharide molecules. The third glycoprotein is fibronectin, the adhesive that attaches the ECM to the plasma membrane of the cell. Membrane proteins called integrins are bound to the ECM on one side and to the microfilaments of the cytoskeleton on the other. This linkage can transmit stimuli between the cell's external environment and its interior.

secreted by the cells. (Recall that glycoproteins are proteins with covalently bonded carbohydrate, usually short chains of sugars.) The most abundant glycoprotein in the ECM of most animal cells is **collagen**, which forms strong fibers outside the cells. In fact, collagen accounts for about half of the total protein in the human body. The collagen fibers are embedded in a network woven from **proteoglycans**, which are glycoproteins of another class. Proteoglycan molecules are especially rich in carbohydrate—up to 95%—and they can form large complexes, as shown in FIGURE 7.29. Some cells are attached to the ECM by still other kinds of glycoproteins, most commonly **fibronectins**. Fibronectins bind to receptor proteins called **integrins** that are built into the plasma membrane. Integrins span the membrane and bind on their cytoplasmic side to microfilaments of the cytoskeleton. Thus, integrins are in a position to transmit changes in the ECM to the cytoskeleton, and vice versa—to integrate changes occurring outside and inside the cell.

Current research on fibronectins and integrins is revealing the influential role of the extracellular matrix in the lives of cells. Communicating with a cell through integrins, the ECM can regulate a cell's behavior. For example, some cells in a developing embryo migrate along specific pathways by matching the orientation of their microfilaments to the "grain" of fibers in the extracellular matrix. Researchers are also learning that the extracellular matrix around a cell can influence the activity of genes in the nucleus. Information about the ECM probably reaches the nucleus by a combination of mechanical and chemical signaling pathways. Mechanical signaling involves fibronectins, integrins, and the cytoskeleton. Changes in the cytoskeleton may in turn trigger chemical signaling pathways inside the cell. In this way, the extracellular matrix of a particular tissue could help coordinate the behavior of all the cells within that tissue. Direct connections between cells also function in this coordination, as we discuss next.

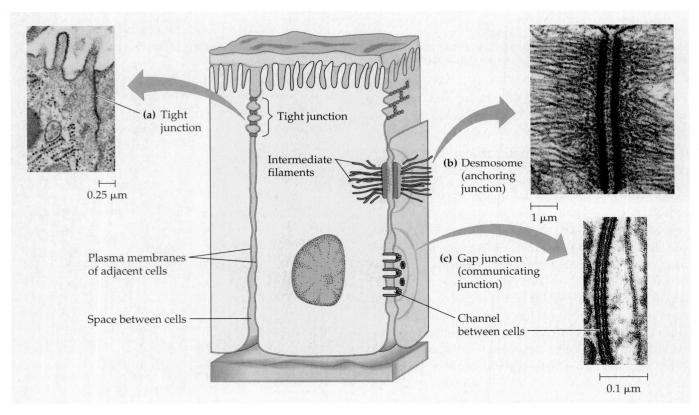

FIGURE 7.30 · Intercellular junctions in animals. These specialized connections are especially common in epithelial tissue, which lines the internal surfaces of the body. Here, we use epithelial cells lining the intestine to describe three kinds of intercellular junctions, each with a structure well adapted for its function. **(a)** Tight junctions. These connections form continuous belts around the cell. The membranes of neighboring cells are actually fused at a tight junction, forming a seal that prevents leakage of extracellular fluid across a layer of epithelial cells. For example, the tight junctions of the intestinal epithelium keep the contents of the intestine separate from the body fluid on the opposite side of the epithelium (TEM).
(b) Desmosomes (anchoring junctions). These junctions function like rivets, fastening cells together into strong epithelial sheets. Intermediate filaments made of the sturdy protein keratin reinforce desmosomes (TEM).
(c) Gap junctions (communicating junctions). These connections provide cytoplasmic channels between adjacent cells. Special membrane proteins surround each pore, which is wide enough for salts, sugars, amino acids, and other small molecules to pass (TEM). In the muscle tissue of the heart, the flow of ions through gap junctions coordinates the contractions of the cells. Gap junctions are especially common in animal embryos, in which chemical communication between cells is essential for development.

7.30b from L. Orci and A. Perrelet, *Freeze-Hetch Histology*, (Heidelberg: Springer-Verlag, 1975). ©1975 Springer-Verlag.

Intercellular junctions help integrate cells into higher levels of structure and function

The many cells of an animal or plant are organized into tissues, organs, and organ systems. Neighboring cells often adhere, interact, and communicate through special patches of direct physical contact.

It might seem that the nonliving cell walls of plants would isolate cells from one another. In fact, as already mentioned, the walls are perforated with channels called **plasmodesmata** (singular, **plasmodesma**; Gr. *desmos,* "to bind"). Cytoplasm passes through the plasmodesmata and connects the living contents of adjacent cells (see FIGURES 7.8 and 7.28). This unifies most of the plant into one living continuum. The plasma membranes of adjacent cells are continuous through a plasmodesma; the membrane lines the channel. Water and small solutes can pass freely from cell to cell, and recent experiments have shown that, in certain circumstances, particular proteins and RNA molecules can also do so. The macromolecules to be transported seem to reach the plasmodesmata by moving along fibers of the cytoskeleton.

In animals, there are three main types of intercellular junctions: **tight junctions, desmosomes**, and **gap junctions**. These are illustrated and described in detail in FIGURE 7.30.

■   ■   ■

The cell is a living unit greater than the sum of its parts

From our panoramic view of the cell's overall compartmental organization to our closeup inspection of each organelle's architecture, this tour of the cell has provided many opportunities to correlate structure with function. (This would be a good time to review cell structure by returning to FIGURES 7.7 and 7.8.) But even as we dissect the cell, remember that none of its organelles works alone. As an example of cellular inte-

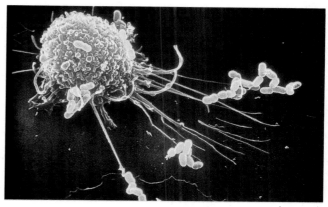

5 µm

FIGURE 7.31 ▪ **The emergence of cellular functions from the cooperation of many organelles.** The ability of this macrophage (brown) to recognize, apprehend, and destroy bacteria (yellow) is a coordinated activity of the whole cell. The cytoskeleton, lysosomes, and plasma membrane are among the components that function in phagocytosis. Other cellular functions are also emergent properties that depend on interactions of the cell's parts (colorized SEM).

gration, consider the microscopic scene in FIGURE 7.31. The large cell is a macrophage. It helps defend the body against infections by ingesting bacteria (the smaller yellow cells). The macrophage crawls along a surface and reaches out to the bacteria with thin pseudopodia ("filopodia"). Actin filaments interact with other elements of the cytoskeleton in these movements. After the macrophage engulfs the bacteria, they are destroyed by lysosomes. The elaborate endomembrane system, which includes the ER and the Golgi apparatus, produces the lysosomes. The digestive enzymes of the lysosomes and the proteins of the cytoskeleton are all made on ribosomes. And the synthesis of these proteins is programmed by genetic messages dispatched from the DNA in the nucleus. All these processes require energy, which mitochondria supply in the form of ATP. Cellular functions arise from cellular order: The cell is a living unit greater than the sum of its parts.

CHAPTER REVIEW

REVIEW OF KEY CONCEPTS

(with page numbers and key figures)

HOW WE STUDY CELLS

■ **Microscopes provide windows to the world of the cell (pp. 102–105, FIGURE 7.1)** Improvements in microscopy have catalyzed progress in the study of cell structure.

■ **Cell biologists can isolate organelles to study their functions (p. 105, FIGURE 7.3)** They use the ultracentrifuge to produce pellets enriched in specific organelles.

A PANORAMIC VIEW OF THE CELL

➡ **7.1** **Prokaryotic and eukaryotic cells differ in size and complexity (pp. 105–107, FIGURE 7.5)** All cells are bounded by a plasma membrane. Bacteria and archaea have prokaryotic cells, without nuclei

or other membrane-enclosed organelles. All other organisms have eukaryotic cells, with membrane-enclosed nuclei and other specialized organelles in their cytoplasm. The need for a high surface-to-volume ratio limits cell size.

➡ **7.2 7.3** **Internal membranes compartmentalize the functions of a eukaryotic cell (p. 107, FIGURES 7.7–7.8)** Plant and animal cells have most of the same organelles.

THE NUCLEUS AND RIBOSOMES

■ **The nucleus contains a eukaryotic cell's genetic library (pp. 107–111, FIGURE 7.9)** DNA is organized with proteins into chromosomes, which exist as chromatin in nondividing cells. Associated with the chromatin are one or more nucleoli, sites of ribosome synthesis. Macromolecules pass between nucleus and cytoplasm through pores in the nuclear envelope.

- Ribosomes build a cell's proteins (p. 111, FIGURE 7.10) Free ribosomes in the cytosol, and bound ribosomes on the outside of endoplasmic reticulum, synthesize proteins.

THE ENDOMEMBRANE SYSTEM

Many of the eukaryotic cell's membranes are connected either by physical continuity or through transport vesicles made of pinched-off pieces of membrane.

- The endoplasmic reticulum manufactures membranes and performs many other biosynthetic functions (pp. 111–113, FIGURE 7.11) Continuous with the nuclear envelope, the endoplasmic reticulum (ER) is a network of cisternae, membrane-enclosed compartments. Smooth ER lacks ribosomes; it synthesizes steroids, metabolizes carbohydrates, stores calcium in muscle, and detoxifies poisons in liver. Rough ER has bound ribosomes and produces cell membrane and secretory proteins. These products are distributed by transport vesicles budded from the ER.

- The Golgi apparatus finishes, sorts, and ships cell products (pp. 113–114, FIGURE 7.12) Stacks of separate cisternae make up the Golgi. Its *cis* face receives secretory proteins from the ER in transport vesicles. They are modified, sorted, and released in transport vesicles from the *trans* face.

- Lysosomes are digestive compartments (pp. 114–115, FIGURE 7.14) Lysosomes are membranous sacs of hydrolytic enzymes. They break down cell macromolecules for recycling as well as substances ingested by phagocytosis.

- Vacuoles have diverse functions in cell maintenance (pp. 115–116, FIGURE 7.15) A plant cell's central vacuole functions in storage, waste disposal, cell growth, and protection.

OTHER MEMBRANOUS ORGANELLES

- Mitochondria and chloroplasts are the main energy transformers of cells (p. 118, FIGURE 7.17–7.18) Mitochondria, the sites of cellular respiration in eukaryotes, have an outer membrane and an inner membrane that is folded into cristae. Some reactions of respiration occur in the mitochondrial matrix enclosed by the inner membrane, and others are catalyzed by enzymes built into the inner membrane. Chloroplasts, a type of plastid, contain chlorophyll and other pigments, which function in photosynthesis. In chloroplasts, two membranes surround the fluid stroma, which contains thylakoids, often stacked into grana.

- Peroxisomes consume oxygen in various metabolic functions (p. 118, FIGURE 7.19) Peroxisomes carry out processes that produce hydrogen peroxide as waste, and their enzymes convert the toxic peroxide to water.

THE CYTOSKELETON

- Providing structural support to the cell, the cytoskeleton also functions in cell motility and regulation (pp. 119–124, TABLE 7.2, FIGURES 7.22–7.24) The cytoskeleton is made of microtubules, microfilaments, and intermediate filaments. Microtubules are hollow cylinders; they radiate from the centrosome, a region near the nucleus that includes two centrioles in many animal cells. Microtubules shape the cell, guide movement of organelles, and aid chromosome separation in dividing cells. Cilia and flagella are motile appendages containing microtubule doublets that are moved past each other by the protein dynein. Microfilaments are thin rods built from the protein actin; they function in muscle contraction, ameboid movement, cytoplasmic streaming, and support for cellular projections. Intermediate filaments support cell shape and fix organelles in place.

CELL SURFACES AND JUNCTIONS

- Plant cells are encased by cell walls (pp. 124–125, FIGURE 7.28) Plant cell walls are composed of cellulose fibers embedded in other polysaccharides and protein.

- The extracellular matrix (ECM) of animal cells functions in support, adhesion, movement, and regulation (pp. 125–126, FIGURE 7.29) The cells secrete glycoproteins that form the ECM. Important components include collagen, proteoglycan complexes, and fibronectin attached to integrins in the plasma membrane.

- Intercellular junctions help integrate cells into higher levels of structure and function (p. 127, FIGURE 7.30) Plants have plasmodesmata, cytoplasmic channels that pass through adjoining cell walls. Animal cell contact is by tight junctions, desmosomes, and gap junctions.

- The cell is a living unit greater than the sum of its parts (p. 127, FIGURE 7.31)

SELF-QUIZ

1. The symptoms of a certain inherited disorder in humans include respiratory problems and, in males, sterility. Which of the following is a reasonable hypothesis for the molecular basis of this disorder? (Explain your answer.)
   a. a defective respiratory enzyme in the mitochondria
   b. defective actin molecules in cellular microfilaments
   c. defective dynein molecules in cilia and flagella
   d. abnormal hydrolytic enzymes in the lysosomes
   e. a defective secretory protein

2. From the following, choose the statement that correctly characterizes bound ribosomes.
   a. Bound ribosomes are enclosed in their own membrane.
   b. Bound ribosomes are structurally different from free ribosomes.
   c. Bound ribosomes generally synthesize membrane proteins and secretory proteins.
   d. The most common location for bound ribosomes is the cytoplasmic surface of the plasma membrane.
   e. Bound ribosomes are concentrated in the cisternal space of rough ER.

3. Which of the following organelles is least closely associated with the endomembrane system?
   a. nuclear envelope   d. plasma membrane
   b. chloroplast   e. ER
   c. Golgi apparatus

4. Cells of the pancreas will incorporate radioactively labeled amino acids into proteins. This "tagging" of newly synthesized proteins enables a researcher to track the location of these proteins in a cell. In this case, we are tracking an enzyme that is eventually secreted by pancreatic cells. Which of the following is the most likely pathway for movement of this protein in the cell?
   a. ER $\longrightarrow$ Golgi $\longrightarrow$ nucleus
   b. Golgi $\longrightarrow$ ER $\longrightarrow$ lysosome
   c. nucleus $\longrightarrow$ ER $\longrightarrow$ Golgi
   d. ER $\longrightarrow$ Golgi $\longrightarrow$ vesicles that fuse with plasma membrane
   e. ER $\longrightarrow$ lysosomes $\longrightarrow$ vesicles that fuse with plasma membrane

5. Which of the following organelles is common to plant *and* animal cells?
   a. chloroplasts   d. mitochondria
   b. wall made of cellulose e. centrioles
   c. tonoplast

6. Which of the following components is present in a prokaryotic cell?

   a. mitochondria   d. chloroplasts
   b. ribosomes   e. ER
   c. nuclear envelope

7. Which type of cell would probably provide the best opportunity to study lysosomes? Explain your answer.

   a. muscle cell   d. leaf cell of a plant
   b. nerve cell   e. bacterial cell
   c. phagocytic white blood cell

8. Which of the following statements is a correct distinction between prokaryotic and eukaryotic cells attributable to the absence of a prokaryotic cytoskeleton?

   a. Compartmentalized organelles are found only in eukaryotic cells.
   b. Cytoplasmic streaming is not observed in prokaryotes.
   c. Only eukaryotic cells are capable of movement.
   d. Prokaryotic cells are usually 10 μm or less in diameter.
   e. Only the eukaryotic cell concentrates its genetic material in a region separate from the rest of the cell.

9. Which of the following structure-function pairs is *mismatched*?

   a. nucleolus; ribosome production
   b. lysosome; intracellular digestion
   c. ribosome; protein synthesis
   d. Golgi; secretion of cell products
   e. microtubules; muscle contraction

10. Cyanide binds with at least one of the molecules involved in the production of ATP. Following exposure of a cell to cyanide, most of the cyanide could be expected to be found within the

    a. mitochondria   d. lysosomes
    b. ribosomes   e. endoplasmic reticulum
    c. peroxisomes

CHALLENGE QUESTIONS

1. After very small viruses infect a plant cell by crossing its membrane, the viruses often spread rapidly throughout the entire plant without crossing additional membranes. Explain how this occurs.

2. Write a short essay describing similarities and differences between plant cells and animal cells.

SCIENCE, TECHNOLOGY, AND SOCIETY

1. Researchers working with breast-tumor cells in culture have made a startling discovery: The cell's transformation from a benign to a malignant state involves signaling across the membrane. When antibodies were used to block specific integrins, the cells lost their ability to become malignant. These observations suggested the possibility of a new treatment strategy for breast cancer. Current treatments seek to kill cancer cells through the accumulated uptake of toxic chemotherapeutic drugs that inhibit cell division. A treatment that inhibited integrins might spare the patient the unpleasant side effects of chemotherapy. Of course, it would also leave living tumor cells in the body. Would you accept a treatment that simply blocked the action of cancerous cells as opposed to destroying them? Explain your reasoning.

2. Doctors at a California university removed a man's spleen, standard treatment for a type of leukemia. The disease did not recur. Researchers kept some of the spleen cells alive in a nutrient medium. They found that some of the cells produced a blood protein called GM-CSF, which they are now testing to fight cancer and AIDS. The researchers patented the cells. The patient sued, claiming a share in profits from any products derived from his cells. In 1988, the California Supreme Court ruled against the plaintiff (patient), stating that his suit "threatens to destroy the economic incentive to conduct important medical research." The U.S. Supreme Court agreed. The plaintiff's attorney argued that the ruling left patients "vulnerable to exploitation at the hands of the state." Do you think the plaintiff was treated fairly? Is there anything else you would like to know about this case that might help you make up your mind?

FURTHER READING

Alberts, B., D. Bray, J. Lewis, M. Raff, K. Roberts, and J. D. Watson. *Molecular Biology of the Cell*, 3rd ed. New York: Garland, 1994. The best comprehensive text; lucidly written and illustrated.

Becker, W. M., J. B. Reece, and M. F. Poenie. *The World of the Cell*, 3rd ed. Menlo Park, CA: Benjamin/Cummings, 1996. Readable and student-oriented.

Gorlich, D., and I. W. Mattaj. "Nucleocytoplasmic Transport." *Science*, March 15, 1996. How proteins and RNA get in and out of the nucleus.

Horwitz, A. F. "Integrins and Health." *Scientific American*, May 1997. These adhesive cell-surface molecules turn out to be crucial to body function.

Ingber, D. E. "The Architecture of Life." *Scientific American*, January 1998. The cytoskeleton and many other biological structures are assembled in accordance with the architectural principle of "tensegrity."

Lichtman, J.W. "Confocal Microscopy." *Scientific American*, August 1994. A powerful window to the cell.

Pelham, H. R. B. "Green Light for Golgi Traffic." *Nature*, September 4, 1997. How vesicles transport proteins from the ER to the Golgi, as revealed by time-lapse video.

Rothman, J. E., and L. Orci. "Budding Vesicles in Living Cells." *Scientific American*, March 1996. More about transport vesicles.

Stossel, T.P. "The Machinery of Cell Crawling." *Scientific American*, September 1994. Cells on the move.

Strange, C. J. "Biological Ties that Bind." *BioScience*, January 1997. The surprisingly varied and important roles of the extracellular matrix in animals.

Zambryski, P. "Plasmodesmata: Plant Channels for Molecules on the Move." *Science*, December 22, 1995. Macromolecular travel between plant cells.

WEB LINKS

Visit the special edition of *The Biology Place* for BIOLOGY, Fifth Edition, at http://www.biology.com/campbell. Go to Chapter 7 for online resources, including learning activities, practice exams, and links to the following web sites:

"The Virtual Cell"
Climb inside this virtual cell and explore its parts.

"The Dictionary of Cell Biology"
An online dictionary of cell biology with over 6000 terms defined.

"Cell and Molecular Biology Online"
A general resource for the biology community with an emphasis on information for cell and molecular biologists.

"CELLS alive"
This site has interesting free pictures and videos of various cell types and processes.

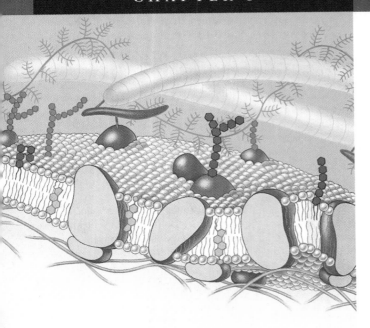

CHAPTER 8

MEMBRANE STRUCTURE AND FUNCTION

Membrane Structure

- Membrane models have evolved to fit new data: *science as a process*
- A membrane is a fluid mosaic of lipids, proteins, and carbohydrates

Traffic Across Membranes

- A membrane's molecular organization results in selective permeability
- Passive transport is diffusion across a membrane
- Osmosis is the passive transport of water
- Cell survival depends on balancing water uptake and loss
- Specific proteins facilitate the passive transport of selected solutes
- Active transport is the pumping of solutes against their gradients
- Some ion pumps generate voltage across membranes
- In cotransport, a membrane protein couples the transport of one solute to another
- Exocytosis and endocytosis transport large molecules

The plasma membrane is the edge of life, the boundary that separates the living cell from its nonliving surroundings. A remarkable film only about 8 nm thick—it would take over 8000 to equal the thickness of this page—the plasma membrane controls traffic into and out of the cell it surrounds. Like all biological membranes, the plasma membrane has **selective permeability**; that is, it allows some substances to cross it more easily than others. One of the earliest episodes in the evolution of life may have been the formation of a membrane that enclosed a solution of different composition from the surrounding solution while still permitting the uptake of nutrients and elimination of waste products. This ability of the cell to discriminate in its chemical exchanges with its environment is fundamental to life, and it is the plasma membrane that makes this selectivity possible.

In this chapter you will learn how cellular membranes control the passage of substances. We will concentrate on the plasma membrane, the outermost membrane of the cell, represented in the drawing on this page. However, the same general principles of membrane traffic also apply to the many varieties of internal membranes that partition the eukaryotic cell. To understand how membranes work, we begin by examining their architecture.

MEMBRANE STRUCTURE

Lipids and proteins are the staple ingredients of membranes, although carbohydrates are also important. Currently, the accepted model for the arrangement of these molecules in membranes is the fluid mosaic model. We will trace the evolution of this model in some detail as an example of how scientists build on earlier observations and ideas and how they use models as hypotheses.

Membrane models have evolved to fit new data: *science as a process*

Scientists began building molecular models of the membrane decades before membranes were first seen with the electron microscope in the 1950s. In 1895, Charles Overton postulated that membranes are made of lipids, based on his observations that substances that dissolve in lipids enter cells much more rapidly than substances that are insoluble in lipids. Twenty years later, membranes isolated from red blood cells were chemically analyzed and found to be composed of lipids and proteins.

Phospholipids are the most abundant lipids in most membranes. The ability of phospholipids to form membranes is built into their molecular structure. A phospholipid is an **amphipathic** molecule, meaning it has both a hydrophilic region and a hydrophobic region (see FIGURE 5.12). Other types of membrane lipids are also amphipathic.

In 1917, Irving Langmuir made artificial membranes by adding phospholipids dissolved in benzene (an organic solvent) to water. After the benzene evaporated, the phospholipids remained as a film covering the surface of the water, with only the hydrophilic heads of the phospholipids immersed in the water (FIGURE 8.1a). In 1925, two Dutch scientists, E. Gorter and F. Grendel, reasoned that cell membranes must actually be phospholipid bilayers, two molecules thick. Such a bilayer could exist as a stable boundary between two aqueous compartments because the molecular arrangement shelters the hydrophobic tails of the phospholipids from water while exposing the hydrophilic heads to water (FIGURE 8.1b). Gorter and Grendel measured the phospholipid content of membranes isolated from red blood cells and found just enough of the lipid to cover the cells with two layers. (Ironically, Gorter and Grendel underestimated both the phospholipid content and the surface area of the cells, but the two errors canceled each other. Thus, what turned out to be a correct conclusion was based on flawed measurements.)

If we assume that a phospholipid bilayer is the main fabric of the membrane, where do we place the proteins? Although the heads of phospholipids are hydrophilic, the surface of an artificial membrane consisting of a phospholipid bilayer adheres less strongly to water than does the surface of an actual biological membrane. This difference could be accounted for if the membrane were coated on both sides with hydrophilic proteins. In 1935, Hugh Davson and James Danielli proposed a sandwich model: a phospholipid bilayer between two layers of globular protein (FIGURE 8.2a).

When researchers first used electron microscopes to study cells in the 1950s, the pictures seemed to support the Davson-Danielli model. In electron micrographs of cells stained with atoms of heavy metals, the plasma membrane is triple-layered, having two dark ("stained") bands separated by an unstained layer (see FIGURE 7.6a, p. 107). Most early electron

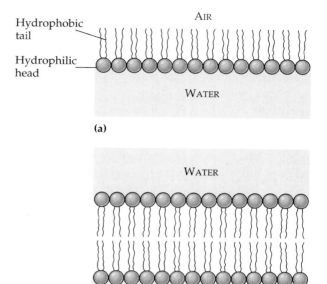

(a)

(b)

FIGURE 8.1 ▪ **Artificial membranes (cross sections). (a)** Water can be coated with a single layer of phospholipid molecules. The hydrophilic heads of the phospholipids are immersed in water, and the hydrophobic tails are excluded from water. **(b)** A bilayer of phospholipids forms a stable boundary between two aqueous compartments. This arrangement exposes the hydrophilic parts of the molecules to water and shields the hydrophobic parts from water.

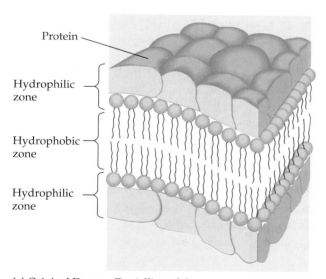

(a) Original Davson-Danielli model

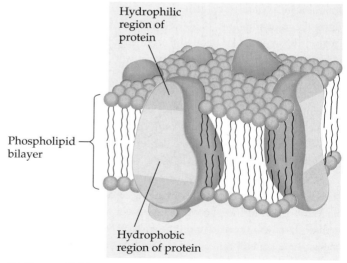

(b) Current fluid mosaic model

FIGURE 8.2 ▪ **Two generations of membrane models. (a)** The Davson-Danielli model, proposed in 1935, sandwiched the phospholipid bilayer between two protein layers. With later modifications, this model was widely accepted until about 1970. **(b)** The fluid mosaic model disperses the proteins and immerses them in the phospholipid bilayer, which is in a fluid state. Shown here in simplified form, this is our present working model of the membrane.

microscopists assumed that the stain adhered to the proteins and hydrophilic heads of the phospholipids, leaving the hydrophobic core of the membrane unstained. In a somewhat circular manner, the electron micrographs and the membrane model became increasingly accepted as explanations for each other. By the 1960s, the Davson-Danielli sandwich had become widely accepted as the structure not only of the plasma membrane, but of all the internal membranes of the cell. However, by the end of that decade, many cell biologists recognized two problems with the model.

First, the generalization that all membranes of the cell are identical was challenged. Not all membranes look alike through the electron microscope. For example, whereas the plasma membrane is 7–8 nm thick and has the three-layered structure, the inner membrane of the mitochondrion is only 6 nm thick and in electron micrographs looks like a row of beads. Mitochondrial membranes also have a substantially greater percentage of proteins than plasma membranes, and there are differences in the specific kinds of phospholipids and other lipids. Membranes with different functions differ in chemical composition and structure.

A more serious problem with the sandwich model is in the placement of the proteins. Unlike proteins dissolved in the cytosol, membrane proteins are not very soluble in water. Membrane proteins have hydrophobic and hydrophilic regions; they are amphipathic, as are their phospholipid partners in membranes. If proteins were layered on the surface of the membrane, their hydrophobic parts would be in an aqueous environment.

In 1972, S. J. Singer and G. Nicolson advocated a revised membrane model that placed the proteins in a location compatible with their amphipathic character. They proposed that membrane proteins are dispersed and individually inserted into the phospholipid bilayer, with only their hydrophilic regions protruding far enough from the bilayer to be exposed to water. This molecular arrangement would maximize contact of hydrophilic regions of proteins and phospholipids with water while providing their hydrophobic parts with a non-aqueous environment. According to this model, the membrane is a mosaic of protein molecules bobbing in a fluid bilayer of phospholipids; hence the term **fluid mosaic model** (FIGURE 8.2b).

A method of preparing cells for electron microscopy called freeze-fracture has provided convincing evidence that proteins are embedded in the phospholipid bilayer of the membrane, rather than being spread upon the surface. Freeze-fracture can delaminate a membrane along the middle of the bilayer, splitting the membrane into outer and inner faces (see the Methods Box, p. 138). When the halves of the fractured membrane are viewed in the electron microscope, the interior of the bilayer appears cobblestoned, with protein particles interspersed in a smooth matrix. Proteins clearly penetrate into the hydrophobic interior of the membrane.

We have examined the evolution of our understanding of membrane structure as a case history of how science works. Models are proposed by scientists as hypotheses, ways of organizing and explaining existing information. Replacing one model of membrane structure with another does not imply that the original model was worthless. The acceptance or rejection of a model depends on how well it fits observations and explains experimental results. A good model also makes predictions that shape future research. Models inspire experiments, and few models survive these tests without modification. New findings may make a model obsolete; even then, it may not be totally scrapped, but revised to incorporate the new observations. Like its predecessor, which endured for 35 years, the fluid mosaic model is continually being refined and may one day undergo major revision.

A membrane is a fluid mosaic of lipids, proteins, and carbohydrates

What exactly does it mean to describe a membrane as a fluid mosaic? Let's begin with the word *fluid*.

The Fluid Quality of Membranes

Membranes are not static sheets of molecules locked rigidly in place. A membrane is held together primarily by hydrophobic interactions, which are much weaker than covalent bonds (see Chapter 5). Most of the lipids and some of the proteins can drift about randomly in the plane of the membrane (FIGURE 8.3a). It is rare, however, for a molecule to flip-flop transversely across the membrane, switching from one phospholipid layer to the other; to do so, the hydrophilic part of the molecule would have to cross the hydrophobic core of the membrane.

Phospholipids move along the plane of the membrane rapidly, averaging about 2 μm—the length of a typical bacterial cell—per second. Proteins are much larger than lipids and move more slowly, but some membrane proteins do, in fact, drift (FIGURE 8.4). And some membrane proteins seem to move in a highly directed manner, perhaps driven along cytoskeletal fibers by motor proteins connected to the membrane proteins' cytoplasmic ends. However, many other membrane proteins seem to be held virtually immobile by their attachment to the cytoskeleton.

A membrane remains fluid as temperature decreases, until finally, at some critical temperature, the phospholipids settle into a closely packed arrangement and the membrane solidifies, much as bacon grease forms lard when it cools. The temperature at which a membrane solidifies depends on its lipid composition. The membrane remains fluid to a lower temperature if it is rich in phospholipids with unsaturated hydrocarbon tails (see FIGURES 5.11 and 5.12). Because of kinks where double

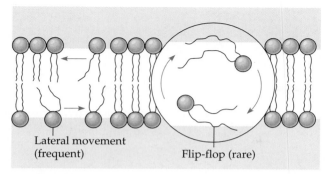

Lateral movement (frequent)

Flip-flop (rare)

(a) Movement of phospholipids

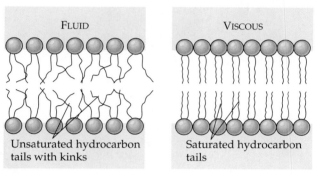

FLUID

VISCOUS

Unsaturated hydrocarbon tails with kinks

Saturated hydrocarbon tails

(b) Membrane fluidity

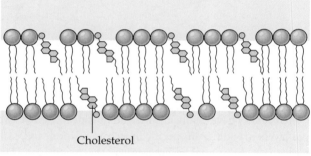

Cholesterol

(c) Cholesterol within the membrane

FIGURE 8.3 ▪ The fluidity of membranes. (a) Lipids move laterally (that is, in two dimensions) in a membrane, but flip-flopping across the membrane (in the third dimension) is rare. **(b)** Unsaturated hydrocarbon tails of phospholipids have kinks that keep the molecules from packing together, enhancing membrane fluidity. **(c)** Cholesterol reduces membrane fluidity by reducing phospholipid movement at moderate temperatures but it also hinders solidification at low temperatures.

bonds are located, unsaturated hydrocarbons do not pack together as closely as saturated hydrocarbons (see FIGURE 8.3b).

The steroid cholesterol, which is wedged between phospholipid molecules in the plasma membranes of animals, helps stabilize the membrane (see FIGURE 8.3c). At relatively warm temperatures—at 37°C, the body temperature of humans, for example—cholesterol makes the membrane less fluid by restraining the movement of phospholipids. However, because cholesterol also hinders the close packing of phospholipids, it lowers the temperature required for the membrane to solidify.

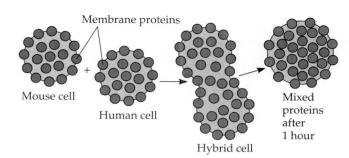

Membrane proteins

Mouse cell

Human cell

Hybrid cell

Mixed proteins after 1 hour

FIGURE 8.4 ▪ Evidence for the drifting of membrane proteins. When researchers fuse a human cell with a mouse cell, it takes less than an hour for the membrane proteins of the two species to completely intermingle in the membrane of the hybrid cell.

Membranes must be fluid to work properly; they are usually about as fluid as salad oil. When a membrane solidifies, its permeability changes, and enzymatic proteins in it may become inactive. A cell can alter the lipid composition of its membranes to some extent as an adjustment to changing temperature. For instance, in many plants that tolerate extreme cold, such as winter wheat, the percentage of unsaturated phospholipids increases in autumn, an adaptation that keeps the membranes from solidifying during winter.

Membranes as Mosaics of Structure and Function

Now we come to the word *mosaic*. A membrane is a collage of many different proteins embedded in the fluid matrix of the lipid bilayer (FIGURE 8.5, p. 134). The lipid bilayer is the main fabric of the membrane, but proteins determine most of the membrane's specific functions. The plasma membrane and the membranes of the various organelles each have unique collections of proteins. More than 50 kinds of proteins have been found to date in the plasma membrane of red blood cells, for example.

Notice in FIGURE 8.5 that there are two major populations of membrane proteins. **Integral proteins** are generally transmembrane proteins, with hydrophobic regions that completely span the hydrophobic interior of the membrane. The hydrophobic regions of an integral protein consist of one or more stretches of nonpolar amino acids (see FIGURE 5.15), usually coiled into α-helices (FIGURE 8.6, p. 134). The hydrophilic ends of the molecule are exposed to the aqueous solutions on either side of the membrane. **Peripheral proteins** are not embedded in the lipid bilayer at all; they are appendages loosely bound to the surface of the membrane, often to the exposed parts of integral proteins (see FIGURE 8.5).

On the cytoplasmic side of the plasma membrane, some membrane proteins are held in place by attachment to the cytoskeleton. And on the exterior side, certain membrane proteins are attached to fibers of the extracellular matrix (see Chapter 7). These attachments combine to give animal cells a stronger external framework than the plasma membrane itself could provide.

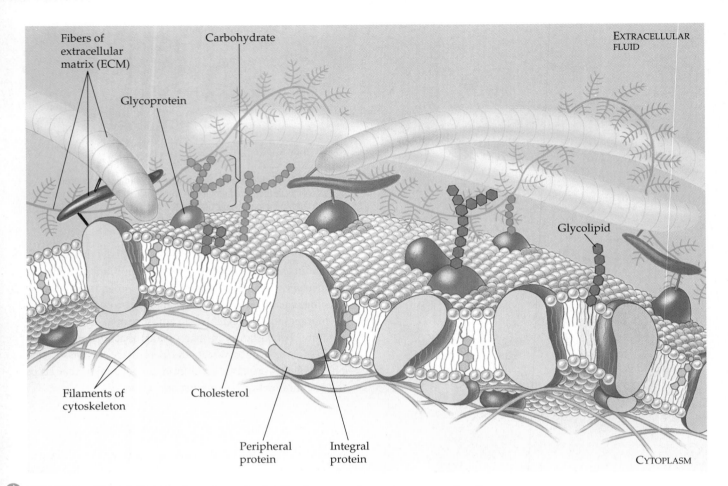

Fibers of
extracellular
matrix (ECM)

Carbohydrate

Glycoprotein

Glycolipid

Filaments of
cytoskeleton

Cholesterol

Peripheral
protein

Integral
protein

CYTOPLASM

FIGURE 8.5 · The detailed structure of an animal cell's plasma membrane, in cross section. See
8.1 Figure 7.29 for details of the ECM.

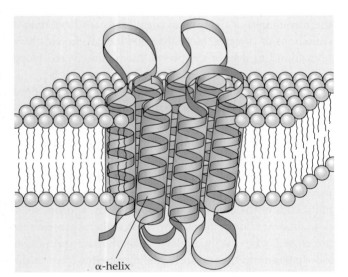

α-helix

FIGURE 8.6 · The structure of a transmembrane protein. This ribbon model highlights the α-helical secondary structure of the hydrophobic parts of the protein, which lie mostly within the hydrophobic core of the membrane. This particular protein, bacteriorhodopsin, has seven transmembrane helices (outlined with cylinders for emphasis). Joining the helices are hydrophilic polypeptide segments that together form the parts of the protein in contact with the aqueous solutions on either side of the membrane. Bacteriorhodopsin is a specialized transport protein found in certain bacteria.

Membranes have distinct inside and outside faces. The two lipid layers may differ in specific lipid composition, and each protein has directional orientation in the membrane. The plasma membrane also has carbohydrates, which are restricted to the exterior surface. This asymmetrical distribution of proteins, lipids, and carbohydrates is determined as the membrane is being built by the endoplasmic reticulum. Molecules that start out on the *inside* face of the ER end up on the *outside* face of the plasma membrane (FIGURE 8.7).

FIGURE 8.8 gives an overview of six major kinds of function exhibited by proteins of the plasma membrane. A single cell may have membrane proteins performing several of these functions, and a single protein may have multiple functions. Thus the membrane is indeed a functional mosaic, as well as a structural one.

Membrane Carbohydrates and Cell-Cell Recognition

Cell-cell recognition, a cell's ability to distinguish one type of neighboring cell from another, is crucial to the functioning of an organism. It is important, for example, in the sorting of cells into tissues and organs in an animal embryo. It is also the basis for the rejection of foreign cells (including those of

FIGURE 8.8 · **Some functions of membrane proteins.** In many cases, a single protein performs some combination of these tasks.

transplanted organs) by the immune system, an important line of defense in vertebrate animals (see Chapter 43). The way cells recognize other cells is by keying on surface molecules, often carbohydrates, on the plasma membrane.

Membrane carbohydrates are usually branched oligosaccharides with fewer than 15 sugar units. (*Oligo* is Greek for "few"; an oligosaccharide is a short polysaccharide.) Some of these oligosaccharides are covalently bonded to lipids, forming molecules called glycolipids. (Recall that *glyco* refers to the presence of carbohydrate.) Most, however, are covalently bonded to proteins, which are thereby glycoproteins.

The oligosaccharides on the external side of the plasma membrane vary from species to species, among individuals of the same species, and even from one cell type to another in a single individual. The diversity of the molecules and their location on the cell's surface enable oligosaccharides to function as markers that distinguish one cell from another. For example, the four human blood groups designated A, B, AB, and O reflect variation in the oligosaccharides on the surfaces of red blood cells.

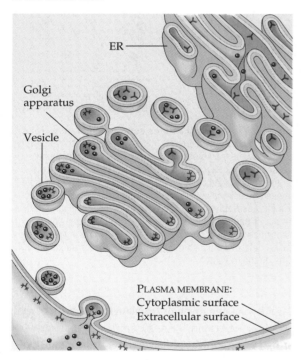

FIGURE 8.7 · **Sidedness of the plasma membrane.** The membrane has distinct cytoplasmic and extracellular sides. This bifacial quality is determined when the membrane is first synthesized and modified by the ER and Golgi. The diagram color-codes the two sides of the membranes of the endomembrane system, to illustrate that the side facing the inside of the ER, Golgi, and vesicles is topologically equivalent to the extracellular surface of the plasma membrane. The other side always faces the cytosol, from the time the membrane is made by the ER to the time it is added to the plasma membrane by fusion of a vesicle. The small green "trees" represent membrane carbohydrates that are synthesized in the ER and modified in the Golgi. Vesicle fusion with the plasma membrane is also responsible for secretion of cell products (purple).

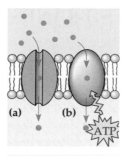

Transport (a) A protein that spans the membrane may provide a hydrophilic channel across the membrane that is selective for a particular solute. (b) Some transport proteins hydrolyze ATP as an energy source to actively pump substances across the membrane.

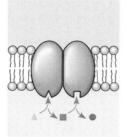

Enzymatic activity A protein built into the membrane may be an enzyme with its active site exposed to substances in the adjacent solution. In some cases, several enzymes in a membrane are ordered as a team that carries out sequential steps of a metabolic pathway.

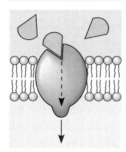

Signal transduction A membrane protein may have a binding site with a specific shape that fits the shape of a chemical messenger, such as a hormone. The external messenger (signal) may cause a conformational change in the protein that relays the message to the inside of the cell.

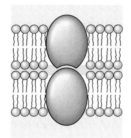

Intercellular joining Membrane proteins of adjacent cells may be hooked together in various kinds of junctions (see Figure 7.30).

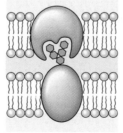

Cell-cell recognition Some glycoproteins (proteins with short chains of sugars) serve as identification tags that are specifically recognized by other cells.

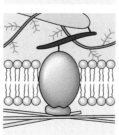

Attachment to the cytoskeleton and extracellular matrix (ECM) Microfilaments or other elements of the cytoskeleton may be bonded to membrane proteins, a function that helps maintain cell shape and fixes the location of certain membrane proteins. Proteins that adhere to the ECM can coordinate extracellular and intracellular changes.

TRAFFIC ACROSS MEMBRANES

The biological membrane is an exquisite example of a supramolecular structure—many molecules ordered into a higher level of organization—with emergent properties beyond those of the individual molecules. The remainder of this chapter focuses on one of the most important of those properties: the ability to regulate transport across cellular boundaries, a function essential to the cell's existence as an open system. We will see once again that form fits function: The fluid mosaic model helps explain how membranes regulate the cell's molecular traffic.

A membrane's molecular organization results in selective permeability

A steady traffic of small molecules and ions moves across the plasma membrane in both directions. Consider the chemical exchanges between a muscle cell and the extracellular fluid that bathes it. Sugars, amino acids, and other nutrients enter the cell, and metabolic waste products leave. The cell takes in oxygen for cellular respiration and expels carbon dioxide. It also regulates its concentrations of inorganic ions, such as Na^+, K^+, Ca^{2+}, and Cl^-, by shuttling them one way or the other across the plasma membrane. Although traffic through the membrane is extensive, cell membranes are selectively permeable, and substances do not cross the barrier indiscriminately. The cell is able to take up many varieties of small molecules and ions and exclude others. Moreover, substances that move through the membrane do so at different rates.

Permeability of the Lipid Bilayer

The hydrophobic core of the membrane impedes the transport of ions and polar molecules, which are hydrophilic. Hydrophobic molecules, such as hydrocarbons, carbon dioxide, and oxygen, can dissolve in the membrane and cross it with ease. Very small molecules that are polar but uncharged can also pass through the membrane rapidly. Examples are water and ethanol, which are tiny enough to pass between the lipids of the membrane. The lipid bilayer is not very permeable to larger, uncharged polar molecules, such as glucose and other sugars. It is also relatively impermeable to all ions, even such small ones as H^+ and Na^+. A charged atom or molecule and its shell of water find the hydrophobic layer of the membrane difficult to penetrate. However, the lipid bilayer is only part of the story of a membrane's selective permeability. Proteins built into the membrane play a key role in regulating transport.

Transport Proteins

Cell membranes are permeable to specific ions and polar molecules. These hydrophilic substances avoid contact with the

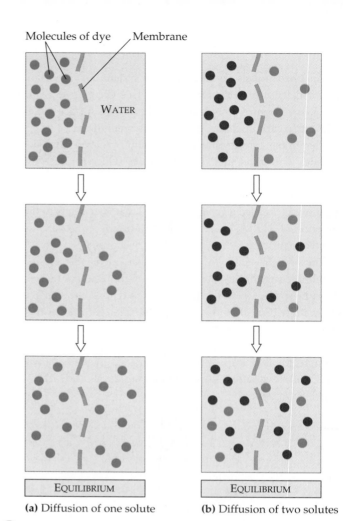

Molecules of dye — Membrane

WATER

EQUILIBRIUM — EQUILIBRIUM

(a) Diffusion of one solute — (b) Diffusion of two solutes

FIGURE 8.9 · The diffusion of solutes across membranes. (a) A substance will diffuse from where it is more concentrated to where it is less concentrated. The membrane, viewed here in cross section, has pores large enough for molecules of dye to pass. Diffusion down the concentration gradient leads to a dynamic equilibrium; the solute molecules continue to cross the membrane, but at equal rates in both directions. **(b)** In this case, solutions of two different dyes are separated by a membrane that is permeable to both dyes. Each dye diffuses down its own concentration gradient. There will be a net diffusion of the green dye toward the left, even though the *total* solute concentration was initially greater on the left side.

lipid bilayer by passing through **transport proteins** that span the membrane (see FIGURE 8.8, top). Some transport proteins function by having a hydrophilic channel that certain molecules use as a tunnel through the membrane. Other transport proteins bind to their passengers and physically move them across the membrane. In both cases, each transport protein is specific for the substances it translocates (moves), allowing only a certain substance or class of closely related substances to cross the membrane. For example, glucose carried in blood to the human liver enters liver cells rapidly through specific transport proteins in the plasma membrane. The protein is so selective that it even rejects fructose, a structural isomer of glucose.

Thus the selective permeability of a membrane depends on both the discriminating barrier of the lipid bilayer and the specific transport proteins built into the membrane. But what determines the *direction* of traffic across a membrane? At a given time, will a particular substance enter the cell or leave? And what mechanisms actually drive molecules across membranes? We will address these questions next as we explore two modes of membrane traffic: passive transport and active transport.

Passive transport is diffusion across a membrane

8.2 Molecules have intrinsic kinetic energy called thermal motion (heat). One result of thermal motion is **diffusion**, the tendency for molecules of any substance to spread out into the available space. Each molecule moves randomly, yet diffusion of a *population* of molecules may be directional. For example, imagine a membrane separating pure water from a solution of a dye in water. Assume that this membrane is permeable to the dye molecules (FIGURE 8.9a). Each dye molecule wanders randomly, but there will be a *net* movement of the dye molecules across the membrane to the side that began as pure water. The spreading of the dye across the membrane will continue until both solutions have equal concentrations of the dye. Once that point is reached, there will be a dynamic equilibrium, with as many dye molecules crossing the membrane in one direction as in the other each second.

We can now state a simple rule of diffusion: In the absence of other forces, a substance will diffuse from where it is more concentrated to where it is less concentrated. Put another way, any substance will diffuse down its **concentration gradient**. No work must be done to make this happen; diffusion is a spontaneous process because it decreases free energy (see FIGURE 6.4b). Recall that in any system there is a tendency for entropy, or disorder, to increase. Diffusion of a solute in water increases entropy by producing a more random mixture than exists when there are localized concentrations of the solute. It is important to note that each substance diffuses down its *own* concentration gradient, unaffected by the concentration differences of other substances (FIGURE 8.9b).

Much of the traffic across cell membranes occurs by diffusion. When a substance is more concentrated on one side of a membrane than on the other, there is a tendency for the substance to diffuse across the membrane down its concentration gradient (assuming that the membrane is permeable to that substance). One important example is the uptake of oxygen by a cell performing cellular respiration. Dissolved oxygen diffuses into the cell across the plasma membrane. As long as cellular respiration consumes the O_2 as it enters, diffusion into the cell will continue, because the concentration gradient favors movement in that direction.

The diffusion of a substance across a biological membrane is called **passive transport**, because the cell does not have to

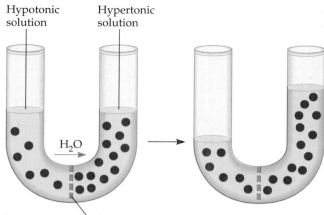

FIGURE 8.10 · Osmosis. Two sugar solutions of different concentration are separated by a porous membrane that is permeable to the solvent (water) but not to the solute (sugar). Water diffuses from the hypotonic solution to the hypertonic solution. This passive transport of water, or osmosis, reduces the difference in sugar concentrations.

8.3 expend energy to make it happen. The concentration gradient itself represents potential energy and drives diffusion. Remember, however, that membranes are selectively permeable and therefore affect the rates of diffusion of various molecules. One molecule that diffuses freely across most membranes is water, a fact that has important consequences for cells.

Osmosis is the passive transport of water

8.3 In comparing two solutions of unequal solute concentration, the solution with a higher concentration of solutes is said to be **hypertonic**. The solution with a lower solute concentration is **hypotonic**. (*Hyper* and *hypo* mean "more" and "less," respectively, referring here to solute concentration.) These are relative terms that are meaningful only in a comparative sense. For example, tap water is hypertonic to distilled water but hypotonic to seawater. In other words, tap water has a higher solute concentration than distilled water, but a lower concentration than seawater. Solutions of equal solute concentration are said to be **isotonic** (*iso* means "the same").

Picture a U-shaped vessel with a selectively permeable membrane separating two sugar solutions of different concentrations (FIGURE 8.10). Pores in this synthetic membrane are too small for sugar molecules to pass but large enough for water molecules to cross the membrane. In effect, the solution with higher solute concentration (hypertonic) has a lower water concentration.* Therefore the water will diffuse across

---

* Actually, at any instant, a fraction of the water molecules in a solution lose their freedom of independent movement by being bound to solute molecules in hydration shells. It is not really a difference in *total* water concentration that causes osmosis, but a difference in the concentration of *unbound* water molecules that are free to cross the membrane.

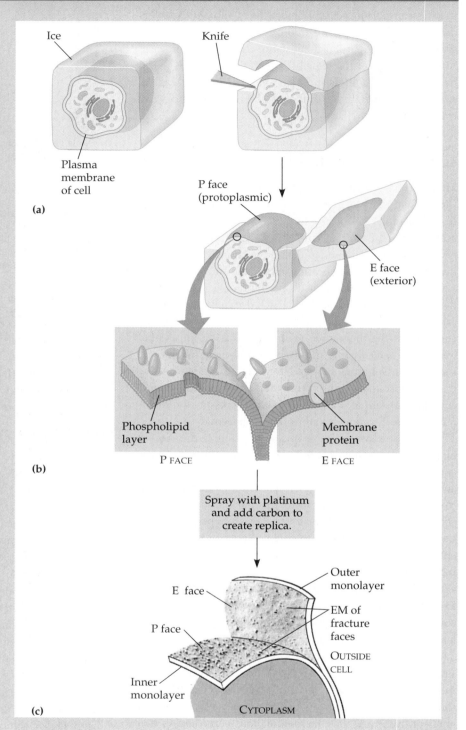

(a) A researcher freezes the specimen at the temperature of liquid nitrogen, then fractures the cells with a cold knife.

(b) The knife does not cut cleanly through the frozen cells; instead, it cracks the specimen, with the fracture plane following the path of least resistance. The fracture plane often follows the hydrophobic interior of a membrane, splitting the lipid bilayer down the middle into a P ("protoplasmic"—that is, cytoplasmic) face and an E (exterior) face. The membrane proteins are not split but go with one or the other of the phospholipid layers. The topography of the fractured surface may be enhanced by etching, the removal of water by sublimation (direct evaporation of frozen water to water vapor).

(c) A fine mist of platinum is sprayed from an angle onto the fractured surface of the cell. There will be "shadows" where elevated regions of the fractured cell block the platinum. Adding a film of carbon strengthens the platinum coat.

The original specimen is digested away with bleach, acids, and enzymes, leaving the platinum-carbon film as a replica of the fractured surface. It is this replica, not the membrane itself, that is examined through the electron microscope.

Electron micrographs have been inserted into this drawing of a delaminated membrane. Notice the protein particles (the "bumps").

the membrane from the hypotonic solution to the hypertonic solution. This diffusion of water across a selectively permeable membrane is a special case of passive transport called **osmosis**.

The direction of osmosis is determined only by a difference in *total* solute concentration. Water moves from a hypotonic to a hypertonic solution even if the hypotonic solution has more *kinds* of solutes. Seawater, which has a great variety of solutes, will lose water to a very concentrated solution of a single sugar, because the total solute concentration of the seawater is lower. If two solutions are isotonic, water moves across a membrane separating the solutions at an equal rate in both directions; that is, there is no net osmosis between isotonic solutions. (In Units Six and Seven, we will look at osmosis in a more quantitative way.)

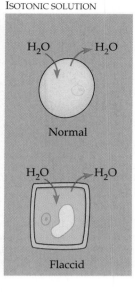

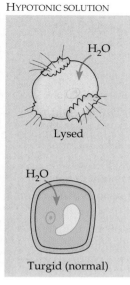

HYPERTONIC SOLUTION	ISOTONIC SOLUTION	HYPOTONIC SOLUTION

ANIMAL CELL

H₂O (Shriveled) | H₂O H₂O (Normal) | H₂O (Lysed)

PLANT CELL

H₂O (Plasmolyzed) | H₂O H₂O (Flaccid) | H₂O (Turgid (normal))

FIGURE 8.11 · **The water balance of living cells.** How living cells react to changes in the solute concentrations of their environments depends on whether or not they have cell walls. Animal cells do not have cell walls; plant cells do. Unless it has special adaptations to offset the osmotic uptake or loss of water, an animal cell fares best in an isotonic environment. Plant cells are turgid (firm) and generally healthiest in a hypotonic environment, where the tendency for continued uptake of water is balanced by the elastic wall pushing back on the cell. (Arrows indicate net water movement when the cells are *first* placed in these solutions.)

Cell survival depends on balancing water uptake and loss

The movement of water across cell membranes and the balance of water between the cell and its environment are crucial to organisms. Let's now apply to living cells what we have learned about osmosis in artificial systems.

Water Balance of Cells Without Walls

If an animal cell is immersed in an environment that is isotonic to the cell, there will be no net movement of water across the plasma membrane. Water flows across the membrane, but at the same rate in both directions. In an isotonic environment, the volume of an animal cell is stable (FIGURE 8.11). Now let's transfer the cell to a solution that is hypertonic to the cell. The cell will lose water to its environment, shrivel, and probably die. This is one reason why an increase in the salinity (saltiness) of a lake can kill the animals there. However, taking up too much water can be just as hazardous to an animal cell as losing water. If we place the cell in a solution that is hypotonic to the cell, water will enter faster than it leaves, and the cell will swell and lyse (burst) like an overfilled water balloon.

A cell without rigid walls can tolerate neither excessive uptake nor excessive loss of water. This problem of water balance is automatically solved if such a cell lives in isotonic surroundings. Seawater is isotonic to many marine invertebrates. The cells of most terrestrial (land-dwelling) animals are bathed in an extracellular fluid that is isotonic to the cells. Animals and other organisms without rigid cell walls living in hypertonic or hypotonic environments must have special adaptations for **osmoregulation**, the control of water balance. For example, the protist *Paramecium* lives in pond water, which is hypotonic to the cell (FIGURE 8.12). Water continually tends to

enter the cell, but *Paramecium* has a plasma membrane that is much less permeable to water than the membranes of most other cells. Also, *Paramecium* is equipped with a contractile vacuole, an organelle that functions as a bilge pump to force

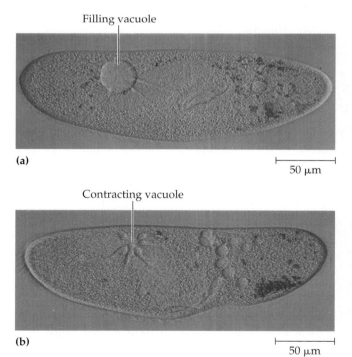

Filling vacuole

(a)

50 μm

Contracting vacuole

(b)

50 μm

FIGURE 8.12 · **Evolutionary adaptations for osmoregulation in** ***Paramecium.*** *Paramecium* is a freshwater protist. Pond water, which is hypotonic to the cell, surrounds a *Paramecium,* and water tends to enter the cell by osmosis. What keeps the cell, which lacks a cell wall, from bursting? Compared to the plasma membranes of most other organisms, the *Paramecium* membrane is less permeable to water. However, this adaptation only slows the uptake of water. The contractile vacuole offsets osmosis by bailing water out of the cell. **(a)** A contractile vacuole fills with fluid that enters from a system of canals radiating throughout the cytoplasm (LM). **(b)** When full, the vacuole and canals contract, expelling fluid from the cell (LM).

water out of the cell as fast as it enters by osmosis. We will examine other adaptations for osmoregulation in Chapter 44.

Water Balance of Cells with Walls

The cells of plants, prokaryotes, fungi, and some protists have walls. When such a cell is in a hypotonic solution—when bathed by rainwater, for example—the wall helps maintain the cell's water balance. Consider a plant cell. Like an animal cell, the plant cell swells as water enters by osmosis (see FIGURE 8.11). However, the elastic wall will expand only so much before it exerts a back pressure on the cell that opposes further water uptake. At this point, the cell is **turgid** (very firm), which is the healthy state for most plant cells. Plants that are not woody, such as most house plants, depend for mechanical support on cells kept turgid by a surrounding hypotonic solution. If a plant's cells and their surroundings are isotonic, there is no net tendency for water to enter, and the cells become **flaccid** (limp), causing the plant to wilt.

On the other hand, a wall is of no advantage if the cell is immersed in a hypertonic environment. In this case, a plant cell, like an animal cell, will lose water to its surroundings and shrink. As the plant cell shrivels, its plasma membrane pulls away from the wall. This phenomenon, called **plasmolysis**, is usually lethal. The walled cells of bacteria and fungi also plasmolyze in hypertonic environments.

Specific proteins facilitate the passive transport of selected solutes

Let's now turn our attention from the transport of water across a membrane to the traffic of specific solutes dissolved in the water. As mentioned earlier, many polar molecules and ions impeded by the lipid bilayer of the membrane diffuse with the help of transport proteins that span the membrane. This phenomenon is called **facilitated diffusion**.

A transport protein has many of the properties of an enzyme. Just as an enzyme is specific for its substrate, a transport protein is specialized for the solute it transports and may even have a specific binding site akin to the active site of an enzyme. Like enzymes, transport proteins can be saturated. There are only so many molecules of each type of transport protein built into the plasma membrane, and when these molecules are translocating passengers as fast as they can, transport is occurring at a maximum rate. Also like enzymes, transport proteins can be inhibited by molecules that resemble the normal "substrate." This occurs when the imposter competes with the normally transported solute by binding to the transport protein. Unlike enzymes, however, transport proteins do not usually catalyze chemical reactions. Their function is to catalyze a *physical* process—the faster transport of a molecule across a membrane that would otherwise be relatively impermeable to the substance.

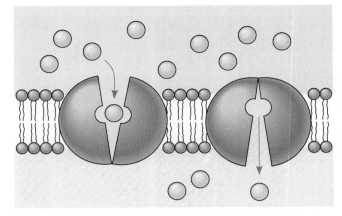

FIGURE 8.13 ▪ **One model for facilitated diffusion.** The transport protein (purple) alternates between two conformations, moving a solute across the membrane as the shape of the protein changes. The protein can transport the solute in either direction, with the net movement being down the concentration gradient of the solute.

Cell biologists are still trying to learn how various transport proteins facilitate diffusion. In many cases, the protein probably undergoes a subtle change in shape that translocates the solute-binding site from one side of the membrane to the other (FIGURE 8.13). The changes in shape could be triggered by the binding and release of the transported molecule. Other transport proteins simply provide selective corridors allowing a specific solute to cross the membrane (see FIGURE 8.8, top, part (a)). Some of these proteins function as **gated channels**; a stimulus causes them to open or close. The stimulus may be electrical or chemical; if chemical, it is a substance other than the one to be transported. For example, stimulation of a nerve cell by neurotransmitter molecules opens gated channels that allow sodium ions into the cell.

In certain inherited diseases, specific transport systems are either defective or missing altogether. An example is cystinuria, a human disease characterized by the absence of a protein that transports cystine and other amino acids across the membranes of kidney cells. Kidney cells normally reabsorb these amino acids from the urine and return them to the blood, but an individual afflicted with cystinuria develops painful stones from amino acids that accumulate and crystallize in the kidneys.

Active transport is the pumping of solutes against their gradients

Despite the help of a transport protein, facilitated diffusion is still considered passive transport because the solute is moving down its concentration gradient. Facilitated diffusion speeds the transport of a solute by providing an efficient passage through the membrane, but it does not alter the direction of transport. Some transport proteins, however, *can* move solutes against their concentration gradients, across the plasma membrane from the side where they are less concentrated to the side

where they are more concentrated. This transport is "uphill" and therefore requires work. To pump a molecule across a membrane against its gradient, the cell must expend its own metabolic energy; therefore, this type of membrane traffic is called **active transport**.

Active transport is a major factor in the ability of a cell to maintain internal concentrations of small molecules that differ from concentrations in its environment. For example, compared to its surroundings, an animal cell has a much higher concentration of potassium ions and a much lower concentration of sodium ions. The plasma membrane helps maintain these steep gradients by pumping sodium out of the cell and potassium into the cell.

The work of active transport is performed by specific proteins embedded in membranes. As in other types of cellular work, ATP supplies the energy for most active transport. One way ATP can power active transport is by transferring its ter-

minal phosphate group directly to the transport protein. This may induce the protein to change its conformation in a manner that translocates a solute bound to the protein across the membrane. One transport system that works this way is the **sodium-potassium pump**, which exchanges sodium (Na^+) for potassium (K^+) across the plasma membrane of animal cells (FIGURE 8.14). FIGURE 8.15 (p. 142) reviews the distinction between passive transport and active transport.

Some ion pumps generate voltage across membranes

All cells have voltages across their plasma membranes. Voltage is electrical potential energy—a separation of opposite charges. The cytoplasm of a cell is negative in charge compared to the extracellular fluid because of an unequal distribution of anions and cations on opposite sides of the

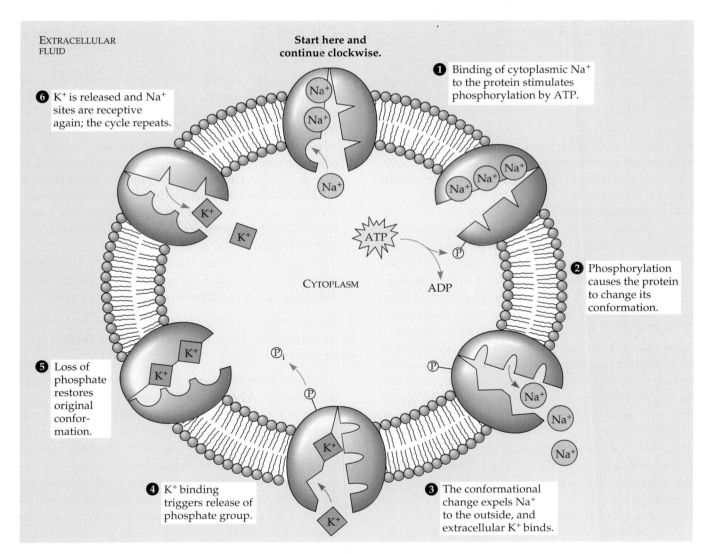

FIGURE 8.14 ▪ The sodium-potassium pump: a specific case of active transport. This transport system pumps ions against steep concentration gradients. The pump oscillates between two conformational states in a pumping cycle that translocates three Na^+ ions out of the cell for every two K^+ ions pumped into the cell. ATP powers the changes in conformation by phosphorylating the transport protein (that is, by transferring a phosphate group to the protein).

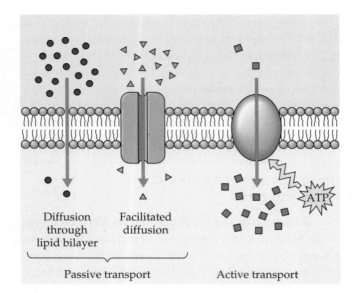

Passive transport

Active transport

FIGURE 8.15 · Review: passive and active transport compared.
In passive transport, a substance diffuses spontaneously down its concentration gradient with no need for the cell to expend energy. Hydrophobic molecules and very small uncharged polar molecules diffuse directly across the membrane. Hydrophilic substances diffuse through transport proteins in a process called facilitated diffusion. In active transport, a transport protein moves substances across the membrane "uphill" against their concentration gradients. Active transport requires an expenditure of energy, usually supplied by ATP.

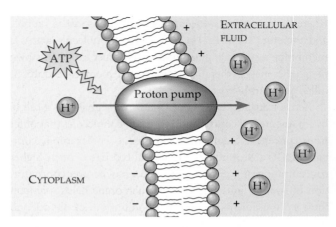

FIGURE 8.16 · An electrogenic pump. Proton pumps are examples of membrane proteins that store energy by generating voltage (charge separation) across membranes. Using ATP for power, a proton pump translocates positive charge in the form of hydrogen ions. The voltage and H$^+$ gradient represent a dual energy source that can be tapped by the cell to drive other processes, such as the uptake of sugar and other nutrients. Proton pumps are the main electrogenic pumps of plants, fungi, and bacteria.

membrane. The voltage across a membrane, called a **membrane potential**, ranges from about −50 to −200 millivolts. (The minus sign indicates that the inside of the cell is negative compared to the outside.)

The membrane potential acts like a battery, an energy source that affects the traffic of all charged substances across the membrane. Because the inside of the cell is negative compared to the outside, the membrane potential favors the passive transport of cations into the cell and anions out of the cell. Thus, *two* forces drive the diffusion of ions across a membrane: a chemical force (the ion's concentration gradient) and an electrical force (the effect of the membrane potential on the ion's movement). This combination of forces acting on an ion is called the **electrochemical gradient**. In the case of ions, we must refine our concept of passive transport: An ion does not simply diffuse down its *concentration* gradient, but diffuses down its *electrochemical* gradient. For example, the concentration of sodium ions (Na$^+$) inside a resting nerve cell is much lower than outside it. When the cell is stimulated, gated channels that facilitate Na$^+$ diffusion open. Sodium ions then "fall" down their electrochemical gradient, driven by the concentration gradient of Na$^+$ and by the attraction of cations to the negative side of the membrane.

Some membrane proteins that actively transport ions contribute to the membrane potential. An example is the sodium-potassium pump. Notice in FIGURE 8.14 that the pump does not translocate Na$^+$ and K$^+$ one for one, but actually pumps three sodium ions out of the cell for every two potassium ions

it pumps into the cell. With each crank of the pump, there is a net transfer of one positive charge from the cytoplasm to the extracellular fluid, a process that stores energy in the form of voltage. A transport protein that generates voltage across a membrane is called an **electrogenic pump**. The sodium-potassium pump seems to be the major electrogenic pump of animal cells. The main electrogenic pump of plants, bacteria, and fungi is a **proton pump**, which actively transports hydrogen ions (protons) out of the cell. The pumping of H$^+$ transfers positive charge from the cytoplasm to the extracellular solution (FIGURE 8.16).

By generating voltage across membranes, electrogenic pumps store energy that can be tapped for cellular work, including a type of membrane traffic called cotransport.

In cotransport, a membrane protein couples the transport of one solute to another

A single ATP-powered pump that transports a specific solute can indirectly drive the active transport of several other solutes in a mechanism called **cotransport**. A substance that has been pumped across a membrane can do work as it leaks back by diffusion, analogous to water that has been pumped uphill and performs work as it flows back down. Another specialized transport protein, separate from the pump, can couple the "downhill" diffusion of this substance to the "uphill" transport of a second substance against its own concentration gradient. For example, a plant cell uses the gradient of hydrogen ions generated by its proton pumps to drive the active transport of amino acids, sugars, and several other nutrients into the cell. One specific transport protein couples the return of hydrogen ions to the transport of sucrose into the cell (FIG-

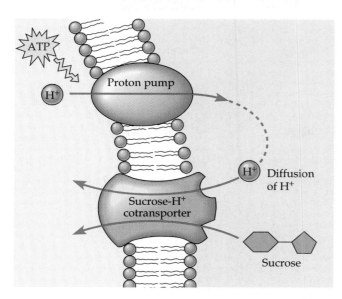

FIGURE 8.17 ▪ **Cotransport.** An ATP-driven pump stores energy by concentrating a substance (H⁺, in this case) on one side of the membrane. As the substance leaks back across the membrane through specific transport proteins, it escorts other substances into the cell. In this case, the proton pump of the membrane is indirectly driving sucrose accumulation by a plant cell, with the help of a protein that cotransports the two solutes.

URE 8.17). The protein can translocate sucrose into the cell against a concentration gradient, but only if the sucrose molecule travels in the company of a hydrogen ion. The sucrose rides on the coattails of the hydrogen ion, which uses the common transport protein as an avenue to diffuse down the concentration gradient maintained by the proton pump. Plants use the mechanism of sucrose-H⁺ cotransport to load sucrose produced by photosynthesis into specialized cells in the veins of leaves. The sugar can then be distributed by the vascular tissue of the plant to nonphotosynthetic organs, such as roots.

Exocytosis and endocytosis transport large molecules

8.6 Water and small solutes enter and leave the cell by passing through the lipid bilayer of the plasma membrane, or by being pumped or carried across the membrane by transport proteins. Large molecules, such as proteins and polysaccharides, generally cross the membrane by a different mechanism involving vesicles. As we described in Chapter 7, the cell secretes macromolecules by the fusion of vesicles with the plasma membrane; this is **exocytosis**. A transport vesicle budded from the Golgi apparatus is moved by the cytoskeleton to the plasma membrane. When the vesicle membrane and plasma membrane come into contact, the lipid molecules of the two bilayers rearrange themselves so that the two membranes fuse. The contents of the vesicle then spill to the outside of the cell (see FIGURE 8.7).

Many secretory cells use exocytosis to export their products. For example, certain cells in the pancreas manufacture the hormone insulin and secrete it into the blood by exocytosis. Another example is the neuron, or nerve cell, which uses exocytosis to release chemical signals that stimulate other neurons or muscle cells (see FIGURE 2.16). When plant cells are making walls, exocytosis delivers carbohydrates from Golgi vesicles to the outside of the cell.

In **endocytosis**, the cell takes in macromolecules and particulate matter by forming new vesicles from the plasma membrane. The steps are basically the reverse of exocytosis. A small area of the plasma membrane sinks inward to form a pocket. As the pocket deepens, it pinches in, forming a vesicle containing material that had been outside the cell.

There are three types of endocytosis: phagocytosis ("cellular eating"), pinocytosis ("cellular drinking"), and receptor-mediated endocytosis. In **phagocytosis**, a cell engulfs a particle by wrapping pseudopodia around it and packaging it within a membrane-enclosed sac large enough to be classified as a vacuole (FIGURE 8.18a, p. 144). The particle is digested after the vacuole fuses with a lysosome containing hydrolytic enzymes. In **pinocytosis**, the cell "gulps" droplets of extracellular fluid in tiny vesicles (FIGURE 8.18b). Because any and all solutes dissolved in the droplet are taken into the cell, pinocytosis is unspecific in the substances it transports. In contrast, **receptor-mediated endocytosis** is very specific (FIGURE 8.18c). Embedded in the membrane are proteins with specific receptor sites exposed to the extracellular fluid. The extracellular substances that bind to the receptors are called **ligands**, a general term for any molecule that binds specifically to a receptor site of another molecule (from the Latin *ligare*, "to bind"). The receptor proteins are usually clustered in regions of the membrane called coated pits, which are lined on their cytoplasmic side by a fuzzy layer of protein. These coat proteins probably help deepen the pit and form the vesicle.

Receptor-mediated endocytosis enables the cell to acquire bulk quantities of specific substances, even though those substances may not be very concentrated in the extracellular fluid. For example, human cells use the process to take in cholesterol for use in the synthesis of membranes and as a precursor for the synthesis of other steroids. Cholesterol travels in the blood in particles called low-density lipoproteins (LDLs), complexes of lipids and proteins. These particles bind to LDL receptors on membranes, and then enter the cell by endocytosis. In humans with familial hypercholesterolemia, an inherited disease characterized by a very high level of cholesterol in the blood, the LDL receptor proteins are defective, and the LDL particles cannot enter cells. Cholesterol accumulates in the blood, where it contributes to early atherosclerosis (the buildup of fat deposits on blood vessel linings).

Vesicles not only transport substances between the cell and its surroundings, they also provide a mechanism for rejuvenating or remodeling the plasma membrane. Endocytosis and

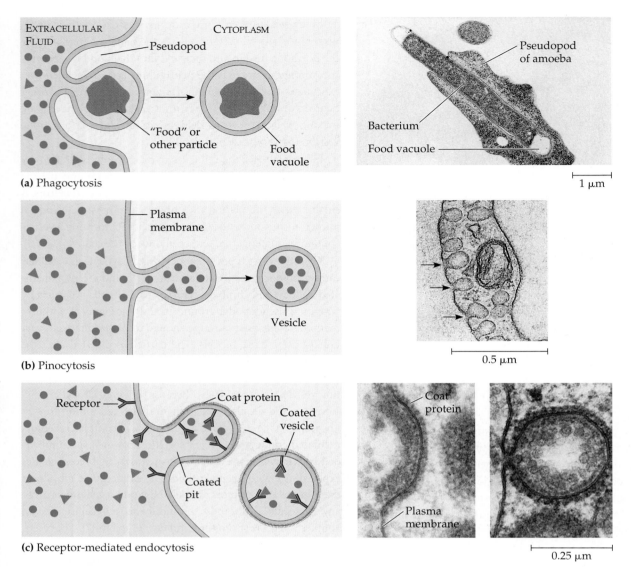

EXTRACELLULAR FLUID   CYTOPLASM

Pseudopod

"Food" or other particle

Food vacuole

(a) Phagocytosis

Pseudopod of amoeba

Bacterium

Food vacuole

1 μm

Plasma membrane

Vesicle

(b) Pinocytosis

0.5 μm

Receptor   Coat protein   Coated vesicle

Coated pit

Coat protein

Plasma membrane

(c) Receptor-mediated endocytosis

0.25 μm

FIGURE 8.18 ▪ **The three types of endocytosis in animal cells.**

8.6   **(a)** In phagocytosis, pseudopodia engulf a particle and package it in a vacuole. The micrograph shows an amoeba engulfing a bacterium (TEM). **(b)** In pinocytosis, droplets of extracellular fluid are incorporated into the cell in small vesicles. The micrograph shows pinocytotic vesicles forming (arrows) in a cell lining a small blood vessel (TEM). **(c)** In receptor-mediated endocytosis, coated pits form vesicles when specific molecules (ligands) bind to receptors on the cell surface. Notice that there is a greater relative number of bound molecules (purple) inside the vesicles, though other molecules (green) are also present. The micrographs show two progressive stages of receptor-mediated endocytosis (TEMs). After the ingested material is liberated from the vesicle for metabolism, the receptors are recycled to the plasma membrane.

exocytosis occur continually to some extent in most eukaryotic cells, yet the amount of plasma membrane in a nongrowing cell remains fairly constant over the long run. Apparently, the addition of membrane by one process offsets the loss of membrane by the other.

▪   ▪   ▪

Energy and cellular work have figured prominently in our study of membranes. We have seen, for example, that active transport is powered by ATP. In the next two chapters you will learn more about how cells acquire chemical energy to do the work of life. We'll call membranes back for an encore in these chapters, as they play a major role in how mitochondria and chloroplasts make energy available to cells.

(with page numbers and key figures)

MEMBRANE STRUCTURE

■ **Membrane models have evolved to fit new data:** *science as a process* (pp. 130–132, FIGURE 8.2) The Davson-Danielli model, placing layers of proteins on either side of a phospholipid bilayer, has been replaced by the fluid mosaic model.

➡ **8.1** **A membrane is a fluid mosaic of lipids, proteins, and carbohydrates** (pp. 132–135, FIGURE 8.5) Integral proteins are embedded in the lipid bilayer; peripheral proteins are attached to the surface. The inside and outside membrane faces differ in composition. Carbohydrates linked to proteins and lipids in the plasma membrane are important for cell-cell recognition.

TRAFFIC ACROSS MEMBRANES

■ **A membrane's molecular organization results in selective permeability** (pp. 136–137) A cell must exchange small molecules and ions with its surroundings, a process controlled by the plasma membrane. Hydrophobic substances such as CO_2 are soluble in lipid and pass through membranes rapidly. Small polar molecules such as H_2O also pass through the membrane. Larger polar molecules and ions require specific transport proteins to help them cross.

➡ **8.2** **Passive transport is diffusion across a membrane** (p. 137, FIGURE 8.9) Diffusion is the spontaneous movement of a substance down its concentration gradient.

➡ **8.3** **Osmosis is the passive transport of water** (pp. 137–138, FIGURE 8.10) Water flows across a membrane from the side where solute is less concentrated (hypotonic) to the side where solute is more concentrated (hypertonic). If the concentrations are equal (isotonic), no net osmosis occurs.

■ **Cell survival depends on balancing water uptake and loss** (pp. 139–140, FIGURE 8.11) Cells lacking walls (as in animals and some protists) are isotonic with their environments or have adaptations for osmoregulation. Plants, prokaryotes, fungi, and some protists have elastic cell walls, so the cells don't burst in a hypotonic environment.

➡ **8.4** **Specific proteins facilitate the passive transport of selected solutes** (p. 140, FIGURE 8.13) In facilitated diffusion, a transport protein speeds movement of a solute across a membrane down its concentration gradient.

➡ **8.5** **Active transport is the pumping of solutes against their gradients** (pp. 140–141, FIGURE 8.14) Specific membrane proteins use energy, usually in the form of ATP, to do this work.

■ **Some ion pumps generate voltage across membranes** (pp. 141–142, FIGURE 8.16) Ions can have both a concentration (chemical) gradient and an electric gradient (voltage). These forces combine in the electrochemical gradient, which determines the net direction of ionic diffusion. Electrogenic pumps, such as sodium-potassium pumps and proton pumps, are transport proteins that contribute to electrochemical gradients.

■ **In cotransport, a membrane protein couples the transport of one solute to another** (pp. 142–143, FIGURE 8.17) One solute's "downhill" diffusion drives the other's "uphill" transport.

➡ **8.6** **Exocytosis and endocytosis transport large molecules** (pp. 143–144, FIGURE 8.18) In exocytosis, transport vesicles migrate to the plasma membrane, fuse with it, and release their contents. In endocytosis, large molecules enter cells within vesicles pinched inward from the plasma membrane. The three types of endocytosis are phagocytosis, pinocytosis, and receptor-mediated endocytosis.

1. In what way do the various membranes of a eukaryotic cell differ?
   a. Phospholipids are found only in certain membranes.
   b. Certain proteins are unique to each membrane.
   c. Only certain membranes of the cell are selectively permeable.
   d. Only certain membranes are constructed from amphipathic molecules.
   e. Some membranes have hydrophobic surfaces exposed to the cytosol, while others have hydrophilic surfaces facing the cytosol.

2. According to the fluid mosaic model of membrane structure, proteins of the membrane are mostly
   a. spread in a continuous layer over the inner and outer surfaces of the membrane
   b. confined to the hydrophobic core of the membrane
   c. embedded in a lipid bilayer
   d. randomly oriented in the membrane, with no fixed inside-outside polarity
   e. free to depart from the fluid membrane and dissolve in the surrounding solution

3. Which of the following factors would tend to increase membrane fluidity?
   a. a greater proportion of unsaturated phospholipids
   b. a lower temperature
   c. a relatively high protein content in the membrane
   d. a greater proportion of relatively large glycolipids compared to lipids having smaller molecular weights
   e. a high membrane potential

4. Which of the following processes includes all others in the list?
   a. osmosis
   b. diffusion of a solute across a membrane
   c. facilitated diffusion
   d. passive transport
   e. transport of an ion down its electrochemical gradient

5. Based on the model of sucrose uptake in FIGURE 8.17, which of the following experimental treatments would increase the rate of sucrose transport into the cell?
   a. decreasing extracellular sucrose concentration
   b. decreasing extracellular pH
   c. decreasing cytoplasmic pH
   d. adding an inhibitor that blocks the regeneration of ATP
   e. adding a substance that makes the membrane more permeable to hydrogen ions

Questions 6–10

An artificial cell consisting of an aqueous solution enclosed in a selectively permeable membrane has just been immersed in a beaker containing a different solution. The membrane is permeable to water and to the simple sugars glucose and fructose but completely impermeable to the disaccharide sucrose.

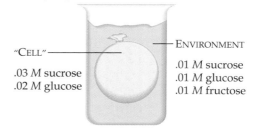

"CELL"
.03 *M* sucrose
.02 *M* glucose

ENVIRONMENT
.01 *M* sucrose
.01 *M* glucose
.01 *M* fructose

6. Which solute(s) will exhibit a net diffusion into the cell?

7. Which solute(s) will exhibit a net diffusion out of the cell?

8. Which solution—the *cell contents* or the *environment*—is hypertonic?

9. In which direction will there be a net osmotic movement of water?

10. After the cell is placed in the beaker, which of the following changes will occur?

    a. The artificial cell will become more flaccid.

    b. The artificial cell will become more turgid.

    c. The entropy of the system (cell plus surrounding solution) will decrease.

    d. The overall free energy stored in the system will increase.

    e. The membrane potential will decrease.

CHALLENGE QUESTIONS

1. The cells of plant seeds store oils in the form of droplets enclosed by membranes. Unlike the membranes you studied in this chapter, the oil droplet membrane probably consists of a single layer of phospholipids rather than a bilayer. Draw a model for a membrane around an oil droplet, and explain why this arrangement is more stable than a bilayer.

2. An experiment is designed to study the mechanism of sucrose uptake by plant cells. Cells are immersed in a sucrose solution, and the pH of the surrounding solution is monitored with a pH meter. The measurements show that sucrose uptake by the plant cells raises the pH of the surrounding solution. The magnitude of the pH change is proportional to the starting concentration of sucrose in the extracellular solution. A metabolic poison that blocks the ability of the cells to regenerate ATP also inhibits the pH changes in the surrounding solution. Propose a hypothesis accounting for these results. Suggest an additional experiment to test your hypothesis.

3. In an adaptation of the preceding experiment, the rates of sucrose uptake from solutions of different sucrose concentrations are compared.

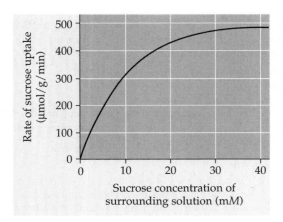

Explain the shape of the curve above in terms of what is happening at the membranes of the plant cells.

SCIENCE, TECHNOLOGY, AND SOCIETY

1. A U.S. government panel has recommended that all people in the United States over age 20 should have their blood cholesterol level measured, and that those with high cholesterol levels should be put on a special diet or drug therapy. The annual cost of this program could be $10–$50 billion. Research suggests that relatively few people benefit from drug treatment, mainly those suffering from abnormal conditions like familial hypercholesterolemia. Do you think it is worth the effort and expense of testing and medicating everyone with high cholesterol to help only 1% or 2% of the population? Why or why not?

2. Extensive irrigation in arid regions causes salts to accumulate in the soil. (The water contains low concentrations of salts, but when the water evaporates from the fields, the salts are left behind to concentrate in the soil.) Based on what you have learned about water balance in plant cells, explain why increasing soil salinity (saltiness) has an adverse effect on agriculture. Suggest some ways to minimize this damage. What costs are attached to your solutions?

FURTHER READING

Alberts, B., D. Bray, J. Lewis, M. Raff, K. Roberts, and J. D. Watson. *Molecular Biology of the Cell.* 3rd ed. New York: Garland, 1994. A description of the structure and functions of the plasma membrane is in Chapter 10.

De Camilli, P., S. D. Emr, P. S. McPherson, and P. Novick. "Phosphoinositides as Regulators in Membrane Traffic." *Science,* March 15, 1996. This issue also has other articles on macromolecular transport across membranes.

Jacobson, K., E. D. Sheets, and R. Simson. "Revisiting the Fluid Mosaic Model of Membranes." *Science.* June 9, 1995. A refinement of the current model.

Lang, F., and Waldegger, S. "Regulating Cell Volume." *American Scientist,* September–October 1997. The effects of osmosis on cell function.

Morré, D. J., and T. W. Keenan. "Membrane Flow Revisited." *BioScience,* September 1997. How molecules move through the endomembrane system.

Sharon, N., and H. Lis. "Carbohydrates in Cell Recognition." *Scientific American,* January 1993. How do membrane markers enable an organism to distinguish "self" cells from "nonself" cells?

WEB LINKS

Visit the special edition of *The Biology Place* for BIOLOGY, Fifth Edition, at http://www.biology.com/campbell. Go to Chapter 8 for online resources, including learning activities, practice exams, and links to the following web sites:

"Bioenergetics"
Membranes house proteins that carry out many important biochemical pathways. This well-written and nicely illustrated site describes the role of the inner mitochondrial membrane in cellular respiration, among other topics.

"Center of Membrane Sciences"
The Center of Membrane Sciences was established to foster multidisciplinary research on both biological and synthetic membranes.

"The UNESCO Centre for Membrane Science & Technology"
Based at the University of New South Wales, this site deals with research on biological membranes and with possible applications to the development of synthetic membranes for industrial purposes.

"Bioenergetics Links"
Many links to sites related to membrane-bound proteins that participate in bioenergetic pathways.

CHAPTER 9

*L*iving is work. A cell organizes small organic molecules into polymers, such as proteins and DNA. It pumps substances across membranes. Many cells move or change their shapes. They grow and reproduce. A cell must work just to maintain its complex structure, because order is intrinsically unstable. To perform their many tasks, cells require transfusions of energy from outside sources. Energy enters most ecosystems in the form of sunlight, the energy source for plants and other photosynthetic organisms (FIGURE 9.1, p. 148). Animals, such as the orangutan in the photograph to the right, obtain fuel by eating plants, or by eating other organisms that eat plants. In this chapter you will learn how cells harvest the chemical energy stored in organic molecules and use it to regenerate ATP, the molecule that drives most cellular work.

CELLULAR RESPIRATION: HARVESTING CHEMICAL ENERGY

PRINCIPLES OF ENERGY HARVEST

In harvesting chemical energy, cells usually employ metabolic pathways with many steps. Fortunately, we can organize this complexity with the help of just a handful of general principles. The first part of this chapter develops these principles, which will then enable you to make sense of cellular respiration and related pathways.

Cellular respiration and fermentation are catabolic (energy-yielding) pathways

Organic compounds store energy in their arrangements of atoms. With the help of enzymes, a cell systematically degrades complex organic molecules that are rich in potential energy to simpler waste products that have less energy. Some of the energy taken out of chemical storage can be used to do work; the rest is dissipated as heat. As you learned in Chapter 6, metabolic pathways that release stored energy by breaking down complex molecules are called catabolic pathways. One catabolic process, **fermentation**, is a partial degradation of sugars that occurs without the help of oxygen. However, the most prevalent and efficient catabolic pathway is **cellular respiration**, in which oxygen is consumed as a reactant along with the organic fuel. In eukaryotic cells, mitochondria house most of the metabolic equipment for cellular respiration.

Although very different in mechanism, respiration is in principle similar to the combustion of gasoline in an automobile engine after oxygen is mixed with the fuel (hydrocarbons). Food is the fuel for respiration, and the exhaust is carbon dioxide and water. The overall process can be summarized as follows:

$$\text{Organic compounds} + \text{Oxygen} \longrightarrow \text{Carbon dioxide} + \text{Water} + \text{Energy}$$

Principles of Energy Harvest
- Cellular respiration and fermentation are catabolic (energy-yielding) pathways
- Cells recycle the ATP they use for work
- Redox reactions release energy when electrons move closer to electronegative atoms
- Electrons "fall" from organic molecules to oxygen during cellular respiration
- The "fall" of electrons during respiration is stepwise, via NAD^+ and an electron transport chain

The Process of Cellular Respiration
- Respiration involves glycolysis, the Krebs cycle, and electron transport: *an overview*
- Glycolysis harvests chemical energy by oxidizing glucose to pyruvate: *a closer look*
- The Krebs cycle completes the energy-yielding oxidation of organic molecules: *a closer look*
- The inner mitochondrial membrane couples electron transport to ATP synthesis: *a closer look*
- Cellular respiration generates many ATP molecules for each sugar molecule it oxidizes: *a review*

Related Metabolic Processes
- Fermentation enables some cells to produce ATP without the help of oxygen
- Glycolysis and the Krebs cycle connect to many other metabolic pathways
- Feedback mechanisms control cellular respiration

147

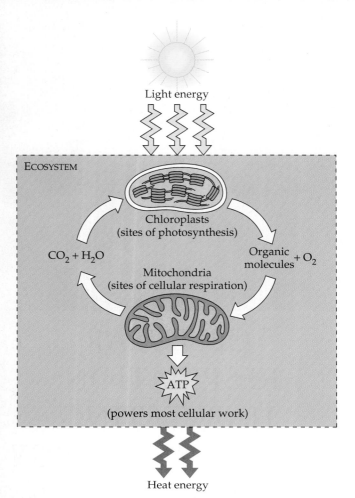

Light energy

ECOSYSTEM

Chloroplasts
(sites of photosynthesis)

$CO_2 + H_2O$

Organic molecules $+ O_2$

Mitochondria
(sites of cellular respiration)

ATP

(powers most cellular work)

Heat energy

FIGURE 9.1 ▪ **Energy flow and chemical recycling in ecosystems.** The mitochondria of eukaryotes (including plants) use the organic products of photosynthesis as fuel for cellular respiration, which also consumes the oxygen produced by photosynthesis. Respiration harvests the energy stored in organic molecules to generate ATP, which powers most cellular work. The waste products of respiration, carbon dioxide and water, are the very substances that chloroplasts use as raw materials for photosynthesis. Thus, the chemical elements essential to life are recycled. But energy is not: It flows into an ecosystem as sunlight and leaves it as heat.

Although carbohydrates, fats, and proteins can all be processed and consumed as fuel, it is traditional to learn the steps of cellular respiration by tracking the degradation of the sugar glucose ($C_6H_{12}O_6$):

$$C_6H_{12}O_6 + 6\,O_2 \longrightarrow 6\,CO_2 + 6\,H_2O$$
$$+ \text{Energy (ATP + heat)}$$

This breakdown of glucose is exergonic, having a free-energy change of −686 kcal (−2870 kJ) per mole of glucose decomposed ($\Delta G = -686$ kcal/mol; recall that a negative ΔG indicates that the products of the chemical process store less energy than the reactants).

Catabolic pathways do not directly move flagella, pump solutes across membranes, polymerize monomers, or perform other cellular work. Catabolism is linked to work by a chemi-

cal drive shaft: ATP. The processes of cellular respiration and fermentation are complex and challenging to learn. Therefore, in studying this chapter it will help you to keep in mind your main objective: discovering how cells use the energy stored in food molecules to make ATP.

Cells recycle the ATP they use for work

The molecule known as ATP, short for adenosine triphosphate, is the central character in bioenergetics. Recall from Chapter 6 that the triphosphate tail of ATP is the chemical equivalent of a loaded spring; the close packing of the three negatively charged phosphate groups is an unstable, energy-storing arrangement (because like charges repel each other). The chemical "spring" tends to "relax" by losing the terminal phosphate (see FIGURE 6.6). The cell taps this energy source by using enzymes to transfer phosphate groups from ATP to other compounds, which are then said to be phosphorylated. Phosphorylation primes a molecule to undergo some kind of change that performs work, and the molecule loses its phosphate group in the process (FIGURE 9.2). The price of most cellular work, then, is the conversion of ATP to ADP and inorganic phosphate (abbreviated Ⓟ$_i$ in this book), products that store less energy than ATP. To keep working, the cell must regenerate its supply of ATP from ADP and inorganic phosphate. A working muscle cell, for example, recycles its ATP at a rate of about 10 million molecules per second. To understand how cellular respiration regenerates ATP, we need to examine the fundamental chemical processes known as oxidation and reduction.

Redox reactions release energy when electrons move closer to electronegative atoms

Just what happens when cellular respiration decomposes glucose and other organic fuels? And why does this metabolic pathway yield energy? The answers are based on the transfer of electrons during the chemical reactions. The relocation of electrons releases the energy stored in food molecules, and this energy is used to synthesize ATP.

In many chemical reactions, there is a transfer of one or more electrons (e^-) from one reactant to another. These electron transfers are called oxidation-reduction reactions, or **redox reactions** for short. In a redox reaction, the loss of electrons from one substance is called **oxidation**, and the addition of electrons to another substance is known as **reduction**.* Consider, for example, the reaction between sodium and chlorine to form table salt:

---

* This term defies intuition; *adding* electrons is called *reduction.* The term was derived from the electrical effects of adding electrons: Negatively charged electrons added to a cation *reduce* the amount of positive charge of the cation.

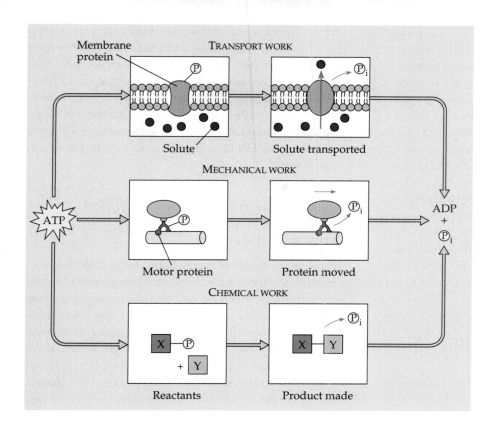

FIGURE 9.2 · **A review of how ATP drives cellular work.** Phosphate-group transfer is the mechanism responsible for most types of cellular work. Enzymes shift a phosphate group ($\textcircled{P}$) from ATP to some other molecule, and this phosphorylated molecule undergoes a change that performs work. For example, ATP drives active transport by phosphorylating specialized proteins built into membranes; drives mechanical work by phosphorylating motor proteins, such as the ones that move organelles along cytoskeletal "tracks" in the cell; and drives chemical work by phosphorylating key reactants. The phosphorylated molecules lose the phosphate groups as work is performed, leaving ADP and inorganic phosphate ($\textcircled{P}_i$) as products. Cellular respiration replenishes the ATP supply by powering the phosphorylation of ADP.

$$
\begin{array}{c}
\overset{\displaystyle\longmapsto \text{Oxidation} \longrightarrow}{} \\
Na \;+\; Cl \longrightarrow Na^+ \;+\; Cl^- \\
\underset{\displaystyle\longmapsto \text{Reduction} \longleftarrow}{}
\end{array}
$$

Or we could generalize a redox reaction this way:

$$
\begin{array}{c}
\overset{\displaystyle\longmapsto \text{Oxidation} \longrightarrow}{} \\
Xe^- \;+\; Y \longrightarrow X \;+\; Ye^- \\
\underset{\displaystyle\longmapsto \text{Reduction} \longleftarrow}{}
\end{array}
$$

In the generalized reaction, substance X, the electron donor, is called the **reducing agent**; it reduces Y. Substance Y, the electron acceptor, is the **oxidizing agent**; it oxidizes X.

Because an electron transfer requires both a donor and an acceptor, oxidation and reduction always go together.

Not all redox reactions involve the complete transfer of electrons from one substance to another; some change the degree of electron sharing in covalent bonds. The reaction between methane and oxygen to form carbon dioxide and water, shown in FIGURE 9.3, is an example. As explained in Chapter 2, the covalent electrons in methane are shared equally between the bonded atoms because carbon and hydrogen have about the same affinity for valence electrons; they are about equally electronegative. But when methane reacts with oxygen to form carbon dioxide, electrons are shifted away from the carbon atoms to their new covalent partner, oxygen, which is very electronegative. Methane has thus been oxidized. The two atoms of the oxygen molecule

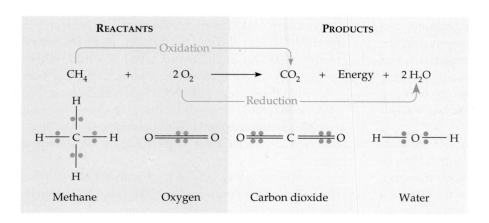

FIGURE 9.3 · **Methane combustion as an energy-yielding redox reaction.** During the reaction, covalently shared electrons move away from carbon and hydrogen atoms and closer to oxygen, which is very electronegative. The reaction releases energy to the surroundings, because the electrons lose potential energy as they move closer to electronegative atoms.

also share their electrons equally. But when the oxygen reacts with the hydrogen from methane to form water, the electrons of the covalent bonds are drawn closer to the oxygen; the oxygen molecule has been reduced. Because oxygen is so electronegative, it is one of the most potent of all oxidizing agents.

Energy must be added to pull an electron away from an atom, just as energy must be added to push a large ball uphill. The more electronegative the atom (the stronger its pull on electrons), the more energy is required to keep the electron away from it, just as more energy is required to push a ball up a steeper hill. An electron *loses* potential energy when it shifts from a less electronegative atom (one with a weaker pull on electrons) *toward* a more electronegative one, just as a ball loses potential energy when it rolls downhill. A redox reaction that relocates electrons closer to oxygen, such as the burning of methane, releases chemical energy that can be put to work.

Electrons "fall" from organic molecules to oxygen during cellular respiration

The oxidation of methane by oxygen is the main combustion reaction that occurs at the burner of a gas stove. Combustion of gasoline in an automobile engine is also a redox reaction, and the energy released pushes the pistons. But the energy-yielding redox process of greatest interest here is respiration: the oxidation of glucose and other fuel molecules in food. Examine again the summary equation for cellular respiration, but this time think of it as a redox process:

$$\overbrace{C_6H_{12}O_6 \quad + \quad \underbrace{6\,O_2 \quad \longrightarrow \quad 6\,CO_2}_{\text{Reduction}} + \quad 6\,H_2O}^{\text{Oxidation}}$$

As in the combustion of methane or gasoline, the fuel (sugar) is oxidized and oxygen is reduced, and the electrons lose potential energy along the way.

In general, organic molecules that have an abundance of hydrogen are excellent fuels because their bonds are a source of "hilltop" electrons with the potential to "fall" closer to oxygen. The summary equation for respiration indicates that hydrogen is transferred from glucose to oxygen. But the important point, not visible in the summary equation, is that the change in the covalent status of electrons as hydrogen is transferred to oxygen is what liberates energy. By oxidizing glucose, respiration takes energy out of storage and makes it available for ATP synthesis.

The main energy foods, carbohydrates and fats, are reservoirs of electrons associated with hydrogen. Only the barrier of activation energy holds back the flood of electrons to a lower energy state (see Chapter 6). Without this barrier, a food substance like glucose would combine spontaneously with O_2. When we supply the activation energy by igniting glucose, it burns in air, releasing 686 kcal (2870 kJ) of heat per mole of glucose (about 180 g). Body temperature is not high enough to initiate burning, which is the rapid oxidation of fuel accompanied by an enormous release of energy as heat. But swallow some glucose in the form of a spoonful of honey, and when the molecules reach your cells, enzymes will lower the barrier of activation energy, allowing the sugar to be oxidized slowly.

The "fall" of electrons during respiration is stepwise, via NAD$^+$ and an electron transport chain

The wholesale release of energy from a fuel is difficult to harness efficiently for constructive work: The explosion of a gasoline tank cannot drive a car very far. Cellular respiration does not oxidize glucose in a single explosive step that would transfer all the hydrogen from the fuel to the oxygen at one time. Rather, glucose and other organic fuels are broken down gradually in a series of steps, each one catalyzed by an enzyme. At key steps, hydrogen atoms are stripped from the glucose, but they are not transferred directly to oxygen. They are usually passed first to a coenzyme called NAD$^+$ (nicotinamide adenine dinucleotide). Thus, NAD$^+$ functions as an oxidizing agent during respiration.

How does NAD$^+$ trap electrons from glucose and other fuel molecules? Enzymes called dehydrogenases remove a pair of hydrogen atoms from the substrate, a sugar or some other fuel. We can think of this as the removal of two electrons and two protons (the nuclei of hydrogen atoms). The enzyme delivers the *two* electrons along with *one* proton to its coenzyme, NAD$^+$ (FIGURE 9.4). The other proton is released as a hydrogen ion (H$^+$) into the surrounding solution:

$$H-\overset{|}{\underset{|}{C}}-OH + NAD^+ \xrightarrow{\text{Dehydrogenase}} \overset{|}{\underset{|}{C}}=O + NADH + H^+$$

Though the oxidized form, NAD$^+$, has a positive charge, the reduced form, NADH, is electrically neutral. By receiving two negatively charged electrons but only one positively charged proton, NAD$^+$ has its charge neutralized. The name NADH for the reduced form shows the hydrogen that has been received in the reaction. Since NAD$^+$ gains electrons, it is an electron acceptor (a synonym for oxidizing agent). The most versatile electron acceptor in cellular respiration, NAD$^+$ functions in many of the redox steps during the breakdown of sugar.

Electrons lose very little of their potential energy when they are transferred from food to NAD$^+$. Each NADH molecule formed during respiration represents stored energy that

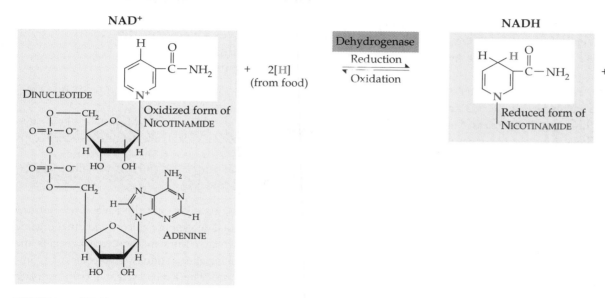

NAD⁺

$+$ $2[H]$ (from food)

Dehydrogenase

Reduction ⇌ Oxidation

NADH

$+$ H^+

DINUCLEOTIDE

Oxidized form of NICOTINAMIDE

ADENINE

Reduced form of NICOTINAMIDE

FIGURE 9.4 · **NAD⁺ as an electron shuttle.** The full name for NAD⁺, nicotinamide adenine dinucleotide, describes its structure; the molecule consists of two nucleotides joined together. (Nicotinamide is a nitrogenous base, although not one that is present in DNA or RNA.) The enzymatic transfer of two electrons and one proton from some organic substrate to NAD⁺ reduces the NAD⁺ to NADH. Most of the electrons removed from food are transferred initially to NAD⁺.

can be tapped to make ATP when the electrons complete their "fall" from NADH to oxygen.

How do electrons extracted from food and stored by NADH finally reach oxygen? It will help to compare this complex redox chemistry of cellular respiration to a much simpler reaction: the reaction between hydrogen and oxygen to form water (FIGURE 9.5a). Mix H_2 and O_2, provide a spark for activation energy, and the gases combine explosively. The explosion represents a release of energy as the electrons of hydrogen

fall closer to the electronegative oxygen. Cellular respiration also brings hydrogen and oxygen together to form water, but there are two important differences. First, in cellular respiration, the hydrogen that reacts with oxygen is derived from organic molecules. Second, respiration uses an **electron transport chain** to break the fall of electrons to oxygen into several energy-releasing steps instead of one explosive reaction (FIGURE 9.5b). The transport chain consists of a number of molecules, mostly proteins, built into the inner membrane of a

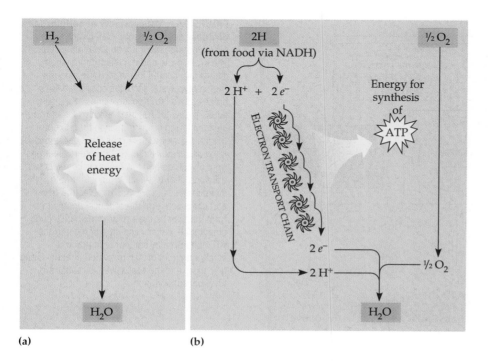

(a)

(b)

FIGURE 9.5 · **An introduction to electron transport chains. (a)** The exergonic reaction of hydrogen with oxygen to form water releases a large amount of energy in the form of heat and light: an explosion. **(b)** In cellular respiration, an electron transport chain breaks the "fall" of electrons in this reaction into a series of smaller steps and stores some of the released energy in a form that can be used to make ATP (the rest of the energy is released as heat).

mitochondrion. Electrons removed from food are shuttled by NADH to the "top" end of the chain. At the "bottom" end, oxygen captures these electrons along with hydrogen nuclei (H^+), forming water.

Electron transfer from NADH to oxygen is an exergonic reaction with a free energy change of −53 kcal/mol (−222 kJ/mol). Instead of this energy being released and wasted in a single explosive step, electrons cascade down the chain from one carrier molecule to the next, losing a small amount of energy with each step until they finally reach oxygen, the terminal electron acceptor. What keeps the electrons moving is that each carrier is more electronegative than its "uphill" neighbor in the chain. At the bottom of the chain is oxygen, which has a very great affinity for electrons. Thus, electrons removed from food by NAD^+ fall down the electron transport chain to a far more stable location in the electronegative oxygen atom. Put another way, oxygen pulls electrons down the chain in an energy-yielding tumble analogous to gravity pulling objects downhill.

Thus, during cellular respiration, most electrons travel this "downhill" route: food ⟶ NADH ⟶ electron transport chain ⟶ oxygen. In the next major section of the chapter, you will learn more about how respiration uses the energy released from this exergonic electron fall to regenerate the cell's supply of ATP.

THE PROCESS OF CELLULAR RESPIRATION

Now that we have covered the basic redox mechanisms of respiration, let's look at the entire process.

Respiration involves glycolysis, the Krebs cycle, and electron transport: *an overview*

9.1 Respiration is a cumulative function of three metabolic stages, which are diagrammed in FIGURE 9.6:

1. Glycolysis (color-coded teal throughout the chapter).
2. The Krebs cycle (color-coded salmon).
3. The electron transport chain and oxidative phosphorylation (color-coded violet).

The first two stages, glycolysis and the Krebs cycle, are the catabolic pathways that decompose glucose and other organic fuels. **Glycolysis**, which occurs in the cytosol, begins the degradation by breaking glucose into two molecules of a compound called pyruvate. The **Krebs cycle**, which takes place within the mitochondrial matrix, completes the job by decomposing a derivative of pyruvate to carbon dioxide.

Thus, the carbon dioxide produced by respiration represents fragments of oxidized organic molecules. Some of the steps of glycolysis and the Krebs cycle are redox reactions in which dehydrogenase enzymes transfer electrons from substrates to NAD^+, forming NADH. In the third stage of respiration, the electron transport chain accepts electrons from the breakdown products of the first two stages (usually via NADH) and passes these electrons from one molecule to another. At the end of the chain, the electrons are combined with hydrogen ions and molecular oxygen to form water (see FIGURE 9.5b). The energy released at each step of the chain is stored in a form the mitochondrion can use to make ATP. This mode of ATP synthesis is called **oxidative phosphoryla-**

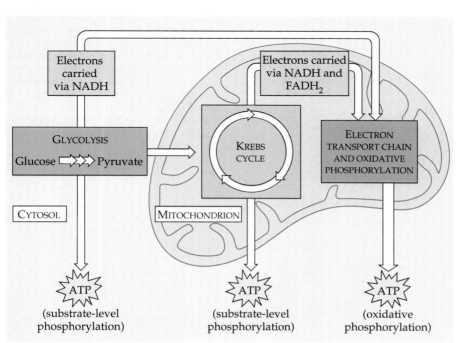

FIGURE 9.6 ▪ An overview of cellular respiration. In a eukaryotic cell, glycolysis occurs outside the mitochondria in the cytosol. The Krebs cycle and the electron transport chains are located inside the mitochondria. During glycolysis, each glucose molecule is broken down into two molecules of the compound pyruvate. The pyruvate crosses the double membrane of the mitochondrion to enter the matrix, where the Krebs cycle decomposes it to carbon dioxide. NADH transfers electrons from glycolysis and the Krebs cycle to electron transport chains, which are built into the membrane of the cristae. The electron transport chain converts the chemical energy to a form that can be used to drive oxidative phosphorylation, which accounts for most of the ATP generated by cellular respiration. A smaller amount of ATP is formed directly during glycolysis and the Krebs cycle by substrate-level phosphorylation.

tion because it is powered by the redox reactions that transfer electrons from food to oxygen.

The site of electron transport and oxidative phosphorylation is the inner membrane of the mitochondrion (see FIGURE 7.18). Oxidative phosphorylation accounts for almost 90% of the ATP generated by respiration. A smaller amount of ATP is formed directly in a few reactions of glycolysis and the Krebs cycle by a mechanism called **substrate-level phosphorylation** (FIGURE 9.7). This mode of ATP synthesis occurs when an enzyme transfers a phosphate group from a substrate to ADP. ("Substrate" here refers to an organic molecule generated during the sequential catabolism of glucose.)

Respiration cashes in the large denomination of energy banked in glucose for the small change of ATP, which is more practical for the cell to spend on its work. For each molecule of glucose degraded to carbon dioxide and water by respiration, the cell makes up to about 38 molecules of ATP.

This overview has introduced how glycolysis, the Krebs cycle, and electron transport fit into the overall process of cellular respiration. We are now ready to take a closer look at each of these three stages of respiration.

Glycolysis harvests chemical energy by oxidizing glucose to pyruvate: *a closer look*

9.2 The word *glycolysis* means "splitting of sugar," and that is exactly what happens during this pathway. Glucose, a six-

carbon sugar, is split into two three-carbon sugars. These smaller sugars are then oxidized, and their remaining atoms rearranged to form two molecules of pyruvate. (Pyruvate is the ionized form of a three-carbon acid, pyruvic acid.)

The catabolic pathway of glycolysis consists of ten steps, each catalyzed by a specific enzyme. We can divide these ten steps into two phases. The energy-investment phase includes the first five steps, and the energy-payoff phase includes the next five steps. During the energy-investment phase, the cell actually spends ATP to phosphorylate the fuel molecules (FIGURE 9.8). This investment is repaid with dividends during the energy-payoff phase, when ATP is produced by substrate-level phosphorylation and NAD$^+$ is reduced to NADH by oxidation of the food. On the next two pages you will find a detailed diagram of glycolysis (FIGURE 9.9). Do not let the details obscure the main functions of glycolysis: Glycolysis is a source of ATP and NADH and also prepares organic molecules for further oxidation in the Krebs cycle.

As summarized in FIGURE 9.8, the net energy yield from glycolysis, per glucose molecule, is 2 ATP plus 2 NADH. Notice that all of the carbon originally present in glucose is accounted for in the two molecules of pyruvate; no CO_2 is

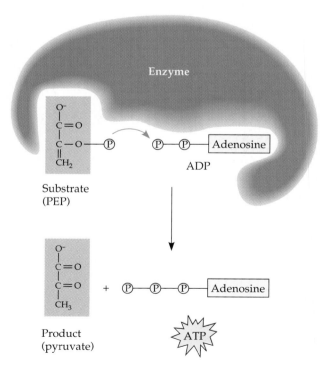

FIGURE 9.7 ▪ **Substrate-level phosphorylation.** Some ATP is made by direct enzymatic transfer of a phosphate group from a substrate to ADP. The phosphate donor in this case is phosphoenolpyruvate (PEP), which is formed from the breakdown of sugar during glycolysis.

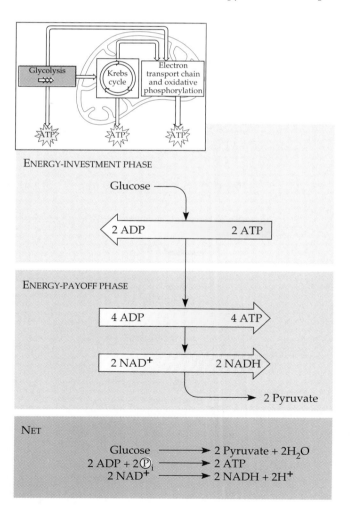

FIGURE 9.8 ▪ **The energy input and output of glycolysis.**

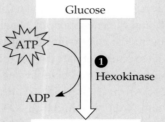

Glucose

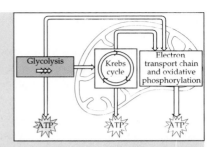

ATP

① Hexokinase

ADP

CH$_2$O—Ⓟ

Glucose 6-phosphate

② Phosphoglucoisomerase

CH$_2$O—Ⓟ

Fructose 6-phosphate

ATP

③ Phosphofructokinase

ADP

Ⓟ—O—CH$_2$ CH$_2$—O—Ⓟ

Fructose
1, 6-bisphosphate

④ Aldolase

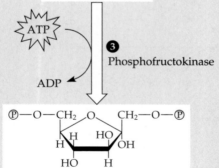

Ⓟ—O—CH$_2$

⑤ Isomerase

C=O

CH$_2$OH

Dihydroxyacetone
phosphate

H

C=O

CHOH

CH$_2$—O—Ⓟ

Glyceraldehyde
phosphate

ENERGY-INVESTMENT PHASE

① Glucose enters the cell and is phosphorylated by the enzyme hexokinase, which transfers a phosphate group from ATP to the sugar. The electrical charge of the phosphate group traps the sugar in the cell because of the impermeability of the plasma membrane to ions. Phosphorylation of glucose also makes the molecule more chemically reactive. In this diagram, the transfer of a phosphate group or pair of electrons from one reactant to another is indicated by coupled arrows:)[

② Glucose 6-phosphate is rearranged to convert it to its isomer, fructose 6-phosphate.

③ In this step, still another molecule of ATP is invested in glycolysis. An enzyme transfers a phosphate group from ATP to the sugar. So far, the ATP ledger shows a debit of 2. With phosphate groups on its opposite ends, the sugar is now ready to be split in half.

④ This is the reaction from which glycolysis gets its name. An enzyme cleaves the sugar molecule into two different three-carbon sugars: glyceraldehyde phosphate and dihydroxyacetone phosphate. These two sugars are isomers of each other.

⑤ Another enzyme catalyzes the reversible conversion between the two three-carbon sugars, and if left alone in a test tube, the reaction reaches equilibrium. This does not happen in the cell, however, because the next enzyme in glycolysis uses only glyceraldehyde phosphate as its substrate and is unreceptive to dihydroxyacetone phosphate. This pulls the equilibrium between the two three-carbon sugars in the direction of glyceraldehyde phosphate, which is removed as fast as it forms. Thus, the net result of steps 4 and 5 is cleavage of a six-carbon sugar into two molecules of glyceraldehyde phosphate; each will progress through the remaining steps of glycolysis.

ENERGY-PAYOFF PHASE

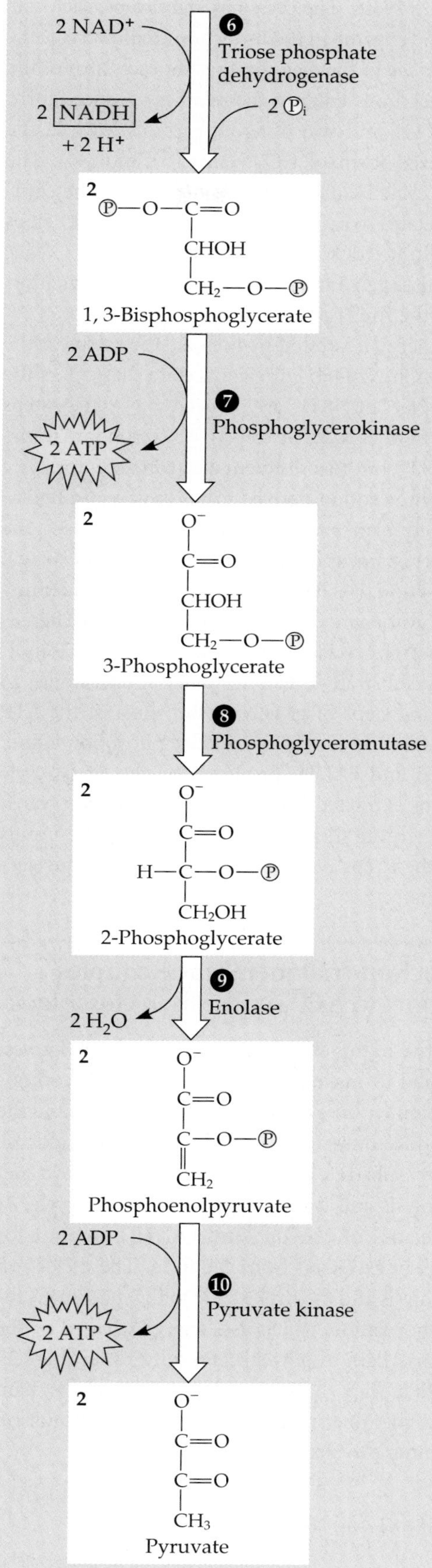
2 NAD+
6
Triose phosphate dehydrogenase
2 NADH
+ 2 H+
2 Pi
2
1, 3-Bisphosphoglycerate
2 ADP
7
Phosphoglycerokinase
2 ATP
2
3-Phosphoglycerate
8
Phosphoglyceromutase
2
2-Phosphoglycerate
9
Enolase
2 H2O
2
Phosphoenolpyruvate
2 ADP
10
Pyruvate kinase
2 ATP
2
Pyruvate

6 An enzyme now catalyzes two sequential reactions while it holds glyceraldehyde phosphate in its active site. First, the sugar is oxidized by the transfer of electrons and H^+ to NAD^+, forming NADH. Here we see in metabolic context the type of redox reaction described earlier. This reaction is very exergonic, and the enzyme uses the energy released to attach a phosphate group to the oxidized substrate, making a product of very high potential energy. The source of the phosphate is inorganic phosphate, which is always present in the cytosol. Notice that the coefficient 2 precedes all molecules in the energy-payoff phase; these steps occur after glucose is split into two three-carbon sugars.

7 Finally, glycolysis produces some ATP. The phosphate group added in the previous step is transferred to ADP in an exergonic reaction. For each glucose molecule that began glycolysis, step 7 produces two molecules of ATP, since every product after the sugar-splitting step (step 4) is doubled. Of course, two ATPs were invested to get sugar ready for splitting. The ATP ledger now stands at zero. By the end of step 7, glucose has been converted to two molecules of 3-phosphoglycerate. This compound is not a sugar. The carbonyl group that characterizes a sugar has been oxidized to a carboxyl group, the hallmark of an organic acid. The sugar was oxidized in step 6, and now the energy made available by that oxidation has been used to make ATP.

8 Next, an enzyme relocates the remaining phosphate group. This prepares the substrate for the next reaction.

9 An enzyme forms a double bond in the substrate by extracting a water molecule to form phosphoenolpyruvate, or PEP. This results in the electrons of the substrate being rearranged in such a way that the remaining phosphate bond becomes very unstable, preparing the substrate for the next reaction.

10 The last reaction of glycolysis produces more ATP by transferring the phosphate group from PEP to ADP. Since this step occurs twice for each glucose molecule, the ATP ledger now shows a net gain of two ATPs. Steps 7 and 10 each produce two ATPs for a total credit of four, but a debt of two ATPs was incurred from steps 1 and 3. Glycolysis has repaid the ATP investment with 100% interest. Additional energy was stored by step 6 in NADH, which can be used to make ATP by oxidative phosphorylation if oxygen is present. In the meantime, glucose has been broken down and oxidized to two molecules of pyruvate, the end-product of the glycolytic pathway.

released during glycolysis. Also note that glycolysis occurs whether or not molecular oxygen (O_2) is present. However, if oxygen *is* present, the energy stored in NADH can be converted to ATP energy during oxidative phosphorylation. And in the presence of oxygen, the chemical energy left in pyruvate can be extracted by the Krebs cycle.

The Krebs cycle completes the energy-yielding oxidation of organic molecules: *a closer look*

9.3 Glycolysis releases less than a quarter of the chemical energy stored in glucose; most of the energy remains stocked in the two molecules of pyruvate. If molecular oxygen is present, the pyruvate enters the mitochondrion, where the enzymes of the Krebs cycle complete the oxidation of the organic fuel.

Upon entering the mitochondrion, pyruvate is first converted to a compound called **acetyl CoA** (FIGURE 9.10). This step, the junction between glycolysis and the Krebs cycle, is accomplished by a multienzyme complex that catalyzes three reactions: ① Pyruvate's carboxyl group, which has little chemical energy, is removed and given off as a molecule of CO_2. (This is the first step in respiration where CO_2 is released.) ② The remaining two-carbon fragment is oxidized to form a compound named acetate (the ionized form of acetic acid). An enzyme transfers the extracted electrons to NAD^+, storing energy in the form of NADH. ③ Finally, coenzyme A, a sulfur-containing compound derived from a B vitamin, is attached to the acetate by an unstable bond that makes the acetyl group (the attached acetate) very reactive. The product of this chemical grooming, acetyl CoA, is now ready to feed its acetate into the Krebs cycle for further oxidation.

The Krebs cycle is named after Hans Krebs, the German-British scientist who was largely responsible for elucidating

FIGURE 9.10 · Conversion of pyruvate to acetyl CoA, the junction between glycolysis and the Krebs cycle. A protein built into the inner mitochondrial membrane translocates pyruvate from the cytosol into the mitochondrial matrix. Then ① the carboxyl group of pyruvate, already fully oxidized, is removed as a CO_2 molecule, which diffuses out of the cell. ② The remaining two-carbon fragment is oxidized while NAD^+ is reduced to NADH. ③ Finally, the two-carbon acetyl group is attached to coenzyme A (CoA). The coenzyme has a sulfur atom, which attaches to the acetyl fragment by an unstable bond. This activates the acetyl group for the first reaction of the Krebs cycle.

the pathway in the 1930s. The cycle has eight steps, each catalyzed by a specific enzyme in the mitochondrial matrix (FIGURE 9.11). You can see in the diagram that for each turn of the Krebs cycle, two carbons enter in the relatively reduced form of acetate (step ①), and two different carbons leave in the completely oxidized form of CO_2 (steps ③ and ④). The acetate joins the cycle by its enzymatic addition to the compound oxaloacetate, forming citrate. Subsequent steps decompose the citrate back to oxaloacetate, giving off CO_2 as "exhaust." It is this regeneration of oxaloacetate that accounts for the "cycle" in the Krebs cycle.

Most of the energy harvested by the oxidative steps of the cycle is conserved in NADH. For each acetate that enters the cycle, three molecules of NAD^+ are reduced to NADH—steps ③, ④, and ⑧. In one oxidative step, ⑥, electrons are transferred not to NAD^+, but to a different electron acceptor, FAD (flavin adenine dinucleotide, derived from riboflavin, a B vitamin). The reduced form, $FADH_2$, donates its electrons to the electron transport chain, as does NADH. (However, as we will see in the next section, $FADH_2$ feeds its electrons to the transport chain at a lower energy level than does NADH.) There is also a step in the Krebs cycle, step ⑤, that forms an ATP molecule directly by substrate-level phosphorylation, similar to the ATP-generating steps of glycolysis. But most of the ATP output of respiration results from oxidative phosphorylation, when the NADH and $FADH_2$ produced by the Krebs cycle relay the electrons extracted from food to the electron transport chain. Use FIGURE 9.12, page 158, to review the inputs and outputs of the Krebs cycle before proceeding to the electron transport chain.

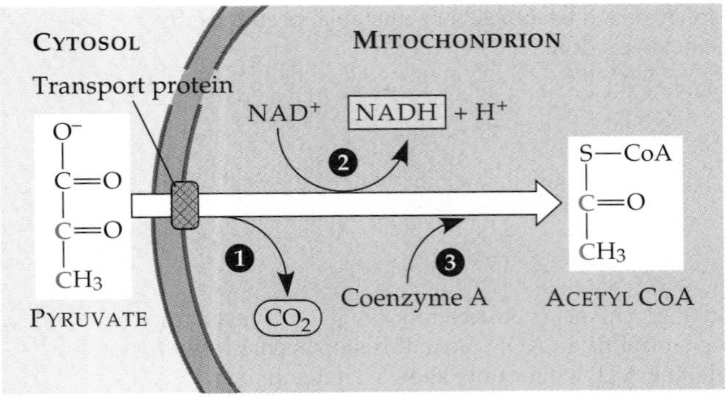

The inner mitochondrial membrane couples electron transport to ATP synthesis: *a closer look*

Our main objective in this chapter is to learn how cells harvest the energy of food to make ATP. But the metabolic components of respiration we have dissected so far, glycolysis and the Krebs cycle, produce only four molecules of ATP per glucose molecule, all by substrate-level phosphorylation: two net ATPs from glycolysis and two ATPs from the Krebs cycle. At this point, molecules of NADH (and $FADH_2$) account for most of the energy extracted from the food. These electron escorts link glycolysis and the Krebs cycle to the machinery for oxidative phosphorylation, which uses energy released by the electron transport chain to power ATP synthesis. In this section, you will first learn how the electron transport chain works, then how the inner membrane of the mitochondrion couples ATP synthesis to electron flow down the chain.

The Pathway of Electron Transport

You learned earlier that the electron transport chain is a collection of molecules embedded in the inner membrane of the

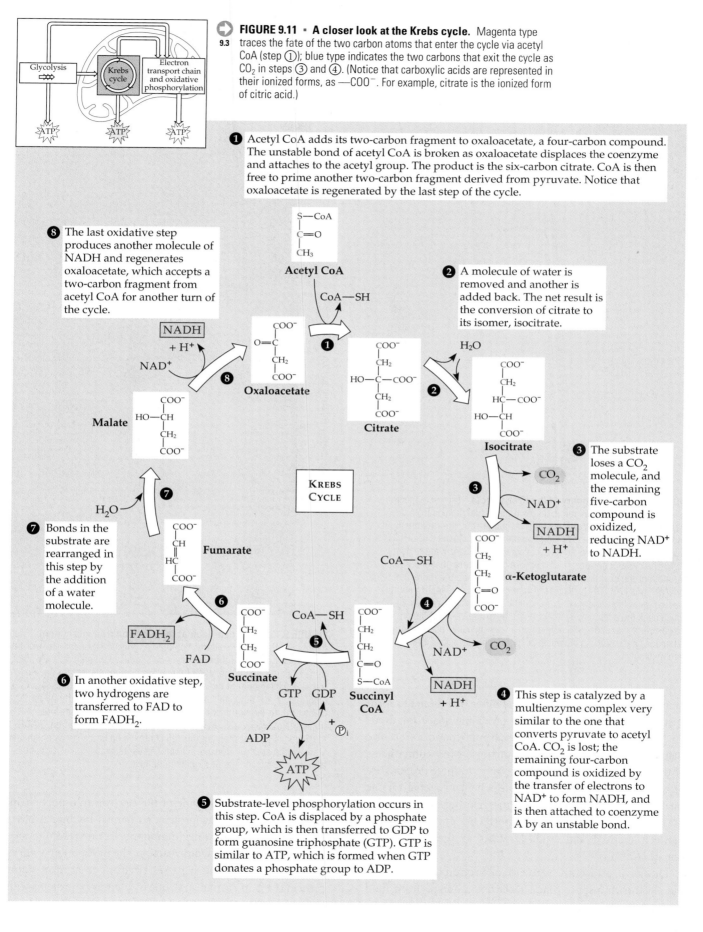

FIGURE 9.11 · A closer look at the Krebs cycle. Magenta type
traces the fate of the two carbon atoms that enter the cycle via acetyl
CoA (step ①); blue type indicates the two carbons that exit the cycle as
CO_2 in steps ③ and ④. (Notice that carboxylic acids are represented in
their ionized forms, as —COO⁻. For example, citrate is the ionized form
of citric acid.)

9.3

❶ Acetyl CoA adds its two-carbon fragment to oxaloacetate, a four-carbon compound.
The unstable bond of acetyl CoA is broken as oxaloacetate displaces the coenzyme
and attaches to the acetyl group. The product is the six-carbon citrate. CoA is then
free to prime another two-carbon fragment derived from pyruvate. Notice that
oxaloacetate is regenerated by the last step of the cycle.

❽ The last oxidative step
produces another molecule of
NADH and regenerates
oxaloacetate, which accepts a
two-carbon fragment from
acetyl CoA for another turn of
the cycle.

❷ A molecule of water is
removed and another is
added back. The net result is
the conversion of citrate to
its isomer, isocitrate.

Acetyl CoA

Oxaloacetate

Citrate

Isocitrate

Malate

KREBS CYCLE

α-Ketoglutarate

❸ The substrate
loses a CO_2
molecule, and
the remaining
five-carbon
compound is
oxidized,
reducing NAD⁺
to NADH.

❼ Bonds in the
substrate are
rearranged in
this step by
the addition
of a water
molecule.

Fumarate

❻ In another oxidative step,
two hydrogens are
transferred to FAD to
form FADH₂.

Succinate

Succinyl CoA

❹ This step is catalyzed by a
multienzyme complex very
similar to the one that
converts pyruvate to acetyl
CoA. CO_2 is lost; the
remaining four-carbon
compound is oxidized by
the transfer of electrons to
NAD⁺ to form NADH, and
is then attached to coenzyme
A by an unstable bond.

❺ Substrate-level phosphorylation occurs in
this step. CoA is displaced by a phosphate
group, which is then transferred to GDP to
form guanosine triphosphate (GTP). GTP is
similar to ATP, which is formed when GTP
donates a phosphate group to ADP.

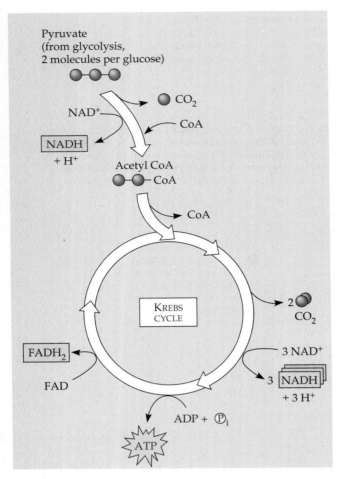

FIGURE 9.12 ▪ **A summary of the Krebs cycle.** The cycle functions as a metabolic "furnace" that oxidizes organic fuel derived from pyruvate, the product of glycolysis. This diagram summarizes the inputs and outputs as pyruvate is broken down to three molecules of CO_2. (The diagram includes the pre-Krebs cycle conversion of pyruvate to acetyl CoA.) The cycle generates 1 ATP per turn by substrate phosphorylation, but most of the chemical energy is transferred during the redox reactions to NAD^+ and FAD. The reduced coenzymes, NADH and $FADH_2$, shuttle their cargo of high-energy electrons to the electron transport chain, which uses the energy to synthesize ATP by oxidative phosphorylation. (To calculate the inputs and outputs on a "per-glucose" basis, multiply by 2, because each glucose molecule is split during glycolysis into two pyruvate molecules.)

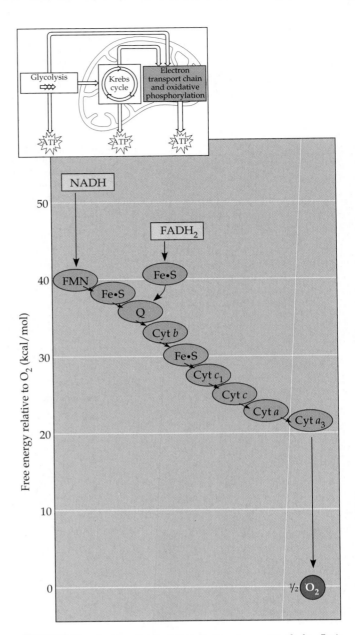

FIGURE 9.13 ▪ **A closer look at the electron transport chain.** Each member of the chain oscillates between a reduced state and an oxidized state. A component of the chain becomes reduced when it accepts electrons from its "uphill" neighbor (which has a lower affinity for the electrons). Each member of the chain returns to its oxidized form as it passes electrons to its "downhill" neighbor (which has a greater affinity for the electrons). At the bottom of the chain is oxygen, which is *very* electronegative. The overall energy drop for electrons traveling from NADH to oxygen is 53 kcal/mol, but this fall is broken up into a series of smaller steps by the electron transport chain. The various molecules of the electron transport chain are described in the text.

mitochondrion. The folding of the inner membrane to form cristae increases its surface area, providing space for thousands of copies of the chain in each mitochondrion. (Once again, we see that structure fits function.) Most components of the chain are proteins. Tightly bound to these proteins are prosthetic groups, nonprotein components essential for the catalytic functions of certain enzymes. During electron transport along the chain, these prosthetic groups alternate between reduced and oxidized states as they accept and donate electrons.

FIGURE 9.13 traces the sequence of electron transfers along the electron transport chain. Electrons removed from food during glycolysis and the Krebs cycle are transferred by NADH to the first molecule of the electron transport chain. This molecule is a flavoprotein, so named because it has a prosthetic group called flavin mononucleotide (FMN in FIGURE 9.13). In the next redox reaction, the flavoprotein returns to its oxidized form as it passes electrons to an iron-sulfur protein (Fe•S in FIGURE 9.13), one of a family of proteins with both iron and sulfur tightly bound. The iron-sulfur protein

then passes the electrons to a compound called ubiquinone (Q in FIGURE 9.13). This electron carrier is a lipid, the only member of the electron transport chain that is not a protein.

Most of the remaining electron carriers between Q and oxygen are proteins called **cytochromes (cyt)**. Their prosthetic group, called a heme group, has four organic rings surrounding a single iron atom. It is similar to the iron-containing prosthetic group found in hemoglobin, the red protein of blood that transports oxygen. But the iron of cytochromes transfers electrons, not oxygen. The electron transport chain has several types of cytochromes, each a different protein with a heme group. The last cytochrome of the chain, cyt a_3, passes its electrons to oxygen, which also picks up a pair of hydrogen ions from the aqueous solution to form water. (An oxygen atom is represented in FIGURE 9.13 as ½ O_2 to emphasize that the electron transport chain reduces molecular oxygen, O_2, not individual oxygen atoms. For every two NADH molecules, one O_2 molecule is reduced to two molecules of water.)

Another source of electrons for the transport chain is $FADH_2$, the other reduced product of the Krebs cycle. Notice in FIGURE 9.13 that $FADH_2$ adds its electrons to the electron transport chain at a lower energy level than NADH does. Consequently, the electron transport chain provides about one-third less energy for ATP synthesis when the electron donor is $FADH_2$ rather than NADH.

The electron transport chain makes no ATP directly. Its function is to ease the fall of electrons from food to oxygen, breaking a large free-energy drop into a series of smaller steps that release energy in manageable amounts. How does the mitochondrion couple this electron transport and energy release to ATP synthesis? The answer is a mechanism called chemiosmosis.

Chemiosmosis: The Energy-Coupling Mechanism

Populating the inner membrane of the mitochondrion are many copies of a protein complex called an **ATP synthase**, the enzyme that actually makes ATP (FIGURE 9.14). It works like an ion pump running in reverse. Recall from Chapter 8 that ion pumps use ATP as an energy source to transport ions against their gradients. In the reverse of that process, an ATP synthase uses the energy of an existing ion gradient to power ATP synthesis. The ion gradient that drives oxidative phosphorylation is a proton (hydrogen ion) gradient; that is, the power source for the ATP synthase is a difference in the concentration of H^+ on opposite sides of the inner mitochondrial membrane. We can also think of this gradient as a difference in pH, since pH is a measure of H^+ concentration.

How does the mitochondrial membrane generate and maintain an H^+ gradient? That is the function of the electron transport chain (FIGURE 9.15, p. 160). The chain is an energy converter that uses the exergonic flow of electrons to pump

H^+ across the membrane, from the matrix into the intermembrane space. The H^+ leaks back across the membrane, diffusing down its gradient. But the ATP synthases are the only patches of the membrane that are freely permeable to H^+. The ions pass through a channel in an ATP synthase, and the complex of proteins functions as a mill that harnesses the exergonic flow of H^+ to drive the phosphorylation of ADP. Thus, an H^+ gradient couples the redox reactions of the electron transport chain to ATP synthesis. This coupling mechanism for oxidative phosphorylation is called **chemiosmosis** (Gr. *osmos*, "push"), a term that highlights the relationship between chemical reactions and transport across a membrane. We have previously used the word *osmosis* in discussing water transport, but here the word refers to the flowing of H^+ across a membrane.

If you have followed this complex story of chemiosmosis so far, you should have at least two questions. How does the electron transport chain pump hydrogen ions? And how does the ATP synthase use H^+ backflow to make ATP? On the first problem, researchers have found that certain members of the electron transport chain accept and release protons (H^+) along with electrons, whereas other carriers transport only electrons. Therefore, at certain steps along the chain, electron transfers cause H^+ to be taken up and released back into the surrounding solution. The electron carriers are spatially

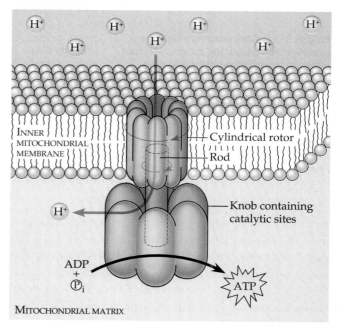

FIGURE 9.14 · ATP synthase, a molecular machine. This protein complex, which uses the energy of an H^+ gradient to drive ATP synthesis, resides in mitochondrial and chloroplast membranes and in the plasma membranes of prokaryotes. ATP synthase has three main parts, each consisting of a number of protein subunits: a cylindrical component within the membrane, a protruding knob (which, in mitochondria, is in the matrix), and a rod (or "stalk") connecting the other two parts. The cylinder is a rotor that spins clockwise when H^+ flows through it down a gradient. The attached rod also spins, activating catalytic sites in the knob, the component that joins inorganic phosphate to ADP to make ATP.

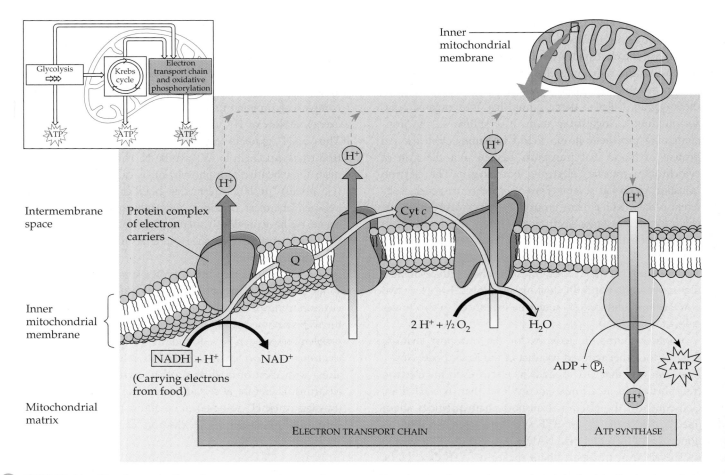

Inner mitochondrial membrane

Intermembrane space

Protein complex of electron carriers

Cyt c

Q

$2\,H^+ + \tfrac{1}{2}\,O_2$ H_2O

Inner mitochondrial membrane

NADH + H+   NAD+
(Carrying electrons from food)

ADP + $\textcircled{P}_i$ ATP

Mitochondrial matrix

ELECTRON TRANSPORT CHAIN   ATP SYNTHASE

FIGURE 9.15 · Chemiosmosis: How the mitochondrial membrane couples electron transport to oxidative phosphorylation.
NADH shuttles high-energy electrons extracted from food during glycolysis and the Krebs cycle to an electron transport chain, which is built into the inner mitochondrial membrane. The gold arrow in this diagram traces the transport of electrons, which pass to oxygen at the "down-hill" end of the chain to form water. Most of the cytochromes and other electron carriers of the chain (see FIGURE 9.13) are collected into three complexes, each represented here by a purple blob embedded in the membrane. Two mobile carriers, ubiquinone (Q) and cytochrome c, move rapidly along the membrane, ferrying electrons between the three large complexes. As each complex of the chain accepts and then donates electrons, it pumps hydrogen ions (protons) from the mitochondrial matrix into the intermembrane space (magenta arrows trace H+ transport). Thus, chemical energy harvested from food is transformed into a proton-motive force, a gradient of H+ across the membrane. The hydrogen ions complete their circuit by flowing down their gradient through an H+ channel in an ATP synthase, another protein complex built into the membrane. The ATP synthase harnesses the proton-motive force to phosphorylate ADP, forming ATP. (This is called oxidative phosphorylation because it is driven by the exergonic transfer of electrons from food to oxygen.) This mechanism for energy coupling—the use of an H+ gradient (proton-motive force) to transfer energy from redox reactions to cellular work (ATP synthesis, in this case)—is called chemiosmosis.

arranged in the membrane in such a way that H+ is accepted from the mitochondrial matrix and deposited in the intermembrane space (see FIGURE 9.15). The H+ gradient that results is referred to as a **proton-motive force**, emphasizing the capacity of the gradient to perform work. The force drives H+ back across the membrane through the specific H+ channels provided by ATP synthase complexes.

Scientists are also learning how the flow of H+ through ATP synthase powers ATP generation. This new understanding of ATP synthase function has emerged from studies of its molecular structure (see FIGURE 9.14). The ATP synthase complex consists of three main parts: a cylinder within the inner mitochondrial membrane, a knob protruding into the mitochondrial matrix, and an internal rod connecting the two. When hydrogen ions flow through the cylinder down their gradient,

they cause the cylinder and the attached rod to rotate, much as a rushing stream turns a water wheel. The spinning rod brings about a conformational change in the knob, activating catalytic sites where ADP and inorganic phosphate combine to make ATP.

In general terms, *chemiosmosis is an energy-coupling mechanism that uses energy stored in the form of an H+ gradient to drive cellular work.* In mitochondria, the energy for gradient formation comes from exergonic redox reactions, and ATP synthesis is the work performed. But chemiosmosis also occurs elsewhere, and in other variations. Chloroplasts use chemiosmosis to generate ATP during photosynthesis; in these organelles, light (rather than chemical energy) drives both electron flow down an electron transport chain and H+-gradient formation. Prokaryotes, which lack both mitochon-

dria and chloroplasts, generate H^+ gradients across their plasma membranes. They then tap the proton-motive force not only to make ATP but also to pump nutrients and waste products across the membrane, and to rotate their flagella.

Experiments with bacteria first led British biochemist Peter Mitchell to propose chemiosmosis as an energy-coupling mechanism in 1961. Nearly two decades later, after many scientists had confirmed the centrality of chemiosmosis in energy conversions within bacteria, mitochondria, and chloroplasts, Mitchell was awarded the Nobel Prize. Chemiosmosis has helped unify the study of bioenergetics.

Cellular respiration generates many ATP molecules for each sugar molecule it oxidizes: *a review*

Now that we have looked more closely at the key processes of cellular respiration, let's return to its overall function: harvesting the energy of food for ATP synthesis.

During respiration, most energy flows in this sequence: Glucose $\longrightarrow$ NADH $\longrightarrow$ electron transport chain $\longrightarrow$ proton-motive force $\longrightarrow$ ATP. We can do some bookkeeping to calculate the ATP profit when cellular respiration oxidizes a molecule of glucose to six molecules of carbon dioxide. The three main departments of this metabolic enterprise are gly-

colysis, the Krebs cycle, and the electron transport chain, which drives oxidative phosphorylation. FIGURE 9.16 gives a detailed accounting of the ATP yield per glucose molecule oxidized. The tally adds the few molecules of ATP produced directly by substrate-level phosphorylation during glycolysis and the Krebs cycle to the many more molecules of ATP generated by oxidative phosphorylation. Each NADH that transfers a pair of electrons from food to the electron transport chain contributes enough to the proton-motive force to generate a maximum of about three ATPs. (The average ATP yield per NADH is probably between two and three; we are rounding off to three here to simplify the bookkeeping.) The Krebs cycle also supplies electrons to the electron transport chain via $FADH_2$, but each molecule of this electron carrier is worth a maximum of only about two molecules of ATP.

In some eukaryotic cells, this lower ATP yield per electron pair also applies to the NADH produced by glycolysis in the cytosol. The mitochondrial inner membrane is impermeable to NADH, so NADH in the cytosol is segregated from the machinery of oxidative phosphorylation. The two electrons of NADH captured in glycolysis must be conveyed into the mitochondrion by one of several electron-shuttle systems. Depending on which shuttle is operating, the electrons are passed either to NAD^+ or to FAD. If the electrons are passed to FAD, only about 2 ATP can result from each cytosolic

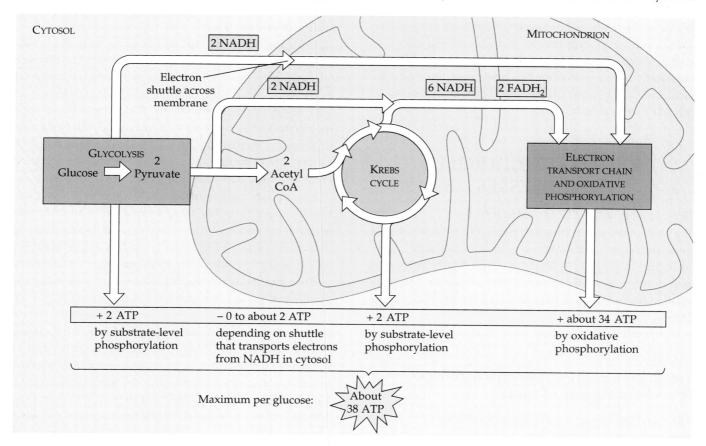

FIGURE 9.16 ▪ **Review: Each molecule of glucose yields many ATP molecules during cellular respiration**. The text explains why the yield of 38 ATP per glucose is only an estimate of the maximum output.

$NADH_2$. If passed to mitochondrial NAD^+, the yield is closer to 3 ATP.

Assuming that the more energy-efficient type of shuttle is active, we can add a maximum of 34 ATP produced by oxidative phosphorylation to the net of 4 ATP from substrate-level phosphorylation to arrive at a bottom line of 38 ATP. This is only an estimate of the maximum ATP yield from a glucose molecule and is undoubtedly somewhat high. One variable that reduces ATP yield is the use of the proton-motive force (generated by the redox reactions of respiration) to drive other kinds of work. For example, the proton-motive force powers the mitochondrion's uptake of pyruvate from the cytoplasm. Also, by rounding up the number of ATP molecules produced per NADH and $FADH_2$ to three and two, respectively, we have inflated the ATP yield of respiration by at least 10%.

We can now make a rough estimate of the efficiency of respiration—that is, the percentage of chemical energy stored in glucose that has been restocked in ATP. Recall that the complete oxidation of a mole of glucose releases 686 kcal of energy ($\Delta G = -686$ kcal/mol). Phosphorylation of ADP to form ATP stores at least 7.3 kcal per mole of ATP (p. 90 explains why this number is probably higher under cellular conditions). Therefore, the efficiency of respiration is 7.3 times 38 (maximum ATP yield per glucose) divided by 686, or about 40%. The rest of the stored energy is lost as heat. We use some of this heat to maintain our relatively high body temperature (37°C), and we dissipate the rest through sweating and other cooling mechanisms. Cellular respiration is remarkably efficient in its energy conversion. By comparison, the most efficient automobile converts about 25% of the energy stored in gasoline to movement of the car.

RELATED METABOLIC PROCESSES

Because most of the ATP generated by cellular respiration is the work of oxidative phosphorylation, our estimate of ATP yield from respiration is contingent upon an adequate supply of oxygen to the cell. Without the electronegative oxygen to pull electrons down the transport chain, oxidative phosphorylation ceases. However, fermentation provides a mechanism by which some cells can oxidize organic fuel and generate ATP *without* the help of oxygen.

Fermentation enables some cells to produce ATP without the help of oxygen

How can food be oxidized without oxygen? Remember, oxidation refers to the loss of electrons to *any* electron acceptor, not just to oxygen. Glycolysis oxidizes glucose to two molecules of pyruvate. The oxidizing agent of glycolysis is NAD^+, *not* oxy-gen. Overall, glycolysis is exergonic, and some of the energy made available is used to produce two ATPs (net) by substrate-level phosphorylation. If oxygen *is* present, then additional ATP is made by oxidative phosphorylation when NADH passes electrons removed from glucose to the electron transport chain. But glycolysis generates two ATPs whether oxygen is present or not—that is, whether conditions are **aerobic** or **anaerobic** (Gr. *aer*, "air," and *bios*, "life"; the prefix *an-* means "without").

Anaerobic catabolism of organic nutrients can occur by fermentation, as mentioned at the beginning of the chapter. Fermentation is an extension of glycolysis that can generate ATP solely by substrate-level phosphorylation—as long as there is a sufficient supply of NAD^+ to accept electrons during the oxidation step of glycolysis. Without some mechanism to recycle NAD^+ from NADH, glycolysis would soon deplete the cell's pool of NAD^+ and shut itself down for lack of an oxidizing agent. Under aerobic conditions, NAD^+ is recycled productively from NADH by the transfer of electrons to the electron transport chain. The anaerobic alternative is to transfer electrons from NADH to pyruvate, the end-product of glycolysis.

Fermentation consists of glycolysis plus reactions that regenerate NAD^+ by transferring electrons from NADH to pyruvate or derivatives of pyruvate. There are many types of fermentation, differing in the waste products formed from pyruvate. Two common types are alcohol fermentation and lactic acid fermentation.

In **alcohol fermentation** (FIGURE 9.17a), pyruvate is converted to ethanol (ethyl alcohol) in two steps. The first step releases carbon dioxide from the pyruvate, which is converted to the two-carbon compound acetaldehyde. In the second step, acetaldehyde is reduced by NADH to ethanol. This regenerates the supply of NAD^+ needed for glycolysis. Alcohol fermentation by yeast, a fungus, is used in brewing and wine making. Many bacteria also carry out alcohol fermentation under anaerobic conditions.

During **lactic acid fermentation** (FIGURE 9.17b), pyruvate is reduced directly by NADH to form lactate as a waste product, with no release of CO_2. (Lactate is the ionized form of lactic acid.) Lactic acid fermentation by certain fungi and bacteria is used in the dairy industry to make cheese and yogurt. Acetone and methanol (methyl alcohol) are among the by-products of other types of microbial fermentation that are commercially important.

Human muscle cells make ATP by lactic acid fermentation when oxygen is scarce. This occurs during the early stages of strenuous exercise, when sugar catabolism for ATP production outpaces the muscle's supply of oxygen from the blood. Under these conditions, the cells switch from aerobic respiration to fermentation. The lactate that accumulates as a waste product may cause muscle fatigue and pain, but it is gradually carried away by the blood to the liver. Lactate is converted back to pyruvate by liver cells.

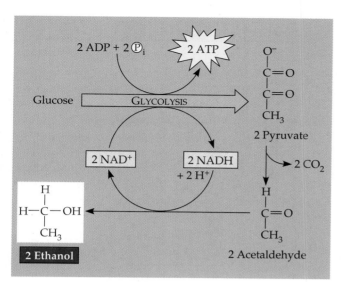

(a) Alcohol fermentation

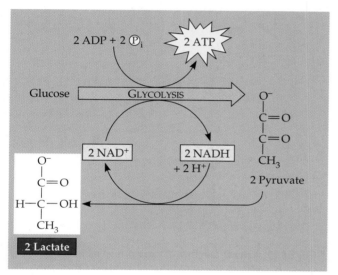

(b) Lactic acid fermentation

FIGURE 9.17 ▪ Fermentation. Pyruvate, the end-product of glycolysis, serves as an electron acceptor for oxidizing NADH back to NAD⁺. The NAD⁺ can then be reused to oxidize sugar during glycolysis, which yields two net molecules of ATP by substrate-level phosphorylation. Two of the common waste products formed from fermentation are **(a)** ethanol and **(b)** lactate, the ionized form of lactic acid.

Fermentation and Respiration Compared

Fermentation and cellular respiration are anaerobic and aerobic alternatives, respectively, for producing ATP by harvesting the chemical energy of food. Both pathways use glycolysis to oxidize glucose and other organic fuels to pyruvate, with a net production of 2 ATP by substrate phosphorylation. And in both fermentation and respiration, NAD⁺ is the oxidizing agent that accepts electrons from food during glycolysis. A key difference is the contrasting mechanisms for oxidizing NADH back to NAD⁺, which is required to sustain glycolysis. In fermentation, the final electron acceptor is an organic molecule

such as pyruvate (lactic acid fermentation) or acetaldehyde (alcohol fermentation). In respiration, by contrast, the final acceptor for electrons from NADH is oxygen. This not only regenerates the NAD⁺ required for glycolysis but pays an ATP bonus when the stepwise electron transport from NADH to oxygen drives oxidative phosphorylation. An even bigger ATP payoff comes from the oxidation of pyruvate in the Krebs cycle, which is unique to respiration. Without oxygen, the energy still stored in pyruvate is unavailable to the cell. Thus, cellular respiration harvests much more energy from each sugar molecule than fermentation can. In fact, respiration yields as much as 19 times more ATP per glucose molecule than does fermentation—38 ATP for respiration, compared to 2 ATP produced by substrate-level phosphorylation in fermentation.

Some organisms, including yeasts and many bacteria, can make enough ATP to survive by either fermentation or respiration. Such species are called **facultative anaerobes**. On the cellular level, our muscle cells behave as facultative anaerobes. In a facultative anaerobe, pyruvate is a fork in the metabolic road that leads to two alternative catabolic routes (FIGURE 9.18). Under aerobic conditions, pyruvate can be converted to acetyl CoA, and oxidation continues in the Krebs cycle. Under anaerobic conditions, pyruvate is diverted from the Krebs

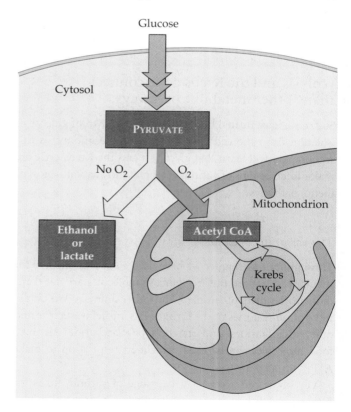

FIGURE 9.18 ▪ Pyruvate as a key juncture in catabolism. Glycolysis is common to fermentation and respiration. The end-product of glycolysis, pyruvate, represents a fork in the catabolic pathways of glucose oxidation. In a cell capable of both respiration and fermentation, pyruvate is committed to one of those two pathways, usually depending on whether or not oxygen is present.

cycle, serving instead as an electron acceptor to recycle NAD$^+$. To make the same amount of ATP, a facultative anaerobe would have to consume sugar at a much faster rate when fermenting than it would when respiring.

The Evolutionary Significance of Glycolysis

The role of glycolysis in both fermentation and respiration has an evolutionary basis. Ancient prokaryotes probably used glycolysis to make ATP long before oxygen was present in the Earth's atmosphere. The oldest known fossils of bacteria date back over 3.5 billion years, but appreciable quantities of oxygen probably did not begin to accumulate in the atmosphere until about 2.5 billion years ago. (According to fossil evidence, the cyanobacteria that produce O_2 as a by-product of photosynthesis had evolved by then.) Therefore, the first prokaryotes may have generated ATP exclusively from glycolysis, which does not require oxygen. In addition, glycolysis is the most widespread metabolic pathway, which suggests that it evolved very early in the history of life. The cytosolic location of glycolysis also implies great antiquity; the pathway does not require any of the membrane-enclosed organelles of the eukaryotic cell, which evolved nearly 2 billion years after the prokaryotic cell. Glycolysis is a metabolic heirloom from the earliest cells that continues to function in fermentation and as the first stage in the breakdown of organic molecules by respiration.

Glycolysis and the Krebs cycle connect to many other metabolic pathways

So far, we have treated the oxidative breakdown of glucose in isolation from the cell's overall metabolic economy. In this section, you will learn that glycolysis and the Krebs cycle are major intersections of various catabolic and anabolic (biosynthetic) pathways.

The Versatility of Catabolism

Throughout this chapter we have used glucose as the fuel for cellular respiration. But free glucose molecules are not common in the diets of humans and other animals. We obtain most of our calories in the form of fats, proteins, sucrose and other disaccharides, and starch, a polysaccharide. All these food molecules can be used by cellular respiration to make ATP (FIGURE 9.19).

Glycolysis can accept a wide range of carbohydrates for catabolism. In the digestive tract, starch is hydrolyzed to glucose, which can then be broken down in the cells by glycolysis and the Krebs cycle. Similarly, glycogen, the polysaccharide that humans and many other animals store in their liver and muscle cells, can be hydrolyzed to glucose between meals as fuel for respiration. The digestion of disaccharides, including

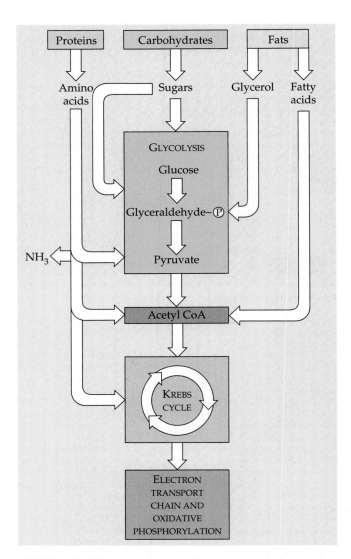

FIGURE 9.19 · The catabolism of various food molecules. Carbohydrates, fats, and proteins can all be used as fuel for cellular respiration. Monomers of these food molecules enter glycolysis or the Krebs cycle at various points. Glycolysis and the Krebs cycle are catabolic funnels through which electrons from all kinds of food molecules flow on their exergonic fall to oxygen.

sucrose, provides glucose and other monosaccharides as fuel for respiration.

Proteins can also be used for fuel, but first they must be digested to their constituent amino acids. Many of the amino acids, of course, are used by the organism to build new proteins. Amino acids present in excess are converted by enzymes to intermediates of glycolysis and the Krebs cycle. Before amino acids can feed into glycolysis or the Krebs cycle, their amino groups must be removed, a process called deamination. The nitrogenous refuse is excreted from the animal in the form of ammonia, urea, or other waste products.

Catabolism can also harvest energy stored in fats obtained either from food or from storage cells in the body. After fats are digested, the glycerol is converted to glyceraldehyde phosphate, an intermediate of glycolysis. Most of the energy of a

fat is stored in the fatty acids. A metabolic sequence called **beta oxidation** breaks the fatty acids down to two-carbon fragments, which enter the Krebs cycle as acetyl CoA. Fats make excellent fuel. A gram of fat oxidized by respiration produces more than twice as much ATP as a gram of carbohydrate. Unfortunately, this also means that a dieter must be patient while using fat stored in the body, because so many calories are stockpiled in each gram of fat.

Biosynthesis (Anabolic Pathways)

Cells need substance as well as energy. Not all the organic molecules of food are destined to be oxidized as fuel to make ATP. In addition to calories, food must also provide the carbon skeletons that cells require to make their own molecules. Some organic monomers obtained from digestion can be used directly. For example, as previously mentioned, amino acids from the hydrolysis of proteins in food can be incorporated into the organism's own proteins. Often, however, the body needs specific molecules that are not present as such in food. Compounds formed as intermediates of glycolysis and the Krebs cycle can be diverted into anabolic pathways as precursors from which the cell can synthesize the molecules it requires. For example, humans can make about half of the 20 amino acids in proteins by modifying compounds siphoned away from the Krebs cycle. Also, glucose can be made from pyruvate, and fatty acids can be synthesized from acetyl CoA. Of course, these anabolic or biosynthetic pathways do not generate ATP, but instead consume it.

In addition, glycolysis and the Krebs cycle function as metabolic interchanges that enable our cells to convert some kinds of molecules to others as we need them. For instance, carbohydrates and proteins can be converted to fats through intermediates of glycolysis and the Krebs cycle. If we eat more food than we need, we store fat even if our diet is fat-free. Metabolism is remarkably versatile and adaptable.

Feedback mechanisms control cellular respiration

Basic principles of supply and demand regulate the metabolic economy. The cell does not waste energy making more of a particular substance than it needs. If there is a glut of a certain amino acid, for example, the anabolic pathway that synthesizes that amino acid from an intermediate of the Krebs cycle is switched off. The most common mechanism for this control is feedback inhibition: The end-product of the anabolic pathway inhibits the enzyme that catalyzes an early step of the pathway (see FIGURE 6.16). This prevents the needless diversion of key metabolic intermediates from uses that are more urgent.

The cell also controls its catabolism. If the cell is working hard and its ATP concentration begins to drop, respiration

speeds up. When there is plenty of ATP to meet demand, respiration slows down, sparing valuable organic molecules for other functions. Again, control is based mainly on regulating the activity of enzymes at strategic points in the catabolic pathway. One important switch is phosphofructokinase, the enzyme that catalyzes step 3 of glycolysis (see FIGURE 9.9). That is the earliest step that commits substrate irreversibly to the glycolytic pathway. By controlling the rate of this step, the cell can speed up or slow down the entire catabolic process; phosphofructokinase is thus the pacemaker of respiration (FIGURE 9.20).

An allosteric enzyme with receptor sites for specific inhibitors and activators, phosphofructokinase is inhibited by ATP and stimulated by AMP, which the cell derives from ADP (see p. 95). As ATP accumulates, inhibition of the enzyme slows down glycolysis. The enzyme becomes active again as

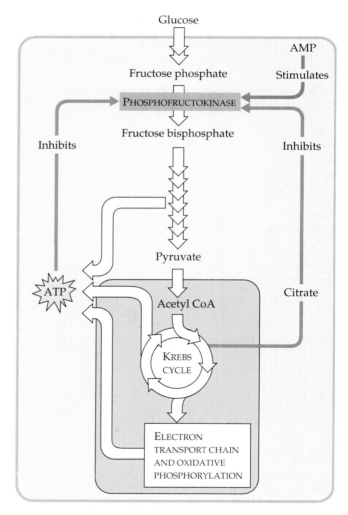

FIGURE 9.20 ▪ The control of cellular respiration. Allosteric enzymes at certain points in the respiratory pathway respond to inhibitors and activators that help set the pace of glycolysis and the Krebs cycle. Phosphofructokinase, the enzyme that catalyzes step 3 of glycolysis, is one such enzyme. It is stimulated by AMP that is derived from ADP, but it is inhibited by ATP and by citrate. This feedback regulation adjusts the rate of respiration as the cell's catabolic and anabolic demands change.

cellular work converts ATP to ADP (and AMP) faster than ATP is being regenerated. Phosphofructokinase is also sensitive to citrate, the first product of the Krebs cycle. If citrate accumulates in mitochondria, some of it passes into the cytosol and inhibits phosphofructokinase. This mechanism helps synchronize the rates of glycolysis and the Krebs cycle. As citrate accumulates, glycolysis slows down, and the supply of acetate to the Krebs cycle decreases. If citrate consumption increases, either because of a demand for more ATP or because anabolic pathways are draining off intermediates of the Krebs cycle, glycolysis accelerates and meets the demand. Metabolic balance is augmented by the control of other enzymes at other key locations in glycolysis and the Krebs cycle. Cells are thrifty, expedient, and responsive in their metabolism.

■   ■   ■

Examine FIGURE 9.1 again to put cellular respiration into the broader context of energy flow and chemical cycling in ecosystems. The energy that keeps us alive is *released*, but not *produced*, by cellular respiration. We are tapping energy that was stored in food by photosynthesis. In the next chapter you will learn how photosynthesis captures light and converts it to chemical energy.

CHAPTER REVIEW

REVIEW OF KEY CONCEPTS

(with page numbers and key figures)

PRINCIPLES OF ENERGY HARVEST

Chemical elements important to life are recycled by respiration and photosynthesis, but energy is not (p. 147, FIGURE 9.1).

■ **Cellular respiration and fermentation are catabolic (energy-yielding) pathways (pp. 147–148)** The breakdown of glucose and other organic fuels to simpler products is exergonic, yielding energy for ATP synthesis.

■ **Cells recycle the ATP they use for work (p. 148, FIGURE 9.2)** ATP transfers phosphate groups to various substrates, priming them to do work. To keep working, a cell must regenerate ATP. Starting with glucose or another organic fuel, and using O_2, cellular respiration yields H_2O, CO_2, and energy in the form of ATP and heat.

■ **Redox reactions release energy when electrons move closer to electronegative atoms (pp. 148–150, FIGURE 9.3)** The cell taps the energy stored in food molecules through redox reactions, in which one substance partially or totally shifts electrons to another. The substance receiving electrons is reduced; the substance losing electrons is oxidized.

■ **Electrons "fall" from organic molecules to oxygen during cellular respiration (p. 150)** Glucose ($C_6H_{12}O_6$) is oxidized to CO_2, and O_2 is reduced to H_2O. Electrons lose potential energy during their transfer from organic compounds to oxygen, and this energy drives ATP synthesis.

■ **The "fall" of electrons during respiration is stepwise, via NAD^+ and an electron transport chain (pp. 150–152, FIGURE 9.5)** Electrons from food are usually passed to NAD^+, reducing it to NADH. NADH passes them to an electron transport chain, which conducts them to O_2 in energy-releasing steps. The energy released is used to make ATP by oxidative phosphorylation.

THE PROCESS OF CELLULAR RESPIRATION

⊃ **Respiration involves glycolysis, the Krebs cycle, and electron**
9.1 **transport (pp. 152–153, FIGURE 9.6)** Glycolysis and the Krebs cycle supply electrons (via NADH) to the transport chain, which drives oxidative phosphorylation. Glycolysis occurs in the cytosol and the Krebs cycle in the mitochondrial matrix. The electron transport chain is built into the inner mitochondrial membrane.

⊃ **Glycolysis harvests chemical energy by oxidizing glucose to pyru-**
9.2 **vate (pp. 153–156, FIGURE 9.8)** Glycolysis nets 2 ATP, produced by substrate-level phosphorylation, and 2 NADH.

⊃ **The Krebs cycle completes the energy-yielding oxidation of**
9.3 **organic molecules (p. 156, FIGURE 9.12)** The conversion of pyruvate to acetyl CoA links glycolysis to the Krebs cycle. The 2-carbon acetate of acetyl CoA joins the 4-carbon oxaloacetate to form the 6-carbon citrate, which is degraded back to oxaloacetate. The cycle releases CO_2, forms 1 ATP by substrate-level phosphorylation, and passes electrons to 3 NAD^+ and 1 FAD.

⊃ **The inner mitochondrial membrane couples electron transport to**
9.4 **ATP synthesis (pp. 156–161, FIGURE 9.15)** Most of the ATP made in cellular respiration is produced by oxidative phosphorylation when NADH and $FADH_2$ donate electrons to the series of electron carriers in the electron transport chain. At the end of the chain, electrons are passed to O_2, reducing it to H_2O. Electron transport is coupled to ATP synthesis by chemiosmosis. At certain steps along the chain, electron transfer causes electron-carrying protein complexes to move H^+ from the matrix to the intermembrane space, storing energy as a proton-motive force (H^+ gradient). As H^+ diffuses back into the matrix through ATP synthase, its exergonic passage drives the endergonic phosphorylation of ADP.

■ **Cellular respiration generates many ATP molecules for each sugar molecule it oxidizes (pp. 161–162, FIGURE 9.16)** The oxidation of glucose to CO_2 in respiration produces a maximum of about 38 ATP.

RELATED METABOLIC PROCESSES

■ **Fermentation enables some cells to produce ATP without the help of oxygen (pp. 162–164, FIGURE 9.17)** Fermentation is anaerobic catabolism of organic nutrients. It yields ATP from glycolysis. The electrons from NADH made in glycolysis are passed to pyruvate, restoring the NAD^+ required to sustain glycolysis. Yeast and certain bacteria are facultative anaerobes, capable of making ATP by either aerobic respiration or fermentation. Of the two pathways, respiration is the more efficient in terms of ATP yield per glucose. Glycolysis occurs in nearly all organisms and probably evolved in ancient prokaryotes before there was O_2 in the atmosphere.

■ **Glycolysis and the Krebs cycle connect to many other metabolic pathways (pp. 164–165, FIGURE 9.19)** These catabolic pathways combine to funnel electrons from all kinds of food molecules into cellular respiration. Carbon skeletons for anabolism (biosynthesis) come directly from digestion or from intermediates of glycolysis and the Krebs cycle.

■ **Feedback mechanisms control cellular respiration (pp. 165–166, FIGURE 9.20)** Cellular respiration is controlled by allosteric enzymes at key points in glycolysis and the Krebs cycle. This helps the cell strike a moment-to-moment balance between catabolism and anabolism.

1. The *immediate* energy source that drives ATP synthesis during oxidative phosphorylation is
   a. the oxidation of glucose and other organic compounds
   b. the flow of electrons down the electron transport chain
   c. the affinity of oxygen for electrons
   d. a difference of H^+ concentration on opposite sides of the inner mitochondrial membrane
   e. the transfer of phosphate from Krebs cycle intermediates to ADP

2. What is the reducing agent in the following reaction?

   $$\text{pyruvate} + \text{NADH} + H^+ \longrightarrow \text{lactate} + \text{NAD}^+$$

   a. oxygen   c. NAD^+ e. pyruvate
   b. NADH   d. lactate

3. Which metabolic pathway is common to both fermentation and cellular respiration?
   a. Krebs cycle
   b. electron transport chain
   c. glycolysis
   d. synthesis of acetyl CoA from pyruvate
   e. reduction of pyruvate to lactate

4. In mitochondria, exergonic redox reactions
   a. are the source of energy driving prokaryotic ATP synthesis
   b. are directly coupled to substrate-level phosphorylation
   c. provide the energy to establish the proton gradient
   d. reduce carbon atoms to carbon dioxide
   e. are coupled via phosphorylated intermediates to endergonic processes

5. The final electron acceptor of the electron transport chain that functions in oxidative phosphorylation is
   a. oxygen   c. NAD^+ e. ADP
   b. water   d. pyruvate

6. When electrons flow along the electron transport chains of mitochondria, which of the following changes occurs? (Explain your answer.)
   a. The pH of the matrix increases.
   b. ATP synthase pumps protons by active transport.
   c. The electrons gain free energy.
   d. The cytochromes of the chain phosphorylate ADP to form ATP.
   e. NAD^+ is oxidized.

7. In the presence of a metabolic poison that specifically and completely inhibits the function of mitochondrial ATP synthase, which of the following would you expect? (Explain your answer.)
   a. a decrease in the pH difference across the inner mitochondrial membrane
   b. an increase in the pH difference across the inner mitochondrial membrane
   c. increased synthesis of ATP
   d. oxygen consumption to cease
   e. proton pumping by the electron transport chain to cease

8. Cells do not catabolize carbon dioxide because
   a. its double bonds are too stable to be broken
   b. CO_2 has fewer bonding electrons than other organic compounds
   c. the carbon atom is already completely reduced
   d. most of the available electron energy was released by the time the CO_2 was formed
   e. the molecule has too few atoms

9. Which of the following is a true distinction between fermentation and cellular respiration?
   a. Only respiration oxidizes glucose.
   b. NADH is oxidized by the electron transport chain only in respiration.
   c. Fermentation, but not respiration, is an example of a catabolic pathway.
   d. Substrate-level phosphorylation is unique to fermentation.
   e. NAD^+ functions as an oxidizing agent only in respiration.

10. Most CO_2 from catabolism is released during
    a. glycolysis
    b. the Krebs cycle
    c. lactate fermentation
    d. electron transport
    e. oxidative phosphorylation

CHALLENGE QUESTION

In the 1940s, some physicians prescribed low doses of a drug called dinitrophenol (DNP) to help patients lose weight. This unsafe method was abandoned after a few patients died. DNP uncouples the chemiosmotic machinery by making the lipid bilayer of the inner mitochondrial membrane leaky to H^+. Explain how this causes weight loss.

SCIENCE, TECHNOLOGY, AND SOCIETY

Nearly all human societies use fermentation to produce alcoholic drinks such as beer and wine. The practice dates back to the earliest days of agriculture. How do you suppose this use of fermentation was first discovered? Why did wine prove to be a more useful beverage, especially to a preindustrial culture, than the grape juice from which it was made?

FURTHER READING

Becker, W. M., J. B. Reece, and M. F. Poenie. *The World of the Cell*, 3rd ed. Menlo Park, CA: Benjamin/Cummings, 1996. Provides particularly clear and comprehensive coverage of how cells harvest energy in Chapters 11 and 12.

Gennis, R. B. "Cytochrome *c* Oxidase: One Enzyme, Two Mechanisms?" *Science*, June 12, 1998. Describes recent discoveries about the third protein complex in the electron transport chain.

Kearney, J. T. "Training the Olympic Athlete." *Scientific American*, June 1996. Includes discussion of how athletes work to achieve an optimum balance between aerobic and anaerobic energy generation.

Mathews, C., and K. van Holde. *Biochemistry*, 2nd ed. Redwood City, CA: Benjamin/Cummings, 1996. Features effective diagrams of catabolism.

Service, R. F. "Chemistry Prize Taps the Energy of Life." *Science*, October 24, 1997. The awarding of the Nobel Prize for research on ATP synthase.

Weiss, R. "Blazing Blossoms." *Science News*, June 24, 1989. How skunk cabbage and other plants use their catabolism to generate heat.

WEB LINKS

Visit the special edition of *The Biology Place* for BIOLOGY, Fifth Edition, at http://www.biology.com/campbell. Go to Chapter 9 for online resources, including learning activities, practice exams, and links to the following web sites:

"DIY Glycolysis Home Page"
To complete "Do It Yourself Glycolysis," you must correctly select the reactions necessary to convert glucose to lactate.

"Metabolism of TCA Intermediates"
From the Argonne National Laboratory, this clickable image map takes you to metabolic pathways linked to the Krebs cycle.

"Biomolecular machines: ATP Synthase"
Animated information on the functioning of ATP synthase.

"The Biology Project—Biochemistry"
Interesting problem sets and tutorials from the Biology Project at the University of Arizona.

PHOTOSYNTHESIS

*L*ife on Earth is solar-powered. The chloroplasts of plants capture light energy that has traveled 160 million kilometers from the sun and convert it to chemical energy stored in sugar and other organic molecules. The process is called **photosynthesis**. In this chapter you will learn how photosynthesis works. We begin by placing photosynthesis in its ecological context.

PHOTOSYNTHESIS IN NATURE

Plants and other autotrophs are the producers of the biosphere

Photosynthesis nourishes almost all of the living world directly or indirectly. An organism acquires the organic compounds it uses for energy and carbon skeletons by one of two major modes: autotrophic or heterotrophic nutrition. At first, the term *autotrophic* (Gr. *autos,* "self," and *trophos,* "feed") may seem to contradict the principle that organisms are open systems, taking in resources from their environment. **Autotrophs** are not totally self-sufficient, however; they are self-feeders only in the sense that they sustain themselves without eating or decomposing other organisms. They make their organic molecules from inorganic raw materials obtained from the environment. It is for this reason that biologists refer to autotrophs as the *producers* of the biosphere.

Plants are autotrophs; the only nutrients they require are carbon dioxide from the air, and water and minerals from the soil. Specifically, plants are *photo*autotrophs, organisms that use light as a source of energy to synthesize carbohydrates, lipids, proteins, and other organic substances. Photosynthesis also occurs in algae, including certain protists, and in some prokaryotes (FIGURE 10.1). In this chapter our emphasis will be on plants. Variations in photosynthesis that occur in algae and bacteria will be discussed in Unit Five. A much rarer form of self-feeding is unique to those bacteria that are *chemo*autotrophs. These organisms produce their organic compounds without the help of light, obtaining their energy by oxidizing inorganic substances, such as sulfur or ammonia. (We will postpone further discussion of this type of autotrophic nutrition until Chapter 27.)

Heterotrophs obtain their organic material by the second major mode of nutrition. Unable to make their own food, they live on compounds produced by other organisms; heterotrophs are the biosphere's *consumers*. The most obvious form of this "other-feeding" (*hetero* means "other, different") occurs when an animal eats plants or other animals. But heterotrophic nutrition may be more subtle. Some heterotrophs consume the remains of dead organisms, decomposing and feeding on organic litter such as carcasses, feces, and fallen

(a)

(b)

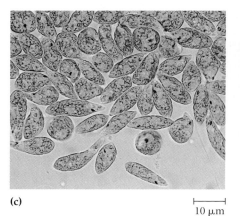

(c)

10 μm

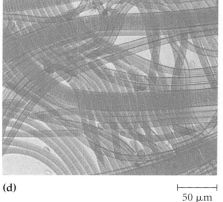

(d)

50 μm

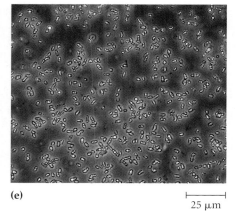

(e)

25 μm

FIGURE 10.1 ▪ **Photoautotrophs: producers for most ecosystems.** These organisms use light energy to drive the synthesis of organic molecules from carbon dioxide and (in most cases) water. They feed not only themselves, but the entire living world. **(a)** On land, plants are the predominant producers of food. Three major groups of land plants—mosses, ferns, and flowering plants—are represented in this scene. In oceans, ponds, lakes, and other aquatic environments, photosynthetic organisms include **(b)** multicellular algae, such as kelp; **(c)** some unicellular protists, such as *Euglena;* **(d)** the prokaryotes called cyanobacteria; and **(e)** other photosynthetic prokaryotes, such as these purple sulfur bacteria (c, d, e: LMs).

leaves; they are known as decomposers. Most fungi and many types of bacteria get their nourishment this way. Almost all heterotrophs, including humans, are completely dependent on photoautotrophs for food, and also for oxygen, a by-product of photosynthesis. Thus, we can trace the food we eat and the oxygen we breathe to the chloroplast.

Chloroplasts are the sites of photosynthesis in plants

All green parts of a plant, including green stems and unripened fruit, have chloroplasts, but the leaves are the

major sites of photosynthesis in most plants (FIGURE 10.2). There are about half a million chloroplasts per square millimeter of leaf surface. The color of the leaf is from **chlorophyll**, the green pigment located within the chloroplasts. It is the light energy absorbed by chlorophyll that drives the synthesis of food molecules in the chloroplast. Chloroplasts are found mainly in the cells of the **mesophyll**, the tissue in the interior of the leaf. Carbon dioxide enters the leaf, and oxygen exits, by way of microscopic pores called **stomata** (singular, **stoma**; Gr. "mouth"). Water absorbed by the roots is delivered to the leaves in veins. Leaves also use veins to export sugar to roots and other nonphotosynthetic parts of the plant.

A typical mesophyll cell has about 30 to 40 chloroplasts, each a watermelon-shaped organelle measuring about 2–4 μm by 4–7 μm. An envelope of two membranes encloses the stroma, the dense fluid within the chloroplast. An elaborate system of interconnected thylakoid membranes segregates the stroma from another compartment, the thylakoid space (or lumen). In some places, thylakoid sacs are stacked in columns called grana. Chlorophyll resides in the thylakoid membranes. (Photosynthetic prokaryotes lack chloroplasts, but, as you will see in Chapter 27, they do have membranes that function in a manner similar to the thylakoid membranes of chloroplasts.) Now that we have looked at the sites of photosynthesis in plants, we are ready to see how these organelles convert the light energy absorbed by chlorophyll to chemical energy.

THE PATHWAYS OF PHOTOSYNTHESIS

Evidence that chloroplasts split water molecules enabled researchers to track atoms through photosynthesis: *science as a process*

Scientists have tried for centuries to piece together the process by which plants make food. Although some of the steps are

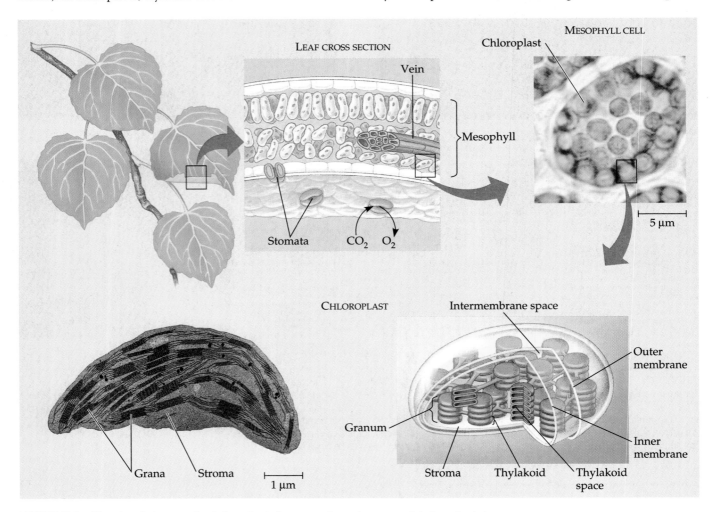

FIGURE 10.2 ▪ **The site of photosynthesis in a plant.** Leaves are the major organs of photosynthesis in plants. Gas exchange between the mesophyll and the atmosphere occurs through microscopic pores called stomata. Chloroplasts, found mainly in the mesophyll, are bounded by two membranes that enclose the stroma, the dense fluid content of the chloroplast. Membranes of the thylakoid system separate the stroma from the thylakoid space. Thylakoids are concentrated in stacks called grana. (Top right, LM; bottom left, TEM.)

still not completely understood, the overall photosynthetic equation has been known since the 1800s: In the presence of light, the green parts of plants produce organic material and oxygen from carbon dioxide and water. Using molecular formulas, we can summarize photosynthesis with this chemical equation:

$$6\ CO_2 + 12\ H_2O + \underset{\text{energy}}{\overset{\text{Light}}{\longrightarrow}} C_6H_{12}O_6 + 6\ O_2 + 6\ H_2O$$

The carbohydrate $C_6H_{12}O_6$ is glucose.* Water appears on both sides of the equation because 12 molecules are consumed and 6 molecules are newly formed during photosynthesis. We can simplify the equation by indicating only the net consumption of water:

$$6\ CO_2 + 6\ H_2O + \text{Light energy} \longrightarrow C_6H_{12}O_6 + 6\ O_2$$

Writing the equation in this form, we can see that the overall chemical change during photosynthesis is the reverse of the one that occurs during cellular respiration. Both of these metabolic processes occur in plant cells. However, as you will soon learn, plants do not make food by simply reversing the steps of respiration.

Now let's divide the photosynthetic equation by 6 to put it in its simplest possible form:

$$CO_2 + H_2O \longrightarrow CH_2O + O_2$$

Here, CH_2O is not an actual sugar but represents the general formula for a carbohydrate. In other words, we are imagining the synthesis of a sugar molecule one carbon at a time. Six repetitions would produce a glucose molecule. Let's now use this simplified formula to see how researchers tracked the chemical elements (C, H, and O) from the reactants of photosynthesis to the products.

The Splitting of Water

One of the first clues to the mechanism of photosynthesis came from the discovery that the oxygen given off by plants is derived from water and not from carbon dioxide. The chloroplast splits water into hydrogen and oxygen. Before this discovery, the prevailing hypothesis was that photosynthesis split carbon dioxide and then added water to the carbon:

$$\text{Step 1: } CO_2 \longrightarrow C + O_2$$

$$\text{Step 2: } C + H_2O \longrightarrow CH_2O$$

This hypothesis predicted that the O_2 released during photosynthesis came from CO_2. This idea was challenged in the 1930s by C. B. van Niel of Stanford University. Van Niel was investigating photosynthesis in bacteria that make their carbohydrate from CO_2 but do not release O_2. Van Niel concluded that, at least in these bacteria, CO_2 is not split into carbon and oxygen. One group of bacteria used hydrogen sul-

fide (H_2S) rather than water for photosynthesis, forming yellow globules of sulfur as a waste product (these globules are visible in FIGURE 10.1e). Here is the chemical equation:

$$CO_2 + 2\ H_2S \longrightarrow CH_2O + H_2O + 2\ S$$

Van Niel reasoned that the bacteria split H_2S and used the hydrogen to make sugar. He then generalized that idea, proposing that all photosynthetic organisms require a hydrogen source, but that the source varies:

$$\text{General: } CO_2 + 2\ H_2X \longrightarrow CH_2O + H_2O + 2\ X$$

$$\text{Sulfur bacteria: } CO_2 + 2\ H_2S \longrightarrow CH_2O + H_2O + 2\ S$$

$$\text{Plants: } CO_2 + 2\ H_2O \longrightarrow CH_2O + H_2O + O_2$$

Thus, van Niel hypothesized that plants split water as a source of hydrogen, releasing oxygen as a by-product.

Nearly 20 years later, scientists confirmed van Niel's hypothesis by using oxygen-18 (^{18}O), a heavy isotope, as a tracer to follow the fate of oxygen atoms during photosynthesis. The O_2 that came from plants was labeled with ^{18}O *only* if water was the source of the tracer. If the ^{18}O was introduced to the plant in the form of CO_2, the label did not turn up in the released O_2. In the following summary of these experiments, red denotes labeled atoms of oxygen:

$$\text{Experiment 1: } CO_2 + 2\ H_2O \longrightarrow CH_2O + H_2O + O_2$$

$$\text{Experiment 2: } CO_2 + 2\ H_2O \longrightarrow CH_2O + H_2O + O_2$$

The most important result of the shuffling of atoms during photosynthesis is the extraction of hydrogen from water and its incorporation into sugar. The waste product of photosynthesis, O_2, restores the atmospheric oxygen consumed during cellular respiration. FIGURE 10.3 shows the fates of all atoms in photosynthesis.

Photosynthesis as a Redox Process

Let's briefly contrast photosynthesis with cellular respiration. During respiration, energy is released from sugar when electrons associated with hydrogen are transported by carriers to oxygen, forming water as a by-product. The electrons lose potential energy as electronegative oxygen pulls them down the electron transport chain, and the mitochondrion uses the energy to synthesize ATP. Photosynthesis, also a redox process, reverses the direction of electron flow. Water is split, and

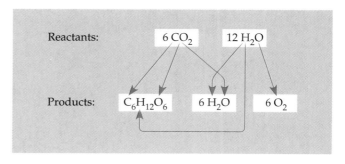

FIGURE 10.3 ▪ **Tracking atoms through photosynthesis.**

---

* The direct product of photosynthesis is actually a three-carbon sugar. Glucose is used here only to simplify the relationship between photosynthesis and respiration.

electrons are transferred along with hydrogen ions from the water to carbon dioxide, reducing it to sugar. The electrons increase in potential energy as they move from water to sugar. The required energy boost is provided by light.

The light reactions and the Calvin cycle cooperate in converting light energy to the chemical energy of food: *an overview*

The equation for photosynthesis is a deceptively simple summary of a very complex process. Actually, photosynthesis is not a single process, but two, each with multiple steps. These two stages of photosynthesis are known as the **light reactions** (the *photo* part of photosynthesis) and the **Calvin cycle** (the *synthesis* part) (FIGURE 10.4).

The light reactions are the steps of photosynthesis that convert solar energy to chemical energy. Light absorbed by chlorophyll drives a transfer of electrons and hydrogen from water to an acceptor called **NADP$^+$** (nicotinamide adenine dinucleotide phosphate), which temporarily stores the energized electrons. Water is split in the process, and thus it is the light reactions of photosynthesis that give off O_2 as a by-product. The electron acceptor of the light reactions, NADP$^+$, is first cousin to NAD$^+$, which functions as an electron carrier in cellular respiration; the two molecules differ only by the presence of an extra phosphate group in the NADP$^+$ molecule. The light reactions use solar power to reduce NADP$^+$ to NADPH by adding a pair of electrons along with a hydrogen nucleus, or H$^+$. The light reactions also generate ATP by powering the addition of a phosphate group to ADP, a process called **photophosphorylation**. Thus, light energy is initially converted to chemical energy in the form of two compounds: NADPH, a source of energized electrons ("reducing power"), and ATP, the versatile energy currency of cells. Notice that the light reactions produce no sugar; that happens in the second stage of photosynthesis, the Calvin cycle.

The Calvin cycle is named for Melvin Calvin, who along with his colleagues began to elucidate its steps in the late 1940s. The cycle begins by incorporating CO_2 from the air into organic molecules already present in the chloroplast. This initial incorporation of carbon into organic compounds is known as **carbon fixation**. The Calvin cycle then reduces the fixed carbon to carbohydrate by the addition of electrons. The reducing power is provided by NADPH, which acquired energized electrons in the light reactions. To convert CO_2 to carbohydrate, the Calvin cycle also requires chemical energy in the form of ATP, which is also generated by the light reactions. Thus, it is the Calvin cycle that makes sugar, but it can do so only with the help of the NADPH and ATP produced by the light reactions. The metabolic steps of the Calvin cycle are sometimes referred to as the dark reactions, or light-independent reactions, because none of the steps requires light *directly*. Nevertheless, the Calvin cycle in most plants occurs during daylight, for only then can the light reactions regenerate the NADPH and ATP spent in the reduction of CO_2 to sugar. In essence, the chloroplast uses light energy to make sugar by coordinating the two stages of photosynthesis.

As FIGURE 10.4 indicates, the thylakoids of the chloroplast are the sites of the light reactions, while the Calvin cycle occurs in the stroma. As molecules of NADP$^+$ and ADP bump into the thylakoid membrane, they pick up electrons and phosphate, respectively, and then transfer their high-energy cargo to the Calvin cycle. The two stages of photosynthesis are

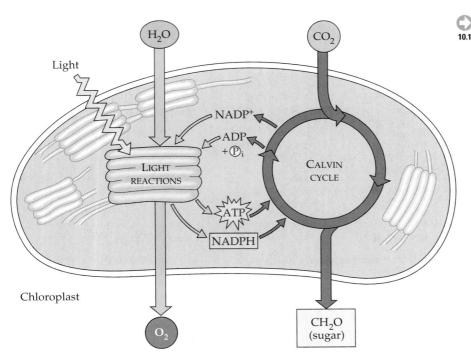

FIGURE 10.4 · An overview of photosynthesis: cooperation of the light reactions and the Calvin cycle. The light reactions use solar energy to make ATP and NADPH, which function as chemical energy and reducing power, respectively, in the Calvin cycle. In contrast to ATP generated by cellular respiration, ATP produced in the light reactions of photosynthesis is usually dedicated to a single kind of cellular work, driving the Calvin cycle. The Calvin cycle incorporates CO_2 into organic molecules, which are converted to sugar. (Recall from Chapter 5 that most simple sugars have formulas that are some multiple of CH_2O.) Thylakoid membranes, especially those of the grana, are the sites of the light reactions, whereas the Calvin cycle occurs in the stroma.

A smaller version of this diagram will reappear in several subsequent figures as a reminder of whether the events being described occur in the light reactions or in the Calvin cycle.

treated in this figure as metabolic modules that take in ingredients and crank out products. Our next step toward understanding photosynthesis is to look more closely at how the two stages work, beginning with the light reactions.

The light reactions convert solar energy to the chemical energy of ATP and NADPH: *a closer look*

Chloroplasts are chemical factories powered by the sun. Their thylakoids transform light energy into the chemical energy of ATP and NADPH. To understand this conversion better, it is first necessary to learn about some important properties of light.

The Nature of Sunlight

Light is a form of energy known as electromagnetic energy, also called radiation. Electromagnetic energy travels in rhythmic waves analogous to those created by dropping a pebble into a puddle of water. Electromagnetic waves, however, are disturbances of electrical and magnetic fields rather than disturbances of a material medium such as water.

The distance between the crests of electromagnetic waves is called the **wavelength**. Wavelengths range from less than a nanometer (for gamma rays) to more than a kilometer (for radio waves). This entire range of radiation is known as the **electromagnetic spectrum** (FIGURE 10.5). The segment most important to life is the narrow band that ranges from about 380 to 750 nm in wavelength. This radiation is known as **visible light**, because it is detected as various colors by the human eye.

The model of light as waves explains many of light's properties, but in certain respects light behaves as though it consists of discrete particles, called **photons**. Photons are not tangible objects, but they act like objects in that each of them has a fixed quantity of energy. The amount of energy is inversely related to the wavelength of the light; the shorter the

wavelength, the greater the energy of each photon of that light. Thus, a photon of violet light packs nearly twice as much energy as a photon of red light.

Although the sun radiates the full spectrum of electromagnetic energy, the atmosphere acts like a selective window, allowing visible light to pass through while screening out a substantial fraction of other radiation. The part of the spectrum we can see—visible light—is also the radiation that drives photosynthesis. Blue and red, the two wavelengths most effectively absorbed by chlorophyll, are the colors most useful as energy for the light reactions.

Photosynthetic Pigments: The Light Receptors

As light meets matter, it may be reflected, transmitted, or absorbed. Substances that absorb visible light are called pigments. Different pigments absorb light of different wavelengths, and the wavelengths that are absorbed disappear. If a pigment is illuminated with white light, the color we see is the color most reflected or transmitted by the pigment. (If a pigment absorbs all wavelengths, it appears black.) We see green when we look at a leaf because chlorophyll absorbs red and blue light while transmitting and reflecting green light (FIGURE 10.6, p. 174). The ability of a pigment to absorb various wavelengths of light can be measured by placing a solution of the pigment in a **spectrophotometer** (see the Methods Box, p. 182). A graph plotting a pigment's light absorption versus wavelength is called an **absorption spectrum**.

FIGURE 10.7a, page 174, shows the absorption spectra of a type of chlorophyll called **chlorophyll *a*** and some other pigments in the chloroplast. The absorption spectrum for chlorophyll *a* provides clues to the relative effectiveness of different wavelengths for driving photosynthesis, since light can perform work in chloroplasts only if it is absorbed. As previously mentioned, blue and red light work best for photosynthesis, while green is the least effective color. An **action spectrum** (FIGURE 10.7b) profiles the relative performance of the different

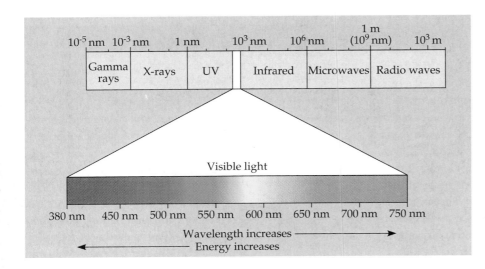

FIGURE 10.5 · The electromagnetic spectrum. Visible light and other forms of electromagnetic energy radiate through space as waves of various lengths. We perceive different wavelengths of visible light as different colors. White light is a mixture of all wavelengths of visible light. A prism can sort white light into its component colors by bending light of different wavelengths varying degrees. Visible light drives photosynthesis.

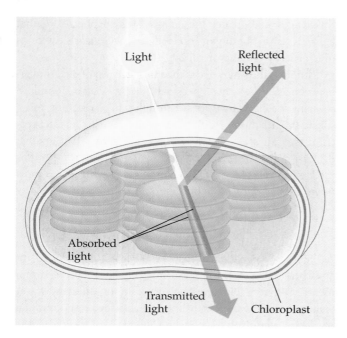

FIGURE 10.6 ▪ **Interactions of light with matter in a chloroplast.** The pigments of chloroplasts absorb blue and red light, the colors most effective in photosynthesis. The pigments reflect or transmit green light, which is why leaves appear green.

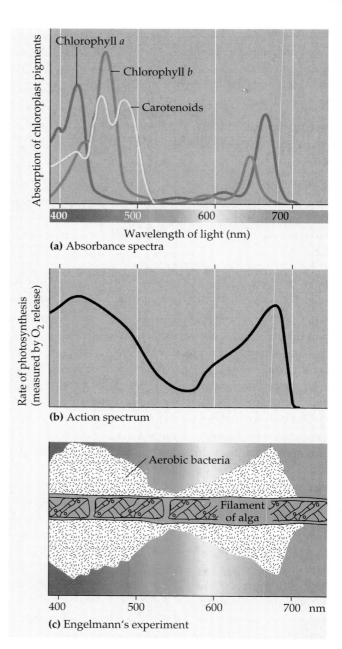

(a) Absorbance spectra

(b) Action spectrum

(c) Engelmann's experiment

FIGURE 10.7 ▪ **Absorption and action spectra for photosynthesis.** **(a)** A comparison of the absorption spectra for chlorophyll *a* and accessory pigments extracted from chloroplasts. **(b)** An action spectrum, profiling the effectiveness of different wavelengths of light in driving photosynthesis. Compared to the peaks in the absorption spectrum for chlorophyll *a* (blue-green line in graph at top), the peaks in the action spectrum are broader, and the valley is narrower and not as deep. This is partly due to the absorption of light by accessory pigments, which broaden the spectrum of colors that can be used for photosynthesis. **(c)** An elegant experiment demonstrating the action spectrum for photosynthesis was first performed in 1883 by Thomas Engelmann, a German botanist. He illuminated a filamentous alga with light that had been passed through a prism, thus exposing different segments of the alga to different wavelengths of light. Engelmann used aerobic bacteria, which concentrate near an oxygen source, to determine which segments of the alga were releasing the most O_2. Bacteria congregated in greatest numbers around the parts of the alga illuminated with red or blue light. Notice the close match of the bacterial distribution to the action spectrum in part b.

wavelengths more accurately than an absorption spectrum. An action spectrum is prepared by illuminating chloroplasts with different colors of light and then plotting wavelength against some measure of photosynthetic rate, such as carbon dioxide consumption or oxygen release (see also FIGURE 10.7c).

Notice by comparing FIGURE 10.7a to FIGURE 10.7b that the action spectrum for photosynthesis does not exactly match the absorption spectrum of chlorophyll *a*. The absorption spectrum underestimates the effectiveness of certain wavelengths in driving photosynthesis. This is partly because chlorophyll *a* is not the only photosynthetically important pigment in chloroplasts. Only chlorophyll *a* can participate directly in the light reactions, which convert solar energy to chemical energy. But other pigments in the thylakoid membrane can absorb light and transfer the energy to chlorophyll *a*, which then initiates the light reactions. One of these accessory pigments is another form of chlorophyll, **chlorophyll *b***. Chlorophyll *b* is almost identical to chlorophyll *a* (FIGURE 10.8), but the slight structural difference between them is enough to give the two pigments slightly different absorption spectra and hence different colors. Chlorophyll *a* is blue-green, whereas chlorophyll *b* is yellow-green. If a photon of sunlight is absorbed by chlorophyll *b*, energy is conveyed to chlorophyll *a*, which then behaves just as though it had absorbed the photon. Other accessory pigments include **carotenoids**, hydrocarbons that are various shades of yellow and orange (see FIGURE 10.7a). Some carotenoids may broaden the spectrum of colors that can drive photosynthesis. However, other carotenoids seem to function primarily in *photoprotection:* Rather than transmit

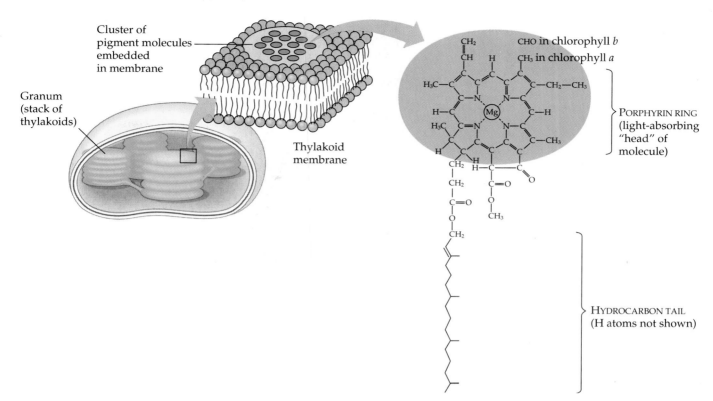

FIGURE 10.8 · **Structure of chlorophyll.** Chlorophyll *a*, the pigment that participates directly in the light reactions of photosynthesis, has a "head," called a porphyrin ring, with a magnesium atom at its center. Attached to the porphyrin is a hydrocarbon tail, which interacts with hydrophobic regions of proteins in the thylakoid membrane. Chlorophyll *b* differs from chlorophyll *a* only in one of the functional groups bonded to the porphyrin. This diagram simplifies by placing chlorophyll at the surface of the membrane; most of the molecule is actually immersed in the hydrophobic core of the membrane.

energy to chlorophyll, these compounds absorb and dissipate excessive light energy that would otherwise damage chlorophyll. (Interestingly, similar carotenoids may have a photoprotective role in the human eye.)

Photoexcitation of Chlorophyll

What exactly happens when chlorophyll and other pigments absorb photons? The colors corresponding to the absorbed wavelengths disappear from the spectrum of the transmitted and reflected light, but energy cannot disappear. When a molecule absorbs a photon, one of the molecule's electrons is elevated to an orbital where it has more potential energy. When the electron is in its normal orbital, the pigment molecule is said to be in its ground state. After absorption of a photon boosts an electron to an orbital of higher energy, the pigment molecule is said to be in an excited state. The only photons absorbed are those whose energy is exactly equal to the energy difference between the ground state and an excited state, and this energy difference varies from one kind of atom or molecule to another. Thus, a particular compound absorbs only photons corresponding to specific wavelengths, which is why each pigment has a unique absorption spectrum.

The energy of an absorbed photon is converted to the potential energy of an electron raised from the ground state to an excited state. But the electron cannot remain there long; the excited state, like all high-energy states, is unstable. Generally, when pigments absorb light, their excited electrons drop back down to the ground-state orbital in a billionth of a second, releasing their excess energy as heat. This conversion of light energy to heat is what makes the top of an automobile so hot on a sunny day. (White cars are coolest because their paint reflects all wavelengths of visible light, although it may absorb ultraviolet and other invisible radiation.) Some pigments, including chlorophyll, emit light as well as heat after absorbing photons. The electron jumps to a state of greater energy, and as it falls back to ground state, a photon is given off. This afterglow is called fluorescence. If a solution of chlorophyll isolated from chloroplasts is illuminated, it will fluoresce in the red part of the spectrum and also give off heat (FIGURE 10.9, p. 176).

Photosystems: Light-Harvesting Complexes of the Thylakoid Membrane

Chlorophyll excited by absorption of light energy produces very different results in an intact chloroplast than it does in

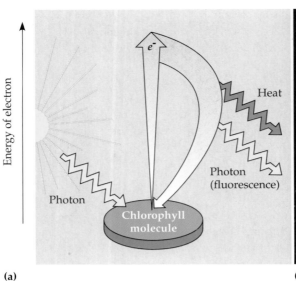

(a)

(b)

FIGURE 10.9 ▪ **Photoexcitation of isolated chlorophyll.** **(a)** Absorption of a photon causes a transition of the chlorophyll molecule from its ground state to its excited state. The photon boosts an electron to an orbital where it has more potential energy. If isolated chlorophyll is illuminated, its excited electron immediately drops back down to the ground-state orbital, giving off its excess energy as heat and fluorescence (light). **(b)** A chlorophyll solution excited with ultraviolet light will fluoresce, giving off a red-orange glow.

isolation. In its native environment of the thylakoid membrane, chlorophyll is organized along with proteins and other kinds of smaller organic molecules into **photosystems**.

A photosystem has a light-gathering "antenna complex" consisting of a cluster of a few hundred chlorophyll *a*, chlorophyll *b*, and carotenoid molecules (FIGURE 10.10). The number and variety of pigment molecules enable a photosystem to harvest light over a larger surface and a larger portion of the spectrum than any single pigment molecule could harvest. When any antenna molecule absorbs a photon, the energy is transmitted from pigment molecule to pigment molecule until it reaches a particular chlorophyll *a*. What is special about *this* chlorophyll *a* molecule is not its molecular structure, but its position. Only this chlorophyll molecule is located in the region of the photosystem called the **reaction center**, where the first light-driven chemical reaction of photosynthesis occurs.

Sharing the reaction center with the chlorophyll *a* molecule is a specialized molecule called the **primary electron acceptor**. In an oxidation-reduction reaction, the chlorophyll *a* molecule at the reaction center loses one of its electrons to the primary electron acceptor. This redox reaction occurs when light excites the electron to a higher energy level in chlorophyll and the electron acceptor traps the high-energy electron before it can return to the ground state in the chlorophyll molecule. Isolated chlorophyll fluoresces because there is no electron acceptor to prevent electrons of photoexcited chlorophyll from dropping right back to the ground state. In a chloroplast, the acceptor molecule functions like a dam that prevents this immediate plunge of high-energy electrons back to the ground state. Thus, each photosystem—reaction-center chlorophyll and electron acceptor surrounded by an antenna complex—functions in the chloroplast as a light-harvesting unit. The solar-powered transfer of electrons from chlorophyll to the primary electron acceptor is the first step of the light reactions.

The thylakoid membrane is populated by two types of photosystems that cooperate in the light reactions of photosynthesis. They are called **photosystem I** and **photosystem II**, in order of their discovery. Each has a characteristic reaction center—a particular kind of primary electron acceptor next to a chlorophyll *a* molecule associated with specific proteins. The reaction-center chlorophyll of photosystem I is known as P700 because this pigment is best at absorbing light having a wavelength of 700 nm (the far-red part of the spectrum). The chlorophyll at the reaction center of photosystem II is called

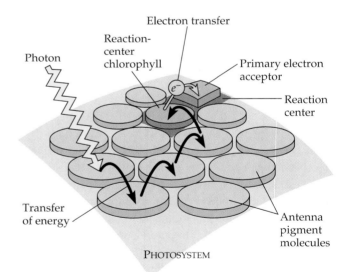

FIGURE 10.10 ▪ **How a photosystem harvests light.** Photosystems are the light-harvesting units of the thylakoid membrane. Each photosystem is a complex of proteins and other kinds of molecules, and includes an antenna consisting of a few hundred pigment molecules. When a photon strikes a pigment molecule, the energy is passed from molecule to molecule until it reaches the reaction center. At the reaction center, the energy drives an oxidation-reduction reaction. An excited electron from the reaction-center chlorophyll is captured by a specialized molecule called the primary electron acceptor.

P680 because its absorption spectrum has a peak at 680 nm (also in the red part of the spectrum). These two pigments, P700 and P680, are actually identical chlorophyll *a* molecules. However, their association with different proteins in the thylakoid membrane affects the electron distribution in the chlorophyll molecules and accounts for the slight differences in light-absorbing properties. Let's now see how the two photosystems work together in using light energy to generate ATP and NADPH, the two main products of the light reactions.

Noncyclic Electron Flow

Light drives the synthesis of NADPH and ATP by energizing the two photosystems embedded in the thylakoid membranes of chloroplasts. The key to this energy transformation is a flow of electrons through the photosystems and other molecular components built into the thylakoid membrane. During the light reactions of photosynthesis, there are two possible routes for electron flow: cyclic and noncyclic. **Noncyclic electron flow**, the predominant route, is shown in FIGURE 10.11. The numbers in the following description correspond to the numbered steps in the figure.

① When photosystem II absorbs light, an electron excited to a higher energy level in the reaction-center chlorophyll (P680) is captured by the primary electron acceptor. The oxidized chlorophyll is now a very strong oxidizing agent; its electron "hole" must be filled.

② An enzyme extracts electrons from water and supplies them to P680, replacing each electron that the chlorophyll molecule lost when it absorbed light energy. This reaction splits a water molecule into two hydrogen ions and an oxygen atom, which immediately combines with another oxygen atom to form O_2. This is the water-splitting step of photosynthesis that releases O_2.

③ Each photoexcited electron passes from the primary electron acceptor of photosystem II to photosystem I via an electron transport chain. This chain is very similar to the one that functions in cellular respiration. The chloroplast version consists of an electron carrier called plastoquinone (Pq), a complex of two cytochromes (closely related to the cytochromes of mitochondria), and a copper-containing protein called plastocyanin (Pc).

④ As electrons cascade down the chain, their exergonic "fall" to a lower energy level is harnessed by the thylakoid membrane to produce ATP. This ATP synthesis is called photophosphorylation because it is driven by light energy.

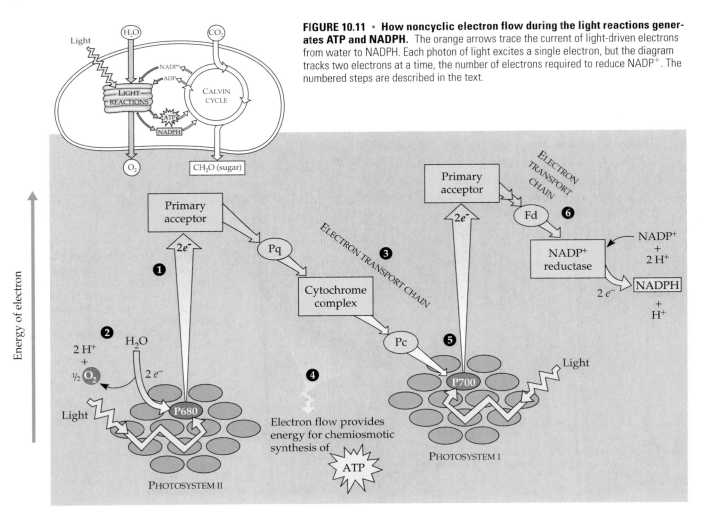

FIGURE 10.11 · **How noncyclic electron flow during the light reactions generates ATP and NADPH.** The orange arrows trace the current of light-driven electrons from water to NADPH. Each photon of light excites a single electron, but the diagram tracks two electrons at a time, the number of electrons required to reduce $NADP^+$. The numbered steps are described in the text.

Specifically, ATP synthesis during noncyclic electron flow is called **noncyclic photophosphorylation**. (As we will discuss, the mechanism for photophosphorylation is chemiosmosis, the same process that operates in respiration.) This ATP generated by the light reactions will provide chemical energy for the synthesis of sugar during the Calvin cycle, the second major stage of photosynthesis.

⑤ When an electron reaches the "bottom" of the electron transport chain, it fills an electron "hole" in P700, the chlorophyll *a* molecule in the reaction center of photosystem I. This hole is created when light energy drives an electron from P700 to the primary acceptor of photosystem I.

⑥ The primary electron acceptor of photosystem I passes the photoexcited electrons to a second electron transport chain, which transmits them to ferredoxin (Fd), an iron-containing protein. An enzyme called NADP⁺ reductase then transfers the electrons from Fd to NADP⁺. This is the redox reaction that stores the high-energy electrons in NADPH, the molecule that will provide reducing power for the synthesis of sugar in the Calvin cycle.

The energy changes of electrons as they flow through the light reactions are analogous to the cartoon in FIGURE 10.12. As complicated as the scheme is, do not lose track of its functions: The light reactions use solar power to generate ATP and NADPH, which provide chemical energy and reducing power, respectively, to the sugar-making reactions of the Calvin cycle.

Cyclic Electron Flow

Under certain conditions, photoexcited electrons take an alternative path called **cyclic electron flow**, which uses photosystem I but not photosystem II. You can see in FIGURE 10.13 that cyclic flow is a short circuit: The electrons cycle back from ferredoxin (Fd) to the cytochrome complex and from there continue on to the P700 chlorophyll. There is no production of NADPH and no release of oxygen. Cyclic flow does, how-

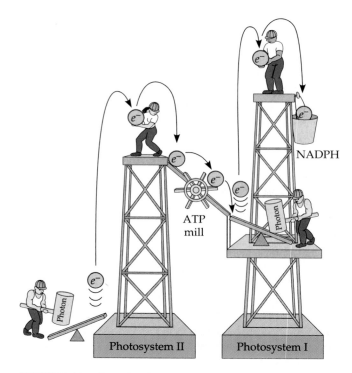

FIGURE 10.12 · A mechanical analogy for the light reactions.

ever, generate ATP. This is called **cyclic photophosphorylation**, to distinguish it from noncyclic photophosphorylation.

What is the function of cyclic electron flow? Noncyclic electron flow produces ATP and NADPH in roughly equal quantities, but the Calvin cycle consumes more ATP than NADPH. Cyclic electron flow makes up the difference. The concentration of NADPH in the chloroplast may help regulate which pathway, cyclic versus noncyclic, electrons take through the light reactions. If the chloroplast runs low on ATP for the Calvin cycle, NADPH will begin to accumulate as the Calvin cycle slows down. The rise in NADPH may stimulate a temporary shift from noncyclic to cyclic electron flow until ATP supply catches up with demand.

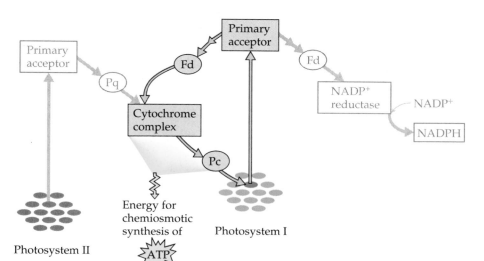

FIGURE 10.13 · Cyclic electron flow.
Photoexcited electrons from photosystem I are occasionally shunted back from ferredoxin (Fd) to chlorophyll via the cytochrome complex and plastocyanin (Pc). This cyclic electron flow supplements the supply of ATP but produces no NADPH. (The two ferredoxin molecules shown in this diagram are actually one and the same—the final electron carrier in the electron transport chain of photosystem I. The "shadow" of noncyclic electron flow is included in the diagram for comparison with the cyclic route.)

Whether photophosphorylation is driven by noncyclic or cyclic electron flow, the actual mechanism for ATP synthesis is the same. This is a good time to review chemiosmosis, the basic process that uses membranes to couple redox reactions to ATP production.

A Comparison of Chemiosmosis in Chloroplasts and Mitochondria

Chloroplasts and mitochondria generate ATP by the same basic mechanism: chemiosmosis. An electron transport chain assembled in a membrane pumps protons across the membrane as electrons are passed through a series of carriers that are progressively more electronegative. Thus, electron transport chains transform redox energy to a proton-motive force, potential energy stored in the form of an H^+ gradient across a membrane. Built into the same membrane is an ATP synthase complex that couples the diffusion of hydrogen ions down their gradient to the phosphorylation of ADP. Some of the electron carriers, including the iron-containing proteins called cytochromes, are very similar in chloroplasts and mitochondria. The ATP synthase complexes of the two organelles are also very much alike. But there are noteworthy differences between oxidative phosphorylation in mitochondria and photophosphorylation in chloroplasts. In mitochondria, the high-energy electrons dropped down the transport chain are extracted by the oxidation of food molecules. Chloroplasts do not need food to make ATP; their photosystems capture light energy and use it to drive electrons to the top of the transport chain. In other words, mitochondria transfer chemical energy from food molecules to ATP, whereas chloroplasts transform light energy into chemical energy.

The spatial organization of chemiosmosis also differs in chloroplasts and mitochondria (FIGURE 10.14). The inner membrane of the mitochondrion pumps protons from the matrix out to the intermembrane space, which then serves as a reservoir of hydrogen ions that powers the ATP synthase. The thylakoid membrane of the chloroplast pumps protons from the stroma into the thylakoid space, which functions as the H^+ reservoir. The membrane makes ATP as the hydrogen ions diffuse from the thylakoid space back to the stroma through ATP synthase complexes, whose catalytic knobs are on the stroma side of the membrane. Thus, ATP forms in the stroma, where it is used to help drive sugar synthesis during the Calvin cycle.

The proton gradient, or pH gradient, across the thylakoid membrane is substantial. When chloroplasts are illuminated, the pH in the thylakoid space drops to about 5, and the pH in the stroma increases to about 8. This gradient of three pH units corresponds to a thousandfold difference in H^+ concentration. If in the laboratory the lights are turned off, the pH gradient is abolished, but it can quickly be restored by turning the lights back on. Such experiments add to the evidence described in Chapter 9 in support of the chemiosmotic model.

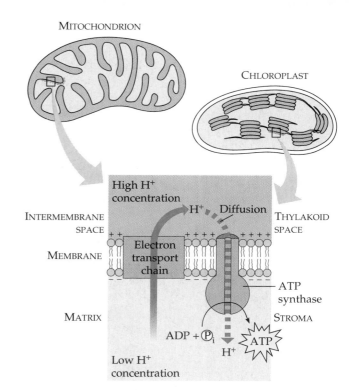

FIGURE 10.14 · The logistics of chemiosmosis in mitochondria and chloroplasts. The inner membrane of the mitochondrion pumps protons (H^+) from the matrix into the intermembrane space (darker brown). ATP is made on the matrix side of the membrane as hydrogen ions diffuse through ATP synthase complexes. In chloroplasts, the thylakoid membrane pumps protons from the stroma into the thylakoid space (lumen). As the hydrogen ions leak back across the membrane through the ATP synthase, phosphorylation of ADP occurs on the stroma side of the membrane.

10.2 Based on studies in several laboratories, FIGURE 10.15 on page 180 shows a current model for the organization of the thylakoid membrane. Each of the molecules and molecular complexes in the figure are present in numerous copies in each thylakoid. Notice that NADPH, like ATP, is produced on the side of the membrane facing the stroma, where sugar is synthesized by the Calvin cycle.

Let's summarize the light reactions. Noncyclic electron flow pushes electrons from water, where they are at a low state of potential energy, to NADPH, where they are stored at a high state of potential energy. The light-driven electron current also generates ATP. Thus, the equipment of the thylakoid membrane converts light energy to the chemical energy stored in NADPH and ATP. (Oxygen is a by-product.) Let's now see how the Calvin cycle uses the products of the light reactions to synthesize sugar from CO_2.

The Calvin cycle uses ATP and NADPH to convert CO_2 to sugar: *a closer look*

10.3 The Calvin cycle is a metabolic pathway similar to the Krebs cycle in that a starting material is regenerated after molecules enter and leave the cycle. Carbon enters the Calvin cycle in the

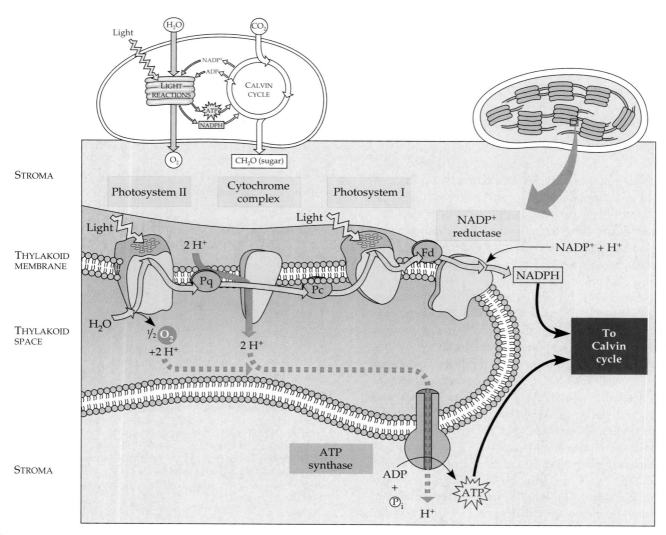

⟳ **FIGURE 10.15** · **A tentative model for the**

10.2 **organization of the thylakoid membrane.**

FIGURE 10.15 · **A tentative model for the organization of the thylakoid membrane.** The orange arrows track electron flow. As electrons pass from carrier to carrier during redox reactions, hydrogen ions removed from the stroma are deposited in the thylakoid space, storing energy as a proton-motive force (H^+ gradient). At least three steps in the light reactions contribute to the proton gradient: Water is split by photosystem II on the side of the membrane facing the thylakoid space; as plastoquinone (Pq), a mobile carrier, transfers electrons to the cytochrome complex, protons are translocated across the membrane; and a hydrogen ion in the stroma is taken up by $NADP^+$ when it is reduced to NADPH. The diffusion of H^+ from the thylakoid space to the stroma (along the H^+ concentration gradient) powers the ATP synthase. These light-driven reactions store chemical energy in NADPH and ATP, which shuttle the energy to the sugar-producing Calvin cycle.

form of CO_2 and leaves in the form of sugar. The cycle spends ATP as an energy source and consumes NADPH as reducing power for adding high-energy electrons to make the sugar (FIGURE 10.16).

The carbohydrate produced directly from the Calvin cycle is actually not glucose, but a three-carbon sugar named **glyceraldehyde 3-phosphate (G3P).** For the net synthesis of one molecule of this sugar, the cycle must take place three times, fixing three molecules of CO_2. (Recall that carbon fixation refers to the initial incorporation of CO_2 into organic material.) As we trace the steps of the cycle, keep in mind that we are following three molecules of CO_2 through the reactions.

FIGURE 10.16 divides the Calvin cycle into three phases:

Phase 1: Carbon fixation. The Calvin cycle incorporates each CO_2 molecule by attaching it to a five-carbon sugar named ribulose bisphosphate (abbreviated RuBP). The enzyme that catalyzes this first step is RuBP carboxylase, or **rubisco.** (It is the most abundant protein in chloroplasts, and probably the most abundant protein on Earth.) The product of the reaction is a six-carbon intermediate so unstable that it immediately splits in half to form two molecules of 3-phosphoglycerate (for each CO_2).

Phase 2: Reduction. Each molecule of 3-phosphoglycerate receives an additional phosphate group. An enzyme transfers the phosphate group from ATP, forming 1,3-bisphosphoglycerate as a product. Next, a pair of electrons donated from NADPH reduces 1,3-bisphosphoglycerate to G3P. Specifically, the electrons from NADPH reduce the carboyxl group of 3-phosphoglycerate to the carbonyl group of G3P, which stores more potential energy. G3P is a

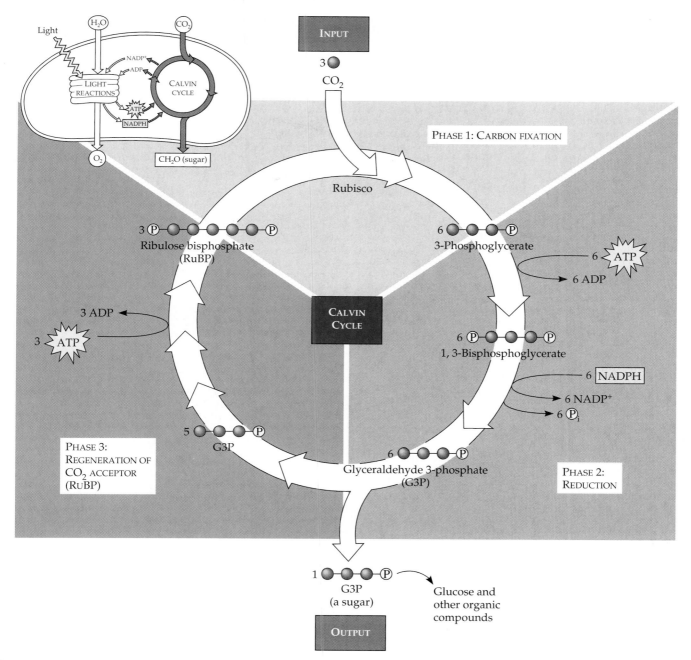

FIGURE 10.16 ▪ The Calvin cycle. This diagram tracks carbon atoms (gray balls) through the cycle. The three phases of the cycle correspond to the phases discussed in the text. For every three molecules of CO_2 that enter the cycle, the net output is one molecule of glyceraldehyde 3-phosphate (G3P), a three-carbon sugar. For each G3P synthesized, the cycle spends nine molecules of ATP and six molecules of NADPH. The light reactions sustain the Calvin cycle by regenerating ATP and NADPH.

sugar—the same three-carbon sugar formed in glycolysis by the splitting of glucose. Notice in FIGURE 10.16 that for every *three* molecules of CO_2, there are *six* molecules of G3P. But only one molecule of this three-carbon sugar can be counted as a net gain of carbohydrate. The cycle began with 15 carbons' worth of carbohydrate in the form of three molecules of the five-carbon sugar RuBP. Now there are 18 carbons' worth of carbohydrate in the form of six molecules of G3P. One molecule exits the cycle to be used by the plant cell, but the other five molecules must be recy-

cled to regenerate the three molecules of RuBP.

Phase 3: Regeneration of CO_2 acceptor (RuBP). In a complex series of reactions, the carbon skeletons of five molecules of G3P are rearranged by the last steps of the Calvin cycle into three molecules of RuBP. To accomplish this, the cycle spends three more molecules of ATP. The RuBP is now prepared to receive CO_2 again, and the cycle continues.

For the net synthesis of one G3P molecule, the Calvin cycle consumes a total of nine molecules of ATP and six molecules

Spectrophotometers are among the most widely used research instruments in biology. A spectrophotometer measures the relative amounts of light of different wavelengths absorbed and transmitted by a pigment solution. Inside the spectrophotometer, white light is separated into colors (wavelengths) by a prism. Then, one by one, the different colors of light are passed through the sample. The transmitted light strikes a photoelectric tube, which converts the light energy to electricity, and the electrical current is measured by a meter. Each time the wavelength of light is changed, the meter indicates the fraction of light transmitted through the sample or, conversely, the fraction of light absorbed. A graph that profiles absorption at different wavelengths is called an absorption spectrum. For example, the absorption spectrum for chlorophyll *a*, the form of chlorophyll most important in photosynthesis, has two peaks, corresponding to blue and red light. These are the colors chlorophyll *a* absorbs best (see FIGURE 10.7a). The absorption spectrum has a valley in the green region because the pigment transmits light of that color.

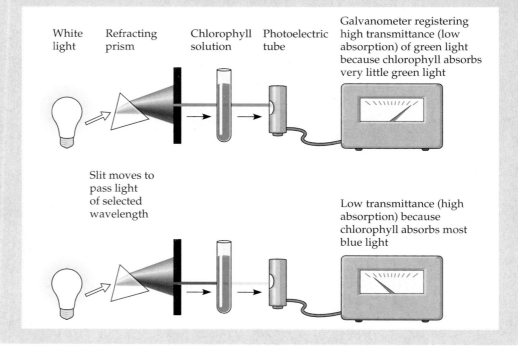

White light Refracting prism Chlorophyll solution Photoelectric tube Galvanometer registering high transmittance (low absorption) of green light because chlorophyll absorbs very little green light

Slit moves to pass light of selected wavelength

Low transmittance (high absorption) because chlorophyll absorbs most blue light

of NADPH. The light reactions regenerate the ATP and NADPH. The G3P spun off from the Calvin cycle becomes the starting material for metabolic pathways that synthesize other organic compounds, including glucose and other carbohydrates. Neither the light reactions nor the Calvin cycle alone can make sugar from CO_2. Photosynthesis is an emergent property of the intact chloroplast, which integrates the two stages of photosynthesis.

Alternative mechanisms of carbon fixation have evolved in hot, arid climates

Since plants first moved onto land about 425 million years ago, they have been adapting to the problems of terrestrial life, particularly the problem of dehydration. In Chapters 29 and 36 we will consider anatomical adaptations that help plants conserve water. Here we are concerned with metabolic adaptations. The solutions often involve trade-offs. An important example is the compromise between photosynthesis and the prevention of excessive water loss from the plant. The CO_2 required for photosynthesis enters a leaf via stomata, the pores through the leaf surface (see FIGURE 10.2). However, stomata are also the main avenues of transpiration, the evaporative loss of water from leaves. On a hot, dry day, most plants close their stomata, a response that conserves water. This response also reduces photosynthetic yield by limiting access to CO_2. With stomata even partially closed, CO_2 concentrations begin to decrease in the air spaces within the leaf, and the concentration of O_2 released from photosynthesis begins to increase. These conditions within the leaf favor a seemingly wasteful process called photorespiration.

Photorespiration: An Evolutionary Relic?

In most plants, initial fixation of carbon occurs via rubisco, the Calvin cycle enzyme that adds CO_2 to ribulose bisphosphate. Such plants are called **C_3 plants** because the first organic product of carbon fixation is a three-carbon compound, 3-phosphoglycerate (see FIGURE 10.16). Rice, wheat, and soybeans are among the C_3 plants that are important in agriculture. These plants produce less food when their stomata close on hot, dry days. The declining level of CO_2 in the

leaf starves the Calvin cycle. Making matters worse, rubisco can accept O_2 in place of CO_2. As O_2 concentrations overtake CO_2 concentrations within the air spaces of the leaf, rubisco adds O_2 to the Calvin cycle instead of CO_2. The product splits, and one piece, a two-carbon compound, is exported from the chloroplast. Mitochondria and peroxisomes then break the two-carbon molecule down to CO_2. The process is called **photorespiration** because it occurs in the light *(photo)* and consumes O_2 *(respiration)*. However, unlike normal cellular respiration, photorespiration generates no ATP. And unlike photosynthesis, photorespiration produces no food. In fact, photorespiration *decreases* photosynthetic output by siphoning organic material from the Calvin cycle.

How can we explain the existence of a metabolic process that seems to be counterproductive to the plant? According to one hypothesis, photorespiration is evolutionary baggage—a metabolic relic from a much earlier time, when the atmosphere had less O_2 and more CO_2 than it does today. In the ancient atmosphere present when rubisco first evolved, the inability of the enzyme's active site to exclude O_2 would have made little difference. The hypothesis speculates that modern rubisco retains some of its ancestral affinity for O_2, which is now so concentrated in the atmosphere that a certain amount of photorespiration is inevitable.

It is not known whether photorespiration is beneficial to plants in any way. It *is* known that in many types of plants—including some of agricultural importance, such as soybeans—photorespiration drains away as much as 50% of the carbon fixed by the Calvin cycle. As heterotrophs that depend on carbon fixation in chloroplasts for our food, we naturally view photorespiration as wasteful. Indeed, if photorespiration

could be reduced in certain plant species without otherwise affecting photosynthetic productivity, crop yields and food supplies would increase.

The environmental conditions that foster photorespiration are hot, dry, bright days—the conditions that cause stomata to close. In certain plant species, alternate modes of carbon fixation that minimize photorespiration—even in hot, arid climates—have evolved. The two most important of these photosynthetic adaptations are C_4 photosynthesis and CAM.

C_4 Plants

The **C_4 plants** are so named because they preface the Calvin cycle with an alternate mode of carbon fixation that forms a four-carbon compound as its first product. Several thousand species in at least 19 plant families use the C_4 pathway. Among the C_4 plants important to agriculture are sugarcane and corn, members of the grass family.

A unique leaf anatomy is correlated with the mechanism of C_4 photosynthesis (FIGURE 10.17a; compare to FIGURE 10.2). In C_4 plants, there are two distinct types of photosynthetic cells: bundle-sheath cells and mesophyll cells. **Bundle-sheath cells** are arranged into tightly packed sheaths around the veins of the leaf. Between the bundle sheath and the leaf surface are the more loosely arranged **mesophyll cells**. The Calvin cycle is confined to the chloroplasts of the bundle sheath. However, the cycle is preceded by incorporation of CO_2 into organic compounds in the mesophyll (FIGURE 10.17b). The first step is the addition of CO_2 to phosphoenolpyruvate (PEP) to form the four-carbon product oxaloacetate. The enzyme **PEP carboxylase** adds CO_2 to PEP. Compared to rubisco, PEP

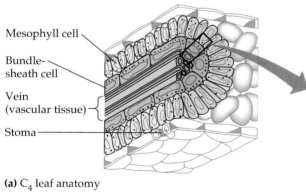

Mesophyll cell

Bundle-sheath cell

Vein (vascular tissue)

Stoma

(a) C_4 leaf anatomy

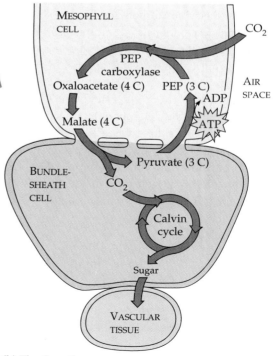

(b) The C_4 pathway

FIGURE 10.17 ▪ **The C_4 anatomy and pathway. (a)** Leaves of C_4 plants contain two types of photosynthetic cells: a cylinder of bundle-sheath cells surrounding the vein, and mesophyll cells located outside the bundle sheath. **(b)** Carbon dioxide is fixed in mesophyll cells by the enzyme PEP carboxylase. A four-carbon compound—malate, in this case—conveys the atoms of the CO_2 into a bundle-sheath cell, via plasmodesmata. There CO_2 is released and enters the Calvin cycle. This adaptation maintains a CO_2 concentration in the bundle sheath that favors photosynthesis over photorespiration.

SUGARCANE

PINEAPPLE

FIGURE 10.18 ▪ **C$_4$ and CAM photosynthesis compared.** Both adaptations are characterized by ① preliminary incorporation of CO$_2$ into organic acids, followed by ② transfer of the CO$_2$ to the Calvin cycle. In C$_4$ plants, such as sugarcane, these two steps are separated spatially; they are segregated into two cell types. In CAM plants, such as pineapple, the two steps are separated temporally; carbon fixation into organic acids occurs at night, and the Calvin cycle operates during the day. The C$_4$ and CAM pathways are two evolutionary solutions to the problem of maintaining photosynthesis with stomata partially or completely closed on hot, dry days.

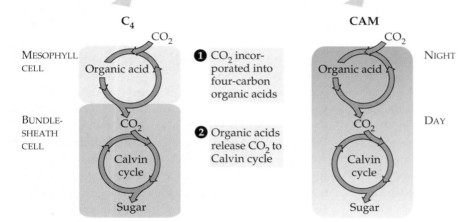

carboxylase has a much higher affinity for CO$_2$. Therefore, PEP carboxylase can fix CO$_2$ efficiently when rubisco cannot—that is, when it is hot and dry and stomata are partially closed, causing CO$_2$ concentration in the leaf to fall and O$_2$ concentration to rise. After the C$_4$ plant fixes CO$_2$, the mesophyll cells export their four-carbon products to bundle-sheath cells through plasmodesmata (see FIGURE 7.28). Within the bundle-sheath cells, the four-carbon compounds release CO$_2$, which is reassimilated into organic material by rubisco and the Calvin cycle.

In effect, the mesophyll cells of a C$_4$ plant pump CO$_2$ into the bundle sheath, keeping the CO$_2$ concentration in the bundle-sheath cells high enough for rubisco to accept carbon dioxide rather than oxygen. In this way, C$_4$ photosynthesis minimizes photorespiration and enhances sugar production. This adaptation is especially advantageous in hot regions with intense sunlight, and it is in such environments that C$_4$ plants evolved and thrive today.

CAM Plants

A second photosynthetic adaptation to arid conditions has evolved in succulent (water-storing) plants (including ice plants), many cacti, pineapples, and representatives of several other plant families. These plants open their stomata during the night and close them during the day, just the reverse of

how other plants behave. Closing stomata during the day helps desert plants conserve water, but it also prevents CO$_2$ from entering the leaves. During the night, when their stomata are open, these plants take up CO$_2$ and incorporate it into a variety of organic acids. This mode of carbon fixation is called **crassulacean acid metabolism**, or **CAM**, after the plant family Crassulaceae, the succulents in which the process was first discovered. The mesophyll cells of **CAM plants** store the organic acids they make during the night in their vacuoles until morning, when the stomata close. During the day, when the light reactions can supply ATP and NADPH for the Calvin cycle, CO$_2$ is released from the organic acids made the night before to become incorporated into sugar in the chloroplasts.

Notice in FIGURE 10.18 that the CAM pathway is similar to the C$_4$ pathway in that carbon dioxide is first incorporated into organic intermediates before it enters the Calvin cycle. The difference is that in C$_4$ plants, the initial steps of carbon fixation are separated structurally from the Calvin cycle, whereas in CAM plants the two steps occur at separate times. Keep in mind that CAM, C$_4$, and C$_3$ plants all eventually use the Calvin cycle to make sugar from carbon dioxide.

Photosynthesis is the biosphere's metabolic foundation: *a review*

In this chapter we have followed photosynthesis from photons to food (FIGURE 10.19). The light reactions capture solar

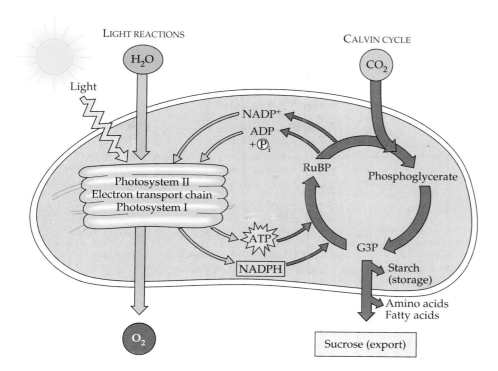

LIGHT REACTIONS

H_2O

Light

CALVIN CYCLE

CO_2

$NADP^+$
ADP
$+ P_i$

RuBP

Phosphoglycerate

Photosystem II
Electron transport chain
Photosystem I

ATP

NADPH

G3P

Starch
(storage)

Amino acids
Fatty acids

O_2

Sucrose (export)

FIGURE 10.19 ▪ A review of photosynthesis. This diagram outlines the main reactants and products of photosynthesis as it occurs in the chloroplasts of plant cells. The light reactions convert light energy to the chemical energy of ATP and NADPH. The pigment and protein molecules that carry out the light reactions are found in the thylakoid membranes and include the molecules of two photosystems and electron transport chains. The light reactions split H_2O and release O_2 to Earth's atmosphere. The Calvin cycle, which takes place in the stroma of the chloroplast, uses ATP and NADPH to convert CO_2 to carbohydrate (three key compounds of the cycle are shown). The direct product of the Calvin cycle is the three-carbon sugar glyceraldehyde 3-phosphate (G3P). Enzymes in the chloroplast and cytosol convert this small sugar to a diversity of other organic compounds. The Calvin cycle returns ADP, inorganic phosphate, and $NADP^+$ to the light reactions. The entire ordered operation depends on the structural integrity of the chloroplast and its membranes.

energy and use it to make ATP and transfer electrons from water to $NADP^+$. The Calvin cycle uses the ATP and NADPH to produce sugar from carbon dioxide. The energy that entered the chloroplasts as sunlight becomes stored as chemical energy in organic compounds.

What are the fates of photosynthetic products? The sugar made in the chloroplasts supplies the entire plant with chemical energy and carbon skeletons to synthesize all the major organic molecules of cells. About 50% of the organic material made by photosynthesis is consumed as fuel for cellular respiration in the mitochondria of the plant cells. Sometimes there is a loss of photosynthetic products to photorespiration.

Technically, green cells are the only autotrophic parts of the plant. The rest of the plant depends on organic molecules exported from leaves via veins. In most plants, carbohydrate is transported out of the leaves in the form of sucrose, a disaccharide. After arriving at nonphotosynthetic cells, the sucrose provides raw material for cellular respiration and a multitude of anabolic pathways that synthesize proteins, lipids, and other products. A considerable amount of sugar in the form of glucose is linked together to make the polysaccharide cellulose, especially in plant cells that are still growing and matur-

ing. Cellulose, the main ingredient of cell walls, is the most abundant organic molecule in the plant—and probably on the surface of the planet.

Most plants manage to make more organic material each day than they need to use as respiratory fuel and precursors for biosynthesis. They stockpile the extra sugar by synthesizing starch, storing some in the chloroplasts themselves and some in storage cells of roots, tubers, seeds, and fruits. In accounting for the consumption of the food molecules produced by photosynthesis, let's not forget that most plants lose leaves, roots, stems, fruits, and sometimes their entire bodies to heterotrophs, including humans.

On a global scale, the collective productivity of the minute chloroplasts is prodigious; it is estimated that photosynthesis makes about 160 billion metric tons of carbohydrate per year (a metric ton is 1000 kg, about 1.1 tons). That's organic matter equivalent to a stack of about 60 trillion copies of this textbook—17 stacks of books reaching from Earth to the sun! No other chemical process on the planet can match the output of photosynthesis. And no process is more important than photosynthesis to the welfare of life on Earth.

CHAPTER REVIEW

REVIEW OF KEY CONCEPTS

(with page numbers and key figures)

PHOTOSYNTHESIS IN NATURE

▪ **Plants and other autotrophs are the producers of the biosphere** (pp. 168–169, FIGURE 10.1) Autotrophs nourish themselves with-

out ingesting organic molecules. Photoautotrophs use the energy of sunlight to synthesize organic molecules from CO_2 and H_2O. Heterotrophs ingest organic molecules from other organisms to get energy and carbon.

▪ **Chloroplasts are the sites of photosynthesis in plants** (pp. 169–170, FIGURE 10.2) In autotrophic eukaryotes, photosynthesis

occurs in chloroplasts, organelles containing thylakoid membranes that separate the thylakoid space from the chloroplast's stroma. Stacks of thylakoids form grana.

THE PATHWAYS OF PHOTOSYNTHESIS

■ **Evidence that chloroplasts split water molecules enabled researchers to track atoms through photosynthesis (pp. 170–172, FIGURE 10.3)** Photosynthesis is summarized as:

$$6\,CO_2 + 12\,H_2O + \frac{Light}{energy} \longrightarrow C_6H_{12}O_6 + 6\,O_2 + 6\,H_2O$$

Experiments show that the chloroplast splits water into hydrogen and oxygen, incorporating the electrons of hydrogen into the bonds of sugar molecules. Photosynthesis is a redox process: H_2O is oxidized, CO_2 is reduced.

10.1 **The light reactions and the Calvin cycle cooperate in converting light energy to the chemical energy of food (pp. 172–173, FIGURE 10.4)** The light reactions in the grana produce ATP and split water, releasing O_2 and forming NADPH by transferring electrons from water to $NADP^+$. The Calvin cycle in the stroma forms sugar from CO_2, using ATP for energy and NADPH for reducing power.

10.2 **The light reactions convert solar energy to the chemical energy of ATP and NADPH (pp. 173–179, FIGURE 10.11)** Light is a form of electromagnetic energy, which travels in waves. The colors we see as visible light are a part of the electromagnetic spectrum. A pigment is a substance that absorbs visible light of specific wavelengths. The action spectrum of photosynthesis does not exactly match the absorption spectrum of chlorophyll *a*, the main photosynthetic pigment in plants, because accessory pigments (chlorophyll *b* and various carotenoids) absorb different wavelengths of light and pass the energy on to chlorophyll *a*.

A pigment goes from a ground state to an excited state when a photon boosts one of its electrons to a higher-energy orbital. The pigments of chloroplasts are built into the thylakoid membrane near molecules called primary electron acceptors, which trap the excited electrons before they return to the ground state. Pigment molecules are clustered in an antenna complex surrounding a chlorophyll *a* molecule at the reaction center. Photons absorbed anywhere in the antenna can pass their energy along to energize this chlorophyll *a*, which then passes an electron to a nearby primary electron acceptor. The antenna complex, the reaction-center chlorophyll, and the primary electron acceptor make up a photosystem, a light-harvesting unit built into the thylakoid membrane. There are two kinds of photosystems. Photosystem I contains P700 chlorophyll *a* molecules at the reaction center; photosystem II contains P680 molecules.

Noncyclic electron flow involves both photosystems and produces NADPH, ATP, and oxygen. Cyclic electron flow employs only photosystem I, producing ATP but no NADPH or O_2. ATP production during the light reactions is called photophosphorylation. The mechanism is chemiosmosis. The redox reactions of the electron transport chain that connects the two photosystems generate an H^+ gradient across the thylakoid membrane. An ATP synthase uses this proton-motive force to make ATP.

10.3 **The Calvin cycle uses ATP and NADPH to convert CO_2 to sugar (pp. 179–182, FIGURE 10.16)** The Calvin cycle is a metabolic pathway in the chloroplast stroma. An enzyme (rubisco) combines CO_2 with ribulose bisphosphate (RuBP), a five-carbon sugar. Then, using electrons from NADPH and energy from ATP, the cycle synthesizes the three-carbon sugar glyceraldehyde 3-phosphate. Most of the G3P is reused in the cycle to reconstitute RuBP, but some exits the cycle and is converted to glucose and other essential organic molecules.

■ **Alternative mechanisms of carbon fixation have evolved in hot, arid climates (pp. 182–184, FIGURE 10.18)** On dry, hot days, plants close their stomata, conserving water. Oxygen from the light reactions builds up. When O_2 substitutes for CO_2 in the active site of rubisco, the product formed leaves the cycle and is oxidized to CO_2

and H_2O in the peroxisomes and mitochondria. This process, photorespiration, consumes organic fuel without producing ATP. C_4 plants avert photorespiration by incorporating CO_2 into four-carbon compounds in mesophyll cells. These compounds are exported to photosynthetic bundle-sheath cells, where they release carbon dioxide for use in the Calvin cycle. CAM plants open their stomata during the night, incorporating the CO_2 that enters into organic acids, which they store in mesophyll cells. During the day the stomata close, and the CO_2 is released from the organic acids for use in the Calvin cycle.

■ **Photosynthesis is the biosphere's metabolic foundation (pp. 184–185, FIGURE 10.19)** The organic compounds produced by photosynthesis provide the energy and building material for ecosystems.

SELF-QUIZ

1. The light reactions of photosynthesis supply the Calvin cycle with
   a. light energy
   b. CO_2 and ATP
   c. H_2O and NADPH
   d. ATP and NADPH
   e. sugar and O_2

2. Which of the following sequences correctly represents the flow of electrons during photosynthesis?
   a. NADPH $\longrightarrow O_2 \longrightarrow CO_2$
   b. $H_2O \longrightarrow$ NADPH $\longrightarrow$ Calvin cycle
   c. NADPH $\longrightarrow$ chlorophyll $\longrightarrow$ Calvin cycle
   d. $H_2O \longrightarrow$ photosystem I $\longrightarrow$ photosystem II
   e. NADPH $\longrightarrow$ electron transport chain $\longrightarrow O_2$

3. Which of the following conclusions does *not* follow from studying the absorption spectrum for chlorophyll *a* and the action spectrum for photosynthesis?
   a. Not all wavelengths are equally effective for photosynthesis.
   b. There must be accessory pigments that broaden the spectrum of light that contributes energy for photosynthesis.
   c. The red and blue areas of the spectrum are most effective in driving photosynthesis.
   d. Chlorophyll owes its color to the absorption of green light.
   e. Chlorophyll *a* has two absorption peaks.

4. Cooperation of the *two* photosystems of the chloroplast is required for
   a. ATP synthesis
   b. reduction of $NADP^+$
   c. cyclic photophosphorylation
   d. oxidation of the reaction center of photosystem I
   e. generation of a proton-motive force

5. In *mechanism*, photophosphorylation is most similar to
   a. substrate-level phosphorylation in glycolysis
   b. oxidative phosphorylation in cellular respiration
   c. the Calvin cycle
   d. carbon fixation
   e. reduction of $NADP^+$

6. In what respect are the photosynthetic adaptations of C_4 plants and CAM plants similar?
   a. In both cases, the stomata normally close during the day.
   b. Both types of plants make their sugar without the Calvin cycle.
   c. In both cases, an enzyme other than rubisco carries out the first step in carbon fixation.
   d. Both types of plants make most of their sugar in the dark.
   e. Neither C_4 plants nor CAM plants have grana in their chloroplasts.

7. Which of the following processes is most directly driven by light energy?

a. creation of a pH gradient by pumping protons across the thylakoid membrane
b. carbon fixation in the stroma
c. reduction of NADP molecules
d. removal of electrons from membrane-bound chlorophyll molecules
e. ATP synthesis

8. Which of the following statements is a correct distinction between cyclic and noncyclic photophosphorylation?
   a. Only noncyclic photophosphorylation produces ATP.
   b. In addition to ATP, noncyclic photophosphorylation also produces O_2 and NADPH.
   c. Only cyclic photophosphorylation utilizes light at 700 nm.
   d. Chemiosmosis is unique to noncyclic photophosphorylation.
   e. Only cyclic photophosphorylation can operate in the absence of photosystem II.

9. Which of the following statements is a correct distinction between autotrophs and heterotrophs?
   a. Only heterotrophs require chemical compounds from the environment.
   b. Cellular respiration is unique to heterotrophs.
   c. Only heterotrophs have mitochondria.
   d. Autotrophs, but not heterotrophs, can nourish themselves beginning with CO_2 and other nutrients that are entirely inorganic.
   e. Only heterotrophs require oxygen.

10. Which of the following processes could still occur in a chloroplast in the presence of an inhibitor that prevents H^+ from passing through ATP synthase complexes? (Explain your answer.)
    a. sugar synthesis
    b. generation of a proton-motive force
    c. photophosphorylation
    d. the Calvin cycle
    e. oxidation of NADPH

CHALLENGE QUESTION

The diagram below represents an experiment with isolated chloroplasts. The chloroplasts were first made acidic by soaking them in a solution at pH 4. After the thylakoid space reached pH 4, the chloroplasts were transferred to a basic solution at pH 8. The chloroplasts then made ATP, in the dark. Explain this result.

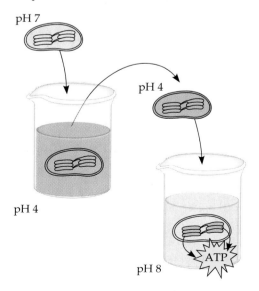

SCIENCE, TECHNOLOGY, AND SOCIETY

Tropical rain forests cover only about 3% of Earth's surface, but they are estimated to be responsible for more than 20% of global photosynthesis. It seems reasonable to expect that the lush growth of jungle foliage would produce large amounts of oxygen and reduce global warming by consuming carbon dioxide. But in fact, many experts now believe that rain forests make little or no net contribution to global oxygen production or reduction of global warming. Using your knowledge of photosynthesis and cellular respiration, explain what the basis of this hypothesis might be. What happens to the food produced by a rain forest tree when it is eaten by animals or the tree dies?

FURTHER READING

Bazzazz, F. A., and E. D. Fajer. "Plant Life in a CO_2-Rich World." *Scientific American*, January 1992. How will increasing atmospheric CO_2 and global warming affect the relative success of C_3 and C_4 plants?

Becker, W. M., J. B. Reece, and M. F. Poenie. *The World of the Cell*, 3rd ed. Menlo Park, CA: Benjamin/Cummings, 1996. Chapter 13 explains photosynthesis in some detail.

Caldwell, M. "The Amazing All-Natural Light Machine." *Discover*, December 1995. Discusses the elegant and efficient antenna complexes of a photosynthetic prokaryote.

Galston, A. W. "Photosynthesis as a Basis for Life Support on Earth and in Space." *Bioscience*, July/August 1992. Plants in space.

Govindjee and W. J. Coleman. "How Plants Make Oxygen." *Scientific American*, February 1990.

Hendry, G. "Oxygen, the Great Destroyer." *Natural History*, August 1992. Explores photorespiration and other problems associated with an oxygen-rich atmosphere.

Walker, D. *Energy, Plants, and Man*. Mill Valley, CA: University Science Books, 1992. Contains cartoons and stories that make bioenergetics fun.

Williams, N. "Mutant Alga Blurs Classic Picture of Photosynthesis." *Science*, July 19, 1996. Mutants with photosystem I disabled carry out photosynthesis with photosystem II alone.

WEB LINKS

Visit the special edition of *The Biology Place* for BIOLOGY, Fifth Edition, at http://www.biology.com/campbell. Go to Chapter 10 for online resources, including learning activities, practice exams, and links to the following web sites:

"Photosynthesis: An Interactive Study Guide"
Visit Campbell's Biology Place where you can use the activities of this tutorial to review photosynthesis. Your tutor is Dr. Graham Kent of Smith College.

"ASU Photosynthesis Center"
The main page of a comprehensive site on photosynthesis from the Arizona State University Photosynthesis Center (ASUPC). Includes links to global photosynthesis resources, including educational resources.

"Virtual Photosynthesis Experiments"
A chatty, interactive site at ASUPC that demonstrates some of the ways scientists study photosynthesis.

"Photosynthesis and Time"
An interactive "experiment" looking at the rate of the light reactions of photosynthesis.

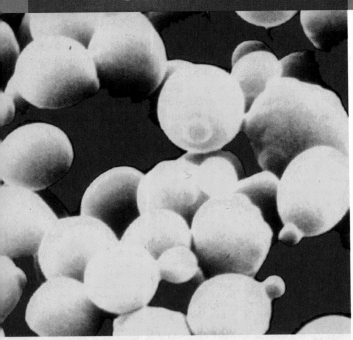

CHAPTER 11

CELL COMMUNICATION

An Overview of Cell Signaling

- Cell signaling evolved early in the history of life
- Communicating cells may be close together or far apart
- The three stages of cell signaling are reception, transduction, and response

Signal Reception and the Initiation of Transduction

- A signal molecule binds to a receptor protein, causing the protein to change shape
- Most signal receptors are plasma-membrane proteins

Signal-Transduction Pathways

- Pathways relay signals from receptors to cellular responses
- Protein phosphorylation, a common mode of regulation in cells, is a major mechanism of signal transduction
- Certain small molecules and ions are key components of signaling pathways (second messengers)

Cellular Responses to Signals

- In response to a signal, a cell may regulate activities in the cytoplasm or transcription in the nucleus
- Elaborate pathways amplify and specify the cell's response to signals

"*Watch out! There's a car coming!*"—We don't really need such a warning to remind us of the importance of communication in our lives as human beings. Perhaps less obvious is the critical role of communication in life at the cellular level. Cell-to-cell communication is absolutely essential for multicellular organisms. The billions of cells of a human or an oak tree must communicate in order to coordinate their activities in a way that enables the organism to develop from a fertilized egg and then survive and reproduce in turn. Communication among cells is also important for many unicellular organisms, such as the yeast pictured in the adjacent micrograph.

As you read in Chapter 1, regulation is a unifying theme in biology, and in recent years cell signaling has emerged as a universal mode of regulation in living things. In many lines of biological research, the same small set of cell-signaling mechanisms are showing up again and again. To the delight of scientists, studies of cell signaling are helping to answer some of the most important questions in biology and medicine—in areas ranging from embryological development to hormone action to the development of cancer and other kinds of disease.

The signals received by cells, whether originating from another cell or from some change in the organism's physical surroundings, take various forms. For instance, cells can sense and respond to electromagnetic signals, such as light, and to mechanical signals, such as touch. (In later units of this text, we discuss cellular detection of these and other types of physical signals.) However, cells most often communicate with each other using chemical signals. In this chapter we focus on the main mechanisms by which cells detect, process, and respond to chemical signals sent from other cells.

AN OVERVIEW OF CELL SIGNALING

What do cells talk about? What kinds of things does a "talking" cell say to a "listening" cell, and how does the latter cell respond to the message? Let's approach these questions by first looking at communication among microorganisms, for modern microbes are a window to the role of cell signaling in the evolution of life on Earth.

Cell signaling evolved early in the history of life

One topic of cell "conversation" is sex—at least for the yeast *Saccharomyces cerevisiae*, the fungus people have used for millennia for making bread, wine, and beer. Researchers have learned that cells of this yeast identify their mates by chemical signaling (FIGURE 11.1). There are two sexes, or mating types, called **a** and α. Cells of mating type **a** secrete a chemical signal called **a**-factor, which can bind to specific receptor proteins on

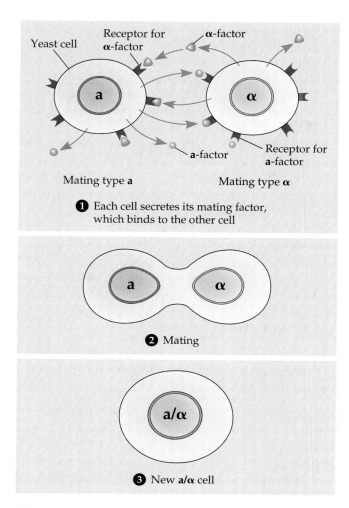

Yeast cell **Receptor for α-factor** **α-factor**

a

α

α-factor

a-factor **Receptor for a-factor**

Mating type **a** Mating type **α**

❶ Each cell secretes its mating factor, which binds to the other cell

a   α

❷ Mating

a/α

❸ New a/α cell

FIGURE 11.1 ▪ **Communication between mating yeast cells.** Cells of the yeast *Saccharomyces cerevisiae* use chemical signaling to identify cells of opposite mating type and initiate the mating process. ① Cells of mating type **a** release **a**-factor, which binds to receptors on nearby cells of mating type α. Meanwhile, α cells release α-factor, which binds to specific receptors on **a** cells. (Both factors are peptides about 12 amino acids in length.) ② Binding of the factors to receptors induces changes in the cells that lead to their fusion, or mating. ③ The resulting **a**/α cell combines in its nucleus all the genes from the **a** and α cells.

nearby α cells. At the same time, α cells secrete α-factor, which binds to receptors on **a** cells. Without actually entering the cells, the receptor-bound molecules of the two mating factors cause the cells to grow toward each other and bring about other cellular changes. The result is the fusion, or mating, of two cells of opposite type. The new **a**/α cell contains all the genes of both original cells, a combination of genetic resources that provides advantages to this cell's descendants.

How is the mating signal at the yeast cell surface transduced, or changed, into a form that brings about the cellular response of mating? The process by which a signal on a cell's surface is converted into a specific cellular response, a series of steps called a **signal-transduction pathway**, has been extensively studied in both yeast and animal cells. Amazingly, the molecular details of signal transduction in yeast and mammals are strikingly similar, even though the last common ancestor of these two groups of organisms lived over a billion years ago. These similarities—and others newly uncovered between signaling systems in bacteria and plants—suggest that early versions of the cell-signaling mechanisms used today evolved well before the first multicellular creatures appeared on Earth. Scientists think that signaling mechanisms evolved first in ancient prokaryotes and single-celled eukaryotes and were then adopted for new uses by their multicellular descendants. Meanwhile, cell signaling has remained important in the microbial world. FIGURE 11.2 shows an example in a sophisticated modern bacterium.

Communicating cells may be close together or far apart

Like microbes, cells in a multicellular organism usually communicate by releasing chemical messengers targeted for cells that may not be immediately adjacent. Some messengers travel only short distances: The transmitting cell secretes molecules of a **local regulator**, a substance that influences cells in

Individual rod-shaped cells   Aggregation in progress   Spore-forming structure |—————| 0.5 mm

FIGURE 11.2 ▪ **Communication among bacteria.** Soil-dwelling bacteria called myxobacteria ("slime bacteria") use chemical signaling to share information about nutrient availability. When food is scarce, starving cells secrete a molecule that enters neighboring cells and stimulates them to aggregate. The cells form a structure that produces thick-walled spores capable of surviving until the environment improves. The bacteria shown here are *Myxococcus xanthus* (SEMs).

the vicinity (FIGURE 11.3a). One class of local regulators in animals, growth factors, are compounds that stimulate nearby target cells to grow and multiply. Numerous cells can simultaneously receive and respond to the molecules of growth factor produced by a single cell in their vicinity. This type of local signaling in animals is called paracrine signaling.

Another, more specialized type of local signaling occurs in the animal nervous system. Here a nerve cell produces a chemical signal, a neurotransmitter, that diffuses to a single target cell that is almost touching the first cell. An electrical signal transmitted the length of the nerve cell triggers the secretion of neurotransmitter molecules into the synapse, the narrow space between the nerve cell and its target cell (often another nerve cell). Because specific nerve cells are so close together at synapses, a nerve signal can travel from your brain to your big toe, for example, without causing unwanted responses in other parts of your body.

Local signaling in plants is less well understood. Because of their cell walls, plants must use some mechanisms different from those operating locally in animals.

Both animals and plants use chemicals called **hormones** for signaling at greater distances. In hormonal signaling in animals, also known as endocrine signaling, specialized cells release hormone molecules into vessels of the circulatory system, by which they travel to target cells in other parts of the body (FIGURE 11.3b). In plants, hormones sometimes travel in vessels but more often reach their targets by moving through cells (see FIGURE 39.4) or by diffusion through the air as a gas. Hormones range widely in molecular size and type, as do local regulators. For instance, the plant hormone ethylene, a

gas that promotes fruit ripening and helps regulate growth, is a hydrocarbon of only six atoms (C_2H_4). In contrast, the mammalian hormone insulin, which regulates sugar levels in the blood, is a protein with thousands of atoms.

Cells may also communicate by direct contact, as we saw in Chapters 7 and 8. Both animals and plants have cell junctions that, where present, provide cytoplasmic continuity between adjacent cells (FIGURE 11.4a). In these cases, signaling substances dissolved in the cytosol can pass freely between adjacent cells. Moreover, animal cells may communicate via direct contact between molecules on their surfaces (FIGURE 11.4b). This sort of signaling is important in embryonic development and in the operation of the immune system.

What happens when a cell encounters a signal? The signal must be recognized by a specific receptor molecule and the information it carries must be changed into another form—transduced—inside the cell before the cell can respond. The remainder of the chapter discusses this process, primarily as it occurs in animal cells.

The three stages of cell signaling are reception, transduction, and response

Our current understanding of how chemical messengers act via signal-transduction pathways had its origins in the pioneering work of Earl W. Sutherland, whose research led to a Nobel Prize in 1971. Sutherland and his colleagues at Vanderbilt University were investigating how the animal hormone epinephrine stimulates breakdown (depolymerization) of the storage polysaccharide glycogen within liver cells and skeletal

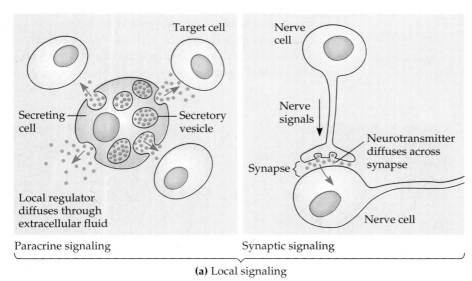

(a) Local signaling

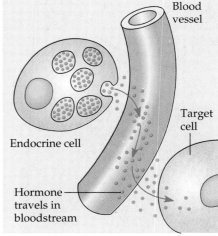

(b) Hormonal signaling

FIGURE 11.3 · Local and distant cell communication in animals. (a) Animals have two main kinds of local chemical signaling. In paracrine signaling, a secreting cell acts on nearby target cells by discharging molecules of a local regulator into the extracellular fluid. In synaptic signaling, a nerve cell releases neurotransmitter molecules into a synapse, the narrow space between the transmitting cell and the target cell, here another nerve cell. **(b)** Hormones signal target cells at much greater distances. In animals, specialized endocrine cells secrete hormones into body fluids, often the blood. Hormones may reach virtually all body cells, but, as with local regulators, only specific target cells recognize and respond to a given chemical signal. (Plants also use hormones for signaling from one part of the plant to another.)

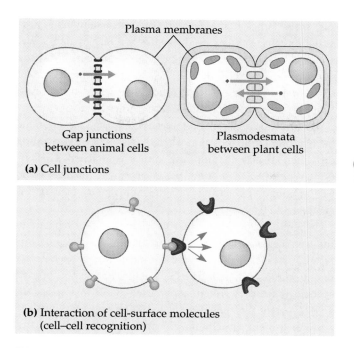

(a) Cell junctions

(b) Interaction of cell-surface molecules
(cell–cell recognition)

FIGURE 11.4 · **Communication by direct contact between cells.**
(a) Both animals and plants have cell junctions that allow molecules to pass readily between adjacent cells without crossing plasma membranes. **(b)** Two cells in an animal may communicate by interaction between molecules protruding from their surfaces.

muscle cells. Glycogen depolymerization releases the sugar glucose-1-phosphate, which the cell converts to glucose-6-phosphate. The cell can then use this compound, an early intermediate in glycolysis, for energy production. Alternatively, the compound can be stripped of phosphate and released into the blood as glucose that can fuel cells throughout the body. Thus one effect of epinephrine, which is secreted from the adrenal gland during times of physical or mental stress, is the mobilization of fuel reserves.

Sutherland's research team discovered that epinephrine stimulates glycogen breakdown by somehow activating a cytosolic enzyme, glycogen phosphorylase. However, when epinephrine was added to a test-tube mixture containing the phosphorylase and its substrate, glycogen, no depolymeriza-

tion occurred. Epinephrine could activate glycogen phosphorylase only when the hormone was added to a solution containing *intact* cells. This result told Sutherland two things. First, epinephrine does not interact directly with the enzyme responsible for glycogen breakdown; an intermediate step or series of steps must be occurring inside the cell. Second, the plasma membrane is somehow involved in transmitting the epinephrine signal.

Thus Sutherland's early work suggested that the process going on at the receiving end of a cellular conversation can be dissected into three stages: reception, transduction, and response (FIGURE 11.5):

1. Reception is the target cell's detection of a signal coming from outside the cell. A chemical signal is "detected" when it binds to a cellular protein, usually at the cell's surface.

2. The binding of the signal molecule changes the receptor protein in some way, thus initiating the process of transduction. The transduction stage converts the signal to a form that can bring about a specific cellular response. In Sutherland's system, the binding of epinephrine to the outside of a receptor protein in a liver cell's plasma membrane leads via a series of steps to activation of glycogen phosphorylase. Transduction sometimes occurs in a single step but more often requires a sequence of changes in a series of different molecules—a signal-transduction *pathway*. The molecules in the pathway are often called relay molecules.

3. In the third stage of cell signaling, the transduced signal finally triggers a specific cellular response. The response may be almost any imaginable cellular activity—such as catalysis by an enzyme (such as glycogen phosphorylase), rearrangement of the cytoskeleton, or activation of specific genes in the nucleus. The cell-signaling process helps ensure that crucial activities like these occur in the right cells, at the right time, and in proper coordination with the other cells of the organism. We'll now explore the mechanisms of cell signaling in more detail.

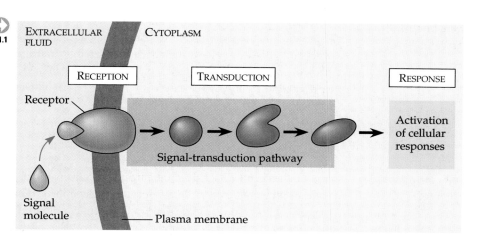

EXTRACELLULAR FLUID CYTOPLASM

RECEPTION TRANSDUCTION RESPONSE

Receptor

Signal-transduction pathway

Activation of cellular responses

Signal molecule

Plasma membrane

FIGURE 11.5 · **Overview of cell signaling.**
From the perspective of the cell receiving the message, cell signaling can be divided into three stages: signal reception, signal transduction, and cellular response. When reception occurs at the plasma membrane, as shown here, the transduction stage is usually a pathway of several steps, with each molecule in the pathway bringing about a change in the next. The last molecule in the pathway triggers the cell's response.

SIGNAL RECEPTION AND THE INITIATION OF TRANSDUCTION

When we speak to someone, others nearby may hear our message, sometimes with unfortunate consequences. However, errors of this kind rarely occur between cells. The signals emitted by an α yeast cell are "heard" only by its prospective mates, **a** cells. Similarly, although epinephrine encounters many types of cells as it circulates in the blood, only certain target cells detect and react to the hormone. The signal receptor is the identity tag on the target cell.

A signal molecule binds to a receptor protein, causing the protein to change shape

A cell targeted by a particular chemical signal has molecules of a receptor protein that recognizes the signal molecule. The signal molecule is complementary in shape to a specific site on the receptor and attaches there, like a key in a lock—or like a substrate in the catalytic site of an enzyme. The signal molecule behaves as a **ligand**, the term for a small molecule that specifically binds to a larger one. Ligand binding generally causes a receptor protein to undergo a change in conformation—that is, to change shape. For many receptors, this shape change directly activates the receptor so that it can interact with another cellular molecule. For other kinds of receptors, as we'll see shortly, the immediate effect of ligand binding is more limited, mainly causing the aggregation of two or more receptor molecules.

Most signal receptors are plasma-membrane proteins

Most signal molecules are water-soluble and too large to pass freely through the plasma membrane. But, as Sutherland learned for epinephrine, they still influence cellular activity in major ways. Like yeast mating factors, most water-soluble signal molecules bind to specific sites on receptor proteins embedded in the cell's plasma membrane. Such a receptor transmits information from the extracellular environment to the inside of the cell by changing shape or aggregating when a specific ligand binds to it.

We'll see how membrane receptors work by looking at three major types: G-protein-linked receptors, tyrosine-kinase receptors, and ion-channel receptors.

G-Protein-Linked Receptors

A **G-protein-linked receptor** is a plasma-membrane receptor that works with the help of a protein called a G protein (FIGURE 11.6a). Many different signal molecules use G-protein-linked receptors, including yeast mating factors, epinephrine and many other hormones, and neurotransmitters. These receptors vary in their binding sites for recognizing signal molecules and for recognizing different G proteins inside the cell. Nevertheless, G-protein-linked receptor proteins are all remarkably similar in structure. They each have seven α-helices spanning the membrane, as shown in FIGURE 11.7.

Loosely attached to the cytoplasmic side of the membrane, the **G protein** functions as a switch that is on or off depending on which of two guanine nucleotides is attached, GDP or GTP. When GDP is bound, the G protein is inactive; when GTP is bound, it is active. (GTP, or guanosine triphosphate, is similar to ATP.)

When the appropriate chemical signal binds as a ligand to the extracellular side of a G-protein-linked receptor, the receptor is activated, changing conformation in such a way that it, in turn, can activate a G protein: The receptor binds a specific, inactive G protein and causes a GTP to displace the GDP (FIGURE 11.6b). The activated G protein then binds to another protein, usually an enzyme, and alters *its* activity. These changes are only temporary, however, for the G protein also functions as a GTPase enzyme and soon hydrolyzes its bound GTP to GDP (FIGURE 11.6c). Now inactive again, the G protein leaves the enzyme. The GTPase function of the G protein allows the pathway to shut down rapidly when the extracellular signal molecule is no longer present.

G-protein receptor systems are extremely widespread and diverse in their functions. In addition to the functions already mentioned, they are important in embryonic development, as indicated by genetic studies. For instance, mutant mouse embryos lacking a certain G protein do not develop normal blood vessels and die in utero. Furthermore, G proteins are involved in sensory reception; in humans, for example, both vision and smell depend on such proteins. Similarities in structure among G proteins and G-protein-linked receptors of modern organisms suggest that G proteins and G-protein-linked receptors evolved very early, possibly as sensory receptors of ancient microbes.

G-protein systems are involved in many human diseases, including bacterial infections. The bacteria that cause cholera, pertussis (whooping cough), and botulism, among others, make their victims ill by producing toxins that interfere with G-protein function. Although drugs for treating infections and other kinds of diseases have often been discovered by trial and error, pharmacologists now realize that up to 60% of all medicines used today exert their effects by influencing G-protein pathways.

Tyrosine-Kinase Receptors

Among the chemical signals impinging on cells in an animal's body are growth factors, the local regulators that stimulate cells to grow and reproduce. As we'll see in Chapter 12, cell reproduction involves a variety of activities by different parts of the

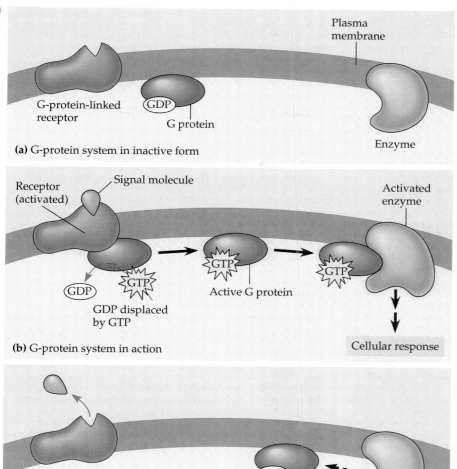

Plasma membrane

(a) G-protein system in inactive form

G-protein-linked receptor · GDP · G protein · Enzyme

Receptor (activated) · Signal molecule · Activated enzyme

GDP · GDP displaced by GTP · GTP · Active G protein · GTP · Cellular response

(b) G-protein system in action

(c) Return to inactive form · GDP · P_i

FIGURE 11.6 · The functioning of a G-protein-linked receptor. (a) This type of receptor is a membrane protein that works in conjunction with a G protein and another protein, usually an enzyme. In the absence of the extracellular signal molecule specific for the receptor, all three proteins are in inactive form. The inactive G protein has a GDP molecule bound to it. **(b)** When the signal molecule binds to the receptor, the receptor changes shape in such a way that it binds and activates the G protein. A molecule of GTP replaces the GDP on the G protein. The active G protein (moving freely along the membrane) binds to and activates the enzyme, which triggers the next step in the pathway leading to the cell's responses. **(c)** The G protein then catalyzes the hydrolysis of its GTP and dissociates from the enzyme, becoming available for reuse. All three proteins remain attached to the plasma membrane.

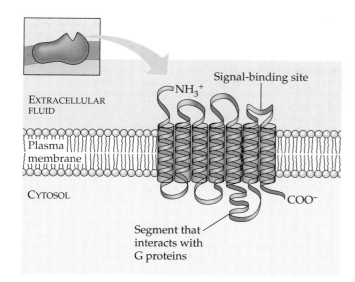

Signal-binding site

NH_3^+

EXTRACELLULAR FLUID

Plasma membrane

CYTOSOL

COO^-

Segment that interacts with G proteins

FIGURE 11.7 · The structure of a G-protein-linked receptor. A large family of eukaryotic receptor proteins have this secondary structure: The single polypeptide, represented as a ribbon, has seven transmembrane α helices. Specific loops correspond to the sites where signal molecules and G-protein molecules bind. The α helices are depicted as cylinders for emphasis.

cell, including protein synthesis in the cytoplasm, chromosome duplication in the nucleus, and the rearrangement of elements of the cytoskeleton. Helping the cell regulate and coordinate these activities is a type of receptor specialized for triggering more than one signal-transduction pathway at once.

The receptor for a growth factor is often a tyrosine-kinase receptor, one of a major class of plasma-membrane receptors characterized by having enzymatic activity. Part of the receptor protein on the cytoplasmic side of the membrane functions as an enzyme, called a **tyrosine kinase**, that catalyzes the transfer of phosphate groups from ATP to the amino acid tyrosine on a substrate protein. Thus **tyrosine-kinase receptors** are membrane receptors that attach phosphates to protein tyrosines.

Tyrosine-kinase receptors often have the structure shown in rough schematic form in FIGURE 11.8, page 194. Before the signal molecule binds, the receptors exist as individual polypeptides. Notice that each has an extracellular signal-binding site, an intracellular tail containing a number of tyrosines, and a single α helix spanning the membrane. The binding of a signal molecule to such a receptor does not cause

enough of a conformational change to activate the cytoplasmic side of the protein directly. Instead, the activation occurs in three steps: (1) The ligand binding causes two receptor polypeptides to aggregate, forming a dimer (a protein consisting of two polypeptides). (2) This aggregation activates the tyrosine-kinase parts of both polypeptides, each of which then (3) phosphorylates the tyrosines on the tail of the other polypeptide. In summary, the effect of the signal molecule on a tyrosine-kinase receptor is polypeptide aggregation and phosphorylation of the receptor.

The receptor protein is now recognized by specific relay proteins inside the cell. Each such protein binds to a specific phosphorylated tyrosine, undergoing a structural change that activates it (the relay protein may or may not be phosphorylated by the tyrosine kinase). One tyrosine-kinase receptor dimer may activate ten or more different intracellular proteins simultaneously, triggering as many different transduction pathways and particular cellular responses. The ability of a single ligand-binding event to trigger so many pathways is a key difference between these receptors and G-protein-linked receptors. Abnormal tyrosine-kinase receptors that aggregate even without ligand cause some kinds of cancer.

Ion-Channel Receptors

Some membrane receptors of chemical signals are **ligand-gated ion channels**. These channels are protein pores in the plasma membrane that open or close in response to a chemical signal, allowing or blocking the flow of specific ions, such as Na^+ or Ca^{2+}. Like the other receptors we have discussed, these channel proteins bind a signal molecule as a ligand at a specific site on their extracellular side (FIGURE 11.9). The shape change produced in the channel protein immediately leads to a change in the concentration of a particular ion inside the cell. Often this change directly affects cell functioning in some way. At a synapse between nerve cells, for example, it may trigger an electrical signal that propagates down the length of the receiving cell. Ligand-gated ion channels are very important in the nervous system, as are gated ion channels that are controlled by electrical signals (see Chapter 48).

Intracellular Receptors

Not all signal receptors are membrane proteins. Some are proteins located in the cytoplasm or nucleus of target cells. To reach such a receptor, a chemical messenger must be able to pass through the target cell's plasma membrane. A number of important signaling molecules can do just that, either because they are small enough to pass between the membrane phospholipids or because they are themselves lipids and therefore soluble in the membrane. Chemical messengers with intracellular receptors include the steroid hormones and thyroid hormones of animals, which are lipids; the small gaseous molecule nitric oxide (NO); and certain small signal molecules used by bacteria.

The behavior of testosterone is representative of steroid hormones: Secreted by cells of the testis, the hormone travels through the blood and enters cells all over the body. In target cells—those with testosterone receptor molecules in their cytosol—the hormone binds to the receptor, activating it. The

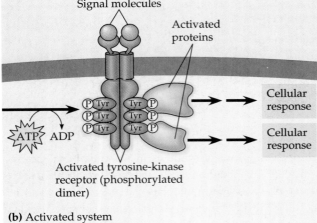

(a) Inactive tyrosine-kinase receptor system

(b) Activated system

FIGURE 11.8 · **The structure and function of a tyrosine-kinase receptor. (a)** In the absence of specific signal molecules, tyrosine-kinase receptors exist as single polypeptides in the plasma membrane. The extracellular portion of the protein, with the signal-molecule binding site, is connected by a single transmembrane α helix to the protein's cytoplasmic portion. This part of the protein is responsible for the receptor's tyrosine-kinase activity and also has a series of tyrosine amino acids. **(b)** When signal molecules (such as a growth factor) attach to their binding sites, two polypeptides aggregate, forming a dimer. Using phosphate groups from ATP, the tyrosine-kinase region of each polypeptide phosphorylates the tyrosines on the other polypeptide. In other words, the dimer is both an enzyme and its own substrate. Now fully activated, the receptor protein can bind specific intracellular proteins, which attach to particular phosphorylated tyrosines and are themselves activated. Each can then initiate a signal-transduction pathway leading to a specific cellular response. Tyrosine-kinase receptors often activate several different signal-transduction pathways at once, helping regulate such complicated functions as cell reproduction (cell division). Inappropriate activation of these receptors can lead to uncontrolled cell growth—cancer (see Chapter 19).

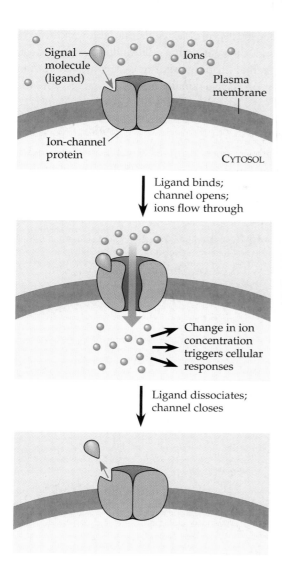

FIGURE 11.9 · A ligand-gated ion-channel receptor. This signal receptor is a transmembrane protein in the plasma membrane that opens to allow the flow of a specific kind of ion across the membrane when a specific signal molecule binds to the extracellular side of the protein.

active form of the receptor protein can then bind to and turn on genes in the nucleus that control male sex characteristics. Thus, the receptor carries out the complete transduction of the signal. We will look more closely at steroids and other hormones with intracellular receptors in Chapter 45. In the next section we discuss the signal-transduction pathways often triggered by membrane receptors.

SIGNAL-TRANSDUCTION PATHWAYS

When signal receptors are plasma-membrane proteins, like most of those we have discussed, the transduction stage of cell signaling is usually a multistep pathway. One benefit of such pathways is signal amplification. If some of the molecules in a pathway transmit the signal to multiple molecules of the next

component in the series, the result can be a large number of activated molecules at the end of the pathway. In other words, a very small number of extracellular signal molecules can produce a major cellular response. Moreover, multistep pathways provide more opportunities for coordination and regulation than simpler systems do, as we'll discuss later.

Pathways relay signals from receptors to cellular responses

The binding of a specific extracellular signal molecule to a receptor in the plasma membrane triggers the first step in the chain of molecular interactions—the signal-transduction pathway—that leads to a particular response within the cell. Like falling dominoes, the signal-activated receptor activates another protein, which activates another molecule, and so on, until the protein that produces the final cellular response is activated. The molecules that relay a signal from receptor to response, sometimes called relay molecules, are mostly proteins. The interaction of proteins is a major theme of cell signaling. Indeed, protein interaction is a unifying theme of all regulation at the cellular level.

Keep in mind that the original signal molecule is not physically passed along a signaling pathway; in most cases, it never even enters the cell. When we say that the signal is relayed along a pathway, we mean that certain *information* is passed on. At each step the signal is transduced into a different form, commonly a conformational change in a protein. Very often, the conformational change is brought about by phosphorylation.

Protein phosphorylation, a common mode of regulation in cells, is a major mechanism of signal transduction

⟳
11.3
Previous chapters introduced the concept of activating a protein by adding one or more phosphate groups to it (see FIGURE 9.2). In this chapter we have already seen how phosphorylation is involved in the activation of tyrosine-kinase receptors. In fact, the phosphorylation of proteins is a widespread cellular mechanism for regulating protein activity. The general name for an enzyme that transfers phosphate groups from ATP to a protein is **protein kinase**. Unlike receptor tyrosine kinases, most cytoplasmic protein kinases act not on themselves, but on other substrate proteins; also, they phosphorylate their substrates on either of two amino acids, serine or threonine. Such serine/threonine kinases are widely involved in signaling pathways in animals, fungi, and plants.

Many of the relay molecules in signal-transduction pathways are protein kinases, and they often act on each other. FIGURE 11.10, page 196, shows a hypothetical pathway containing three different protein kinases. This sequence is similar to many known pathways, including those triggered in yeast by mating factors and in animal cells by many growth factors.

The signal is transmitted by a cascade of protein phosphorylations, each bringing with it a conformational change. Each shape change results from the interaction of the charged phosphate groups with charged and polar amino acids (see FIGURE 5.15). The addition of phosphates often changes a protein from an inactive form to an active form (although in other cases phosphorylation *decreases* the activity of the protein).

The importance of protein kinases can hardly be overstated. Fully 1% of our own genes are thought to code for protein kinases. A single cell may have hundreds of different kinds, each with specificity for a different substrate protein.

Together, they probably regulate a large proportion of the thousands of proteins in a cell. Among these are most of the proteins that, in turn, regulate cell reproduction. Abnormal activity of such a kinase frequently causes abnormal cell growth and contributes to the development of cancer.

For a cell to respond normally to an extracellular signal, it must have mechanisms for turning off the signal-transduction pathway when the initial signal is no longer present. The effects of protein kinases are rapidly reversed in the cell by **protein phosphatases**, enzymes that remove phosphate groups from proteins. At any given moment, the activity of a

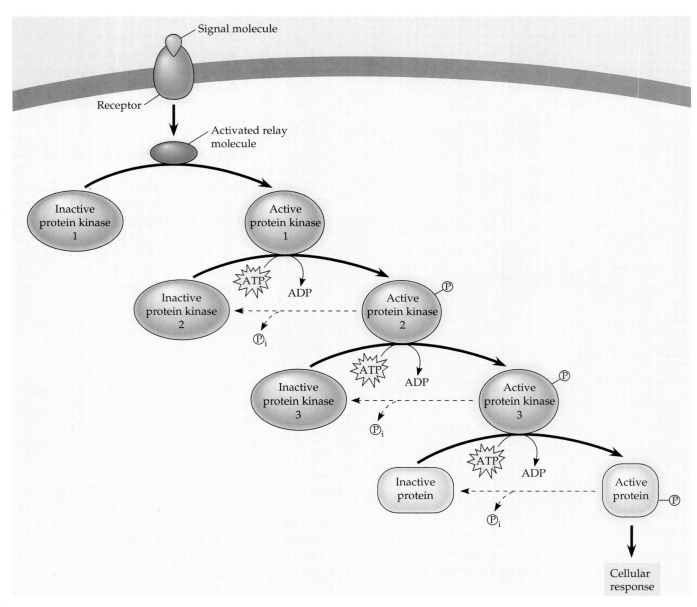

FIGURE 11.10 · A phosphorylation cascade.
11.3 This hypothetical signaling pathway begins when a signal molecule binds to a membrane receptor. The receptor then activates a relay molecule, which activates protein kinase 1. Active protein kinase 1 transfers a phosphate from ATP to an inactive molecule of protein kinase 2, thus activating this second kinase. In turn, active protein kinase 2 catalyzes the phosphorylation (and activation) of protein kinase 3. Finally, active protein kinase 3 phosphorylates a protein that brings about the cell's final response to the signal. The dashed arrows represent inactivation of the phosphorylated proteins, making them available for reuse; enzymes called phosphatases catalyze the removal of the phosphate groups. The active and inactive proteins are represented by different shapes to remind you that activation is usually associated with a change in molecular conformation.

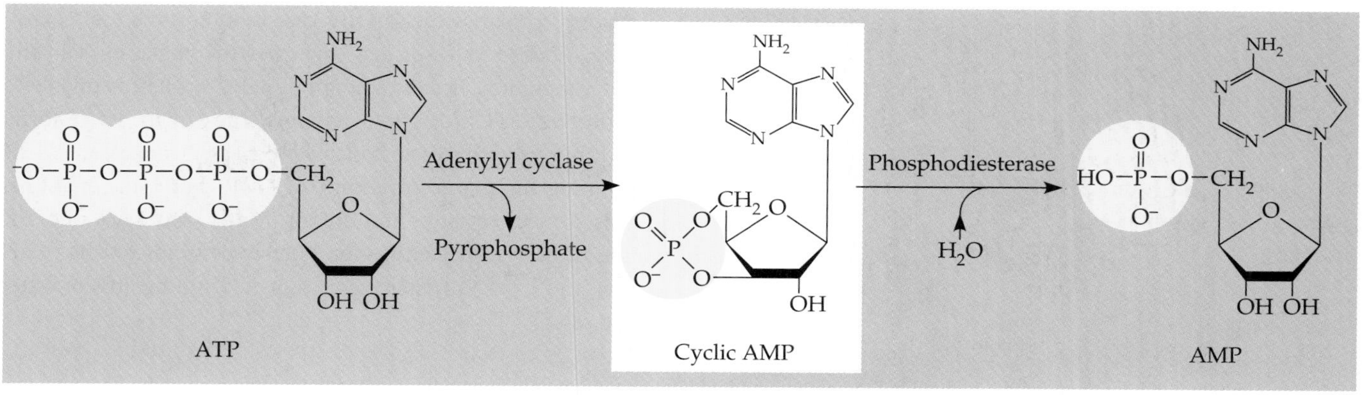

FIGURE 11.11 ▪ **Cyclic AMP.** Cyclic AMP (cAMP) is made from ATP by adenylyl cyclase, an enzyme embedded in the plasma membrane. The enzyme is activated as a consequence of binding of a signal molecule (such as the hormone epinephrine) to a membrane receptor. Cyclic AMP functions as a second messenger that relays the signal from the membrane to the metabolic machinery of the cytoplasm. Cyclic AMP is inactivated by phosphodiesterase, an enzyme that converts it to inactive AMP.

protein regulated by phosphorylation depends on the balance in the cell between active kinase and active phosphatase molecules. When the extracellular signal molecule is not present, active phosphatase molecules predominate, and the signaling pathway and cellular response shut down.

Certain small molecules and ions are key components of signaling pathways (second messengers)

11.3 Not all components of signal-transduction pathways are proteins. Many signaling pathways also involve small, nonprotein, water-soluble molecules or ions, called **second messengers**. (The extracellular signal molecule that binds to the membrane receptor is a pathway's "first messenger.") Because second messengers are both small and water-soluble, they can readily spread throughout the cell by diffusion. For example, as we'll see shortly, it is a second messenger called cyclic AMP that carries the signal initiated by epinephrine from the plasma membrane of a liver or muscle cell into the cell's interior, where it brings about glycogen breakdown. Second messengers participate in pathways initiated by both G-protein-linked receptors and tyrosine-kinase receptors. The two most widely used second messengers are cyclic AMP and calcium ions, Ca^{2+}. A large variety of relay proteins are sensitive to the cytosolic concentration of one or the other of these second messengers.

Cyclic AMP

Once Earl Sutherland had established that epinephrine somehow causes glycogen breakdown without passing through the plasma membrane, the search began for the second messenger (he coined the term) that transmits the signal from the plasma membrane to the metabolic machinery in the cytoplasm.

Sutherland found that the binding of epinephrine to the plasma membrane of a liver cell elevates the cytoplasmic concentration of a compound called cyclic adenosine monophosphate, abbreviated **cyclic AMP** or **cAMP** (FIGURE 11.11). An enzyme built into the plasma membrane, **adenylyl cyclase**, converts ATP to cAMP in response to an extracellular signal—in this case, epinephrine. Adenylyl cyclase becomes active only after epinephrine binds to a specific receptor protein. Thus the first messenger, the hormone, causes a membrane enzyme to synthesize cAMP, which broadcasts the signal to the cytoplasm. The cAMP does not persist for long in the absence of the hormone, because another enzyme converts the cAMP to an inactive product, AMP. Another surge of epinephrine is needed to boost the cytosolic concentration of cAMP again.

Subsequent research revealed that epinephrine is only one of many hormones and other signal molecules that trigger pathways involving cAMP. It also brought to light the other components of cAMP pathways, including G proteins, G-protein-linked receptors, and protein kinases (FIGURE 11.12 on page 198). The relay molecule immediately after cAMP in a signaling pathway is usually *protein kinase A,* a serine/threonine kinase. Cyclic AMP activates this kinase. The active kinase then phosphorylates various other proteins, depending on the cell. (The complete pathway for epinephrine's stimulation of glycogen breakdown is shown in FIGURE 11.15.)

Further fine-tuning of cell metabolism is provided by other G-protein systems that *inhibit* adenylyl cyclase. In these systems, a different signal molecule activates a different receptor, which activates an inhibitory G protein.

Now that we know about the role of cAMP in G-protein-signaling pathways, we can explain in molecular detail how certain microbes cause disease. Consider cholera, a disease that is frequently epidemic in places where the water supply is contaminated with human feces. People acquire the cholera bacterium, *Vibrio cholerae,* by drinking contaminated water. The bacteria colonize the lining of the small intestine and

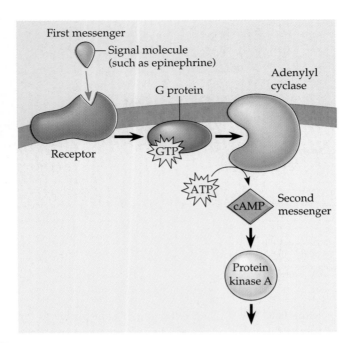

FIGURE 11.12 · cAMP as a second messenger. Cyclic AMP is a component of many G-protein-signaling pathways. The signal molecule—the "first messenger"—activates a G-protein-linked receptor, which activates a specific G protein. In turn, the G protein activates adenylyl cyclase, which catalyzes the conversion of ATP to cAMP. The cAMP then activates another protein, most often protein kinase A. The role of cAMP was discovered in research on a hormonal signal molecule, epinephrine.

produce a toxin, which in this case is an enzyme that chemically modifies a G protein involved in regulating salt and water secretion. Because the modified G protein is unable to hydrolyze GTP to GDP, it remains stuck in its active form, continuously stimulating adenylyl cyclase to make cAMP. The resulting high concentration of cAMP causes the intestinal cells to secrete large amounts of water and salts into the intestines. An infected person quickly develops profuse diarrhea and if left untreated can easily die from the loss of water and salts.

Calcium Ions and Inositol Trisphosphate

Many signal molecules in animals, including neurotransmitters, growth factors, and some hormones, induce responses in their target cells via signal-transduction pathways that increase the cytosolic concentration of calcium ions (Ca^{2+}). Calcium is even more widely used than cAMP as a second messenger. Increasing the cytosolic concentration of Ca^{2+} causes many responses in animal cells, including muscle cell contraction, secretion of certain substances, and cell division. In plant cells, calcium functions as a second messenger in signaling pathways plants have evolved for coping with environmental stresses, such as drought or cold. Cells use Ca^{2+} as a second messenger in both G-protein pathways and tyrosine-kinase receptor pathways.

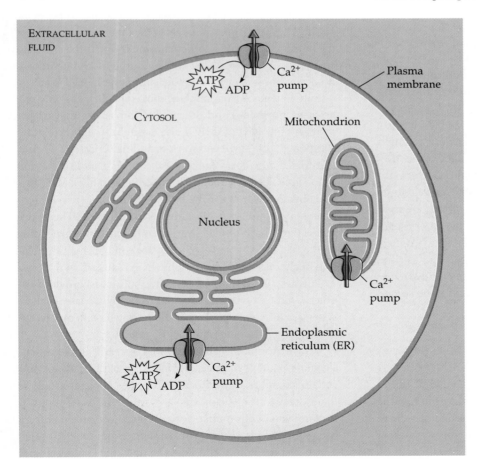

FIGURE 11.13 · Calcium ion concentrations in an animal cell. Calcium ions (Ca^{2+}) are actively transported out of the cytosol by a variety of protein pumps. Pumps in the plasma membrane move Ca^{2+} into the extracellular fluid, and ones in the ER membrane move Ca^{2+} into the lumen of the ER. Consequently, the Ca^{2+} concentration in the cytosol is usually much lower (light blue) than in the extracellular fluid and ER (darker blue). Additional Ca^{2+} pumps in the mitochondrial inner membrane operate when the calcium level in the cytosol rises significantly. These pumps are driven by the proton-motive force generated across the membrane by mitochondrial electron transport chains (see Chapter 9).

Although cells always contain some Ca^{2+}, this ion can function as a second messenger because its concentration in the cytosol is normally much lower than the concentration outside the cell. In fact, the level of Ca^{2+} in the blood and extracellular fluid of an animal often exceeds that in the cytosol by more than 10,000 times. Calcium ions are actively transported out of the cell and are actively imported from the cytosol into the endoplasmic reticulum (and, under some conditions, into mitochondria and chloroplasts). As a result, the calcium concentration in the ER is usually much higher than in the cytosol (FIGURE 11.13). Because the cytosolic calcium level is low, a small change in absolute numbers of ions represents a relatively large percentage change in calcium concentration.

In response to a signal relayed by a signal-transduction pathway, the cytosolic calcium level may rise, usually by a mechanism that releases Ca^{2+} from the cell's ER. The pathways leading to calcium release involve still other second messengers, **diacylglycerol (DAG)** and **inositol trisphosphate (IP_3)**. These two messengers are produced by cleavage of a certain kind of phospholipid in the plasma membrane. FIGURE 11.14 shows how this occurs and how IP_3 stimulates the release of calcium from the ER. Because IP_3 acts before calcium in the pathway, calcium could be considered a "*third* messenger." However, scientists use the term *second messenger* for all small, nonprotein components of signal-transduction pathways.

In some cases, calcium ions activate a signal-transduction protein directly, but often they function by means of **calmodulin**, a Ca^{2+}-binding protein present at high levels in eukaryotic cells (in an animal cell, for example, calmodulin may

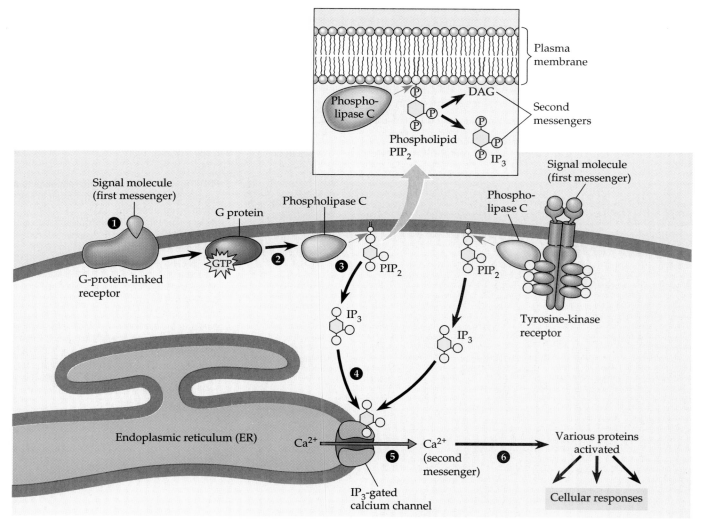

FIGURE 11.14 · **Calcium and inositol trisphosphate in signaling pathways.** Calcium ions (Ca^{2+}) and inositol trisphosphate (IP_3) function as second messengers in many signal-transduction pathways. The process is initiated by the binding of a signal molecule to either a G-protein-linked receptor (left) or a tyrosine-kinase receptor (right). The circled numbers trace the former pathway. ① A signal molecule binds to a receptor, leading to ② activation of an enzyme called phospholipase C. ③ This enzyme cleaves a plasma-membrane phospholipid called PIP_2 into DAG and IP_3 (inset). Both can function as second messengers. ④ IP_3, a small molecule, quickly diffuses through the cytosol and binds to a ligand-gated calcium channel in the ER membrane, causing it to open. ⑤ Calcium ions flow out of the ER (down their gradient), raising the Ca^{2+} level in the cytosol. ⑥ The calcium ions activate the next protein in one or more signaling pathways, often acting via calmodulin, a ubiquitous Ca^{2+}-binding protein. DAG functions as a second messenger in still other pathways.

represent as much as 1% of the total protein). Calmodulin mediates many calcium-regulated processes in cells. When calcium ions bind to it, calmodulin changes conformation and then binds to other proteins, activating or inactivating them. The proteins most often regulated by calmodulin are protein kinases and phosphatases—the most common relay proteins in signaling pathways.

CELLULAR RESPONSES TO SIGNALS

We now take a closer look at the cell's eventual response to an extracellular signal—what some researchers call the "output response." What is the nature of the final step in a signaling pathway?

In response to a signal, a cell may regulate activities in the cytoplasm or transcription in the nucleus

11.4 Ultimately, a signal-transduction pathway leads to the regulation of one or more cellular activities. The regulated activities may occur in the cytoplasm, such as a rearrangement of the cytoskeleton, the opening or closing of an ion channel in the plasma membrane, or some aspect of cell metabolism. As we have discussed already, the response of liver cells to signaling by the hormone epinephrine helps regulate cellular energy metabolism. The final step in the signaling pathway activates the enzyme that catalyzes the breakdown of glycogen. FIGURE 11.15 shows the complete pathway leading to the release of glucose-1-phosphate from glycogen.

Many other signaling pathways ultimately regulate not the *activity* of an enzyme but the *synthesis* of enzymes or other proteins, usually by turning specific genes on or off. Recall that the genes in a cell's DNA function by being transcribed into an RNA version called messenger RNA (mRNA), which leaves the nucleus and is translated into a specific protein by ribosomes in the cytoplasm (see FIGURE 5.26). Special proteins called *transcription factors* control which genes are turned on—that is, transcribed into mRNA—in a particular cell at a particular time. The activity of a transcription factor may itself be regulated by a signaling pathway that extends into the cell nucleus (FIGURE 11.16). All the different kinds of signal receptors and relay molecules introduced in this chapter participate in gene-regulating pathways, as well as in pathways leading to other kinds of responses. The molecular messengers that produce gene-regulation responses include growth factors and certain plant and animal hormones. Malfunctioning of growth-factor pathways like the one in FIGURE 11.16 can cause cancer, as we will see in Chapter 19.

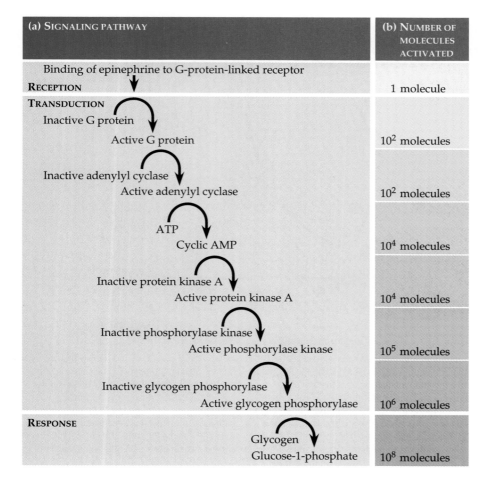

FIGURE 11.15 ▪ **Cytoplasmic response to a signal: The stimulation of glycogen breakdown by epinephrine.** **(a)** In this signaling system, the hormone epinephrine acts through a G-protein-linked receptor to activate a succession of relay molecules, including cAMP and two protein kinases. The final protein to be activated is the cytosolic enzyme glycogen phosphorylase, which releases glucose-1-phosphate units from glycogen. **(b)** As discussed in the next section of the text, this pathway *amplifies* the hormonal signal, because the receptor protein can activate many molecules of G protein, and each enzyme molecule in the pathway can act on many molecules of its substrate, the next molecule in the cascade. The number of activated molecules given for each step is only approximate.

(a) SIGNALING PATHWAY | **(b)** NUMBER OF MOLECULES ACTIVATED

Binding of epinephrine to G-protein-linked receptor
RECEPTION — 1 molecule
TRANSDUCTION
Inactive G protein
Active G protein — 10^2 molecules
Inactive adenylyl cyclase
Active adenylyl cyclase — 10^2 molecules
ATP
Cyclic AMP — 10^4 molecules
Inactive protein kinase A
Active protein kinase A — 10^4 molecules
Inactive phosphorylase kinase
Active phosphorylase kinase — 10^5 molecules
Inactive glycogen phosphorylase
Active glycogen phosphorylase — 10^6 molecules
RESPONSE
Glycogen
Glucose-1-phosphate — 10^8 molecules

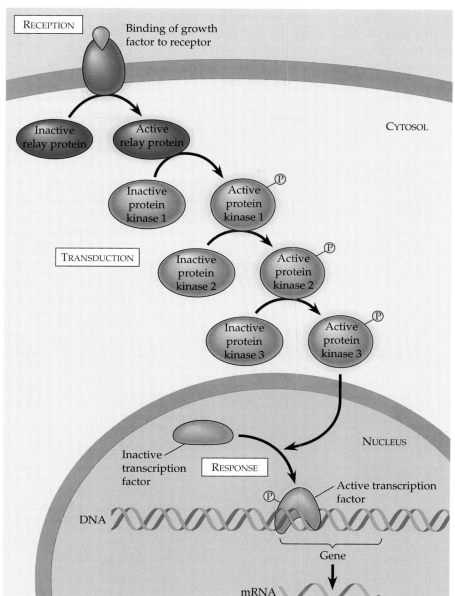

FIGURE 11.16 ▪ **Nuclear response to a signal: The activation of a specific gene by a growth factor.** This diagram is a simplified representation of a typical signaling pathway that leads to the regulation of gene activity in the cell nucleus. The initial signal molecule, a local regulator called a growth factor, triggers a phosphorylation cascade. The last kinase in the sequence enters the nucleus and there activates a gene-regulating protein, a transcription factor. This protein stimulates a specific gene to be transcribed into mRNA, which then directs the synthesis of a particular protein in the cytoplasm. Sometimes a transcription factor turns on several different genes.

Elaborate pathways amplify and specify the cell's response to signals

Why are there often so many steps between the original signaling event at the cell surface and the cell's response? As mentioned earlier, signaling pathways with a multiplicity of steps have two important benefits: They amplify the signal (and thus the response), and they contribute to the specificity of response.

Signal Amplification

Elaborate enzyme cascades amplify the cell's response to a signal. At each catalytic step in the cascade, the number of activated products is much greater than in the preceding step. For example, in the epinephrine-triggered pathway in FIGURE

11.15, each adenylyl cyclase molecule catalyzes the formation of many cAMP molecules, each molecule of protein kinase A phosphorylates many molecules of the next kinase in the pathway, and so on. The amplification effect depends on the fact that these proteins persist in active form long enough to process numerous molecules of substrate before they become inactive again. As a result of the signal's amplification, a small number of epinephrine molecules binding to receptors on the surface of a liver cell or skeletal muscle cell can lead to the release of hundreds of millions of glucose molecules from glycogen.

The Specificity of Cell Signaling

Consider two different cells in your body—a liver cell and a heart muscle cell, for example. Both are in contact with your

bloodstream and are therefore constantly exposed to many different hormone molecules, as well as to local regulators secreted by nearby cells. Yet the liver cell responds to some signals but ignores others, and the same is true for the heart cell. And some kinds of signals trigger responses in both cells—but different responses. For instance, epinephrine stimulates the liver cell to break down glycogen, but the main response of the heart cell to epinephrine is contraction, leading to a more rapid heartbeat. How do we account for this difference?

The explanation for the specificity exhibited in cellular responses to signals is the same as the basic explanation for virtually all differences between cells: *Different kinds of cells have different collections of proteins* (FIGURE 11.17). The response of a particular cell to a signal depends on its particular collection of signal receptor proteins, relay proteins, and proteins needed to carry out the response. A liver cell, for

example, is poised to respond appropriately to epinephrine by having the proteins shown in FIGURE 11.15, as well as those needed to manufacture glycogen.

Thus two cells that respond differently to the same signal differ in one or more of the proteins that handle and respond to the signal. Notice in FIGURE 11.17 that pathways may have some molecules in common. For example, cells A, B, and C all use the same receptor protein for the triangular signal molecule; differences in other proteins account for their differing responses. Also note that in cell B, a pathway triggered by a single kind of signal diverges to produce two responses, and that in cell C, two pathways triggered by separate signals converge to modulate a single response. Branching of pathways and "cross-talk" between pathways are important in regulating and coordinating a cell's responses to incoming information. Moreover, the use of some of the same proteins in more

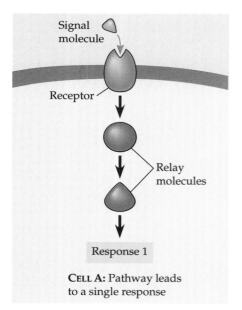

CELL A: Pathway leads to a single response

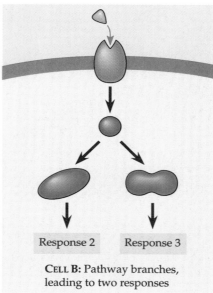

CELL B: Pathway branches, leading to two responses

FIGURE 11.17 · The specificity of cell signaling. The particular proteins a cell possesses determine what signal molecules it responds to and the nature of the response. All four cells in these simplified diagrams respond to the signal molecule represented by the orange triangle, but in different ways, because each has a different set of proteins. Note, however, that the same kinds of molecules can participate in more than one pathway; for example, cells A, B, and C have identical receptors for the orange triangle. Cell B has a branched pathway, as is found especially often in pathways that use tyrosine-kinase receptors (which can activate multiple relay proteins) or second messengers (which can regulate numerous proteins). Cell C exhibits cross-talk between two pathways, enabling the cell to integrate information from two different signals. Cell D has a receptor for the orange triangle that differs from the ones in cells A, B, and C.

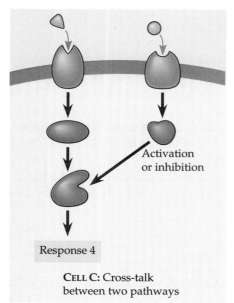

CELL C: Cross-talk between two pathways

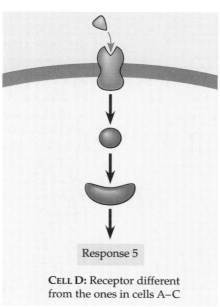

CELL D: Receptor different from the ones in cells A–C

than one pathway allows the cell to economize on the number of different proteins it must make.

The importance of the relay proteins that serve as points of branching or intersection in signaling pathways is highlighted by the problems arising when these proteins are defective or missing. For instance, in an inherited disorder called Wiskott-Aldrich syndrome (WAS), the absence of a single relay protein leads to such diverse effects as abnormal bleeding, eczema, and a predisposition to infections and leukemia. These symptoms are thought to arise primarily from the absence of the protein in cells of the immune system. By studying normal cells, scientists found that the WAS protein is located just beneath the cell surface. The protein interacts both with microfilaments of the cytoskeleton and with several different components of signaling pathways that relay information from the cell surface, including pathways regulating immune-cell proliferation. This multifunctional relay protein is thus both a branch point and an important intersection point in a complex signal transduction network that controls immune-cell behavior. When the WAS protein is absent, the cytoskeleton is not properly organized and signaling pathways are disrupted, leading to the WAS symptoms.

To keep FIGURE 11.17 simple, we have not indicated the *inactivation* mechanisms that are an essential aspect of cell signaling. For a cell of a multicellular organism to remain alert and capable of responding to incoming signals, each molecular change in its signaling pathways must last only a short time. As we saw in the cholera example, if a signaling pathway component becomes locked into one state, whether active or inactive, dire consequences for the organism can result.

Thus a key to a cell's continuing receptiveness to regulation is the reversibility of the changes that signals produce. The binding of signal molecules to receptors is reversible, which means that the lower the concentration of signal molecules, the fewer will be bound at any given moment. When they leave the receptor, the receptor reverts to its inactive form. Then, by a variety of means, the relay molecules return to their inactive forms: The GTPase activity intrinsic to a G protein hydrolyzes its bound GTP; the enzyme phosphodiesterase converts cAMP to AMP; protein phosphatases inactivate phosphorylated kinases and other proteins; and so forth. As a result, the cell is soon ready to respond to a fresh signal.

■   ■   ■

This chapter has introduced you to a number of details of cellular signal processing. More important than the details, however, are the general mechanisms of cell communication—mechanisms involving ligand binding, conformational changes in proteins, interactions among proteins, cascades of interactions that transduce and amplify signals, and protein phosphorylations by kinases. As you continue through the text, you will encounter numerous examples of cell signaling. In the very next chapter, in fact, you'll learn about the enormously important role of cell signaling in the regulation of cell reproduction.

CHAPTER REVIEW

REVIEW OF KEY CONCEPTS

(with page numbers and key figures)

AN OVERVIEW OF CELL SIGNALING

- **Cell signaling evolved early in the history of life (pp. 188–189, FIGURES 11.1, 11.2)** Cell signaling in microorganisms has much in common with the process that goes on in multicellular organisms, indicating that the sending and receiving of signals arose early in the history of life. This chapter concentrates on chemical signaling between cells.

- **Communicating cells may be close together or far apart (pp. 189–190, FIGURES 11.3, 11.4)** Animal cells communicate with nearby cells by secreting local regulators or, if nerve cells, by secreting neurotransmitters at synapses. Both animal and plant cells use hormones for signaling over long distances. Cells can also communicate by direct contact—for example, in plant cells via plasmodesmata or in animal cells via gap junctions.

- **The three stages of cell signaling are reception, transduction, and response (pp. 190–191, FIGURE 11.5)** The pioneering research of Earl Sutherland focused on the effect of the hormone epinephrine on liver and skeletal muscle cells. In this system, the signal molecule epinephrine binds to specific receptors on a cell's surface (reception), leading to a series of changes in the receptor and other molecules inside the cell (transduction, the change in signal form), and finally to the activation of an enzyme that breaks down glycogen to glucose-1-phosphate (response).

SIGNAL RECEPTION AND THE INITIATION OF TRANSDUCTION

- **A signal molecule binds to a receptor protein, causing the protein to change shape (p. 192).** The binding between signal molecule (ligand) and receptor is highly specific. A conformational change in a receptor is often the initial transduction of the signal.

- **Most signal receptors are plasma-membrane proteins (pp. 192–195, FIGURES 11.6, 11.8, 11.9)** A G-protein-linked receptor is a membrane receptor that works with the help of a cytoplasmic G protein. Ligand binding activates the cytoplasmic side of the receptor, which then activates a specific G protein by causing it to exchange a bound GDP for a GTP. Until the G protein inactivates itself by hydrolyzing its GTP to GDP, it can activate yet another protein in a signal-transduction pathway. Epinephrine uses this sort of receptor.

Membrane receptors called tyrosine-kinase receptors react to the binding of signal molecules by forming dimers and then using an intrinsic enzyme to add phosphate groups to tyrosines on the cytoplasmic side of the receptor. A variety of relay proteins inside the cell can then be activated by binding to different phosphorylated tyrosines, allowing this receptor to trigger several different pathways simultaneously. Growth factors are a type of signal molecule that

commonly uses tyrosine-kinase receptors. Specific signal molecules cause ligand-gated ion channels in a membrane to open or close, regulating the flow of specific ions across the membrane. Such channels are important at nerve cell synapses. Intracellular receptors are cytoplasmic or nuclear proteins. Signal molecules that can readily penetrate the plasma membrane, such as lipid hormones and the gas nitric oxide, use these receptors.

SIGNAL-TRANSDUCTION PATHWAYS

- **Pathways relay signals from receptors to cellular responses (p. 195)** At each step in a signal-transduction pathway, the signal is transduced into a different form, commonly a conformational change in a protein.

Protein phosphorylation, a common mode of regulation in cells,
11.3 is a major mechanism of signal transduction (pp. 195–197, FIGURE 11.10) Many signal-transduction pathways include phosphorylation cascades, in which a series of protein kinases successively add phosphate groups to the next one in line, activating it. Phosphatase enzymes soon remove the phosphates, keeping the pathway open for a new signal.

Certain small molecules and ions are key components of signaling
11.3 pathways (second messengers) (pp. 197–200, FIGURES 11.11–11.14) Second messengers, such as cyclic AMP (cAMP) and Ca^{2+}, diffuse readily through the cytosol and thus help broadcast signals throughout the cell quickly. Many G proteins, including the one operating in the epinephrine signal-transduction pathway, activate adenylyl cyclase, which makes cAMP from ATP. Although continually present in the fluids of organisms, Ca^{2+} can serve as a messenger because protein pumps usually keep it at low concentrations in the cytosol. Many G proteins and tyrosine-kinase receptors activate an enzyme that splits a plasma-membrane phospholipid into two second messengers, one of which is inositol trisphosphate (IP_3). IP_3 is the ligand for a gated calcium channel in the membrane of the ER, which stores Ca^{2+} at high concentrations. When IP_3 binds, Ca^{2+} flows into the cytosol, where it activates proteins of many signaling pathways, often via the protein calmodulin.

CELLULAR RESPONSES TO SIGNALS

In response to a signal, a cell may regulate activities in the cyto-
11.4 plasm or transcription in the nucleus (p. 200, FIGURES 11.15, 11.16) For example, signaling pathways regulate enzyme activity (such as the enzyme that breaks down glycogen) and cytoskeleton rearrangement in the cytoplasm. Other pathways regulate genes; they do this by activating transcription factors, proteins that turn on specific genes.

Elaborate pathways amplify and specify the cell's response to sig-
11.5 nals (pp. 201–203, FIGURE 11.17) Each catalytic protein in a signaling pathway amplifies the signal by activating multiple copies of the next component of the pathway; for long pathways, the total amplification may be a millionfold or more. The particular combination of proteins in a cell gives the cell great specificity in both the signals it detects and the responses it carries out. Pathway branching and cross-talk further help the cell coordinate the signals received and the responses produced.

SELF-QUIZ

1. Phosphorylation cascades involving a series of protein kinases are useful for cellular signal transduction because
   a. they are species specific
   b. they always lead to the same cellular response
   c. they amplify the original signal many fold
   d. they counter the harmful effects of phosphatases
   e. the number of molecules used is small and fixed

2. Binding of a signal molecule to which type of receptor leads to a change in membrane potential?
   a. tyrosine-kinase receptor
   b. G-protein-linked receptor
   c. phosphorylated tyrosine-kinase dimer
   d. ligand-gated ion channel
   e. intracellular receptor

3. The activation of tyrosine-kinase receptors is characterized by
   a. aggregation and phosphorylation
   b. IP_3 binding
   c. calmodulin formation
   d. GTP hydrolysis
   e. channel protein conformational change

4. Cell signaling is believed to have evolved early in the history of life because
   a. it is seen in "primitive" organisms such as bacteria
   b. yeast cells of different mating types signal one another
   c. signal-transduction molecules found in distantly related organisms are similar
   d. signaling can operate over large distances, a function required before the development of multicellular life
   e. signal molecules typically interact with the outer surface of the plasma membrane

5. Which observation suggested to Sutherland the involvement of a second messenger in epinephrine's effect on liver cells?
   a. Enzymatic activity was proportional to the amount of calcium added to a cell-free extract.
   b. Receptor studies indicated epinephrine was a ligand.
   c. Glycogen depolymerization was observed only when epinephrine was administered to intact cells.
   d. Glycogen depolymerization was observed when epinephrine and glycogen phosphorylase were combined.
   e. Epinephrine was known to have different effects on different types of cells.

6. Protein phosphorylation is commonly involved with all of the following *except*
   a. regulation of transcription by extracellular signal molecules
   b. enzyme activation
   c. activation of G-protein-linked receptors
   d. activation of tyrosine-kinase receptors
   e. activation of protein-kinase relay molecules

7. Amplification of a chemical signal occurs when
   a. a receptor in the plasma membrane activates several G-protein molecules while a signal molecule is bound to it
   b. a cAMP molecule activates one protein-kinase molecule before being converted to AMP
   c. phosphorylase and phosphatase activities are balanced
   d. numerous calcium ions flow through an open ligand-gated calcium channel
   e. both a and d occur

8. Lipid-soluble signal molecules, such as testosterone, cross the plasma membranes of all cells but affect only their target cells because
   a. only target cells retain the appropriate DNA segments
   b. intracellular receptors are present only in target cells
   c. most cells lack the *Y* chromosome required
   d. only target cells possess the cytosolic enzymes that transduce the testosterone
   e. only in target cells is testosterone able to initiate the phosphorylation cascade leading to activated transcription factor

9. Signal-transduction pathways benefit cells for all of the following reasons *except*
   a. they help cells respond to signal molecules that are too large or too polar to cross the plasma membrane
   b. they enable different cells to respond appropriately to the same signal
   c. they help cells use up phosphate generated by ATP breakdown
   d. they can amplify a signal
   e. variations in the signal-transduction pathways can enhance response specificity

10. Consider this pathway: epinephrine $\longrightarrow$ G-protein-linked receptor $\longrightarrow$ G protein $\longrightarrow$ adenylyl cyclase $\longrightarrow$ cAMP. Identify the "second messenger."
    a. cAMP
    b. G protein
    c. GTP
    d. adenylyl cyclase
    e. G-protein-linked receptor

CHALLENGE QUESTIONS

1. Cell biologists recently reported the discovery of orexin, a signaling molecule that appears to regulate appetite in humans and other mammals. Orexin concentrations were measurably higher in fasting individuals. Using your knowledge of membrane receptors and signal-transduction pathways, suggest ways in which the understanding of orexin function could lead to treatments for both anorexia and obesity.

2. Explain how the same chemical signal, such as a particular hormone, can have one effect on cell-type A, a different effect on cell-type B, and no effect on cell-type C.

SCIENCE, TECHNOLOGY, AND SOCIETY

A patient with severe epilepsy has recently received an injection of fetal pig cells into the brain. Physicians hope these cells will integrate with the patient's brain cells and eventually produce enough GABA, a signaling molecule, to prevent seizures. The recipient was enthusiastic about the transplant, but medical ethicists were less so, because the long-term effects of this treatment are unknown. In addition, undetected viruses present in the transplanted cells might infect the recipient. Should individuals with severely debilitating or terminal diseases be permitted to receive experimental treatments before they are known to be safe? Develop arguments both for and against such experimental procedures.

FURTHER READING

Alberts, B., et al. *Essential Cell Biology.* New York: Garland, 1998. See Chapter 15. Additional information is available in Chapter 15 of *Molecular Biology of the Cell,* 3rd ed (1994), the much larger book by the same authors.

Becker, W. M., J. B. Reece, and M. F. Poenie. *The World of the Cell,* 3rd ed. Menlo Park, CA: Benjamin/Cummings, 1996. Chapter 23 focuses on chemical signaling.

Bourne, H. R. "Pieces of the True Grail: A G Protein Finds Its Target." *Science,* December 12, 1997. Exactly how certain G proteins interact with adenylyl cyclase.

Cossart, P., P. Boquet, S. Normark, and R. Rappuoli. "Cellular Microbiology Emerging." *Science,* January 19, 1996. How pathogenic bacteria interfere with host-cell signaling pathways and other cell functions, and the use of these pathogens as tools for basic research.

Featherstone, C. "The Many Faces of WAS Protein." *Science,* January 3, 1997. More about the protein that is missing in people with Wiskott-Aldrich syndrome.

Harbron, P. "Conversation in a Cell." *Discover,* February 1996. Stuart Schreiber's research on cell signaling, which began with an investigation of the sex attractant of cockroaches.

Linder, E., and A. Gilman. "G Proteins." *Scientific American,* July 1992. Signal-transduction pathways in the actions of hormones.

Losick, R., and D. Kaiser. "Why and How Bacteria Communicate." *Scientific American,* February 1997. Bacteria "talk" with one another and with plants and animals by emitting and reacting to chemical signals.

Marx, J. "Medicine: A Signal Contribution to Cell Biology." *Science,* October 23, 1992. The Nobel Prize awarded for pioneering work on protein kinases and phosphatases. Also "Medicine: A Signal Award for Discovering G Proteins." *Science,* October 21, 1994. The Nobel Prize awarded for the discovery of G proteins.

WEB LINKS

Visit the special edition of *The Biology Place* for BIOLOGY, Fifth Edition, at http://www.biology.com/campbell. Go to Chapter 11 for online resources, including learning activities, practice exams, and links to the following web sites:

"Yeast (Budding, Fission and Candida)"
A compendium of resources about the yeasts used as model organisms in biological research.

"The G-Protein-Coupled Receptor Database"
Anything you ever wanted to know about G-protein-linked receptors can be found at this site.

"The Dictionary of Cell Biology"
An on-line dictionary of cell biology that defines over 6000 terms.

"The Virtual Cell"
Climb inside this virtual cell and explore its parts.

THE CELL CYCLE

Photograph courtesy of J. M. Murray, University of Pennsylvania Medical School.

*T*he ability of organisms to reproduce their kind is the one characteristic that best distinguishes living things from nonliving matter. This unique capacity to procreate, like all biological functions, has a cellular basis. Rudolf Virchow, a German physician, put it this way in 1855: "Where a cell exists, there must have been a preexisting cell, just as the animal arises only from an animal and the plant only from a plant." He summarized with the Latin axiom, "Omnis cellula e cellula," meaning "Every cell from a cell." The continuity of life is based on the reproduction of cells, or **cell division**. The micrograph on this page shows a cell dividing; only the chromosomes (yellow) and microtubules (red) are visible.

In this chapter you will learn how cells reproduce to form genetically equivalent daughter cells.* This process is an integral part of the **cell cycle**, the life of a cell from its origin in the division of a parent cell until its own division into two.

THE KEY ROLES OF CELL DIVISION

Before describing the cell cycle or the mechanics of cell division, let's look at the roles that cellular reproduction plays in the lives of organisms.

Cell division functions in reproduction, growth, and repair

When a unicellular organism such as *Amoeba* divides to form duplicate offspring, the division of a cell reproduces an entire organism (FIGURE 12.1a). But cell division also enables multicellular organisms, including humans, to grow and develop from a single cell—the fertilized egg (FIGURE 12.1b). Even after the organism is fully grown, cell division continues to function in renewal and repair, replacing cells that die from normal wear and tear or accidents. For example, dividing cells in your bone marrow continuously supply new blood cells (FIGURE 12.1c).

The reproduction of an ensemble as complex as a cell cannot occur by a mere pinching in half; the cell is not like a soap bubble that simply enlarges and splits in two. Cell division involves the distribution of identical genetic material—DNA—to two daughter cells. What is most remarkable about cell division is the fidelity with which the DNA is passed along, without dilution, from one generation of cells to the next. A dividing cell duplicates its DNA, allocates the two copies to opposite ends of the cell, and only then splits into two daughter cells.

---

* Although the terms *daughter cells* and *sister chromatids* (a term you will encounter later in the chapter) are traditional and will be used throughout this book, the structures they refer to have no gender.

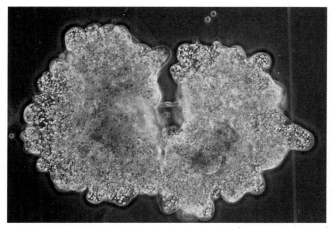

(a) Reproduction

100 μm

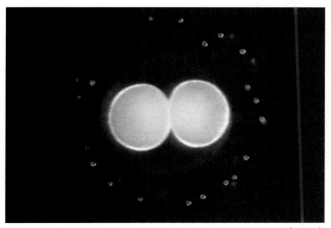

(b) Growth and development

100 μm

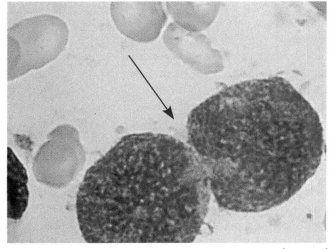

(c) Tissue renewal

10 μm

FIGURE 12.1 ▪ **The functions of cell division. (a)** *Amoeba,* a single-celled eukaryote, divides to form two cells, each an individual organism. In this case, the function of cell division is reproduction. **(b)** For multicellular organisms, the division of embryonic cells is essential for growth and development. This darkfield micrograph shows a sand dollar embryo shortly after the fertilized egg divided to form two cells. **(c)** Even in a mature multicellular organism, cell division continues to function in the renewal and repair of tissues. For example, these dividing bone marrow cells (arrow) give rise to new blood cells. (All LMs.)

Cell division distributes identical sets of chromosomes to daughter cells

A cell's total hereditary endowment of DNA is called its **genome.** Although a prokaryotic genome is often a single long DNA molecule, eukaryotic genomes usually consist of several such molecules. The overall length of DNA in a eukaryotic cell is enormous. A typical human cell, for example, has about 3 meters of DNA—a length about 300,000 times greater than the cell's diameter. Yet before the cell can divide, all of this DNA must be copied and then apportioned to give each daughter cell a complete genome.

The replication and distribution of so much DNA is manageable because the DNA molecules are packaged into chromosomes (FIGURE 12.2). Every eukaryotic species has a

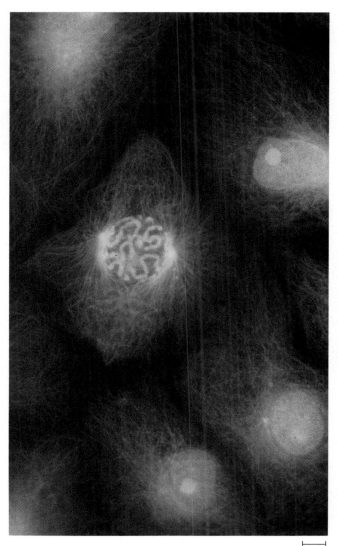

25 μm

FIGURE 12.2 ▪ **Eukaryotic chromosomes.** A tangle of chromosomes (orange) is visible within the nucleus of the kangaroo rat epithelial cell in the center of this micrograph. The cell is preparing to divide (LM). Chromosomes are so named because they take up certain dyes used in microscopy (*chromo,* "colored," and *somes,* "bodies").

Photo courtesy of J. M. Murray, University of Pennsylvania Medical School.

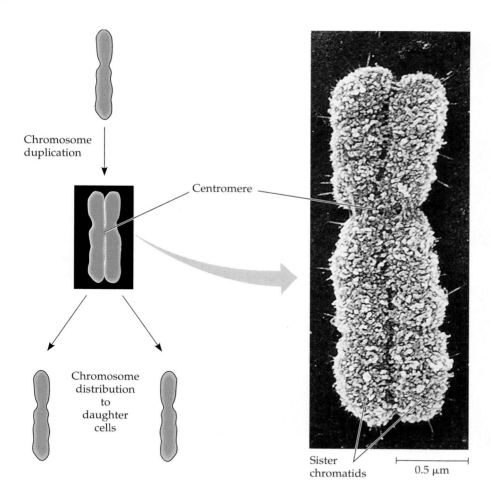

Chromosome
duplication

Centromere

Chromosome
distribution
to
daughter
cells

Sister
chromatids

0.5 μm

FIGURE 12.3 · Chromosome duplication and distribution during mitosis. A eukaryotic cell preparing to divide duplicates each of its multiple chromosomes, one of which is represented here. A duplicated chromosome consists of two sister chromatids, which narrow at their centromeres. The micrograph shows a human chromosome in this state (SEM). The chromosome looks hairy because each chromatid consists of a very long chromatin fiber folded and coiled in a compact arrangement. Each chromatin fiber, in turn, consists of one long DNA molecule associated with a variety of protein molecules. The DNA molecules of the sister chromatids are identical, products of a precise replication process. As mitosis continues, mechanical processes separate the sister chromatids and distribute them to two daughter cells.

characteristic number of chromosomes in each cell nucleus. For example, human **somatic cells** (all body cells except the reproductive cells) contain 46 chromosomes. Reproductive cells, or **gametes**—sperm cells and egg cells—have half as many chromosomes as somatic cells, or 23 chromosomes in humans.

Incorporated into each eukaryotic chromosome is one very long, linear DNA molecule representing thousands of genes, the units that specify an organism's inherited traits. The DNA is associated with various proteins that maintain the structure of the chromosome and help control the activity of the genes. The DNA-protein complex, called **chromatin**, is organized into a long, thin fiber. After a cell duplicates its genome in preparation for division, the chromatin condenses: It becomes densely coiled and folded, making the chromosomes so thick that we can see them with a light microscope.

Each duplicated chromosome consists of two **sister chromatids**. The two chromatids, containing identical copies of the chromosome's DNA molecule, are initially attached along their lengths. In its condensed form, the chromosome has a narrow "waist" at a specialized region called the **centromere** (FIGURE 12.3). Later in the cell division process, the sister chromatids of all the chromosomes are pulled apart and repackaged as complete chromosome sets in two new nuclei, one at

each end of the cell. **Mitosis**, the division of the nucleus, is usually followed immediately by **cytokinesis**, the division of the cytoplasm. Where there was one cell, there are now two, each the genetic equivalent of the parent cell.

What happens to chromosome number as we follow the human life cycle through the generations? You inherited 46 chromosomes, 23 from each parent. They were combined in the nucleus of a single cell when a sperm cell from your father united with an egg cell from your mother to form a fertilized egg, or zygote. Mitosis and cytokinesis produced the trillions of somatic cells that now make up your body, and the same processes continue to generate new cells to replace dead and damaged ones. In contrast, your gametes—eggs or sperm cells—are produced by a variation of cell division called **meiosis**, which yields daughter cells that have half as many chromosomes as the parent cell. Meiosis occurs only in your gonads (ovaries or testes). In each generation of humans, meiosis reduces the chromosome number from 46 to 23. Fertilization joins gametes and doubles the chromosome number to 46 again, and mitosis conserves that number in every somatic cell of the new individual. In Chapter 13 we will examine the role of meiosis in reproduction and inheritance in more detail. In the remainder of this chapter we focus on mitosis and the rest of the mitotic cell cycle.

THE MITOTIC CELL CYCLE

The mitotic phase alternates with interphase in the cell cycle: *an overview*

12.1 Mitosis is just one part of the cell cycle (FIGURE 12.4). In fact, the **mitotic (M) phase**, which includes both mitosis and cytokinesis, is usually the shortest part of the cell cycle. Successive mitotic cell divisions alternate with a much longer **interphase**, which often accounts for about 90% of the cycle. It is during interphase that the cell grows and copies its chromosomes in preparation for cell division. Interphase can be divided into subphases: **G_1 phase** ("first gap"), **S phase**, and **G_2 phase** ("second gap"). During all three subphases, the cell grows by producing proteins and cytoplasmic organelles. However, chromosomes are duplicated only during the S phase (S stands for synthesis of DNA). Thus a cell grows (G_1), continues to grow as it copies its chromosomes (S), grows more as it completes preparations for cell division (G_2), and divides (M). The daughter cells may then repeat the cycle.

12.2 Time-lapse films of living, dividing cells reveal the dynamics of mitosis as a continuum of changes. For purposes of description, however, mitosis is conventionally broken down into five subphases: **prophase, prometaphase, metaphase, anaphase**, and **telophase**. FIGURE 12.5 on the following pages **12.3** describes these stages in an animal cell. Be sure to study this figure thoroughly before progressing to the next section, which examines mitosis more closely.

The mitotic spindle distributes chromosomes to daughter cells: *a closer look*

Many of the events of mitosis depend on the **mitotic spindle**, which begins to form in the cytoplasm during prophase. This structure consists of fibers made of microtubules and associated proteins. While the mitotic spindle assembles, the microtubules of the cytoskeleton partially disassemble, probably providing the material used to construct the spindle. The spindle microtubules elongate by incorporating more subunits of the protein tubulin (see TABLE 7.2, p. 120).

The assembly of spindle microtubules starts in the centrosome, also called the microtubule organizing center. In animal cells, a pair of centrioles is located at the center of the centrosome, but these structures are not essential for cell division. In fact, the centrosomes of most plants lack centrioles, and if a researcher destroys the centrioles of an animal cell with a laser microbeam, a spindle nevertheless forms during mitosis.

During interphase, the single centrosome replicates to form two centrosomes located just outside the nucleus (see FIGURE 12.5). The two centrosomes move farther apart during prophase and prometaphase, as spindle microtubules grow out from them. By the end of prometaphase, the two centrosomes, referred to as *spindle poles* in this context, are at opposite poles of the cell.

Each of the two joined chromatids of a chromosome has a **kinetochore**, a structure of proteins and specific sections of chromosomal DNA at the centromere. The chromosome's two kinetochores face in opposite directions. During prometaphase, some of the spindle microtubules attach to kinetochores. When one of a chromosome's kinetochores is

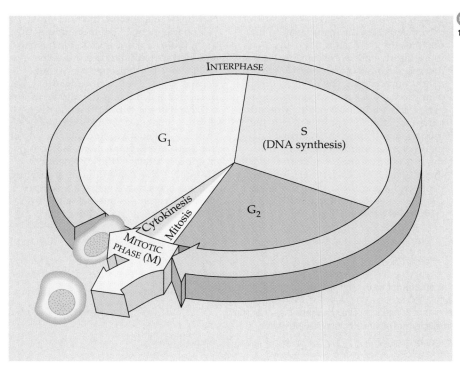

FIGURE 12.4 · The cell cycle. In a dividing **12.1** cell, the mitotic (M) phase alternates with interphase, a growth period. The first part of interphase, called G_1, is followed by the S phase, when the chromosomes replicate; the last part of interphase is called G_2. In the M phase, mitosis divides the nucleus and distributes its chromosomes to the daughter nuclei, and cytokinesis divides the cytoplasm, producing two daughter cells.

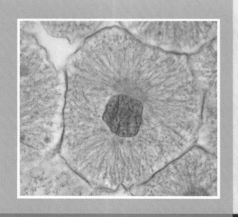
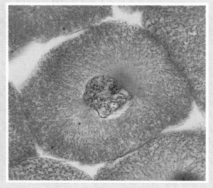
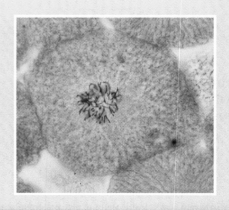

| G₂ OF INTERPHASE | PROPHASE | PROMETAPHASE |

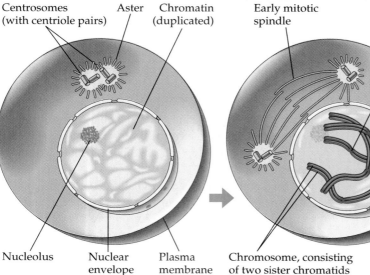

Centrosomes (with centriole pairs)   Aster   Chromatin (duplicated)

Nucleolus   Nuclear envelope   Plasma membrane

Early mitotic spindle   Centromere

Chromosome, consisting of two sister chromatids

Fragments of nuclear envelope   Kinetochore   Nonkinetochore microtubules

Spindle pole   Kinetochore microtubule

During late interphase, the nucleus is well defined and bounded by the nuclear envelope. It contains one or more nucleoli. Just outside the nucleus are two centrosomes, formed earlier by replication of a single centrosome. In animal cells, each centrosome features a pair of centrioles. Microtubules extend from the centrosomes in radial arrays called **asters** ("stars"). The chromosomes have already duplicated (during the S phase), but at this stage they cannot be distinguished individually because they are still in the form of loosely packed chromatin fibers.

During prophase, changes occur in both the nucleus and the cytoplasm. In the nucleus, the chromatin fibers become more tightly coiled, condensing into discrete chromosomes observable with a light microscope. The nucleoli disappear. Each duplicated chromosome appears as two identical sister chromatids joined together. In the cytoplasm, the mitotic spindle begins to form; it is made of microtubules radiating from the two centrosomes. The centrosomes move away from each other, apparently propelled along the surface of the nucleus by the lengthening bundles of microtubules between them.

During prometaphase, the nuclear envelope fragments. The microtubules of the spindle can now invade the nucleus and interact with the chromosomes, which have become even more condensed. Bundles of microtubules extend from each pole toward the middle of the cell. Each of the two chromatids of a chromosome now has a specialized structure called a **kinetochore,** located at the centromere region. Some of the microtubules attach to the kinetochores. This interaction causes the chromosomes to begin jerky movements. Nonkinetochore microtubules interact with those from the opposite pole of the cell.

 FIGURE 12.5 · The stages of mitotic cell division in an animal cell. The light micrographs, similar to
12.2 slides you are likely to see in lab, show dividing cells from a fish embryo. (In plant cells, centrioles are lacking
12.3 and cytokinesis occurs by a different mechanism; see FIGURES 12.8b and 12.9.) The schematic drawings show
details not visible in the micrographs. For the sake of simplicity, only four chromosomes are drawn.

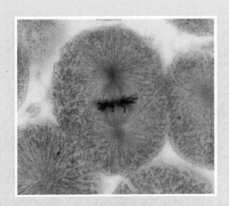

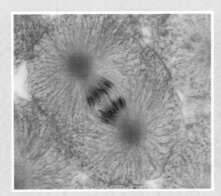

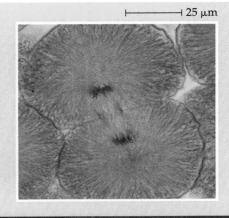

METAPHASE | **ANAPHASE** | **TELOPHASE AND CYTOKINESIS**

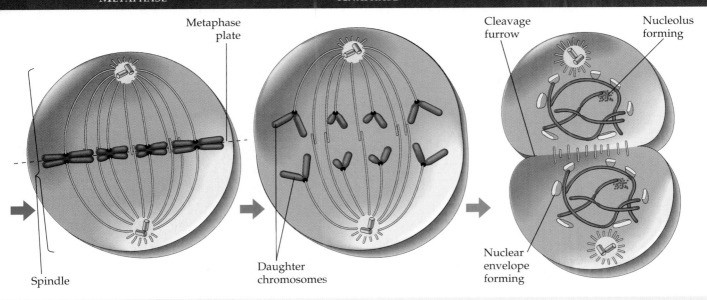

25 μm

Metaphase plate

Spindle

Daughter chromosomes

Cleavage furrow

Nucleolus forming

Nuclear envelope forming

The centrosomes are now at opposite poles of the cell. The chromosomes convene on the **metaphase plate,** an imaginary plane that is equidistant between the spindle's two poles. The centromeres of all the chromosomes are aligned with one another, and the sister chromatids of each chromosome straddle the metaphase plate. For each chromosome, the kinetochores of the sister chromatids are attached to microtubules coming from opposite poles of the cell. The entire apparatus of microtubules is called the spindle because of its shape.

Anaphase begins when the paired centromeres of each chromosome separate, finally liberating the sister chromatids from each other. Each chromatid is now considered a full-fledged chromosome. The once-joined sisters begin moving toward opposite poles of the cell, as their kinetochore microtubules shorten. Because the kinetochore microtubules are attached at the centromere, the chromosomes move centromere first (their pace is about 1 μm/min). At the same time, the poles of the cell move farther apart, as the nonkinetochore microtubules lengthen. By the end of anaphase, the two poles of the cell have equivalent—and complete—collections of chromosomes.

At telophase, the nonkinetochore microtubules elongate the cell still more, and daughter nuclei form at the two poles of the cell. Nuclear envelopes arise from the fragments of the parent cell's nuclear envelope and other portions of the endomembrane system. In a further reversal of prophase and prometaphase events, the chromatin fiber of each chromosome becomes less tightly coiled. Mitosis, the equal division of one nucleus into two genetically identical nuclei, is now complete. Cytokinesis, the division of the cytoplasm, is usually well under way by this time, so the appearance of two separate daughter cells follows shortly after the end of mitosis. In animal cells, cytokinesis involves the formation of a cleavage furrow, which pinches the cell in two.

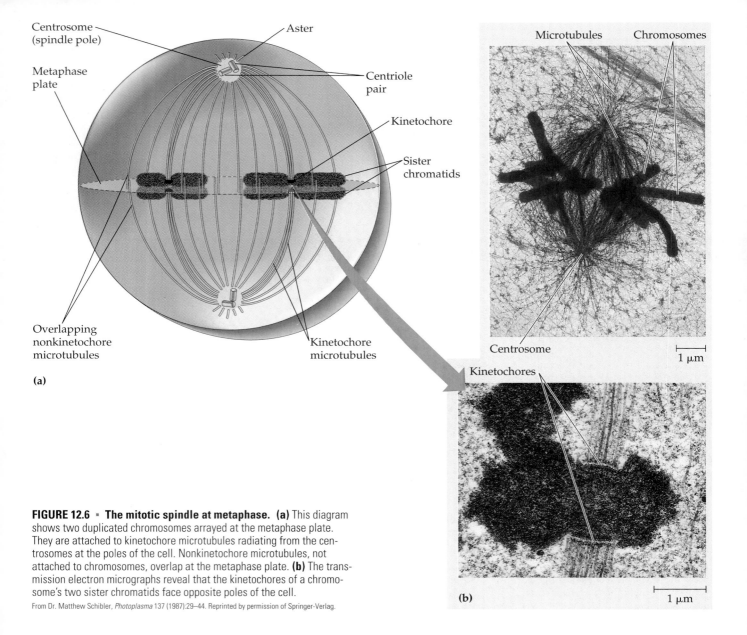

FIGURE 12.6 ▪ **The mitotic spindle at metaphase.** **(a)** This diagram shows two duplicated chromosomes arrayed at the metaphase plate. They are attached to kinetochore microtubules radiating from the centrosomes at the poles of the cell. Nonkinetochore microtubules, not attached to chromosomes, overlap at the metaphase plate. **(b)** The transmission electron micrographs reveal that the kinetochores of a chromosome's two sister chromatids face opposite poles of the cell.

From Dr. Matthew Schibler, *Photoplasma* 137 (1987):29–44. Reprinted by permission of Springer-Verlag.

"captured" by microtubules, the chromosome begins to move toward the pole from which those microtubules come. However, this movement is checked as soon as microtubules from the opposite pole attach to the other kinetochore. What happens next is like a tug-of-war that ends in a draw. The chromosome moves first in one direction, then the other, back and forth, finally settling midway between the two poles of the cell (FIGURE 12.6). Meanwhile, microtubules that do not attach to kinetochores interact with nonkinetochore microtubules from the opposite pole of the cell. At metaphase, these microtubules overlap, and the centromeres of all the duplicated chromosomes are on a plane midway between the two poles. This plane is called the **metaphase plate** of the cell. The spindle is now complete.

Let's now see how the structure of the completed spindle correlates with its function during anaphase. Anaphase com-

mences rather suddenly, with the separation of the sister chromatids of each chromosome. Now full-fledged chromosomes, they move toward opposite poles of the cell. How do the kinetochore microtubules function in this poleward movement of chromosomes? Experimental evidence indicates that kinetochore microtubules shorten during anaphase by depolymerizing at their kinetochore ends (FIGURE 12.7). A chromosome migrates poleward while its kinetochore somehow hangs onto the remaining tips of microtubules just ahead of the zone of depolymerization. The exact mechanism of this interaction between kinetochores and microtubules is not yet fully understood, but there is much evidence that the kinetochore is equipped with motor proteins that "walk" a chromosome along the shortening microtubules. (To review the relationship between motor proteins and the cytoskeleton, see Chapter 7.)

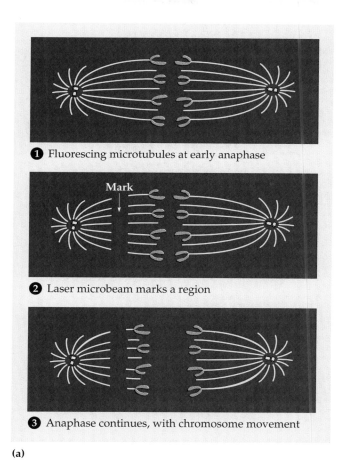

① Fluorescing microtubules at early anaphase

② Laser microbeam marks a region

③ Anaphase continues, with chromosome movement

(a)

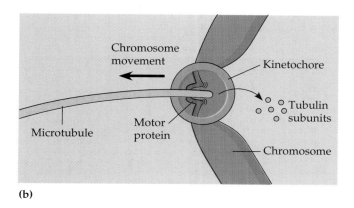

(b)

FIGURE 12.7 ▪ **Testing a hypothesis for chromosome migration during anaphase. (a)** In this experiment, ① the microtubules of a dividing cell were labeled with a fluorescent dye that glows in the microscope (yellow). ② During early anaphase, the researchers aimed a laser microbeam at the kinetochore microtubules about midway between one spindle pole and the chromosomes. The laser marked the microtubules by eliminating fluorescence at the targeted region, but the microtubules still functioned. The researchers could now monitor changes in the lengths of the microtubules on either side of the nonfluorescing mark. ③ As anaphase proceeded and the chromosomes moved toward the poles, the microtubule segments on the kinetochore side of the laser mark shortened while the portions of the microtubules on the centrosome side of the mark stayed the same length. This is one of the experiments supporting **(b)**, the hypothesis that chromosomes track along microtubules as the microtubules depolymerize at their kinetochore ends, releasing tubulin subunits.

What is the function of the nonkinetochore microtubules? In a dividing animal cell, these microtubules, which interact at the middle of the cell, are responsible for elongating the whole cell along the polar axis during anaphase (see FIGURE 12.5). The interdigitating microtubules move past each other away from the metaphase plate. The mechanism seems to be similar to the one that slides neighboring microtubules in a flagellum: Motor proteins attached to the nonkinetochore microtubules drive them past one another, using energy from ATP.

At the end of anaphase, duplicate sets of chromosomes have arrived at opposite poles of the elongated parent cell. Nuclei re-form during telophase. Cytokinesis generally begins during this last stage of mitosis.

Cytokinesis divides the cytoplasm: *a closer look*

In animal cells, cytokinesis occurs by a process known as cleavage. The first sign of cleavage is the appearance of a **cleavage furrow**, which begins as a shallow groove in the cell surface near the old metaphase plate (FIGURE 12.8a, p. 214). On the cytoplasmic side of the furrow is a contractile ring of actin microfilaments associated with molecules of the protein myosin. Actin and myosin are the same proteins that are responsible for muscle contraction, as well as many other

kinds of cell movement. The contraction of the dividing cell's ring of microfilaments is like the pulling of drawstrings. The cleavage furrow deepens until the parent cell is pinched in two, producing two completely separated cells.

Cytokinesis in plant cells, which have walls, is markedly different. There is no cleavage furrow. Instead, during telophase, vesicles derived from the Golgi apparatus move along microtubules to the middle of the cell, where they coalesce, producing a **cell plate** (FIGURE 12.8b). Cell-wall materials carried in the vesicles collect in the cell plate as it grows. The cell plate enlarges until its surrounding membrane fuses with the plasma membrane along the perimeter of the cell. Two daughter cells result, each with its own plasma membrane. Meanwhile, a new cell wall has formed between them.

FIGURE 12.9 on page 215 is a series of micrographs of a dividing plant cell. Examining this figure will help you review mitosis and cytokinesis.

Mitosis in eukaryotes may have evolved from binary fission in bacteria

The complex cellular choreography of mitotic cell division solves the problem of correctly distributing copies of eukaryotic

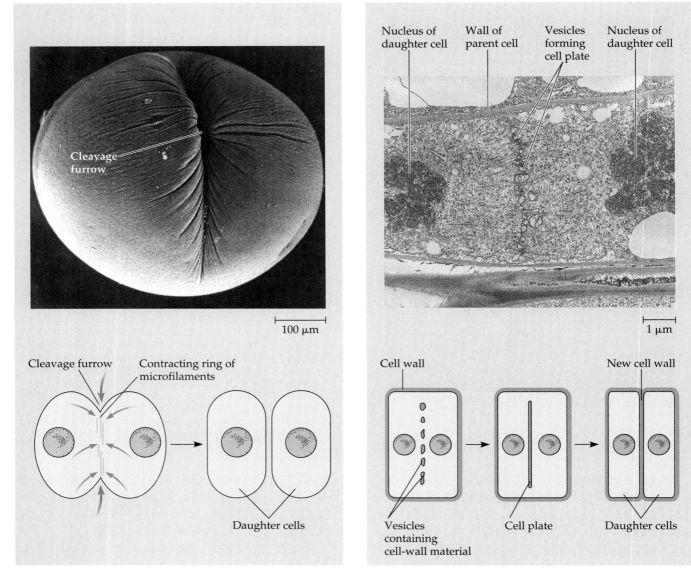

(a) Cleavage of an animal cell

(b) Cell plate formation in a plant cell

FIGURE 12.8 · Cytokinesis in animal and plant cells. (a) The micrograph (SEM) shows the cleavage furrow of a dividing animal cell as it appears on the cell surface. Just inside the plasma membrane at the location of furrowing, microfilaments form a ring. These actin filaments interact with molecules of myosin, causing the ring to contract. The cleavage furrow deepens until the cell is pinched in two. **(b)** In this micrograph (TEM) of a soybean root cell at telophase, you can see the new nuclei at the two poles and vesicles from the Golgi apparatus that are coming together to form a cell plate at the equatorial plane of the cell. These vesicles, laden with cell-wall material, fuse to form a bigger and bigger cell plate, until the plate's membrane fuses at its edges with the plasma membrane, dividing the cell in two. New cell wall between the daughter cells arises from the contents of the cell plate.

genomes to daughter cells. How did mitosis evolve? Given that prokaryotes preceded eukaryotes on Earth by billions of years, we might hypothesize that mitosis had its origins in simpler bacterial mechanisms of cell reproduction.

Prokaryotes (bacteria) reproduce by a type of cell division called **binary fission**, meaning literally "division in half" (FIGURE 12.10). Most bacterial genes are carried on a single chromosome that consists of a circular DNA molecule and

associated proteins. Although bacteria are smaller and simpler than eukaryotic cells, the problem of replicating their genomes in an orderly fashion and distributing the copies equally to two daughter cells is still formidable. The chromosome of the bacterium *Escherichia coli*, for example, when it is fully stretched out, is about 500 times longer than the length of the cell. Clearly, such a long chromosome must be highly folded within the cell.

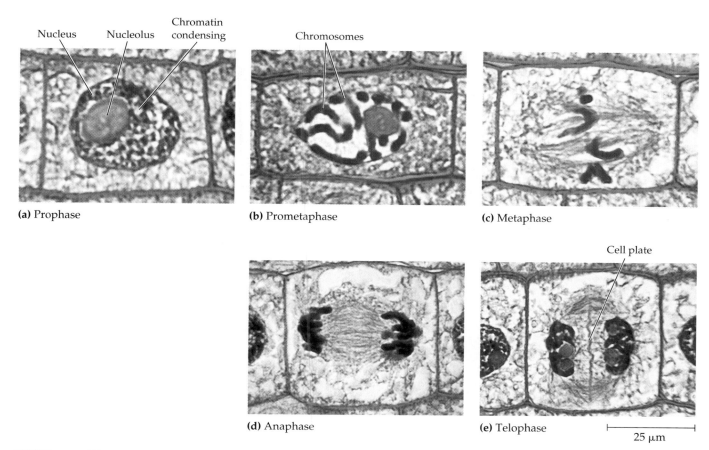

FIGURE 12.9 · **Mitosis in a plant cell.** These light micrographs show the process of mitosis in cells of an onion root.

(a) Prophase. The chromatin is condensing. The nucleolus is still clearly present but will soon begin to disappear. Although not yet visible in the micrograph, the mitotic spindle is starting to form.

(b) Prometaphase. We now see discrete chromosomes; each consists of two identical sister chromatids attached all along their lengths. Later in prometaphase, the nuclear envelope will fragment, and spindle microtubules will attach to the kinetochores of the chromosomes.

(c) Metaphase. The spindle is complete, and the chromosomes, pulled equally by kinetochore microtubules coming from opposite poles of the cell, are lined up at the metaphase plate.

(d) Anaphase. The chromatids of each chromosome have separated, and the daughter chromosomes are moving to the poles of the cell as their kinetochore microtubules shorten.

(e) Telophase. Daughter nuclei are forming. Meanwhile, cytokinesis has started: The cell plate, which will divide the cytoplasm in two, is growing toward the perimeter of the parent cell.

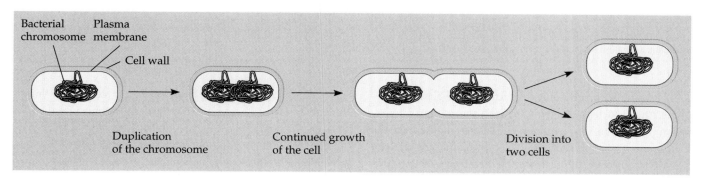

FIGURE 12.10 · **Bacterial cell division (binary fission).** Allocation of identical genomes to daughter cells depends on the attachment of duplicated chromosomes to the plasma membrane of the parent cell. Continued growth of the cell gradually separates the chromosomes. Eventually the plasma membrane grows inward to divide the cell in two as a new cell wall is deposited between the daughter cells.

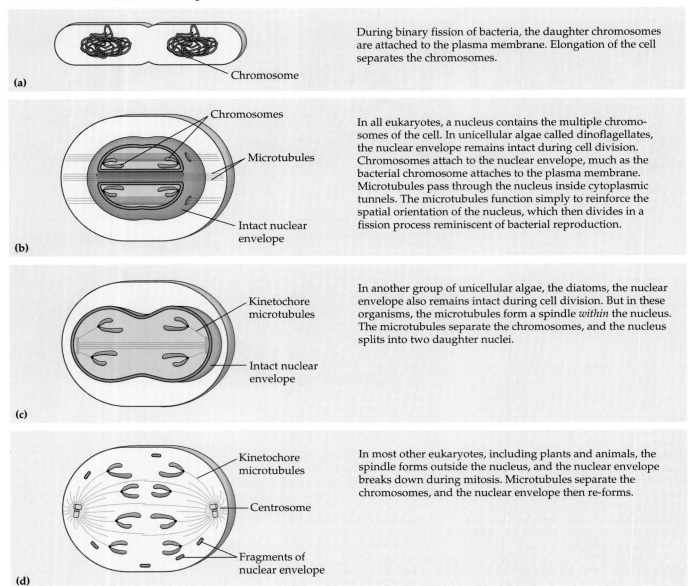

(a) Chromosome

During binary fission of bacteria, the daughter chromosomes are attached to the plasma membrane. Elongation of the cell separates the chromosomes.

(b) Chromosomes / Microtubules / Intact nuclear envelope

In all eukaryotes, a nucleus contains the multiple chromosomes of the cell. In unicellular algae called dinoflagellates, the nuclear envelope remains intact during cell division. Chromosomes attach to the nuclear envelope, much as the bacterial chromosome attaches to the plasma membrane. Microtubules pass through the nucleus inside cytoplasmic tunnels. The microtubules function simply to reinforce the spatial orientation of the nucleus, which then divides in a fission process reminiscent of bacterial reproduction.

(c) Kinetochore microtubules / Intact nuclear envelope

In another group of unicellular algae, the diatoms, the nuclear envelope also remains intact during cell division. But in these organisms, the microtubules form a spindle *within* the nucleus. The microtubules separate the chromosomes, and the nucleus splits into two daughter nuclei.

(d) Kinetochore microtubules / Centrosome / Fragments of nuclear envelope

In most other eukaryotes, including plants and animals, the spindle forms outside the nucleus, and the nuclear envelope breaks down during mitosis. Microtubules separate the chromosomes, and the nuclear envelope then re-forms.

FIGURE 12.11 ▪ **A hypothesis for the evolution of mitosis.** Mitotic cell division is unique to eukaryotes. Prokaryotes (bacteria) have much smaller genomes and reproduce by the simpler process of binary fission **(a)**. As eukaryotes, with their larger genomes, evolved, the ancestral process of binary fission somehow gave rise to mitosis. Researchers interested in this evolutionary problem have observed what they believe are mechanisms of cell division intermediate between binary fission and mitosis. Two of these variations in cell division are illustrated in **(b)** and **(c)**, beneath bacterial fission and above mitosis as it occurs in plants and animals **(d)**. The schematic diagrams in this figure do not include cell walls.

The bacterial chromosome is attached to the plasma membrane. After a bacterial cell replicates its chromosome in preparation for fission, the two copies remain attached to the membrane at adjacent sites. Growth of the membrane between the two attachment sites separates the two copies of the chromosome. When the bacterium has reached about twice its initial size, its plasma membrane grows inward, dividing the parent cell into two daughter cells. Each cell inherits a complete genome.

FIGURE 12.11 traces a hypothesis for the stepwise evolution of mitosis from bacterial binary fission. Possible intermediate stages are represented by two unusual types of nuclear division found in certain modern unicellular algae. In both types, the nuclear envelope remains intact. In dinoflagellates, replicated chromosomes are attached to the nuclear envelope and separate as it elongates prior to cell division. In diatoms, a spindle within the nucleus separates the chromosomes.

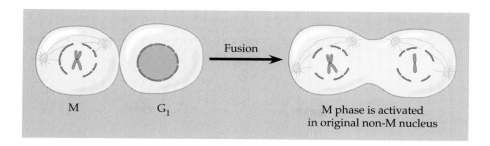

FIGURE 12.12 • **Evidence for cytoplasmic chemical signals in cell-cycle regulation.** Cultured mammalian cells can be induced to fuse, forming a single cell with two nuclei. The results of fusing cells at two different phases of the cell cycle suggested that particular chemicals control the progression of phases. For example, when a cell in M phase was fused with one in any other phase, the nucleus from the latter cell immediately began mitosis. If the second cell was in G_1, the condensed chromosomes that appeared had single chromatids.

REGULATION OF THE CELL CYCLE

The timing and rate of cell division in different parts of a plant or animal are crucial to normal growth, development, and maintenance. The frequency of cell division varies with the type of cell. For example, human skin cells divide frequently throughout life, whereas liver cells maintain the ability to divide but keep it in reserve until an appropriate need arises—say, to repair a wound. Some of the most specialized cells, such as nerve cells and muscle cells, do not divide at all in a mature human. These cell-cycle differences result from regulation at the molecular level. The mechanisms of this regulation are of intense interest, not only for understanding the life cycles of normal cells but also for understanding how cancer cells manage to escape normal controls.

A molecular control system drives the cell cycle

What drives the cell cycle? One reasonable hypothesis might be that each event in the cycle triggers the next. According to this hypothesis, for example, the replication of chromosomes in S phase might cause cell growth during G_2, which might in turn directly trigger the onset of mitosis. However, this apparently logical hypothesis is not in fact correct.

In the early 1970s a variety of experiments suggested an alternative hypothesis: that the cell cycle is driven by specific chemical signals present in the cytoplasm. Some of the first strong evidence for this hypothesis came from experiments with mammalian cells grown in culture (see the Methods Box, p. 219). In these experiments, two cells in different phases of the cell cycle were fused to form a single cell with two nuclei. If one of the original cells was in S phase and the other was in G_1, the G_1 nucleus immediately entered S phase, as though stimulated by chemicals present in the cytoplasm of the first cell. Similarly, if a cell undergoing mitosis (M phase) was fused with another cell in any stage of its cell cycle, even G_1, the second nucleus immediately entered mitosis, with condensation of the chromatin and formation of a spindle (FIGURE 12.12).

These and other experiments demonstrated that the sequential events of the cell cycle are directed by a distinct cell-cycle control system, a cyclically operating set of molecules in the cell that both triggers and coordinates key events in the cell cycle. The cell-cycle control system has been compared to the control device of an automatic washing machine (FIGURE 12.13). Like the washer's device, the cell-cycle control system proceeds on its own, driven by a built-in clock. However, just as a washer's cycle is subject to both external adjustment (such as faucets controlling the water supply) and internal control (such as the sensor that detects when the tub is filled with water), the cell cycle is regulated at certain checkpoints by internal and external controls.

Cell-Cycle Checkpoints

A **checkpoint** in the cell cycle is a critical control point where stop and go-ahead signals can regulate the cycle. Animal cells generally have built-in stop signals that halt the cell cycle at checkpoints until overridden by go-ahead signals. Many signals registered at checkpoints come from cellular surveillance

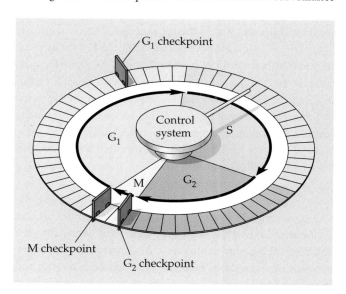

FIGURE 12.13 • **Mechanical analogy for the cell-cycle control system.** In this diagram of the cell cycle, the flat blocks represent sequential events within each phase. Like the control device of an automatic washer, the cell-cycle control system proceeds on its own, driven by a built-in clock. However, the system is subject to regulation at various checkpoints, of which three are shown (red).

mechanisms; the signals report whether crucial cellular processes up to that point have been completed correctly, and thus whether or not the cell cycle should proceed. Checkpoints also register signals from outside the cell, as we will discuss later. Three major checkpoints are found in the G_1, G_2, and M phases.

For many cells, the G_1 checkpoint—dubbed the "restriction point" in mammalian cells—seems to be the most important. If a cell receives a go-ahead signal at the G_1 checkpoint, it will usually complete the cycle and divide. Alternatively, if it does not receive a go-ahead signal at that point, it will exit the cycle, switching into a nondividing state called the **G_0 phase**. Most cells of the human body are actually in the G_0 phase. As mentioned earlier, specialized nerve and muscle cells never divide. Other cells, such as liver cells, can be "called back" to the cell cycle by certain environmental cues, such as growth factors released during injury.

To understand how cell-cycle checkpoints work, we need to see what kinds of molecules make up the cell-cycle control system.

The Cell-Cycle Clock:
Cyclins and Cyclin-Dependent Kinases

Rhythmic fluctuations in the abundance and activity of cell-cycle control molecules pace the sequential events of the cell cycle. These regulatory molecules are proteins of two main types. Some are protein kinases, enzymes that activate or inactivate other proteins by phosphorylating them (see Chapter 11). Particular protein kinases give the go-ahead signals at the G_1 and G_2 checkpoints.

The kinases that drive the cell cycle are actually present at a constant concentration in the growing cell, but much of the time they are in inactive form. To be active, such a kinase must be attached to a **cyclin**, a protein that gets its name from its cyclically fluctuating concentration in the cell. Because of this requirement, these kinases are called **cyclin-dependent kinases**, or **Cdks**. The activity of a Cdk rises and falls with changes in the concentration of its cyclin partner (FIGURE 12.14a).

Let's examine the cyclin-Cdk complex that was discovered first, called **MPF**. The initials stand for "maturation promoting factor," but we can think of it as "M-phase promoting factor," because it triggers the cell's passage past the G_2 checkpoint into M phase (FIGURE 12.14b). When cyclins that accumulate during G_2 associate with Cdk molecules, the resulting MPF complex initiates mitosis, apparently by phosphorylating a variety of proteins. MPF acts both directly and indirectly. For example, it causes the nuclear envelope to fragment by phosphorylating—*and* stimulating other kinases to phosphorylate—proteins of the nuclear lamina, the lining of the nuclear envelope (see FIGURE 7.9).

Later in M phase, MPF helps switch itself off by initiating a process that leads to the destruction of its cyclin by proteolytic

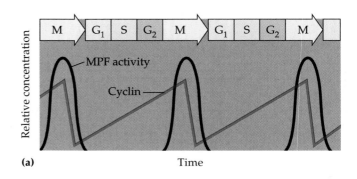

(a)

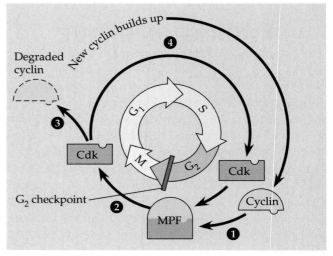

(b)

FIGURE 12.14 · The molecular basis of the cell-cycle control system: control at the G_2 checkpoint. The stepwise processes of the cell cycle are timed by rhythmic fluctuations in the activity of protein kinases, enzymes that switch target proteins on or off by phosphorylating them. These enzymes are called cyclin-dependent kinases (Cdks) because they are active only when bound to a cyclin, a protein whose concentration varies cyclically. Here we focus on a Cdk-cyclin complex called MPF, which acts at the G_2 checkpoint to trigger mitosis. **(a)** The graph shows how MPF activity fluctuates with the level of cyclin in the cell. The cyclin level rises throughout interphase (G_1, S, and G_2 phases), then falls abruptly during mitosis (M phase). The peaks of MPF activity and cyclin concentration correspond. The Cdk itself is present at a constant level (not shown). **(b)** ① By the G_2 checkpoint (red bar), enough cyclin is available to produce many molecules of MPF. ② MPF promotes mitosis by phosphorylating various proteins, including other enzymes. ③ One effect of MPF is the initiation of a sequence of events leading to the breakdown of its own cyclin. ④ The Cdk component of MPF is recycled. Its kinase activity will be restored by association with new cyclin that accumulates during interphase.

(protein-hydrolyzing) enzymes. Proteolytic enzymes are also involved in driving the cycle past the M-phase checkpoint, which controls the onset of anaphase. Anaphase starts when proteins that hold sister chromatids together at metaphase are broken down. The noncyclin part of MPF, the Cdk, persists in the cell in inactive form until it associates with new cyclin molecules synthesized during interphase of the next round of the cycle.

Many types of animal and plant cells can be removed from an organism and cultured in an artificial environment. This makes it possible to study the cell cycle and many other activities of cells under controlled conditions.

In the experiment illustrated here, we test the effect of a specific growth factor on the ability of human fibroblast cells to divide. Fibroblasts are the connective tissue cells that secrete collagen, the protein making up the extracellular fibers that strengthen our tissues and organs. Our source of fibroblasts is a small sample of tissue removed during a biopsy. Two steps are required to isolate these cells. First, small pieces of connective tissue are dissected

from the tissue sample. Second, specific enzymes are added to digest the collagen fibers and other components of the extracellular matrix, resulting in a suspension of free fibroblast cells. The isolated fibroblasts are placed in a culture vessel, a flat flask that lies on its side. The cells adhere to the glass on the inside of the vessel, and they are bathed in a liquid culture medium of known composition. It is essential to sterilize the vessels and the culture medium before use, in order to kill microorganisms that would contaminate the culture. The culture medium is a complex mixture of glucose, amino acids, salts, and antibiotics (as a further precaution against bacterial growth). The cultures are incubated at an

optimal temperature, 37°C for human fibroblast cultures.

In our experiment, some culture vessels contain only this basic medium while others contain the basic medium plus a protein called platelet-derived growth factor, or PDGF. In the intact animal, blood cells called platelets release this growth factor at the site of an injury, stimulating nearby fibroblasts to proliferate. This is an important step in the healing of wounds. Our experiment confirms that PDGF stimulates the cell division of cultured fibroblasts.

SOURCE: Art adapted from R. I. Freshney, *Culture of Animal Cells: A Manual of Basic Technique*, 2nd ed., fig. 1.2, p. 5. © 1989 John Wiley and Sons. Reprinted by permission of Wiley-Liss, a subsidiary of John Wiley and Sons, Inc.

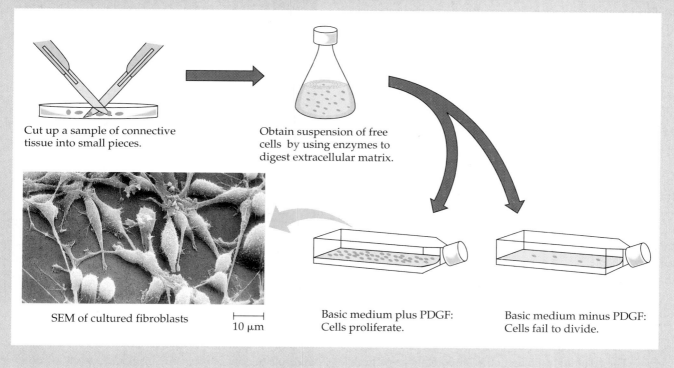

Cut up a sample of connective tissue into small pieces.

Obtain suspension of free cells by using enzymes to digest extracellular matrix.

SEM of cultured fibroblasts

10 μm

Basic medium plus PDGF: Cells proliferate.

Basic medium minus PDGF: Cells fail to divide.

What about the G_1 checkpoint? Recent research suggests the involvement of at least three Cdk proteins and several cyclins at this checkpoint. The fluctuating activities of different cyclin-Cdk complexes probably control all the stages of the cell cycle.

Internal and external cues help regulate the cell cycle

Research scientists are only in the early stages of working out the signaling pathways that link cyclin-dependent kinases to

other molecules and events inside and outside the cell. For example, they know that active Cdks function by phosphorylating substrate proteins that affect particular steps in the cell cycle. But identifying the specific substrates of the various Cdks that become active at different phases of the cell cycle has proven difficult. In other words, scientists don't yet know what Cdks actually do in most cases. However, they have identified some steps of the signaling pathways that convey information to the cell-cycle machinery. We'll next discuss two examples of such signaling, one originating inside the cell and one outside.

Internal Signals: Messages from the Kinetochores

Anaphase, the separation of sister chromatids, does not begin until all the chromosomes are properly attached to the spindle at the metaphase plate. The gatekeeper is the M-phase checkpoint, and it ensures that daughter cells do not end up with missing or extra chromosomes. Researchers have learned that a signal that delays anaphase originates at the kinetochores that are not yet attached to spindle microtubules. Certain associated proteins trigger a signaling pathway that keeps an anaphase-promoting complex (APC) in an inactive state. Only when all the kinetochores are attached to the spindle does this "wait" signal cease. The APC becomes active, and its proteolytic enzymes break down cyclin and the proteins holding the sister chromatids together.

External Signals: Growth Factors

By growing animal cells in culture, researchers have been able to identify many external factors, both chemical and physical, that can influence cell division. For example, cells fail to divide if an essential nutrient is left out of the culture medium. Even if all other conditions are favorable, most types of mammalian cells divide in culture only if the growth medium includes specific growth factors. As mentioned in Chapter 11, a **growth factor** is a protein released by certain body cells that stimulates other cells to divide.

One example of a growth factor is *platelet-derived growth factor (PDGF)*, which is made by blood cells called platelets. Important for wound healing, PDGF is required for the division of fibroblasts. These connective tissue cells have PDGF receptors on their plasma membranes. The binding of PDGF molecules to these receptors (which are tyrosine-kinase receptors; see Chapter 11) triggers a signal-transduction pathway that leads to stimulation of cell division. Presumably the pathway activates one or more components of the cell-cycle control system. PDGF stimulates fibroblast division not only in the artificial conditions of cell culture, but in an animal's body as well. When an injury occurs, platelets release PDGF in the vicinity. The resulting proliferation of fibroblasts helps heal the wound. Researchers have discovered a number of different growth factors. Each cell type probably responds specifically to a certain growth factor or combination of different growth factors.

The discovery of growth factors provided the key to understanding **density-dependent inhibition** of cell division, a phenomenon in which crowded cells stop dividing (FIGURE 12.15a). As first observed many years ago, cultured cells normally divide until they form a single layer of cells on the inner surface of the culture container, at which point the cells stop dividing. If some cells are removed, those bordering the open space begin dividing again and continue until the vacancy is filled. Apparently, when a cell population reaches a certain

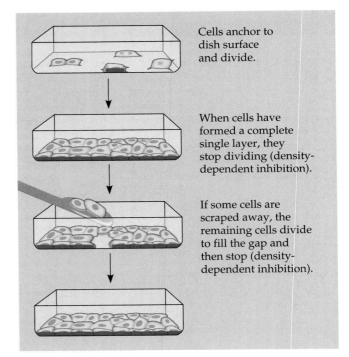

(a)

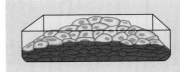

(b)

FIGURE 12.15 · Density-dependent inhibition of cell division.
(a) When grown in cell culture, normal mammalian cells will multiply only until they form a single layer. The availability of nutrients, growth factors, and substratum for attachment limits the density of the cell population. If some cells are removed, those at the border of the resulting gap will divide until the gap is filled with a single layer. **(b)** In contrast, cancer cells are tolerant of crowding and usually continue to divide well beyond a single layer, forming a clump of overlapping cells. (Individual cells are shown disproportionately large in this figure.)

density, the amount of required growth factors and nutrients available to each cell becomes insufficient to allow continued cell growth.

Most animal cells also exhibit **anchorage dependence**. To divide, they must be attached to a substratum, such as the inside of a culture jar or the extracellular matrix of a tissue. Experiments suggest that anchorage is signaled to the cell-cycle control system via pathways involving plasma membrane proteins and elements of the cytoskeleton linked to them. Density-dependent inhibition and anchorage dependence probably function in the body's tissues as well as in cell culture, checking the growth of cells at some optimal density and location. Cancer cells, which we discuss next, exhibit neither density-dependent inhibition nor anchorage dependence (FIGURE 12.15b).

Cancer cells have escaped from cell-cycle controls

Cancer cells do not respond normally to the body's control mechanisms. They divide excessively and invade other tissues. If unchecked, they can kill the organism.

By studying cells growing in culture, researchers have learned that cancer cells do not heed the normal signals that regulate the cell cycle. For example, as FIGURE 12.15b shows, cancer cells do not exhibit density-dependent inhibition when growing in culture; they do not stop dividing when growth factors are depleted. A logical hypothesis to explain this behavior is that cancer cells have no need for growth factors in their culture medium. They may make a required growth factor themselves or have an abnormality in the signaling pathway that conveys the growth factor's signal to the cell-cycle control system—or the cell-cycle control system itself may be abnormal. In fact, as you will learn in Chapter 19, these are some of the possible explanations.

There are other important differences between normal cells and cancer cells that reflect derangements of the cell cycle. If and when they stop dividing, cancer cells do so at random points in the cycle, rather than just at the normal checkpoints. Moreover, in culture, cancer cells can go on dividing indefinitely if they are given a continual supply of nutrients; they are said to be "immortal." A striking example is a cell line that has been reproducing in culture since 1951. Cells of this line are called HeLa cells because their original source was from a tumor removed from a woman named Henrietta Lacks. By contrast, nearly all normal mammalian cells growing in culture divide only about 20–50 times before they stop dividing, age, and die. (We'll see a possible reason for this phenomenon when we discuss chromosome replication in Chapter 16.)

The abnormal behavior of cancer cells can be catastrophic when it occurs in the body. The potential problem begins when a single cell in a tissue undergoes **transformation**, the process that converts a normal cell to a cancer cell. The body's immune system normally recognizes a transformed cell as an insurgent and destroys it. However, if the cell evades destruction, it may proliferate to form a **tumor**, a mass of abnormal cells within an otherwise normal tissue. If the abnormal cells remain at the original site, the lump is called a **benign tumor**. Most benign tumors do not cause serious problems and can be completely removed by surgery. In contrast, a **malignant tumor** becomes invasive enough to impair the functions of one or more organs (FIGURE 12.16). An individual with a malignant tumor is said to have cancer.

The cells of malignant tumors are abnormal in many ways besides their excessive proliferation. They may have unusual numbers of chromosomes. Their metabolism may be deranged, and they cease to function in any constructive way. Also, due to abnormal changes of the cells' surfaces, they lose their attachments to neighboring cells and the extracellular matrix, and can spread into nearby tissues. Cancer cells may also separate from the original tumor, enter the blood and lymph vessels of the circulatory system, and invade other parts of the body, where they proliferate to form more tumors. This spread of cancer cells beyond their original site is called **metastasis**. If a tumor metastasizes, treatments may include high-energy radiation and chemotherapy with toxic drugs that are especially harmful to actively dividing cells.

Researchers are beginning to understand how a normal cell is transformed into a cancer cell. Though the causes of cancer are diverse, cellular transformation always involves the alteration of genes that somehow influence the cell-cycle control system. Our knowledge of how changes in the genome lead to the various abnormalities of cancer cells remains rudimentary, however.

Perhaps the reason we have so many unanswered questions about cancer cells is that there is still so much to learn about how normal cells function. The cell, life's basic unit of structure and function, holds enough secrets to engage researchers well into the future.

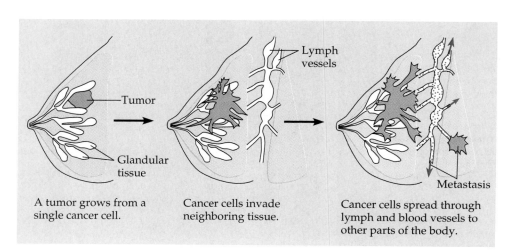

A tumor grows from a single cancer cell.

Cancer cells invade neighboring tissue.

Cancer cells spread through lymph and blood vessels to other parts of the body.

FIGURE 12.16 ▪ **The growth and metastasis of a malignant breast tumor.** The cells of malignant (cancerous) tumors grow in an uncontrolled way and can spread to neighboring tissues and, via the circulatory system, to other parts of the body. The spread of cancer cells beyond their original site is called metastasis.

REVIEW OF KEY CONCEPTS

THE KEY ROLES OF CELL DIVISION

■ **Cell division functions in reproduction, growth, and repair (p. 206, FIGURE. 12.1)** Unicellular organisms reproduce by cell division. Multicellular organisms depend on it for development from a fertilized egg, growth, and repair.

■ **Cell division distributes identical sets of chromosomes to daughter cells (pp. 206–208)** Eukaryotic cell division consists of mitosis (division of the nucleus) and cytokinesis (division of the cytoplasm). DNA is partitioned among chromosomes, making it easier for the eukaryotic cell to replicate and distribute its huge amounts of DNA. Chromosomes consist of chromatin, a complex of DNA and protein that condenses during mitosis. When chromosomes replicate, they form identical sister chromatids. The chromatids separate during mitosis, becoming the chromosomes of the new daughter cells.

THE MITOTIC CELL CYCLE

➡ **The mitotic phase alternates with interphase in the cell cycle: *an overview* (p. 209, FIGURES 12.4, 12.5)** Mitosis and cytokinesis make up the M (mitotic) phase of the cell cycle. Between divisions, cells are in interphase: the G_1, S, and G_2 phases. The cell grows throughout interphase, but DNA is replicated only during the S (synthesis) phase. Mitosis is a continuous process, often described as occurring in five stages: prophase, prometaphase, metaphase, anaphase, and telophase.
12.1
12.2
12.3

■ **The mitotic spindle distributes chromosomes to daughter cells: *a closer look* (pp. 209–213, FIGURE 12.6)** The mitotic spindle is an apparatus of microtubules that controls chromosome movement during mitosis. The spindle arises from the centrosomes, regions near the nucleus associated with centrioles in animal cells. Spindle microtubules attach to the kinetochores of chromatids and move the chromosomes to the metaphase plate. In anaphase, sister chromatids separate and move toward opposite poles of the cell. Using motor proteins, each kinetochore moves along shortening microtubules. Meanwhile, nonkinetochore microtubules slide, elongating the cell. In telophase, daughter nuclei form at opposite ends of the cell.

■ **Cytokinesis divides the cytoplasm: *a closer look* (p. 213, FIGURE 12.8)** Mitosis is usually followed by cytokinesis, involving cleavage furrows in animals and cell plates in plants.

■ **Mitosis in eukaryotes may have evolved from binary fission in bacteria (pp. 213–216, FIGURES 12.10, 12.11)**

REGULATION OF THE CELL CYCLE

■ **A molecular control system drives the cell cycle (pp. 217–219, FIGURES 12.13, 12.14, METHODS BOX)** Cyclical changes in regulatory proteins work as a mitotic clock. The key molecules are cyclin-dependent kinases, complexes of cyclins (whose concentrations build during the cell cycle) and specific protein kinases.

■ **Internal and external cues help regulate the cell cycle (pp. 219–220, FIGURE 12.15)** Cell culture has enabled researchers to study the molecular details of cell division. Both internal signals, such as those emanating from kinetochores not yet attached to the spindle, and external signals, such as growth factors, control the cell-cycle checkpoints via signal-transduction pathways. Growth factor depletion explains density-dependent inhibition.

■ **Cancer cells have escaped from cell-cycle controls (p. 221, FIGURE 12.16)** Cancer cells elude normal regulation and divide out of control, forming tumors. Malignant tumors invade surrounding tissues and can metastasize, exporting cancer cells to other parts of the body.

SELF-QUIZ

1. During the cell cycle, increases in the enzymatic activity of protein kinases are due to
   a. kinase synthesis by ribosomes
   b. activation of inactive kinase by binding to cyclin
   c. conversion of inactive cyclin to the active kinase via phosphorylation
   d. cleavage of the inactive kinase molecules by cytoplasmic proteases
   e. a decline in external growth factors to a concentration below the inhibitory threshold

2. Through a microscope, you can see a cell plate beginning to develop across the middle of the cell and nuclei re-forming at opposite poles of the cell. This cell is most likely a (an)
   a. animal cell in the process of cytokinesis
   b. plant cell in the process of cytokinesis
   c. animal cell in the S phase of the cell cycle
   d. bacterial cell dividing
   e. plant cell in metaphase

3. Vinblastine is a standard chemotherapeutic drug used to treat cancer. Since it interferes with the assembly of microtubules, its effectiveness must be related to
   a. disruption of mitotic spindle formation
   b. inhibition of regulatory protein phosphorylation
   c. suppression of cyclin production
   d. myosin denaturation and inhibition of cleavage furrow formation
   e. inhibition of DNA synthesis

4. A particular cell has half as much DNA as some of the other cells in a mitotically active tissue. The cell in question is most likely in
   a. G_1
   b. G_2
   c. prophase
   d. metaphase
   e. anaphase

5. In the light micrograph below of dividing cells near the tip of an onion root, identify a cell in each of the following stages: interphase, prophase, metaphase, and anaphase. Describe the major events occurring at each stage.

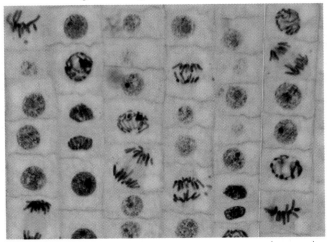

25 μm

6. One difference between a cancer cell and a normal cell is that

   a. the cancer cell is unable to synthesize DNA

   b. the cell cycle of the cancer cell is arrested at the S phase

   c. cancer cells continue to divide even when they are tightly packed together

   d. cancer cells cannot function properly because they suffer from density-dependent inhibition

   e. cancer cells are always in the M phase of the cell cycle

7. The decline of MPF at the end of mitosis is caused by

   a. the destruction of the protein kinase (Cdk)

   b. decreased synthesis of cyclin

   c. the enzymatic destruction of cyclin

   d. synthesis of DNA

   e. an increase in the cell's volume-to-genome ratio

8. A red blood cell (RBC) has a 120-day lifespan. If an average adult has 5 L (5000 cm^3) of blood and each mm^3 contains 5 million RBCs, how many new cells must be produced each second to replace the entire RBC population?

   a. 30,000   d. 18,000

   b. 2400   e. 30,000,000

   c. 2,400,000

9. In *function*, the plant cell structure that is analogous to an animal cell's cleavage furrow is the

   a. chromosome

   b. cell plate

   c. nucleus

   d. centrosome

   e. spindle apparatus

10. In some organisms, mitosis occurs without cytokinesis occurring. This will result in

   a. cells with more than one nucleus

   b. cells that are unusually small

   c. cells lacking nuclei

   d. destruction of chromosomes

   e. cell cycles lacking an S phase

CHALLENGE QUESTION

When a population of cells is examined with a microscope, the percentage of the cells in the M phase is called the mitotic index. The greater the proportion of cells that are dividing, the higher the mitotic index. In a particular study, cells from a cell culture are spread on a slide, preserved and stained, and then inspected in the microscope. A hundred cells are examined: 9 cells are in prophase; 5 cells are in metaphase; 2 cells are in anaphase; 4 cells are in telophase; the remainder, 80 cells, are in interphase. Answer the following questions:

a. What is the mitotic index for this cell culture?

b. The average duration for the cell cycle in this culture is known to be 20 hours. What is the duration of interphase? Of metaphase?

c. Going back to the living culture of these cells, the average quantity of DNA per cell is measured. Of the cells in interphase, 50% contain 10 ng (1 nanogram = 10^{-9} g) of DNA per cell, 20% contain 20 ng DNA per cell, and the remaining 30% of the interphase cells have amounts of DNA between 10 and 20 ng. Based on these data, determine the duration of the G_1, S, and G_2 portions of the cell cycle.

SCIENCE, TECHNOLOGY, AND SOCIETY

Every year about a million Americans are diagnosed as having cancer. This means that about 75 million Americans now living will eventually have cancer, and one in five will die of the disease. There are many kinds of cancers and many causes of the disease. For example, smoking causes most lung cancers, and overexposure to ultraviolet rays in sunlight causes most skin cancers. There is evidence that a high-fat, low-fiber diet is a factor in breast, colon, and prostate cancers. And agents in the workplace such as asbestos and vinyl chloride are also implicated as causes of cancer. Hundreds of millions of dollars are spent each year in the search for effective treatments for cancer; far less money is spent on preventing cancer. Why might this be the case? What kinds of lifestyle changes could we make to help prevent cancer? What kinds of prevention programs could be initiated or strengthened to encourage these changes? What factors might impede such changes and programs?

FURTHER READING

Alberts, B., D. Bray, T. Lewis, M. Raff, K. Roberts, and J. D. Watson. *Molecular Biology of the Cell*, 3rd ed. New York: Garland, 1994. Chapter 13.

Baringa, M. "A New Twist to the Cell Cycle." *Science*, August 4, 1995. How the timed destruction of cyclins regulates cell division.

Becker, W. M., J. Reece, and M. F. Poenie. *The World of the Cell*, 3rd ed. Menlo Park, CA: Benjamin/Cummings, 1996. Chapter 15.

"Cancer." *Scientific American*, September 1996. The entire issue is devoted to the subject of cancer.

Elledge, S. J. "Mitotic Arrest: Mad2 Prevents Sleepy from Waking Up the APC." *Science*, February 13, 1998. How unattached kinetochores control the onset of anaphase. See also "Cell Division Gatekeepers Identified" by E. Pennisi in *Science*, January 23, 1998.

Glover, D. M., C. Gonzalez, and J. W. Raff. "The Centrosome." *Scientific American*, June 1993. Discusses the structure and function of the mitotic spindle.

McIntosh, J. R., and K. L. McDonald. "The Mitotic Spindle." *Scientific American*, October 1989.

Murray, A. W., and T. Hunt. *The Cell Cycle: An Introduction*. New York: W. H. Freeman, 1993. A thorough overview.

Murray, A. W., and M. W. Kirschner. "What Controls the Cell Cycle." *Scientific American*, March 1991.

Orr-Weaver, T. L., and R. A. Weinberg. "A checkpoint on the road to cancer." *Nature*, March 19, 1998. Mutations that disrupt a cell-cycle checkpoint have been identified in cancer cells.

Pluta, A. F., A. M. Mackay, A. M. Ainsztein, I. G. Goldberg, and W. C. Earnshaw. "The Centromere: Hub of Chromosomal Activities." *Science*, December 8, 1995. Discusses the functioning of centromeres and kinetochores.

WEB LINKS

Visit the special edition of *The Biology Place* for BIOLOGY, Fifth Edition, at http://www.biology.com/campbell. Go to Chapter 12 for online resources, including learning activities, practice exams, and links to the following web sites:

"Interactive Mitosis Tutorial"

A small but highly animated tutorial on mitosis. Requires a Shockwave plug-in.

"Online Onion Root Tips"

In this interactive experiment from the Biology Project at the University of Arizona, you score the number of onion root tip cells in various stages of the cell cycle and then calculate the time cells spend in each phase of the cycle.

"The Cell Cycle and Mitosis Tutorial"

Another well-conceived tutorial from the Biology Project at the University of Arizona. It explains the cycle with graphics and animation, and you can take a small interactive test at the end to see how well you understand the concepts.

"The Forsburg Lab Home Pages"

Visit the home pages of this research group at the Salk Institute in La Jolla, California, who study the cell cycle. This site has graphic explanations of their work and provides links to cell cycle resources worldwide.

GENETICS

Mary-Claire King is best known for her research on the genetics of breast cancer, a disease that strikes one out of every ten American women in her lifetime. In this work, and in her research on inherited deafness and inherited susceptibility to HIV infection (among other subjects), Dr. King has demonstrated the power of approaching biological questions from a variety of perspectives. Depending on the question at hand, she may focus on molecules, on cells, on human families, or on whole populations—using whatever techniques are most appropriate. In addition to basic research, King's laboratory group applies the concepts and methods of genetics to solving practical problems relating to human-rights abuses around the world. Jane Reece spoke with Dr. King on these and other topics at the University of Washington, where she is a professor in the Departments of Medicine and Genetics.

How did you get started in biology?

After majoring in math at Carleton College in Minnesota in the mid '60s, I went out to UC Berkeley to study statistics. I wanted to try to integrate math, which was something I liked and was reasonably good at, with some sort of work that mattered to people. In those days we were very much involved with the civil rights movement, and we were becoming increasingly involved in what was going on in Vietnam. It wasn't an era in which it made sense to ignore the world around you. My first quarter at Berkeley, I took Curt Stern's genetics course, just before he retired. I remember going to that class every day at 1 o'clock, and it was like Christmas every day. I couldn't imagine that people got paid to work on these fascinating kinds of problems! That course changed my life. Soon I transferred to Genetics.

What kind of research did you do as a graduate student?

I worked in Allan Wilson's lab on questions relating to human evolution. With little background in biology, I was initially a menace in the lab, but I didn't let that stop me. My dissertation asked, "How similar at the level of genes and proteins are people and chimpanzees?" We discovered, much to our amazement, that they are extraordinarily similar, that we differ in only about one percent of our DNA. Morphologically and behaviorally, humans and chimpanzees seem to be in different taxonomic families. But genetically we are closely related species. How does one resolve this paradox? One possibility is that similar genes in humans and chimps are

turned on and off at different times during embryonic development. The idea that the evolutionary divergence of species might be at least partially explained by changes in the *timing* of gene activity is one that other researchers are exploring.

What led you to study breast cancer?

I finished my Ph. D. in '73 and then went to teach at the University of Chile in a Ford Foundation program. I was in Chile when the Allende government was overthrown. There had been wonderful opportunities for the integration of scientific and economic development of the country, all of which were

INTERVIEW

MARY-CLAIRE KING

destroyed in the coup. I came back to Berkeley at a loss, thinking, "What shall I do next?" I knew that I liked genetics very much, and I also knew that I needed to do work that was important to people in an everyday sort of way. The first thing that came up was the possibility of working at UC San Francisco setting up a modern genetics lab in their cancer epidemiology group. At that time a lot of money was available for bringing approaches from other fields into cancer research. I was hired to set up a cancer genetics lab and was captivated by the question of what causes cancer, in particular breast cancer.

When scientists say that cancer is a genetic disease, what does that mean?

It means two things. Cancer is always genetic in the sense that cancer is always the consequence of changes in DNA. Cells that have cancer-causing mutations no longer divide

and develop in the way that they should. Something goes wrong with cell division; it's no longer under normal control. The great majority of mutations that lead to cancer arise in the tissue where the cancer starts. The first occurrence is in the colon or in the breast, for example. These mutations are what we call somatic mutations; they are in the body but not in the germ line, the cells that give rise to eggs or sperm. But very rarely, in some families, there *are* germ line mutations in one or more of these same genes. These mutations are passed on from parent to child.

So breast cancer is not usually inherited?

The vast majority of breast-cancer cases seem to have nothing to do with inherited mutations. However, there are many accounts, going back to the ancient Greeks, of families in which breast cancer appears frequently, generation after generation. Of course, this doesn't prove that the disease is inherited. Lung cancer, for example, also clusters in families—but mainly because smoking clusters in families. So, does breast cancer cluster in families because of their exposure to some unidentified environmental agent, or because of an inherited genetic trait, or some combination of both? I thought it would be possible to sort that out by combining statistical studies of families with experimental genetics, and it was. But it took 20 years.

Did you first approach the problem, then, by collecting data on families in which breast cancer was common?

Yes. It occurred to me in 1974 that if mutations were involved in familial breast cancer, we might be able to identify some of the genes that are mutated and then figure out how these genes normally work. The results might give us insight into the more common, nonhereditary forms of the disease.

You eventually identified the gene *BRCA1*, which is mutated in many families with inherited breast cancer, and located the gene on chromosome 17. Are mutations in *BRCA1* also found in the tumors of women with *non*familial breast cancer?

If you test tumor cells from women with nonfamilial breast cancer, you find that cells from more than half of the tumors completely lack one copy of the *BRCA1* gene (of the two in each normal cell) and make reduced amounts of *BRCA1's* protein product. But the sorts of breast-cancer mutations inherited in families are not found in tumors from women with

c. telomerase, helicase, single-strand binding protein
d. DNA ligase, replication fork proteins, adenase
e. nuclease, telomerase, primase

10. Of the following, the most reasonable inference from the observation that defects in DNA repair enzymes contribute to some forms of cancer is that
   a. cancer is generally inherited
   b. uncorrected changes in DNA can cause cancer
   c. cancer cannot occur when DNA repair enzymes work properly
   d. mutations generally lead to cancer
   e. cancer is caused by environmental factors that damage DNA repair enzymes

CHALLENGE QUESTIONS

1. Nerve cells do not replicate their DNA after reaching maturity. A cell biologist observed that there was x amount of DNA in a human nerve cell. In four other types of human cells, labeled A–D, she measured the following amounts of DNA: cell A, $2x$; cell B, $1.6x$; cell C, $0.5x$; cell D, x. Match the four cell types with the following choices: (a) sperm cell; (b) bone cell just beginning interphase; (c) skin cell in the S phase; (d) intestinal cell beginning mitosis. (See Chapter 12 to review the cell cycle and mitosis.)

2. Cells proofread and repair errors in the genetic information encoded in DNA. But some lasting mistakes, or mutations, still happen. The most error-prone stage in DNA replication occurs after parent DNA strands have separated but before new complementary strands are in place. Why might permanent errors be more likely then?

3. Write a short essay explaining the evidence that DNA is the genetic material.

SCIENCE, TECHNOLOGY, AND SOCIETY

1. Cooperation and competition are both common in science. What roles did these two social behaviors play in Watson and Crick's discovery of the double helix? How might competition between scientists accelerate progress in a scientific field? How might it slow progress?

2. DNA molecules with any desired base sequence can be synthesized and replicated in large quantities in the laboratory. It is also possible to determine the base sequence of a DNA molecule. For these reasons, it has been suggested that oil shipments could be tagged with DNA of known sequences. If an oil slick were found, the DNA could be sequenced and the offending ship tracked down. Suggest some other potential applications for "DNA labeling."

FURTHER READING

Greider, C. W., and E. H. Blackburn. "Telomeres, Telomerase and Cancer." *Scientific American,* February 1996.

Travis, J. "Crystal Clear: X-ray Snapshots Illuminate How Enzymes Stitch Together DNA." *Science News,* February 14, 1998.

Watson, J. D. *The Double Helix.* New York: Atheneum, 1968. The controversial bestseller by the codiscoverer of the double helix.

WEB LINKS

Visit the special edition of *The Biology Place* for BIOLOGY, Fifth Edition, at http://www.biology.com/campbell. Go to Chapter 16 for online resources, including learning activities, practice exams, and links to the following web sites:

"Primer on Molecular Genetics"
This introduction to molecular genetics contains numerous explanatory figures and is continuously being revised and updated by the Human Genome Management Information System at the Department of Energy.

"A Structure for Deoxyribose Nucleic Acid"
This site includes a full text and graphic reprint of Watson and Crick's groundbreaking paper on the structure of DNA published in *Nature* in 1953.

"James Dewey Watson"
Learn more about Francis Crick, James Watson, and Maurice Wilkins, who were awarded a Nobel Prize for their work in elucidating the structure of DNA.

"DNA Computing and Informatics at Surfaces"
This site gives a fascinating insight into possible future uses of DNA. Its information storage and retrieval powers may make it the best candidate for super computers of the future.

FROM GENE
TO PROTEIN

The information content of DNA, the genetic material, is in the form of specific sequences of nucleotides along the DNA strands. But how is this information related to an organism's inherited traits? Put another way, what does a gene actually say? And how is its message translated by cells into a specific trait, such as brown hair or type A blood?

Consider, once again, Mendel's peas. One of the characters Mendel studied was stem length. Variation in a single gene accounts for the difference between the tall and dwarf varieties of pea plants in the drawing on this page. Mendel did not know the physiological basis of this phenotypic difference, but plant scientists have since worked out the explanation: Dwarf peas lack growth hormones called gibberellins, which stimulate the normal elongation of stems. A dwarf plant treated with gibberellins grows to normal height. Why do dwarf peas fail to make their own gibberellins? They are missing a key protein, an enzyme required for gibberellin synthesis. This example illustrates the main point of this chapter: The DNA inherited by an organism leads to specific traits by dictating the synthesis of proteins. Proteins are the links between genotype and phenotype. This chapter explores the flow of information from genes to proteins.

THE CONNECTION BETWEEN GENES AND PROTEINS

Before going into the details of how genes direct protein synthesis, let's step back and examine the fundamental relationship between genes and proteins and how this connection was discovered.

The study of metabolic defects provided evidence that genes specify proteins: *science as a process*

In 1909, British physician Archibald Garrod first suggested that genes dictate phenotypes through enzymes that catalyze specific chemical processes in the cell. Garrod postulated that the symptoms of an inherited disease reflect a person's inability to make a particular enzyme. He referred to such diseases as "inborn errors of metabolism." Garrod gave as one example the hereditary condition called alkaptonuria, in which the urine appears black because it contains the chemical alkapton, which darkens upon exposure to air. Garrod reasoned that normal individuals have an enzyme that breaks down alkapton, whereas alkaptonuric individuals have inherited an inability to make the enzyme that metabolizes alkapton.

How Genes Control Metabolism

Garrod's idea was ahead of its time, but research conducted several decades later supported his hypothesis that the func-

tion of a gene is to dictate the production of a specific enzyme. Biochemists accumulated much evidence that cells synthesize and degrade most organic molecules via metabolic pathways, in which each chemical reaction in a sequence is catalyzed by a specific enzyme. Such metabolic pathways lead, for instance, to the synthesis of the pigments that give *Drosophila* their eye color (see FIGURE 15.2). In the 1930s, George Beadle and Boris Ephrussi speculated that each of the various mutations affecting eye color in *Drosophila* blocks pigment synthesis at a specific step by preventing production of the enzyme that catalyzes that step. However, neither the chemical reactions nor the enzymes that catalyze them were known at the time.

A breakthrough in demonstrating the relationship between genes and enzymes came a few years later, after Beadle and Edward Tatum began to search for mutants of a bread mold, *Neurospora crassa*. They discovered mutants that differed from the wild-type mold in their nutritional needs (FIGURE 17.1). Wild-type *Neurospora* has modest food requirements. It can

survive in the laboratory on agar (a moist support medium) mixed only with inorganic salts, sucrose, and the vitamin biotin. From this *minimal medium,* the mold uses its metabolic pathways to produce all the other molecules it needs. Beadle and Tatum identified mutants that could not survive on minimal medium, apparently because they were unable to synthesize certain essential molecules from the minimal ingredients. Such nutritional mutants are called **auxotrophs** (Gr. *auxely,* "to increase"; *trophikos,* "nourishment"). Most auxotrophs *can* survive on a *complete growth medium,* minimal medium supplemented with all 20 amino acids and a few other nutrients.

To pinpoint an auxotroph's metabolic defect, Beadle and Tatum took samples from the mutant growing on complete medium and distributed them to several different vials. Each vial contained minimal medium plus a single additional nutrient. The particular supplement that allowed growth indicated the metabolic defect. For example, if the only supplemented vial that supported growth of the mutant was the

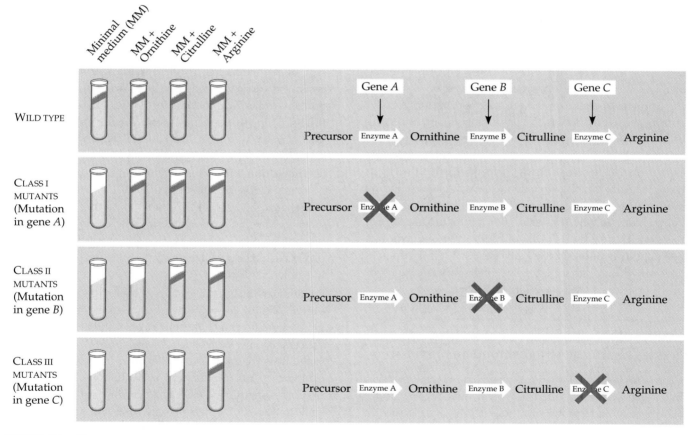

FIGURE 17.1 · **The one gene–one enzyme hypothesis.** Beadle and Tatum based this idea on their study of nutritional mutants of the red bread mold *Neurospora crassa.* The wild-type strain requires only a minimal nutritional medium containing sucrose, essential minerals (inorganic salts), and one vitamin. The mold uses a multistep pathway to synthesize the amino acid arginine from a precursor. Beadle and Tatum

identified three classes of mutants unable to synthesize arginine. Each mutant class had a metabolic block (X in this diagram) at a different step in the pathway. For example, class II mutants failed to grow on minimal medium or minimal medium supplemented with ornithine. Adding either citrulline or arginine to the nutritional medium enabled these mutants to grow. Beadle and Tatum deduced that class II mutants

lacked the enzyme that converts ornithine to citrulline. Adding citrulline to the medium bypasses the metabolic block and allows the mold to survive. The other classes of mutants lacked different enzymes. Beadle and Tatum concluded that various mutations were abnormal variations of different genes, each gene dictating the production of one enzyme; hence, the one gene–one enzyme hypothesis.

one fortified with the amino acid arginine, the researchers could conclude that the mutant was defective in the pathway that normally synthesizes arginine.

With further experimentation, a defect could be described even more specifically. For instance, consider three of the steps in the synthesis of arginine: A precursor nutrient is converted to ornithine, which is converted to citrulline, which is converted to arginine (see FIGURE 17.1). Beadle and Tatum could distinguish among the various arginine auxotrophs they found. Some required arginine, others required either arginine or citrulline, and still others could grow when any of the three compounds—arginine, citrulline, or ornithine—was provided. These three classes of mutants, Beadle and Tatum reasoned, must be blocked at different steps in the pathway that synthesizes arginine. They concluded that each mutant lacked a different enzyme. Assuming that each mutant was defective in a single gene, they formulated the one gene–one enzyme hypothesis, which states that the function of a gene is to dictate the production of a specific enzyme.

One Gene–One Polypeptide

As researchers learned more about proteins, they made minor revisions in the one gene–one enzyme hypothesis. Not all proteins are enzymes. Keratin, the structural protein of animal hair, and the hormone insulin are two examples of nonenzyme proteins. Because proteins that are not enzymes are nevertheless gene products, molecular biologists began to think in terms of one gene–one protein. However, many proteins are constructed from two or more different polypeptide chains (see Chapter 5), and each polypeptide is specified by its own gene. For example, hemoglobin, the oxygen-transporting protein of vertebrate red blood cells, is built from two kinds of polypeptides, and thus *two* genes code for this protein. We can therefore restate Beadle and Tatum's idea as the one gene–one polypeptide hypothesis. Note, however, that it is common to refer to proteins, rather than polypeptides, as the gene products, a practice you will encounter in this book.

Transcription and translation are the two main processes linking gene to protein: *an overview*

17.1 Genes provide the instructions for making specific proteins. But a gene does not build a protein directly. The bridge between DNA and protein synthesis is RNA. You learned in Chapter 5 that RNA is chemically similar to DNA, except that it contains ribose instead of deoxyribose as its sugar and has the nitrogenous base uracil rather than thymine (see FIGURE 5.27). Thus, each nucleotide along a DNA strand has deoxyribose as its sugar and A, G, C, or T as its base; each nucleotide along an RNA strand has ribose as its sugar and A, G, C, or U as its base. An RNA molecule almost always consists of a single strand.

It is customary to describe the flow of information from gene to protein in linguistic terms because both nucleic acids and proteins are polymers with specific sequences of monomers that convey information, much as specific sequences of letters communicate information in a written language. In DNA or RNA, the monomers are the four types of nucleotides, which differ in their nitrogenous bases. Genes are typically hundreds or thousands of nucleotides long, each gene having a specific sequence of bases. Each polypeptide of a protein also has monomers arranged in a particular linear order (the protein's primary structure; see Chapter 5), but its monomers are the 20 amino acids. Thus, nucleic acids and proteins contain information written in two different chemical languages. To get from DNA, written in one language, to protein, written in the other, requires two major stages, transcription and translation.

Transcription is the synthesis of RNA under the direction of DNA. Both nucleic acids use the same language, and the information is simply transcribed, or copied, from one molecule to the other. Just as a DNA strand provides a template for the synthesis of a new complementary strand during DNA replication, it provides a template for assembling a sequence of RNA nucleotides. The resulting RNA molecule is a faithful transcript of the gene's protein-building instructions. This type of RNA molecule is called **messenger RNA (mRNA)**, because it carries a genetic message from the DNA to the protein-synthesizing machinery of the cell (FIGURE 17.2a). (Transcription is the general term for the synthesis of *any* kind of RNA from DNA. Later in this chapter you will learn about other types of RNA produced by transcription.)

Translation is the actual synthesis of a polypeptide, which occurs under the direction of mRNA. During this stage there is a change in language: The cell must translate the base sequence of an mRNA molecule into the amino acid sequence of a polypeptide. The sites of translation are ribosomes, complex particles that facilitate the orderly linking of amino acids into polypeptide chains.

Although the basic mechanics of transcription and translation are similar for prokaryotes and eukaryotes, there is an important difference in the flow of genetic information within the cells. Because bacteria lack nuclei, their DNA is not segregated from ribosomes and the other protein-synthesizing equipment. Transcription and translation are coupled, with ribosomes attaching to the leading end of an mRNA molecule while transcription is still in progress (see FIGURE 17.20, p. 311). In a eukaryotic cell, by contrast, the nuclear envelope separates transcription from translation in space and time. Transcription occurs in the nucleus, and mRNA is dispatched to the cytoplasm, where translation occurs (FIGURE 17.2b). But before they can leave the nucleus, eukaryotic RNA transcripts are modified in various ways to produce the final, functional mRNA. Thus, in a two-step process, the transcription of a eukaryotic gene results in *pre-mRNA,* and **RNA processing**

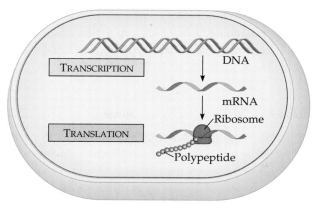

(a) Prokaryotic cell

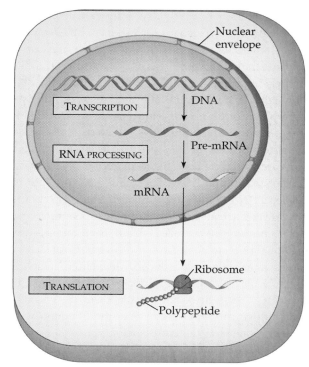

(b) Eukaryotic cell

FIGURE 17.2 ▪ Overview: the roles of transcription and translation in the flow of genetic information. In a cell's chain of command, inherited information flows from DNA to RNA to protein. The two main stages of information flow are transcription and translation. In transcription, a gene provides the instructions for synthesizing a messenger RNA (mRNA) molecule. In translation, the information encoded in mRNA determines the order of amino acids that are joined to form a specific polypeptide. Ribosomes are the sites of translation. **(a)** In a prokaryotic cell, which lacks a nucleus, mRNA produced by transcription is immediately translated without additional processing. **(b)** In a eukaryotic cell, transcription and translation occur in separate compartments, the nucleus and the cytoplasm. The mRNA moves from nucleus to cytoplasm via pores in the nuclear envelope. The original RNA transcript, called pre-mRNA, is processed in various ways by enzymes before leaving the nucleus as mRNA. A miniature version of this illustration (or, in some cases, part a) accompanies several figures later in the chapter as an orientation diagram to help you see where the content of a particular figure fits into the overall scheme.

yields the finished mRNA. A more general term for an initial RNA transcript is **primary transcript**.

Let's summarize the main point of our overview of protein synthesis: Genes program protein synthesis via genetic messages in the form of messenger RNA. Put another way, cells are governed by a molecular chain of command: DNA ⟶ RNA ⟶ protein. The next section discusses how the instructions for assembling amino acids into a specific order are encoded in nucleic acids.

In the genetic code, nucleotide triplets specify amino acids

When biologists began to suspect that the instructions for protein synthesis were encoded in DNA, they recognized a problem: There are only 4 nucleotides to specify 20 amino acids. Thus, the genetic code cannot be a language like Chinese, where each written symbol corresponds to a single word. If each nucleotide base were translated into an amino acid, only 4 of the 20 amino acids could be specified. Would a language of two-letter code words suffice? The base sequence AG, for example, could specify one amino acid, and GT could specify another. Since there are four bases, this would give us 16 (that is, 4^2) possible arrangements—still not enough to code for all 20 amino acids.

Triplets of nucleotide bases are the smallest units of uniform length that can code for all the amino acids. If each arrangement of three consecutive bases specifies an amino acid, there can be 64 ($=4^3$) possible code words—more than enough to specify all the amino acids. Experiments have verified that the flow of information from gene to protein is based on a **triplet code**: The genetic instructions for a polypeptide chain are written in the DNA as a series of three-nucleotide words. For example, the base triplet AGT at a particular position along a DNA strand says to place the amino acid serine at the corresponding position of the polypeptide to be produced.

A cell cannot directly translate a gene into amino acids. The intermediate step is transcription, during which the gene determines the sequence of base triplets along the length of an mRNA molecule. For each gene, only one of the two DNA strands is transcribed. This strand is called the **template strand**, because it provides the template for ordering the

sequence of nucleotides in an RNA transcript. (The other strand provides the instructions for making a new template strand when the DNA replicates.) A given DNA strand can be the template strand in some regions of a DNA molecule, while in other regions along the double helix it is the complementary strand that functions as the template for RNA synthesis.

An mRNA molecule is complementary rather than identical to its DNA template because RNA bases are assembled on the template according to base-pairing rules (FIGURE 17.3). The pairs are similar to those that form during DNA replication, except that U, the RNA substitute for T, pairs with A. Thus, when a DNA strand is transcribed, the base triplet ACC in DNA provides a template for UGG in the mRNA molecule. The mRNA base triplets are called **codons**. For example, UGG is the codon for the amino acid tryptophan (abbreviated Trp).

During translation, the sequence of codons along an mRNA molecule is decoded, or translated, into a sequence of amino acids making up a polypeptide chain. Each codon along the mRNA specifies which one of the 20 amino acids will be incorporated at the corresponding position along a polypeptide. Because codons are base triplets, the number of

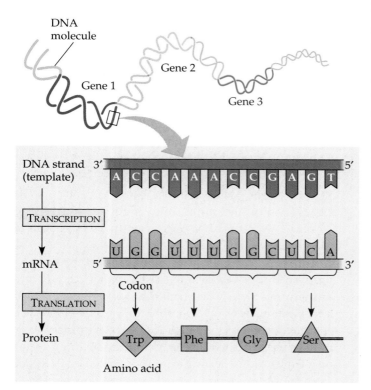

FIGURE 17.3 · The triplet code. For each gene, one of the two strands of DNA functions as a template for transcription—the synthesis of an mRNA molecule of complementary sequence. The same base-pairing rules that apply to DNA synthesis also guide transcription, but the base uracil (U) takes the place of thymine (T) in RNA. During translation, the genetic message (mRNA) is read as a sequence of base triplets, analogous to three-letter code words. Each of these triplets, called a codon (bracketed in the figure), specifies the amino acid to be added at the corresponding position along a growing polypeptide chain. The gene, its mRNA transcript, and the polypeptide product are all much longer than the segments shown here.

nucleotides making up a genetic message must be three times the number of amino acids making up the protein product. For example, it takes 300 nucleotides along an RNA strand to code for a polypeptide that is 100 amino acids long.

Cracking the Genetic Code

Molecular biologists cracked the code of life in the early 1960s, when a series of elegant experiments disclosed the amino acid translations of each of the RNA codons. The first codon was deciphered in 1961 by Marshall Nirenberg of the National Institutes of Health. Nirenberg had synthesized an artificial mRNA by linking identical RNA nucleotides containing uracil as their base. No matter where this message started or stopped, it could contain only one codon in repetition: UUU. Nirenberg added this "poly U" to a test-tube mixture containing amino acids, ribosomes, and the other components required for protein synthesis. His artificial system translated the poly U into a polypeptide containing a single amino acid, phenylalanine (Phe), strung together as a long polyphenylalanine chain. Thus, Nirenberg determined that the mRNA codon UUU specifies the amino acid phenylalanine. Soon, the amino acids specified by the codons AAA, GGG, and CCC were also determined.

Although more elaborate techniques were required to decode mixed triplets such as AUA and CGA, all 64 codons were deciphered by the mid-1960s. As FIGURE 17.4 shows, 61 of the 64 triplets code for amino acids. Notice that the codon AUG has a dual function: It not only codes for the amino acid methionine (Met), but also functions as a "start" signal, or an initiation codon. Genetic messages begin with the mRNA codon AUG, which signals the protein-synthesizing machinery to begin translating the mRNA at that location. (Since AUG also stands for methionine, polypeptide chains begin with methionine when they are synthesized. However, an enzyme may subsequently remove this starter amino acid from a chain.) The remaining three codons do not designate amino acids. Instead, they are "stop" signals, or termination codons, marking the end of translation.

Notice in FIGURE 17.4 that there is redundancy in the genetic code, but no ambiguity. For example, although codons GAA and GAG both specify glutamic acid (redundancy), neither of them ever specifies any other amino acid (no ambiguity). The redundancy in the code is not altogether random. In many cases, codons that are synonyms for a particular amino acid differ only in the third base of the triplet. We will consider a possible explanation for this redundancy later in the chapter.

Our ability to extract the intended message from a written language depends on reading the symbols in the correct sequence and groupings—that is, in the correct **reading frame**. Consider this statement: "The red dog ate the cat." Read the words out of order, and you may get the unintended

		SECOND BASE			
	U	C	A	G	

FIRST BASE (5' end) / **THIRD BASE (3' end)**

	U	C	A	G	
U	UUU ⎤ UUC ⎦ Phe UUA ⎤ UUG ⎦ Leu	UCU ⎤ UCC ⎥ UCA ⎥ UCG ⎦ Ser	UAU ⎤ UAC ⎦ Tyr UAA Stop UAG Stop	UGU ⎤ UGC ⎦ Cys UGA Stop UGG Trp	U C A G
C	CUU ⎤ CUC ⎥ CUA ⎥ CUG ⎦ Leu	CCU ⎤ CCC ⎥ CCA ⎥ CCG ⎦ Pro	CAU ⎤ CAC ⎦ His CAA ⎤ CAG ⎦ Gln	CGU ⎤ CGC ⎥ CGA ⎥ CGG ⎦ Arg	U C A G
A	AUU ⎤ AUC ⎥ Ile AUA ⎦ AUG Met or start	ACU ⎤ ACC ⎥ ACA ⎥ ACG ⎦ Thr	AAU ⎤ AAC ⎦ Asn AAA ⎤ AAG ⎦ Lys	AGU ⎤ AGC ⎦ Ser AGA ⎤ AGG ⎦ Arg	U C A G
G	GUU ⎤ GUC ⎥ GUA ⎥ Val GUG ⎦	GCU ⎤ GCC ⎥ GCA ⎥ GCG ⎦ Ala	GAU ⎤ GAC ⎦ Asp GAA ⎤ GAG ⎦ Glu	GGU ⎤ GGC ⎥ GGA ⎥ Gly GGG ⎦	U C A G

FIGURE 17.4 ▪ The dictionary of the genetic code. The three bases of an mRNA codon are designated here as the first, second, and third bases, reading in the 5'⟶3' direction along the mRNA. Practice using this dictionary by finding the codon UGG, the first codon in FIGURE 17.3. This is the only codon for the amino acid tryptophan, but most amino acids are specified by two or more codons. For example, both UUU and UUC stand for the amino acid phenylalanine (Phe). When either of these codons is read along an mRNA molecule, phenylalanine will be incorporated into the growing polypeptide chain. We can think of UUU and UUC as synonyms in the genetic code. Notice that the codon AUG not only stands for the amino acid methionine (Met) but also functions as a "start" signal for ribosomes, the cell organelles that actually assemble polypeptides, to begin translating the mRNA at that location. Three of the 64 codons function as "stop" signals. Any one of these termination codons marks the end of a genetic message.

message, "The red cat ate the dog." Group the letters incorrectly, and you may think that the first word of the message is "There." The reading frame is also important in the molecular language of cells. The short stretch of polypeptide shown in FIGURE 17.3, for instance, will only be made correctly if the mRNA nucleotides UGGUUUGGCUCA are read from left to right in groups of three. Although a genetic message is written with no spaces between the codons, the cell's protein-synthesizing machinery reads the message as a series of nonoverlapping three-letter words. The message is *not* read as a series of overlapping words—UGG UUU, and so on—which would convey a very different message.

Let's summarize what we have just covered. Genetic information is encoded as a sequence of nonoverlapping base triplets, or codons, each of which is translated into a specific amino acid during protein synthesis.

The genetic code must have evolved very early in the history of life

The genetic code is nearly universal, shared by organisms from the simplest bacteria to the most complex plants and animals. The RNA codon CCG, for instance, is translated as the amino acid proline in all organisms whose genetic code has been examined. In laboratory experiments, genes can be transcribed and translated after they are transplanted from one species to another (FIGURE 17.5). One important application is that bacteria can be programmed by the insertion of human genes to synthesize certain human proteins that have important medical uses. Such applications have produced many exciting developments in biotechnology, which you will learn about in Chapter 20.

There are some exceptions to the universality of the genetic code, translation systems where a few codons differ from the standard ones. The main examples are found in certain single-celled eukaryotes, such as *Paramecium,* an organism you may know from the lab. Other examples are found in certain

FIGURE 17.5 ▪ A tobacco plant expressing a firefly gene.
Because diverse forms of life share a common genetic code, it is possible to program one species to produce proteins characteristic of another species by transplanting DNA. In this experiment, researchers were able to incorporate a gene from a firefly into the DNA of a tobacco plant. The gene codes for the firefly enzyme that catalyzes the chemical reaction that releases energy in the form of light.

mitochondria and chloroplasts, which transcribe and translate the genes carried by their small amount of DNA. However, the evolutionary significance of the code's *near* universality is clear. A language shared by all living things must have been operating very early in the history of life—early enough to be present in the organisms that were the common ancestors of all modern organisms. A shared genetic vocabulary is a reminder of the kinship that bonds all life on Earth.

Now that we have considered the linguistic logic and evolutionary significance of the genetic code, we are ready to reexamine transcription, translation, and related topics in more detail.

THE SYNTHESIS AND PROCESSING OF RNA

Transcription is the DNA-directed synthesis of RNA: *a closer look*

17.2 Messenger RNA, the carrier of information from DNA to the cell's protein-synthesizing machinery, is transcribed from the template strand of a gene. An enzyme called an **RNA polymerase** pries the two strands of DNA apart and hooks together the RNA nucleotides as they base-pair along the DNA tem-

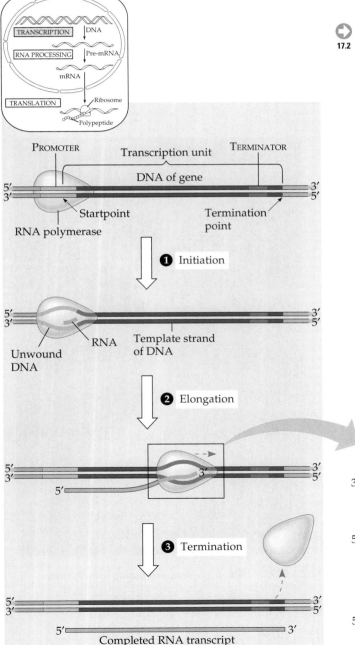

FIGURE 17.6 ▪ The stages of transcription. The enzyme responsible for transcription is RNA polymerase, which moves along a gene from its promoter (green) to just beyond its terminator (red). RNA polymerase assembles an RNA molecule with a nucleotide sequence complementary to that of the gene's template strand. The stretch of DNA that is actually transcribed is called a transcription unit. ① After binding to the promoter, the RNA polymerase unwinds the two DNA strands and initiates RNA synthesis at the startpoint on the template strand. Nucleotide sequences within the promoter determine which way the RNA polymerase faces and hence which strand is used as the template. ② The RNA polymerase works its way "downstream" from the promoter, unwinding the DNA and elongating the growing RNA in the 5'⟶3' direction. In the wake of transcription the DNA strands re-form the double helix. ③ Eventually the RNA polymerase transcribes a terminator, a sequence of nucleotides along the DNA that signals the end of the transcription unit. Shortly thereafter the RNA is released, and the polymerase dissociates from the DNA. In a prokaryote the RNA transcript of a protein-coding gene is immediately usable as mRNA; in a eukaryote the RNA must first undergo additional processing.

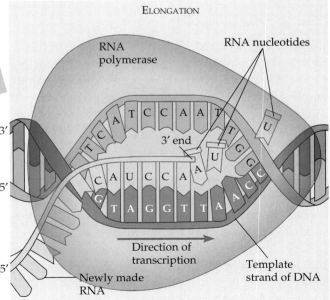

plate. Like the DNA polymerases that function in DNA replication, RNA polymerases can add nucleotides only to the 3′ end of the growing polymer. Thus, an RNA molecule elongates in its 5′ ⟶ 3′ direction. Specific sequences of nucleotides along the DNA mark where transcription of a gene begins and ends. The stretch of DNA that is transcribed into an RNA molecule is called a **transcription unit** (FIGURE 17.6).

Bacteria have a single type of RNA polymerase that synthesizes not only mRNA but also other types of RNA that function in protein synthesis. In contrast, eukaryotes have three types of RNA polymerase in their nuclei, numbered I, II, and III. The one used for mRNA synthesis is RNA polymerase II. In the discussion of transcription that follows, we start with the features of mRNA synthesis common to both prokaryotes and eukaryotes and then describe some key differences.

The three stages of transcription, as shown in FIGURE 17.6, are initiation, elongation, and termination of the RNA chain.

RNA Polymerase Binding and Initiation of Transcription

A region of DNA where RNA polymerase attaches and initiates transcription is known as a **promoter**. A promoter includes the transcription startpoint (the nucleotide where RNA synthesis actually begins) and typically extends several dozen nucleotide pairs "upstream" from the startpoint. In addition to determining where transcription starts, the promoter determines which of the two strands of the DNA helix is used as the template.

Certain sections of a promoter are especially important for binding RNA polymerase. In prokaryotes, the RNA polymerase itself specifically recognizes and binds to the promoter. In eukaryotes, by contrast, a collection of proteins called **transcription factors** mediate the binding of RNA polymerase and the initiation of transcription. Only after certain transcription factors are bound to the promoter does the RNA polymerase bind to it. The completed assembly of transcription factors and RNA polymerase bound to the promoter is called a **transcription initiation complex**.

The interaction between eukaryotic RNA polymerase and transcription factors is an example of the special importance of protein-protein interactions in controlling eukaryotic transcription (as we will discuss further in Chapter 19). FIGURE 17.7 shows the role of transcription factors and a crucial promoter DNA sequence called a **TATA box** in forming the initiation complex. Once the polymerase is firmly attached to the promoter DNA, the two DNA strands unwind there, and the enzyme starts transcribing the template strand.

Elongation of the RNA Strand

As RNA polymerase moves along the DNA, it continues to untwist the double helix, exposing about 10–20 DNA bases at a time for pairing with RNA nucleotides (see FIGURE 17.6).

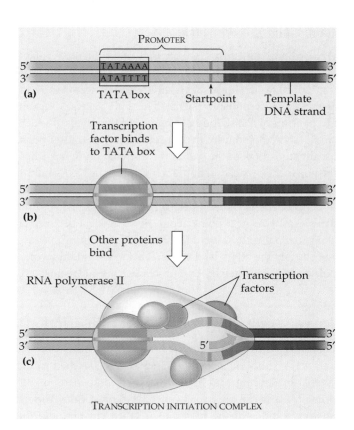

FIGURE 17.7 · **The initiation of transcription at a eukaryotic promoter.** In eukaryotic cells, the enzyme that transcribes protein-coding genes into pre-mRNA is RNA polymerase II. This enzyme initiates RNA synthesis at promoters that commonly include a *TATA box*, a nucleotide sequence typically something like TATAAAA. (By convention, nucleotide sequences are given as they occur on the *non*-template strand.) **(a)** Within the promoter, the TATA box is located about 25 nucleotides upstream from the transcriptional startpoint. **(b)** RNA polymerase II cannot recognize the TATA box and other landmarks of the promoter on its own. Another protein, a transcription factor that recognizes the TATA box, binds to the DNA before the RNA polymerase can do so. **(c)** Additional transcription factors (purple) join the polymerase on the DNA. Protein-protein interactions are critical in the formation of the eukaryotic transcription initiation complex. The DNA double helix unwinds, and RNA synthesis begins at the startpoint on the template strand.

The enzyme adds nucleotides to the 3′ end of the growing RNA molecule as it continues along the double helix. In the wake of this advancing wave of RNA synthesis, the DNA double helix re-forms and the new RNA molecule peels away from its DNA template. Transcription progresses at a rate of about 60 nucleotides per second in eukaryotes.

A single gene can be transcribed simultaneously by several molecules of RNA polymerase following each other like trucks in a convoy. The growing strands of RNA trail off from each polymerase, with the length of each new strand reflecting how far along the template the enzyme has traveled from the startpoint (see FIGURE 17.20, p. 311). The congregation of many polymerase molecules simultaneously transcribing a single gene increases the number of mRNA molecules and helps a cell make a protein in large amounts.

Termination of Transcription

Transcription proceeds until shortly after the RNA polymerase transcribes a DNA sequence called a **terminator**. The transcribed terminator—that is, an *RNA* sequence—functions as the actual termination signal. There are several different mechanisms of transcription termination, the details of which are still somewhat murky. In the prokaryotic cell, transcription usually stops right at the end of the termination signal; when the polymerase reaches that point it releases the RNA and the DNA. By contrast, in the eukaryotic cell the polymerase continues past the termination signal, an AAUAAA sequence in the pre-mRNA. At a point about 10–35 nucleotides farther along, the pre-mRNA is cut free from the enzyme. The cleavage site on the RNA is also the site for the addition of a poly(A) tail—one step of RNA processing, our next topic.

Eukaryotic cells modify RNA after transcription

17.3 Enzymes in the eukaryotic nucleus modify pre-mRNA in various ways before the genetic messages are dispatched to the cytoplasm. During this RNA processing, both ends of the primary transcript are usually altered. In most cases, certain interior sections of the molecule are then cut out, and the remaining parts spliced together.

Alteration of mRNA Ends

Each end of a pre-mRNA molecule is modified in a particular way. The 5′ end, the end made first during transcription, is immediately capped off with a modified form of a guanine (G) nucleotide. This **5′ cap** has at least two important functions. First, it helps protect the mRNA from degradation by hydrolytic enzymes. Second, after the mRNA reaches the cytoplasm, the 5′ cap functions as part of an "attach here" sign for ribosomes. The other end of an mRNA molecule, the 3′ end, is also modified before the message exits the nucleus. To the 3′ end an enzyme adds a **poly(A) tail** consisting of 30 to 200 adenine nucleotides. Like the 5′ cap, the poly(A) tail inhibits degradation of the RNA and helps the ribosome attach to it. The poly(A) tail also seems to facilitate the export of mRNA from the nucleus. FIGURE 17.8 shows a eukaryotic mRNA molecule with cap and tail; it also shows the nontranslated *leader* and *trailer* segments of RNA to which they are attached.

Split Genes and RNA Splicing

The most remarkable stage of RNA processing in the eukaryotic nucleus is the removal of a large portion of the RNA molecule that is initially synthesized—a cut-and-paste job called **RNA splicing** (FIGURE 17.9). The average length of a transcription unit along a eukaryotic DNA molecule is about 8000 nucleotides, so the primary RNA transcript is also that long. But it takes only about 1200 nucleotides to code for an average-sized protein of 400 amino acids. (Remember, each amino acid is encoded by a *triplet* of nucleotides.) This means that most eukaryotic genes and their RNA transcripts have long noncoding stretches of nucleotides, regions that are not translated. Even more surprising is that most of these noncoding sequences are interspersed between coding segments of the gene, and thus between coding segments of the pre-mRNA. In other words, the sequence of DNA nucleotides that codes for a eukaryotic polypeptide is not continuous. The noncoding segments of nucleic acid that lie between coding regions are called intervening sequences, or **introns** for short. The other regions are called **exons**, because they are eventually expressed—that is, translated into amino acid sequences. (The exceptions are the leader and trailer portions of the exons at the two ends of the RNA; see FIGURE 17.9.) Richard Roberts and Phillip Sharp, who independently found evidence of "split genes" in 1977, shared a Nobel Prize in 1993 for this discovery.

RNA polymerase transcribes both introns and exons from the DNA, creating an oversized RNA molecule. But this pre-mRNA never leaves the nucleus; the mRNA molecule that enters the cytoplasm is an abridged version of the primary transcript. The introns are excised from the molecule and the exons joined together to form an mRNA molecule with a continuous coding sequence.

FIGURE 17.8 · RNA processing: addition of the 5′ cap and poly(A) tail. Enzymes modify the two ends of a eukaryotic pre-mRNA molecule. A cap consisting of a modified guanosine triphosphate is added to the 5′ end of the RNA as soon as it is made. A poly(A) tail consisting of up to 200 adenine nucleotides is attached to the 3′ end, the end created by cleavage downstream of the AAUAAA termination signal. The modified ends help protect the RNA from degradation, and the poly(A) tail may facilitate the export of mRNA from the nucleus. When the mRNA reaches the cytoplasm, the modified ends, in conjunction with certain cytoplasmic proteins, signal a ribosome to attach to the mRNA. The leader and trailer segments of RNA are not translated.

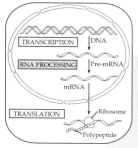

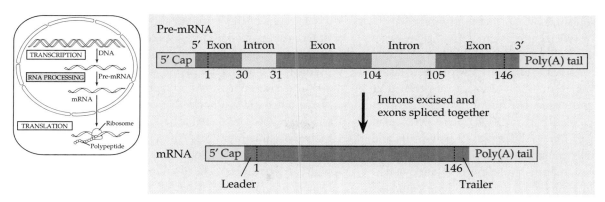

FIGURE 17.9 · RNA processing: RNA splicing. The gene depicted here codes for β-globin, one of the polypeptides of hemoglobin. β-globin is 146 amino acids long. (The numbers under the RNA refer to codons.) Its gene has three segments containing coding regions, called exons, that are separated by noncoding regions, called introns. The entire gene is transcribed to form a molecule of pre-mRNA. However, before the RNA leaves the nucleus as mRNA, the introns are excised and the exons are spliced together. Notice that the exons at the ends of the mRNA include noncoding sections (leader and trailer), to which are attached the cap and tail.

How is mRNA splicing carried out? Researchers have learned that the signals for RNA splicing are short nucleotide sequences at the ends of introns. Particles called *small nuclear ribonucleoproteins,* or *snRNPs* (pronounced "snurps"), recognize these splice sites. As the name implies, snRNPs are located in the cell nucleus and are composed of RNA and protein molecules. The RNA in a snRNP particle is called a *small nuclear RNA (snRNA);* each molecule is about 150 nucleotides long. Several different snRNPs join with additional proteins to form an even larger assembly called a **spliceosome**, which is almost as big as a ribosome. The spliceosome interacts with the splice sites at the ends of an intron. It cuts at specific points to release the intron, then immediately joins together the two exons that flanked the intron (FIGURE 17.10). There is strong evidence that snRNA plays a role in the catalytic process, as well as in spliceosome assembly and splice-site recognition. The idea of a catalytic role for snRNA arose from the discovery of **ribozymes**, RNA molecules that function as enzymes.

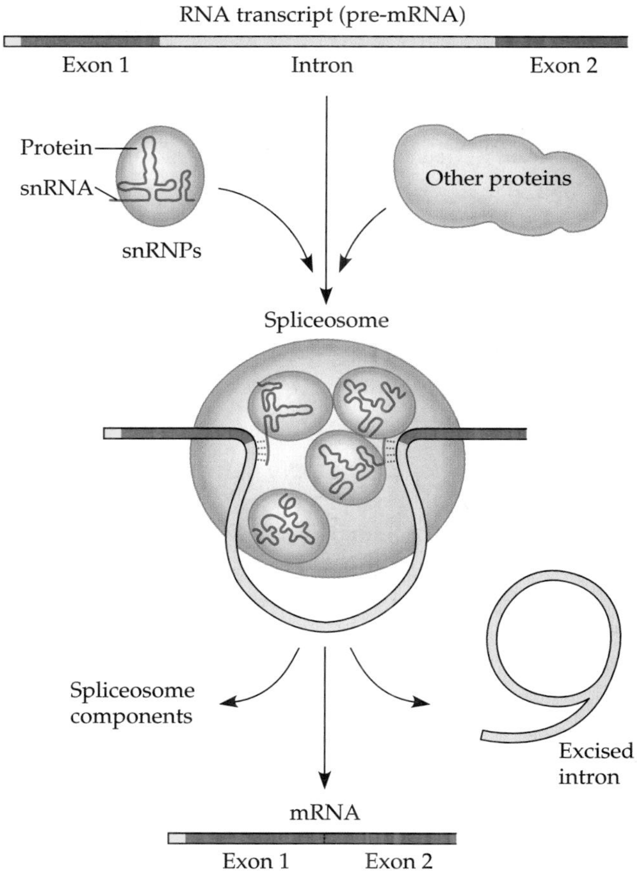

Ribozymes

Like pre-mRNA, other kinds of primary transcripts may also be spliced, but by diverse mechanisms that do not involve spliceosomes. However, as with mRNA splicing, RNA is often involved in catalyzing the reactions. In a few cases the splicing occurs completely without proteins or even extra RNA molecules: The intron RNA itself catalyzes the process! For example, in the protozoan *Tetrahymena,* self-splicing occurs in the production of an RNA component of the organism's ribosomes (ribosomal RNA). Like enzymes, ribozymes function as catalysts. The discovery of ribozymes rendered the statement "All biological catalysts are proteins" obsolete.

The Functional and Evolutionary Importance of Introns

What are the biological functions of introns and RNA splicing? One idea is that introns play regulatory roles in the cell. At

FIGURE 17.10 · The roles of snRNPs and spliceosomes in mRNA splicing. After a eukaryotic gene containing exons and introns is transcribed, the RNA transcript combines with small nuclear ribonucleoproteins (snRNPs) and other proteins to form a molecular complex called a spliceosome. Within the spliceosome the RNA of certain snRNPs base-pairs with nucleotides at the ends of the intron, the RNA transcript is cut to release the intron, and the exons are spliced together. The spliceosome then comes apart, releasing mRNA, which now contains only exons. The diagram shows only a portion of the RNA transcript; additional introns and exons lie downstream from the ones pictured here.

least some introns contain sequences that control gene activity in some way, and the splicing process itself may help regulate the passage of mRNA from nucleus to cytoplasm. Moreover, a number of genes are known to give rise to two or more different proteins, depending on which segments are treated as exons during RNA processing. The fruit fly provides an interesting example of alternative RNA splicing: Sex differences in this animal are largely due to differences in how males and females splice the RNA transcribed from certain genes.

Introns also play an important role in the evolution of new and potentially useful proteins. Many proteins have a modular architecture consisting of discrete structural and functional components called **domains**. One domain of an enzymatic protein, for instance, might include the active site, while another might attach the protein to a cellular membrane. In many cases the exons of a "split gene" code for the different domains of a protein. It is relatively easy for genetic recombination to modify the function of such a protein by changing just one of its domains without altering the other domains. Because the coding regions (exons) for the protein are separated by stretches of noncoding (intron) DNA, the frequency of recombination within a split gene can be higher than for a gene lacking introns. Introns increase the opportunity for crossing over between two alleles of a gene, raising the probability that a crossover will switch one version of an exon for another version found on the homologous chromosome. We can also imagine the occasional mixing and matching of exons between completely different (nonallelic) genes. Exon shuffling of either sort could lead to new proteins with novel combinations of functions.

THE SYNTHESIS OF PROTEIN

We will now examine more closely how genetic information flows from mRNA to protein—the process of translation. As we did for transcription, we'll concentrate on the basic steps of translation that occur in both prokaryotes and eukaryotes while pointing out key differences.

Translation is the RNA-directed synthesis of a polypeptide: *a closer look*

17.4 In the process of translation a cell interprets a genetic message and builds a protein accordingly. The message is a series of codons along an mRNA molecule, and the interpreter is **transfer RNA (tRNA)**. The function of tRNA is to transfer amino acids from the cytoplasm's amino acid pool to a ribosome. A cell keeps its cytoplasm stocked with all 20 amino acids, either by synthesizing them from other compounds or by taking them up from the surrounding solution. The ribosome adds each amino acid brought to it by tRNA to the growing end of a polypeptide chain (FIGURE 17.11).

Molecules of tRNA are not all identical. The key to translating a genetic message into a specific amino acid sequence is that each type of tRNA molecule links a particular mRNA codon with a particular amino acid. As a tRNA molecule arrives at a ribosome, it bears a specific amino acid at one end. At the other end is a nucleotide triplet called an **anticodon**, which binds, according to the base-pairing rules, to a complementary codon on mRNA. For example, consider the mRNA codon UUU, which is translated as the amino acid phenylalanine (see FIGURE 17.4). The tRNA that plugs into this codon by hydrogen bonding has AAA as its anticodon and carries phenylalanine at its other end. As an mRNA molecule slides through a ribosome, phenylalanine will be added to the polypeptide chain whenever the codon UUU is presented for translation. Codon by codon, the genetic message is translated, as tRNAs deposit amino acids in the order prescribed, and the ribosome joins the amino acids into a chain. The tRNA molecule is like a flashcard with a nucleic acid word

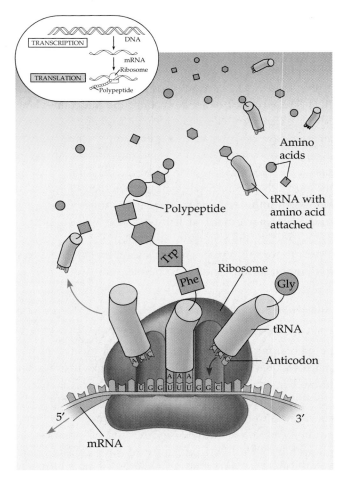

FIGURE 17.11 ▪ **Translation: the basic concept.** As a molecule of mRNA slides through a ribosome, codons are translated into amino acids, one by one. The interpreters are tRNA molecules, each type with a specific anticodon at one end and a certain amino acid at the other end. A tRNA adds its amino acid cargo to a growing polypeptide chain when the anticodon bonds to a complementary codon on the mRNA. The figures that follow show some of the details of translation in the prokaryotic cell.

(anticodon) on one side and a protein word (amino acid) on the other.

Translation is simple in principle but complex in its biochemistry and mechanics, especially in the eukaryotic cell. In dissecting translation we'll concentrate on the slightly less complicated version of the process that occurs in prokaryotes. Let's first look at some of the major players in this cellular drama, then see how they act together to make a polypeptide.

The Structure and Function of Transfer RNA

Like mRNA and other types of cellular RNA, transfer RNA molecules are transcribed from DNA templates. In a eukaryotic cell, tRNA, like mRNA, is made in the nucleus and must travel from the nucleus to the cytoplasm, where translation occurs. In both prokaryotic and eukaryotic cells, each tRNA molecule is used repeatedly, picking up its designated amino acid in the cytosol, depositing this cargo at the ribosome, and leaving the ribosome to pick up another load.

As illustrated in FIGURE 17.12, a tRNA molecule consists of a single RNA strand that is only about 80 nucleotides long (compared to hundreds of nucleotides for most mRNA molecules). This RNA strand folds back upon itself to form a molecule with a three-dimensional structure reinforced by interactions between different parts of the nucleotide chain. Nucleotide bases in certain regions of the tRNA strand form hydrogen bonds with complementary bases of other regions. Flattened into one plane to reveal this hydrogen bonding, a tRNA molecule looks like a cloverleaf. The tRNA actually twists and folds into a compact three-dimensional structure that is roughly L-shaped. The loop protruding from one end of the L includes the anticodon, the specialized base triplet that binds to a specific mRNA codon. From the other end of the L-shaped tRNA molecule protrudes its 3′ end, which is the attachment site for an amino acid. Thus, the structure of a tRNA molecule fits its function

If one tRNA variety existed for each of the mRNA codons that specifies an amino acid, there would be 61 tRNAs (see FIGURE 17.4). The actual number is smaller: about 45. This number is sufficient because some tRNAs have anticodons that can recognize two or more different codons. Such versatility is possible because the rules for base pairing between the third base of a codon and the corresponding base of a tRNA anticodon are not as strict as those for DNA and mRNA codons. For example, the base U of a tRNA anticodon can pair with either A or G in the third position of an mRNA codon. This relaxation of the base-pairing rules is called **wobble**. The most versatile tRNAs are those with inosine (I), a modified base, in the wobble position of the anticodon. Inosine is formed by enzymatic alteration of adenine after tRNA is synthesized. When anticodons associate with codons, the base I can hydrogen-bond with any one of three bases: U, C, or A. Thus, the tRNA molecule that has CCI as its anticodon

can bind to the codons GGU, GGC, and GGA, all of which code for the amino acid glycine. Wobble explains why the synonymous codons for a given amino acid can differ in their third base, but usually not in their other bases.

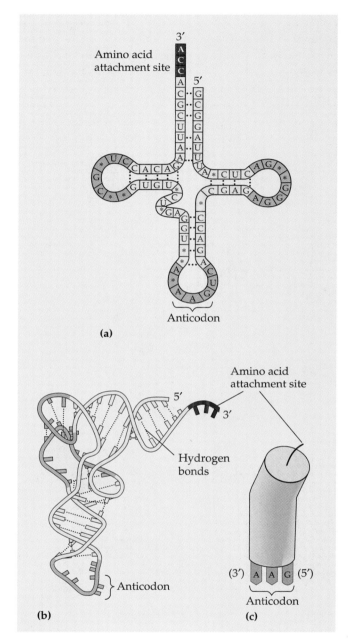

FIGURE 17.12 ▪ The structure of transfer RNA. (a) The two-dimensional structure of a tRNA molecule specific for the amino acid phenylalanine. Notice the four base-paired regions and three loops characteristic of all tRNAs. At the 3′ end of the molecule is the amino acid attachment site, which has the same base sequence for all tRNAs; within the middle loop is the anticodon triplet, which is unique to each tRNA type. (The asterisks mark bases that have been chemically modified, a characteristic of tRNA.) **(b)** The three-dimensional, L-shaped structure of a tRNA. **(c)** This simplified shape is used for tRNA in the figures that follow. Anticodons are conventionally written 3′⟶5′ in order to align properly with codons written 5′⟶3′ (see FIGURE 17.11). For base-pairing, RNA strands must be antiparallel, like DNA (see FIGURE 16.12). For example, anticodon 3′-AAG-5′ pairs with mRNA codon 5′-UUC-3′.

Aminoacyl-tRNA Synthetases

Codon-anticodon bonding is actually the second of two recognition steps required for the accurate translation of a genetic message. It must be preceded by a correct match between tRNA and an amino acid. A tRNA that binds to an mRNA codon specifying a particular amino acid must carry *only* that amino acid to the ribosome. Each amino acid is joined to the correct tRNA by a specific enzyme called an **aminoacyl-tRNA synthetase**. There are 20 of these enzymes in the cell, one enzyme for each amino acid. The active site of each type of aminoacyl-tRNA synthetase fits only a specific combination of amino acid and tRNA. The synthetase catalyzes the covalent attachment of the amino acid to its tRNA in a process driven by the hydrolysis of ATP (FIGURE 17.13). The resulting aminoacyl tRNA is released from the enzyme and delivers its amino acid to a growing polypeptide chain on a ribosome.

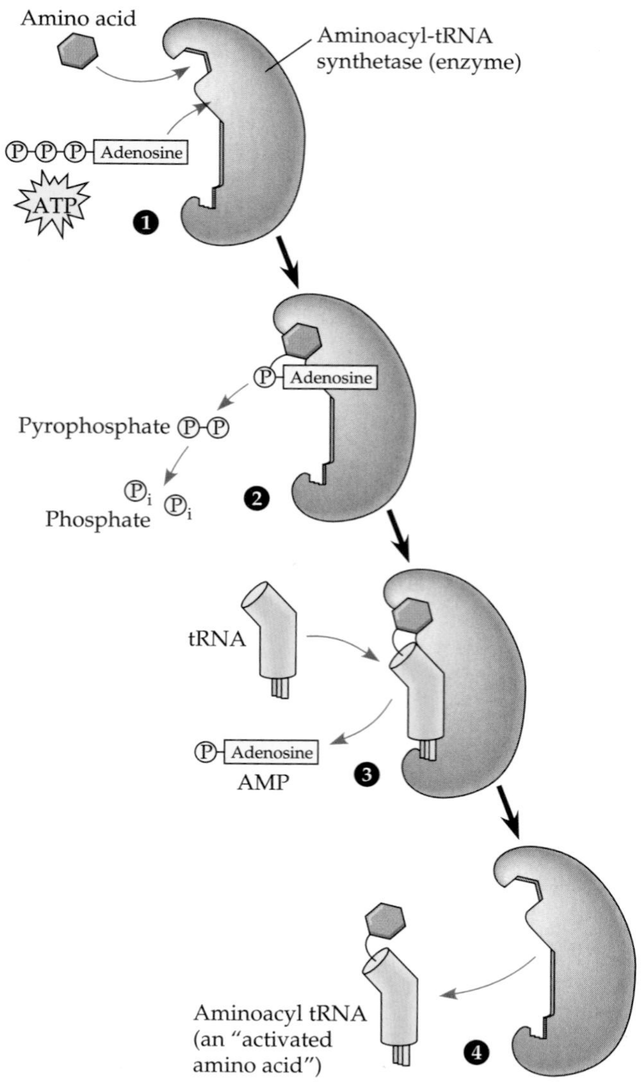

Ribosomes

Ribosomes facilitate the specific coupling of tRNA anticodons with mRNA codons during protein synthesis. A ribosome, which can be seen with the electron microscope, is made up of two subunits, termed the large and small subunits (FIGURE 17.14a). The ribosomal subunits are constructed of proteins and RNA molecules called **ribosomal RNA (rRNA)**. In eukaryotes, the subunits are made in the nucleolus. Ribosomal RNA genes on the chromosomal DNA are transcribed, and the RNA is processed and assembled with proteins imported from the cytoplasm. The resulting ribosomal subunits are then exported via nuclear pores to the cytoplasm. In both prokaryotes and eukaryotes, large and small subunits join to form a functional ribosome only when they attach to an mRNA molecule. About 60% of the weight of each ribosome is rRNA. Because most cells contain thousands of ribosomes, rRNA is the most abundant type of RNA.

Although the ribosomes of prokaryotes and eukaryotes are very similar in structure and function, those of eukaryotes are slightly larger and differ somewhat from prokaryotic ribosomes in their molecular composition. The differences are medically significant. Certain drugs can paralyze prokaryotic ribosomes without inhibiting the ability of eukaryotic ribosomes to make proteins. These drugs, including tetracycline and streptomycin, are used as antibiotics to combat bacterial infection.

The structure of a ribosome reflects its function of bringing mRNA together with amino acid–bearing tRNAs. In addition to a binding site for mRNA, each ribosome has three binding sites for tRNA (FIGURE 17.14b). The **P site** (peptidyl-tRNA site) holds the tRNA carrying the growing polypeptide chain, while the **A site** (aminoacyl-tRNA site) holds the tRNA carrying the next amino acid to be added to the chain. Discharged tRNAs leave the ribosome from the more recently discovered **E site** (exit site). Acting like a vise, the ribosome holds the tRNA and mRNA close together and positions the new amino acid for addition to the carboxyl end of the growing polypeptide (FIGURE 17.14c).

Building a Polypeptide

We can divide translation, the synthesis of a polypeptide chain, into three stages (analogous to those of transcription): initiation, elongation, and termination. All three stages require protein "factors" that aid mRNA, tRNA, and ribosomes in the translation process. For chain initiation and elongation, energy is also required. It is provided by GTP (guanosine triphosphate), a molecule closely related to ATP.

FIGURE 17.13 · An aminoacyl-tRNA synthetase joins a specific amino acid to a tRNA. Linkage of the tRNA and amino acid is an endergonic process that occurs at the expense of ATP. ① The active site of the enzyme binds the amino acid and an ATP molecule. ② The ATP loses two phosphate groups and joins to the amino acid as AMP (adenosine monophosphate). ③ The appropriate tRNA covalently bonds to the amino acid, displacing the AMP from the enzyme's active site. ④ The enzyme releases the aminoacyl tRNA, also called an "activated amino acid."

Initiation. The initiation stage of translation brings together mRNA, a tRNA bearing the first amino acid of the polypeptide, and the two subunits of a ribosome. First, a small ribosomal subunit binds to both mRNA and a special initiator tRNA (FIGURE 17.15). The small ribosomal subunit attaches to the leader segment at the 5' (upstream) end of the mRNA. In bacteria, rRNA of the subunit base-pairs with a specific sequence of nucleotides within the mRNA leader; in eukaryotes the 5' cap first tells the small subunit to attach to the 5' end of the mRNA. Downstream on the mRNA is the initiation codon, AUG, which signals the start of translation. The initiator tRNA, which carries the amino acid methionine, attaches to the initiation codon.

The union of mRNA, initiator tRNA, and a small ribosomal subunit is followed by the attachment of a large ribosomal subunit, completing a translation initiation complex. Proteins called *initiation factors* are required to bring all these components together. The cell also spends energy in the form of a GTP molecule to form the initiation complex. At the completion of the initiation process, the initiator tRNA sits in the P site of the ribosome, and the vacant A site is ready for the next aminoacyl tRNA. The synthesis of a polypeptide is initiated at its amino end.

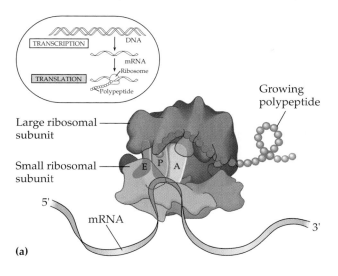

(a)

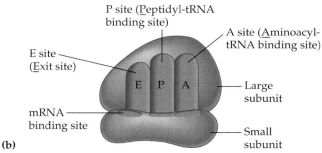

(b)

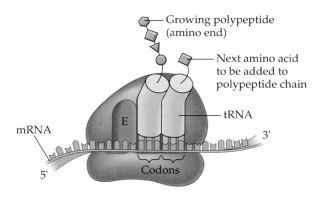

(c)

FIGURE 17.14 ▪ **The anatomy of a ribosome. (a)** A functional ribosome consists of two subunits, each an aggregate of ribosomal RNA and many proteins. This is a model of a bacterial ribosome. The eukaryotic ribosome is roughly similar, but larger, with more proteins and rRNA molecules. **(b)** A ribosome has an mRNA-binding site and three tRNA-binding sites, known as the P, A, and E sites. This is a simplified version of the ribosomal shape that will appear in the next several figures. **(c)** A tRNA fits into a binding site when its anticodon base-pairs with an mRNA codon. The P site holds the tRNA attached to the growing polypeptide. The A site holds the tRNA carrying the next amino acid to be added to the polypeptide chain. Discharged tRNA leaves via the E site.

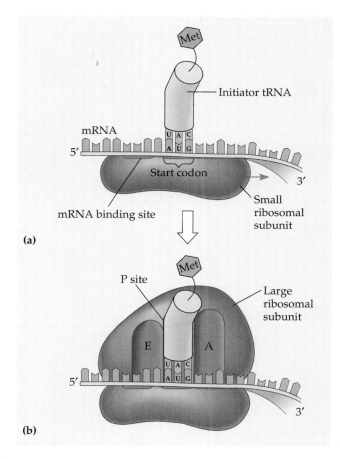

(a)

(b)

FIGURE 17.15 ▪ **Initiation of translation. (a)** A small ribosomal subunit binds to a molecule of mRNA. In a prokaryotic cell, the mRNA-binding site on this subunit recognizes a specific nucleotide sequence on the mRNA just upstream of the start codon. An initiator tRNA, with the anticodon UAC, base-pairs with the start codon, AUG. This tRNA carries the amino acid methionine (Met). **(b)** The arrival of a large ribosomal subunit completes the initiation complex. The initiator tRNA is in the P site. The A site is available to the tRNA bearing the next amino acid. Proteins called initiation factors (not shown) are required to bring all the translation components together. GTP provides the energy for the initiation process.

Elongation. In the elongation stage of translation, amino acids are added one by one to the first amino acid. Each addition involves the participation of several proteins called *elongation factors* and occurs in a three-step cycle (FIGURE 17.16):

① *Codon recognition.* The mRNA codon in the A site of the ribosome forms hydrogen bonds with the anticodon of an incoming molecule of tRNA carrying its appropriate amino acid. An elongation factor ushers the tRNA into the A site. This step also requires the hydrolysis of a GTP.

② *Peptide bond formation.* An rRNA molecule of the large ribosomal subunit, functioning as a ribozyme, catalyzes the formation of a peptide bond that joins the polypeptide extending from the P site to the newly arrived amino acid in the A site. In this step, the polypeptide separates from the tRNA to which it was attached, and the amino acid at its carboxyl end bonds to the amino acid carried by the tRNA in the A site.

③ *Translocation.* The tRNA in the A site, now attached to the growing polypeptide, is translocated to the P site. As the tRNA moves, its anticodon remains hydrogen-bonded to the mRNA codon; the mRNA moves along with it and brings the next codon to be translated into the A site. Meanwhile, the tRNA that was in the P site moves to the E (exit) site and from there leaves the ribosome. The translocation step requires energy, which is provided by hydrolysis of a GTP. The mRNA moves through the ribosome in one direction only, 5′ end first; this is equivalent to the ribosome moving 5′ ⟶ 3′ on the mRNA. The important point is that the ribosome and the mRNA move relative to each other, unidirectionally, codon by codon.

FIGURE 17.16 · The elongation cycle of translation. Not shown in this diagram are the proteins called elongation factors and GTP, whose hydrolysis drives the process.

17.4

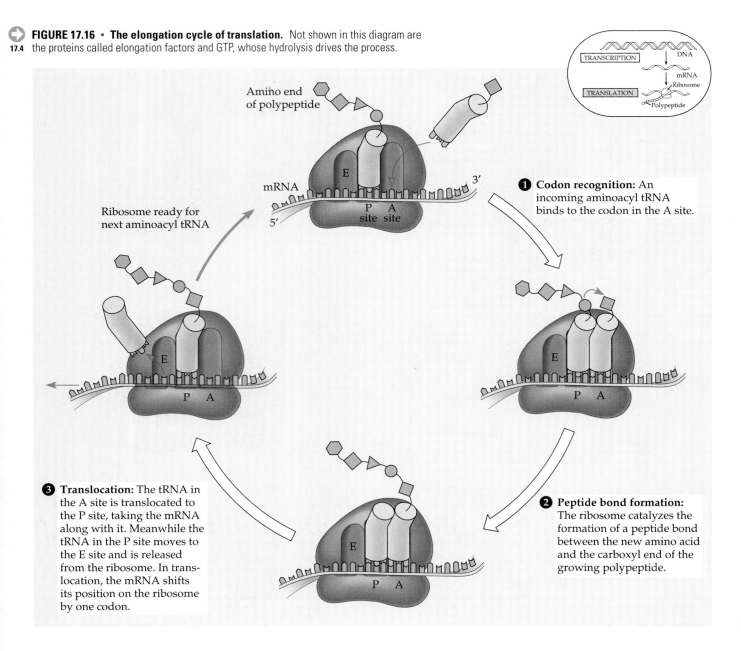

Amino end of polypeptide

mRNA

Ribosome ready for next aminoacyl tRNA

❶ Codon recognition: An incoming aminoacyl tRNA binds to the codon in the A site.

❷ Peptide bond formation: The ribosome catalyzes the formation of a peptide bond between the new amino acid and the carboxyl end of the growing polypeptide.

❸ Translocation: The tRNA in the A site is translocated to the P site, taking the mRNA along with it. Meanwhile the tRNA in the P site moves to the E site and is released from the ribosome. In translocation, the mRNA shifts its position on the ribosome by one codon.

TRANSCRIPTION — DNA
mRNA
Ribosome
TRANSLATION
Polypeptide

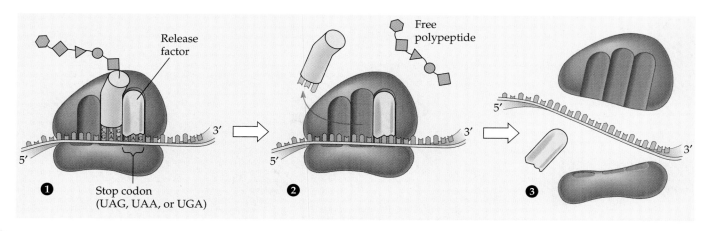

FIGURE 17.17 ▪ Termination of translation. ① When a ribosome reaches a termination codon on a strand of mRNA, the A site of the ribosome accepts a protein called a release factor instead of tRNA. ② The release factor hydrolyzes the bond between the tRNA in the P site and the last amino acid of the polypeptide chain. The polypeptide is thus freed from the ribosome. ③ The two ribosomal subunits and the other components of the assembly dissociate.

The elongation cycle takes less than a tenth of a second and is repeated as each amino acid is added to the chain until the polypeptide is completed.

Termination. The final stage of translation is termination (FIGURE 17.17). Elongation continues until a stop codon reaches the A site of the ribosome. These special base triplets—UAA, UAG, and UGA—do not code for amino acids but instead act as signals to stop translation. A protein called a *release factor* binds directly to the stop codon in the A site. The release factor causes the addition of a water molecule instead of an amino acid to the polypeptide chain. This reaction hydrolyzes the completed polypeptide from the tRNA that is in the P site, freeing the polypeptide from the ribosome. The remainder of the translation assembly then comes apart.

Polyribosomes

A single ribosome can make an average-sized polypeptide in less than a minute. Typically, however, a single mRNA is used to make many copies of a polypeptide simultaneously, because several ribosomes work on translating the message at the same time. Once a ribosome moves past the initiation codon, a second ribosome can attach to the mRNA, and thus several ribosomes may trail along the same mRNA. Such strings of ribosomes, called **polyribosomes**, can be seen with the electron microscope (FIGURE 17.18). Polyribosomes are found in both prokaryotic and eukaryotic cells.

From Polypeptide to Functional Protein

During and after its synthesis a polypeptide chain begins to coil and fold spontaneously, forming a functional protein of specific conformation: a three-dimensional molecule with secondary and tertiary structure. A gene determines primary structure, and primary structure in turn determines conformation. In many cases, chaperone proteins help the polypeptide fold correctly (see Chapter 5).

Additional steps—*posttranslational modifications*—may be required before the protein can begin doing its particular job

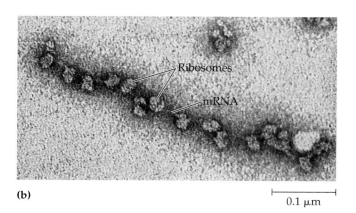

FIGURE 17.18 ▪ Polyribosomes. (a) An mRNA molecule is generally translated simultaneously by several ribosomes in clusters called polyribosomes. **(b)** This micrograph shows a large polyribosome in a prokaryotic cell (TEM).

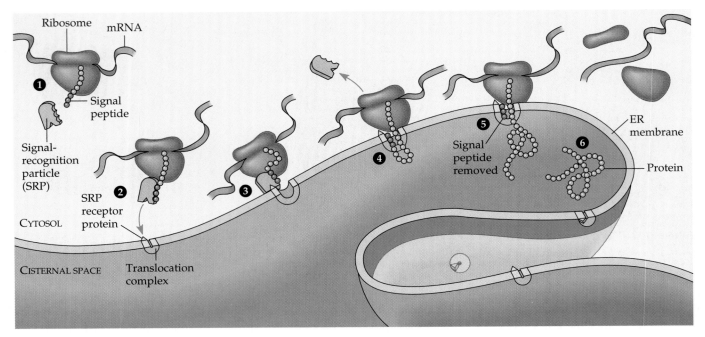

FIGURE 17.19 • The signal mechanism for targeting proteins to the ER. A polypeptide destined for the endomembrane system or for secretion from the cell begins with a signal peptide, a stretch of amino acids that targets it for the ER. This figure shows the synthesis of a secretory protein and its simultaneous import into the ER. ① Polypeptide synthesis begins on a free ribosome in the cytosol. ② A signal-recognition particle (SRP) binds to the signal peptide. ③ The SRP then binds to a receptor protein in the ER membrane. This receptor is part of a protein complex, here called a translocation complex, that also includes a membrane pore and a signal-cleaving enzyme. ④ The SRP is released, and the growing polypeptide translo-cates across the membrane. The signal peptide stays attached to the membrane. ⑤ The signal-cleaving enzyme cuts off the peptide. ⑥ The rest of the completed polypeptide leaves the ribosome and folds into its final conformation. The protein's secretion is accomplished as described in Chapter 7.

in the cell. Certain amino acids may be chemically modified by the attachment of sugars, lipids, phosphate groups, or other additions. Enzymes may remove one or more amino acids from the leading (amino) end of the polypeptide chain. In some cases, a single polypeptide chain may be enzymatically cleaved into two or more pieces. For example, the protein insulin is first synthesized as a single polypeptide chain but becomes active only after an enzyme excises a central part of the chain, leaving a protein made up of two polypeptide chains connected by disulfide bridges. In other cases, two or more polypeptides that are synthesized separately may join to become the subunits of a protein that has quaternary structure. (To review the levels of protein structure, see Chapter 5.)

Signal peptides target some eukaryotic polypeptides to specific destinations in the cell

In electron micrographs of eukaryotic cells active in protein synthesis, two populations of ribosomes (and polyribosomes) are evident: free and bound (see FIGURE 7.10). Free ribosomes are suspended in the cytosol and mostly synthesize proteins that dissolve in the cytosol and function there. In contrast, bound ribosomes are attached to the cytosolic side of the endoplasmic reticulum (ER). They make proteins of the endomembrane system (the nuclear envelope, ER, Golgi apparatus, lysosomes, vacuoles, and plasma membrane) and

proteins that are secreted from the cell. Insulin is an example of a secretory protein. The ribosomes themselves are identical and can switch their status from free to bound.

What determines whether a ribosome will be free in the cytosol or bound to rough ER at any particular time? The synthesis of all proteins begins in the cytosol, when a free ribosome starts to translate an mRNA molecule. There the process continues to completion—*unless* the growing polypeptide itself cues the ribosome to attach to the ER. The polypeptides of proteins destined for the endomembrane system or for secretion are marked by a **signal peptide**, which targets the protein to the ER (FIGURE 17.19). The signal peptide, a sequence of about 20 amino acids at or near the leading (amino) end of the polypeptide, is recognized as it emerges from the ribosome by a protein-RNA complex called a **signal-recognition particle (SRP)**. This particle functions as an adaptor that brings the ribosome to a receptor protein built into the ER membrane. This receptor is part of a multiprotein complex. Polypeptide synthesis continues there, and the growing polypeptide snakes across the membrane into the cisternal space via a protein pore. The signal peptide is usually removed by an enzyme. The rest of the completed polypeptide, if it is to be a secretory protein, is released into solution within the cisternal space (as in FIGURE 17.19). Alternatively, if the polypeptide is to be a membrane protein, it remains partially embedded in the ER membrane.

Other kinds of signal peptides are used to target polypeptides to mitochondria, chloroplasts, the interior of the nucleus, and other organelles that are not part of the endomembrane system. The critical difference in these cases is that translation is completed in the cytosol before the polypeptide is imported into the organelle. The mechanisms of translocation also vary, but in all cases studied to date, the "postal" codes that address proteins to cellular locations are signal peptides of some sort.

RNA plays multiple roles in the cell: *a review*

As we have seen, the cellular machinery of protein synthesis (and ER targeting) is dominated by RNA of various kinds. In addition to mRNA, these include tRNA, rRNA, and, in eukaryotes, snRNA and SRP RNA (TABLE 17.1). The diverse functions of these molecules range from structural to informational to catalytic. The ability of RNA to perform so many different functions is based on two related characteristics of this kind of molecule: RNA can hydrogen-bond to other nucleic acid molecules (DNA or RNA), and it can assume a specific three-dimensional shape by forming hydrogen bonds between bases in different parts of its polynucleotide chain (you saw an example of this intramolecular bonding in tRNA, FIGURE 17.12). DNA may be the genetic material of all living cells today, but RNA is much more versatile. You will learn in Chapter 18 that many viruses even use RNA rather than DNA as their genetic material.

Comparing protein synthesis in prokaryotes and eukaryotes: *a review*

Although bacteria and eukaryotes carry out transcription and translation in very similar ways, we have noted certain differences in cellular machinery and in details of the processes. Prokaryotic and eukaryotic RNA polymerases are different, and those of eukaryotes depend on transcription factors. Transcription is terminated differently in the two kinds of cells. Also prokaryotic and eukaryotic ribosomes are slightly different. The most important differences, however, arise from the eukaryotic cell's compartmental organization. Like a one-room workshop, a prokaryotic cell assures a streamlined operation. In the absence of a nucleus, it can simultaneously transcribe and translate the same gene (FIGURE 17.20), and the newly made protein can quickly diffuse to its site of function. In contrast, the eukaryotic cell's nuclear envelope segregates transcription from translation and provides a compartment for extensive RNA processing. This processing stage provides an additional way to regulate and coordinate the eukaryotic cell's elaborate activities (see Chapter 19). Finally, as we have seen, eukaryotic cells have complicated mechanisms for targeting proteins to the appropriate cellular compartment (organelle).

Table 17.1 ▪ Types of RNA in a Eukaryotic Cell

TYPE OF RNA	FUNCTION
Messenger RNA (mRNA)	Carries information specifying amino acid sequences of proteins from DNA to ribosomes.
Transfer RNA (tRNA)	Serves as adaptor molecule in protein synthesis; translates mRNA codons into amino acids.
Ribosomal RNA (rRNA)	Plays structural and catalytic (ribozyme) roles in ribosomes.
Primary transcript	Serves as a precursor to mRNA, rRNA, or tRNA; this RNA molecule is processed by cleavage or splicing. In eukaryotes, pre-mRNA commonly contains introns, noncoding segments that are spliced out as the primary transcript is processed. Some intron RNA acts as a ribozyme, catalyzing its own splicing.
Small nuclear RNA (snRNA)	Plays structural and catalytic roles in spliceosomes, the complexes of protein and RNA that splice pre-mRNA in the eukaryotic nucleus.
SRP RNA	Acts as a component of the signal-recognition particle (SRP), the protein-RNA complex that recognizes the signal peptides of polypeptides targeted to the ER.

Where did eukaryotes—and prokaryotes, for that matter—get the genes that encode the huge diversity of proteins they synthesize? For the past few billion years the ultimate source of new genes has been the mutation of preexisting genes, the topic of the next section.

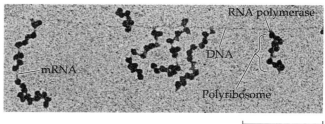

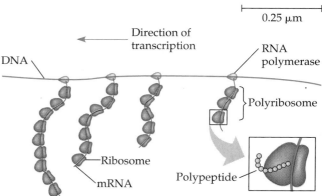

FIGURE 17.20 ▪ Coupled transcription and translation in bacteria. In prokaryotic cells, transcription and translation are not separated by a nuclear envelope. The translation of mRNA can begin as soon as the leading (5′) end of the mRNA molecule peels away from the DNA template. The micrograph shows a strand of *E. coli* DNA being transcribed by RNA polymerase molecules. Attached to each RNA polymerase molecule is a growing strand of mRNA, which is already being translated by ribosomes. The newly synthesized polypeptides are not visible in the micrograph (TEM).

Photo reprinted with permission from O. L. Miller, B. A. Hamkalo, and C. A. Thomas, Jr., *Science* 169 (1970):392. Copyright ©1970 American Association for the Advancement of Science.

Point mutations can affect protein structure and function

Mutations are changes in the genetic material of a cell (or virus). In Chapter 15 we considered large-scale mutations, chromosomal rearrangements that affect long segments of DNA. Now that you have learned about the genetic code and its translation, we can examine **point mutations**, which are chemical changes in just one or a few base pairs in a single gene.

If a point mutation occurs in a gamete, or in a cell that gives rise to gametes, it may be transmitted to offspring and to a succession of future generations. If the mutation has an adverse effect on the phenotype of a human or other animal, the mutant condition is referred to as a genetic disorder, or hereditary disease. For example, we can trace the genetic basis of sickle-cell disease to a mutation of a single base pair in the gene that codes for one of the polypeptides of hemoglobin. The change of a single nucleotide in the DNA's template strand leads to the production of an abnormal protein (FIGURE 17.21). Let's see how different types of point mutations translate into altered proteins.

Types of Point Mutations

Point mutations within a gene can be divided into two general categories: base-pair substitutions and base-pair insertions or deletions. While reading about how these mutations affect proteins, refer to the appropriate parts of FIGURE 17.22.

Substitutions. A **base-pair substitution** is the replacement of one nucleotide and its partner in the complementary DNA strand with another pair of nucleotides. Some substitutions are called *silent mutations* because, due to the redundancy of the genetic code, they have no effect on the encoded protein. In other words, a change in a base pair may transform one codon into another that is translated into the same amino acid. For example, if CCG mutated to CCA, the mRNA codon that used to be GGC would become GGU, and a glycine would still be inserted at the proper location in the protein (see FIGURE 17.4). Other changes of a single nucleotide pair may switch an amino acid but have little effect on the protein. The new amino acid may have properties similar to those of the amino acid it replaces, or it may be in a region of the protein where the exact sequence of amino acids is not essential to the protein's function.

However, the base-pair substitutions of greatest interest are those that cause a readily detectable change in a protein. The alteration of a single amino acid in a crucial area of a protein—in the active site of an enzyme, for example—will significantly alter protein activity. Occasionally, such a mutation leads to an improved protein or one with novel capabilities that enhance the success of the mutant organism and its descendants. But much more often such mutations are detri-

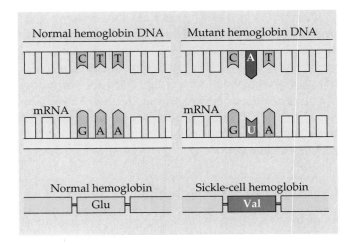

FIGURE 17.21 ▪ **The molecular basis of sickle-cell disease.** The allele that causes sickle-cell disease differs from the normal allele by a change in a single base pair—a point mutation. The top row of this figure shows the template strand of the gene for one of the polypeptides making up the protein hemoglobin. Where the normal allele has the base thymine, the sickle-cell allele has adenine. This alters one of the codons in the mRNA transcribed from the gene, with the result that the amino acid valine appears in the polypeptide in place of the glutamic acid found in the normal polypeptide. In individuals who are homozygous for the mutant allele, the sickling of red blood cells caused by the altered hemoglobin produces the multiple symptoms associated with sickle-cell disease (see FIGURE 14.16).

mental, creating a useless or less active protein that impairs cellular function.

Substitution mutations are usually **missense mutations**; that is, the altered codon still codes for an amino acid and thus makes sense, although not necessarily the *right* sense. But if a point mutation changes a codon for an amino acid into a stop codon, translation will be terminated prematurely, and the resulting polypeptide will be shorter than the polypeptide encoded by the normal gene. Alterations that change an amino acid codon to a stop signal are called **nonsense mutations**, and nearly all nonsense mutations lead to nonfunctional proteins.

Insertions and Deletions. **Insertions** and **deletions** are additions or losses of one or more nucleotide pairs in a gene. These mutations have a disastrous effect on the resulting protein more often than substitutions do. Because mRNA is read as a series of nucleotide triplets during translation, the insertion or deletion of nucleotides may alter the reading frame (triplet grouping) of the genetic message. Such a mutation, called a **frameshift mutation**, will occur whenever the number of nucleotides inserted or deleted is not a multiple of 3. All the nucleotides that are downstream of the deletion or insertion will be improperly grouped into codons, and the result will be extensive missense ending sooner or later in nonsense—premature termination. Unless the frameshift is very near the end of the gene, it will produce a protein that is almost certain to be nonfunctional.

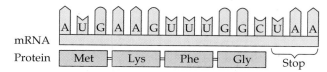

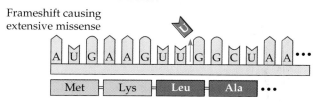

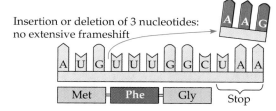

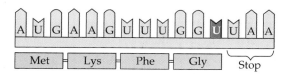

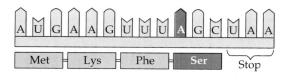

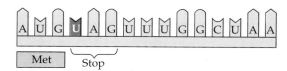

FIGURE 17.22 ▪ Categories and consequences of point mutations. Mutations are changes in DNA, but they are represented here as they are reflected in mRNA and its protein product.

Mutagens

The production of mutations can occur in a number of ways. Errors during DNA replication, repair, or recombination can lead to base-pair substitutions, insertions, or deletions, as well as to mutations affecting longer stretches of DNA. Mutations resulting from such errors are called *spontaneous mutations.*

A number of physical and chemical agents, called **mutagens,** interact with DNA to cause mutations. In the 1920s, Hermann Muller discovered that if he subjected fruit flies to X-rays, genetic changes increased in frequency. Using this method, Muller was able to obtain mutants of *Drosophila* that he could use in his genetic studies. But he also recognized an alarming implication of his discovery: Because they are mutagens, X-rays and other forms of high-energy radiation pose hazards to the genetic material of people as well as laboratory organisms. Mutagenic radiation, a physical mutagen, includes ultraviolet (UV) light, which can produce disruptive thymine dimers in DNA (see FIGURE 16.17).

Chemical mutagens fall into several categories. Base analogues are chemicals that are similar to normal DNA bases but

that pair incorrectly during DNA replication. Some other chemical mutagens interfere with correct DNA replication by inserting themselves into the DNA and distorting the double helix. Still other mutagens cause chemical changes in bases that change their pairing properties.

Researchers have developed various methods to test the mutagenic activity of different chemicals. One of the simplest and most popular methods is the **Ames test**, named for its developer, Bruce Ames (see the Methods Box on the next page). The Ames test uses easily grown bacteria as test organisms. A suspected mutagenic chemical is added to a culture of bacteria that already carry a point mutation rendering them unable to synthesize the amino acid histidine. The only bacteria that will grow to form colonies on a medium lacking histidine will be those that have undergone a back-mutation, a second mutation that restores the ability to make histidine. Thus, the number of colonies that grow on the histidine-lacking medium is a measure of the strength of the mutagen.

A major application of the Ames test is the preliminary screening of chemicals to identify those that may cause cancer. This approach makes sense because most carcinogens

The Ames test, named for its developer, microbiologist Bruce Ames, measures the mutagenic strength of various chemicals. The suspected mutagen is mixed with a culture of bacteria. It is also necessary to add a rat liver extract, which contains enzymes that convert certain chemicals from nonmutagenic to mutagenic forms. (These enzymes, also present in our own livers, normally function to metabolize toxic substances, but unfortunately the chemical modification sometimes makes a bad situation worse by increasing the mutagenicity of the substances.) The bacteria, *Salmonella*, carry a mutation preventing them from synthesizing the amino acid histidine. These bacteria fail to grow when plated on a growth medium lacking histidine. Some of the bacteria, however, undergo a back-mutation that restores the ability to make histidine. Such revertant bacteria give rise to colonies on the histidine-free medium. A mutagen will increase the frequency of these back-mutations, thereby bringing about the appearance of more colonies on the histidine-free medium. The mutagenic activity of a chemical can be quantified by comparing the number of colonies that grow after chemical treatment to control samples not treated with the suspected mutagen. One application of the Ames test is the screening of chemicals to identify those that can cause cancer. Most carcinogens (cancer-causing chemicals) are mutagenic and, conversely, most mutagens are carcinogenic.

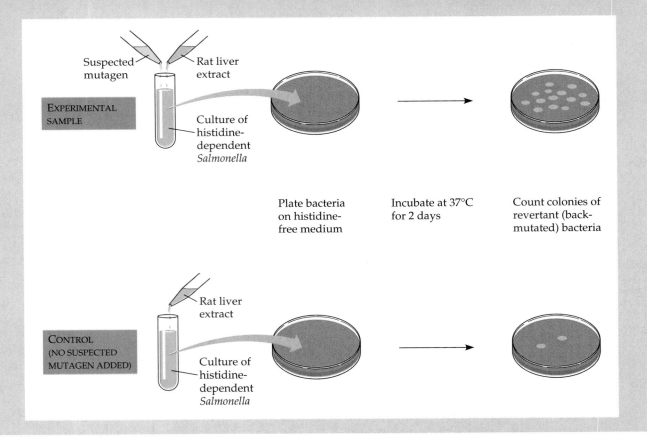

Suspected mutagen / Rat liver extract

EXPERIMENTAL SAMPLE

Culture of histidine-dependent *Salmonella*

Plate bacteria on histidine-free medium

Incubate at 37°C for 2 days

Count colonies of revertant (back-mutated) bacteria

Rat liver extract

CONTROL (NO SUSPECTED MUTAGEN ADDED)

Culture of histidine-dependent *Salmonella*

(cancer-causing chemicals) are mutagenic and, conversely, most mutagens are carcinogenic.

■   ■   ■

What is a gene?: *revisiting the question*

Our definition of a gene has evolved over the past few chapters, as it has through the history of genetics. We began with the Mendelian concept of a gene as a discrete unit of inheritance that affects a phenotypic character (Chapter 14). We saw that Morgan and his colleagues assigned such genes to specific loci on chromosomes and that geneticists sometimes use the term *locus* as a synonym for gene (Chapter 15). We went on to view a gene as a region of specific nucleotide sequence along the length of a DNA molecule (Chapter 16). Finally, in this chapter, we have moved toward a functional definition of a gene as a DNA sequence coding for a specific polypeptide chain. All these definitions are useful, depending on the context in which genes are being studied. (FIGURE 17.23 summarizes the path from gene to polypeptide in a eukaryotic cell.)

Even the one gene–one polypeptide definition must be refined and applied selectively. Most eukaryotic genes contain noncoding segments (introns), so large portions of these

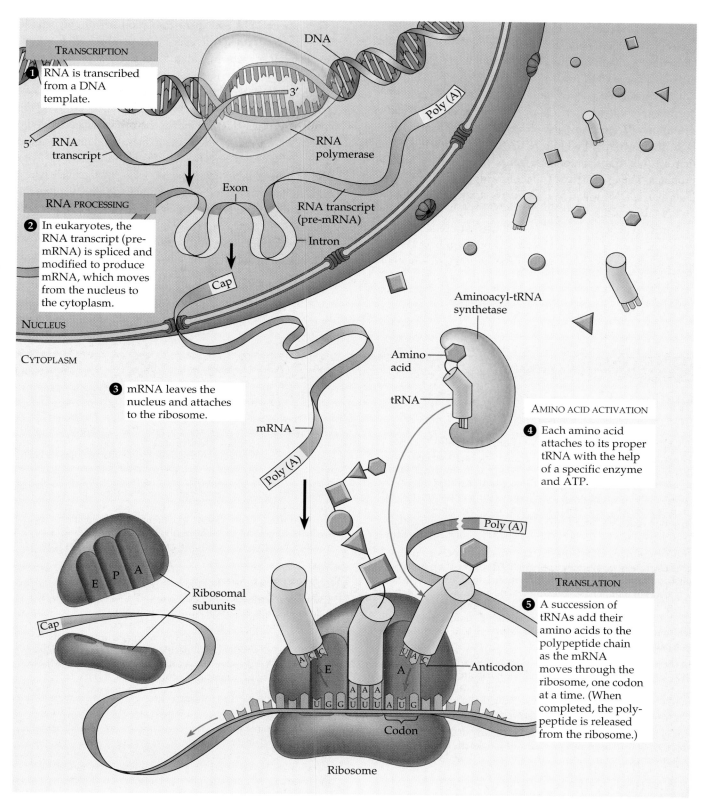

TRANSCRIPTION
1 RNA is transcribed from a DNA template.

DNA — RNA polymerase — Poly (A)

5′ RNA transcript

RNA PROCESSING
2 In eukaryotes, the RNA transcript (pre-mRNA) is spliced and modified to produce mRNA, which moves from the nucleus to the cytoplasm.

Exon — RNA transcript (pre-mRNA) — Intron — Cap

NUCLEUS

CYTOPLASM

3 mRNA leaves the nucleus and attaches to the ribosome.

mRNA — Poly (A)

Aminoacyl-tRNA synthetase — Amino acid — tRNA

AMINO ACID ACTIVATION
4 Each amino acid attaches to its proper tRNA with the help of a specific enzyme and ATP.

E P A — Ribosomal subunits — Cap

TRANSLATION
5 A succession of tRNAs add their amino acids to the polypeptide chain as the mRNA moves through the ribosome, one codon at a time. (When completed, the polypeptide is released from the ribosome.)

Poly (A) — Anticodon — Codon — Ribosome

⊙ **FIGURE 17.23** ▪ **A summary of transcription and translation in a eukaryotic cell.** Keep in mind that each gene in the DNA can be transcribed repeatedly into many RNA molecules, and that each mRNA can be translated repeatedly to yield numerous protein molecules. (Also,

17.2
17.4

remember that the final products of some genes are RNA molecules, including tRNA and rRNA.) In general, the steps of transcription and translation are similar in prokaryotic and eukaryotic cells. The major difference is the occurrence of mRNA processing in the eukaryotic nucleus.

Other significant differences are found in the initiation stages of both transcription and translation and in the termination of transcription.

CHAPTER 17 ▪ FROM GENE TO PROTEIN **315**

genes have no corresponding segments in polypeptides. Molecular biologists also often include promoters and certain other regulatory regions of DNA within the boundaries of a gene. These DNA sequences are not transcribed, but they can be considered part of the functional gene because they must be present for transcription to occur. Our molecular definition of a gene must also be broad enough to include the DNA that is transcribed into rRNA, tRNA, and other RNAs that are not translated. These genes have no polypeptide products. Thus, we arrive at the following definition: *A gene is a region of DNA whose final product is either a polypeptide or an RNA molecule.*

For most genes, however, it is still useful to retain the one gene–one polypeptide idea. In this chapter you have learned in molecular terms how a typical gene is expressed—by tran-

scription into RNA and then translation into a polypeptide that forms a protein of specific structure and function. Proteins, in turn, bring about an organism's observable phenotype.

Genes are subject to regulation. The control of gene expression enables a bacterium, for example, to vary the amounts of particular enzymes as the metabolic needs of the cell change. In multicellular eukaryotes, the control of gene expression makes it possible for cells with the same DNA to diverge during their development into different cell types, such as muscle and nerve cells in animals. We will explore the regulation of gene expression in eukaryotes in Chapters 19 and 21. In the next chapter we begin our discussion of gene regulation by focusing on the simpler molecular biology of bacteria and viruses.

CHAPTER REVIEW

REVIEW OF KEY CONCEPTS

(with page numbers and key figures)

THE CONNECTION BETWEEN GENES AND PROTEINS

■ **The study of metabolic defects provided evidence that genes specify proteins:** *science as a process* (pp. 294–296, FIGURE 17.1) DNA controls metabolism by commanding cells to make specific enzymes and other proteins. Beadle and Tatum's experiments on mutant strains of *Neurospora* gave rise to the one gene–one enzyme hypothesis, later modified to one gene–one polypeptide. A gene determines the amino acid sequence of a polypeptide chain.

➡ **Transcription and translation are the two main processes linking**
17.1 gene to protein: *an overview* (pp. 296–297; FIGURE 17.2) Both nucleic acids and proteins are informational polymers with linear sequences of monomers—nucleotides and amino acids, respectively. Transcription is the nucleotide-to-nucleotide transfer of information from DNA to RNA, while translation is the informational transfer from nucleotide sequence in RNA to amino acid sequence in a polypeptide.

■ **In the genetic code, nucleotide triplets specify amino acids** (pp. 297–299, FIGURES 17.3, 17.4) The three-nucleotide units in DNA are transcribed into mRNA nucleotide triplets called codons. Of the 64 codons, 61 code for amino acids, with many synonyms. A few codons are start and stop signals for the genetic message.

■ **The genetic code must have evolved very early in the history of life** (pp. 299–300) The near universality of the genetic code suggests that it was present in ancestors common to all kingdoms of life.

THE SYNTHESIS AND PROCESSING OF RNA

➡ **Transcription is the DNA-directed synthesis of RNA:** *a closer look*
17.2 (pp. 300–302, FIGURES 17.6, 17.7) RNA synthesis on a DNA template is catalyzed by RNA polymerase. It follows the same base-pairing rules as DNA replication, except that in RNA, uracil substitutes for thymine. Promoters, specific nucleotide sequences at the start of a gene, signal the initiation of RNA synthesis. Transcription factors (proteins) help eukaryotic RNA polymerase recognize promoter sequences. Transcription continues until a particular RNA sequence signals termination.

➡ **Eukaryotic cells modify RNA after transcription** (pp. 302–304,
17.3 FIGURES 17.8–17.10) Eukaryotic mRNA molecules are processed before leaving the nucleus by modification of their ends and by RNA splicing. The 5′ end receives a modified nucleotide cap, and the 3′ end a poly(A) tail. These probably protect the molecule from degradation and enhance translation. Most eukaryotic genes have introns, noncoding regions interspersed among the coding regions, exons. In RNA splicing, introns are removed and exons joined. RNA splicing is catalyzed by small nuclear ribonucleoproteins (snRNPs), operating within larger assemblies called spliceosomes. In some cases, RNA alone catalyzes splicing. Catalytic RNA molecules are called ribozymes. The shuffling of exons by recombination may contribute to the evolution of protein diversity.

THE SYNTHESIS OF PROTEIN

➡ **Translation is the RNA-directed synthesis of a polypeptide:**
17.4 *a closer look* (pp. 304–310, FIGURE 17.15–17.17) After picking up specific amino acids, transfer RNA (tRNA) molecules line up by means of their anticodon triplets at complementary codons on mRNA. The attachment of a specific amino acid to its particular tRNA is an ATP-driven process catalyzed by an aminoacyl-tRNA synthetase enzyme. Ribosomes coordinate the three stages of translation: initiation, elongation, and termination. Each ribosome is composed of two subunits made of protein and ribosomal RNA (rRNA). Ribosomes have a binding site for mRNA; P and A sites that hold adjacent tRNAs as amino acids are linked in the growing polypeptide chain; and an E site for release of tRNA. A number of ribosomes can work on a single mRNA molecule simultaneously, forming a polyribosome. After translation the protein may be modified in ways that affect its three-dimensional shape.

■ **Signal peptides target some eukaryotic polypeptides to specific destinations in the cell** (pp. 310–311, FIGURE 17.19) Proteins that will remain in the cytosol are made on free ribosomes. Proteins destined for membranes or for export from the cell are synthesized on ribosomes bound to the endoplasmic reticulum. A signal-recognition particle binds to a signal sequence on the leading end of the growing polypeptide, enabling the ribosome to bind to the ER. Other signal sequences target proteins for mitochondria or chloroplasts.

- **RNA plays multiple roles in the cell:** *a review* (p. 311, TABLE 17.1) More versatile than DNA, RNA performs structural, informational and catalytic roles.

- **Comparing protein synthesis in prokaryotes and eukaryotes:** *a review* (p. 311) In a bacterial cell, which lacks a nuclear envelope, translation of an mRNA can begin while transcription is still in progress. In a eukaryotic cell, the nuclear envelope separates transcription from translation; extensive RNA processing occurs in the nucleus.

- **Point mutations can affect protein structure and function** (pp. 312–314, FIGURE 17.22) Point mutations are changes in one or a few sequential base pairs. Base-pair substitutions can cause missense or nonsense mutations, which are often detrimental to protein function. Base-pair insertions or deletions may produce frameshift mutations that disrupt the codon messages downstream of the mutation. Spontaneous mutations can occur during DNA replication or repair. Various chemical and physical mutagens can also alter genes.

- **What is a gene?:** *revisiting the question* (pp. 314–316, FIGURE 17.23) A gene is usually a region of DNA encoding a polypeptide, but some genes have RNA molecules as their final products.

SELF-QUIZ

1. Base-pair substitutions involving the third base of a codon are unlikely to result in an error in the polypeptide. This is because
   a. base-pair substitutions are corrected before transcription begins
   b. base-pair substitutions are restricted to introns, and these regions are later deleted from the mRNA
   c. most tRNAs bind tightly to a codon with only the first two bases of the anticodon
   d. a signal-recognition particle corrects coding errors before the mRNA reaches the ribosome
   e. transcribed errors attract snRNPs, which then stimulate splicing and correction

2. In eukaryotic cells, transcription cannot begin until
   a. the two DNA strands have completely separated and exposed the promoter
   b. the appropriate transcription factors have bound to the promoter
   c. the 5′ caps are removed from the mRNA
   d. the DNA introns are removed from the template
   e. DNA nucleases have isolated the transcription unit from the noncoding DNA

3. Which of the following is *not* true of a codon?
   a. It consists of three nucleotides.
   b. It may code for the same amino acid as another codon does.
   c. It never codes for more than one amino acid.
   d. It extends from one end of a tRNA molecule.
   e. It is the basic unit of the genetic code.

4. Beadle and Tatum discovered several classes of *Neurospora* mutants that were able to grow on minimal medium with arginine added. Class I mutants were also able to grow on medium supplemented with either ornithine or citrulline, whereas class II mutants could grow on citrulline medium but not on ornithine medium. The metabolic pathway of arginine synthesis is as follows:

Precursor $\longrightarrow$ Ornithine $\longrightarrow$ Citrulline $\longrightarrow$ Arginine
$\qquad\qquad\quad$ A $\qquad\qquad$ B $\qquad\qquad$ C

From the behavior of their mutants, Beadle and Tatum could conclude that
   a. one gene codes for the entire metabolic pathway
   b. the genetic code of DNA is a triplet code
   c. class I mutants have their mutations later in the nucleotide chain than do class II mutants and thus have more functional enzymes
   d. class I mutants have a nonfunctional enzyme at step A, and class II mutants have a nonfunctional enzyme at step B
   e. class I mutants have a nonfunctional enzyme at step B, and class II mutants have a nonfunctional enzyme at step C

5. The anticodon of a particular tRNA molecule is
   a. complementary to the corresponding mRNA codon
   b. complementary to the corresponding triplet in rRNA
   c. the part of tRNA that bonds to a specific amino acid
   d. changeable, depending on the amino acid that attaches to the tRNA
   e. catalytic, making the tRNA a ribozyme

6. Which of the following is *not* true of RNA processing?
   a. Exons are excised and hydrolyzed before mRNA moves out of the nucleus.
   b. The existence of exons and introns may facilitate crossing over between regions of a gene that code for polypeptide domains.
   c. Ribozymes function in RNA splicing.
   d. RNA splicing may be catalyzed by spliceosomes.
   e. A primary transcript is often much longer than the final RNA molecule that leaves the nucleus.

7. Which of the following terms includes all others in the list?
   a. ribozyme
   b. enzyme
   c. catalyst
   d. snRNP
   e. aminoacyl-tRNA synthetase

8. Using the genetic code in FIGURE 17.4, identify a possible 5′⟶3′ sequence of nucleotides in the *DNA template strand* for an mRNA coding for the polypeptide sequence Phe-Pro-Lys.
   a. UUU-GGG-AAA   d. CTT-CGG-GAA
   b. GAA-CCC-CTT   e. AAA-CCC-UUU
   c. AAA-ACC-TTT

9. Which of the following mutations would be *most* likely to have a harmful effect on an organism? Explain your answer.
   a. a base-pair substitution
   b. a deletion of three bases near the middle of the gene
   c. a single base deletion near the middle of an intron
   d. a single base deletion close to the end of the coding sequence
   e. a single base insertion near the start of the coding sequence

10. Which component is *not directly* involved in the process known as translation?
   a. mRNA   d. ribosomes
   b. DNA   e. GTP
   c. tRNA

CHALLENGE QUESTIONS

1. The base sequence of the template strand of an unusual gene, which codes for an extremely short polypeptide, is CTACGCTAGGCGAT-TCAT. Which is the 5′ end of this DNA sequence? How do you know? What would be the base sequence of the mRNA transcribed

from this gene? Using the genetic code chart (FIGURE 17.4), give the amino acid sequence of the polypeptide translated from this mRNA.

2. A biologist inserted a gene from a human liver cell into the chromosome of a bacterium. The bacterium then transcribed this gene into mRNA and translated the mRNA into protein. The protein produced was useless; it contained many more amino acids than the protein made by the eukaryotic cell, and the amino acids were in a different sequence. Explain why.

3. Choose one catalyst, either an enzyme or a ribozyme, and write a paragraph explaining how it functions in the pathway from gene to protein.

SCIENCE, TECHNOLOGY, AND SOCIETY

1. Our civilization generates many potentially mutagenic chemicals (pesticides, for example) and modifies the environment in ways that increase exposure to other mutagens, notably UV radiation. What role should government play in identifying mutagens and regulating their release to the environment?

2. As part of the Human Genome Project (discussed in Chapter 20), researchers are determining the nucleotide sequences of human genes and identifying the proteins coded by the genes. Labs of the U.S. National Institutes of Health (NIH), for example, have worked out thousands of sequences, and similar analysis is being carried out by many private companies. Knowing the nucleotide sequence of a gene and identifying its product can be useful; this information might be used to treat genetic defects or produce life-saving medicines. U.S. law allows the first person or research group to isolate a pure protein or a gene to patent it, whether or not a practical use for the discovery has been demonstrated. The NIH and biotechnology companies have applied for patents on their discoveries. What are the purposes of a patent? How might the discoverer of a gene benefit from a patent? How might the public benefit? What kinds of negative impacts might result from patenting genes? Do you think individuals and companies should be able to patent genes and gene products? Why or why not? Under what conditions should such patenting be permitted?

FURTHER READING

Becker, W. M., J. B. Reece, and M. F. Poenie. *The World of the Cell*, 3rd ed. Menlo Park, CA: Benjamin/Cummings, 1996. Chapters 17 and 18 present the topics of this chapter in more detail.

Hartl, F. U. "Molecular Chaperones in Cellular Protein Folding." *Nature*, June 13, 1996. Describes the critically important roles of chaperones in protein folding and related activities, including protein translocation into organelles.

Hentze, M. W. "elF4G: A Multipurpose Ribosome Adapter?" *Science*, January 24, 1997. Discusses the roles of 5′ cap, poly(A) tail, leader sequences, and protein factors in the binding of the eukaryotic small ribosomal subunit to mRNA.

Landick, R., and J. W. Roberts. "The Shrewd Grasp of RNA Polymerase." *Science*, July 12, 1996. Provides the details of the transcription elongation stage in bacteria.

Pennisi, E. "How the Nucleus Gets It Together." *Science*, June 6, 1997. Eukaryotic mRNA synthesis and processing seem to occur at particular locations within the nucleus.

Radetsky, P. "Genetic Heretic." *Discover*, November 1990. The story of how the discovery of ribozymes led to a Nobel Prize.

Stoltzfus, A., et al. "Testing the Exon Theory of Genes: The Evidence from Protein Structure." *Science*, July 8, 1994. Did introns first arise in prokaryotes or eukaryotes? This article reports evidence for a eukaryotic origin.

Tijan, R. "Molecular Machines That Control Genes." *Scientific American*, February 1995. Transcription is a team effort.

WEB LINKS

Visit the special edition of *The Biology Place* for BIOLOGY, Fifth Edition, at http://www.biology.com/campbell. Go to Chapter 17 for online resources, including learning activities, practice exams, and links to the following web sites:

"From Gene to Function"

The first topic in Genetech's Access Excellence Graphics Gallery, this is a sequence of illustrated pages describing how cells use the information encoded in genes to make proteins.

"The Central Dogma Directory"

This is a chapter from the MIT HyperTextbook that deals with DNA replication, transcription, and translation.

"Nucleic Acids Problem Sets"

Use this problem set to test your understanding of nucleic acids.

"From Gene to Protein"

Visit Campbell's Biology Place for access to these interactive exercises on transcription and translation by Peter Russell of Reed College.

Harwell, M. A. "Ecosystem Management of South Florida." *BioScience*, September 1997. A case study of the potential for cooperation between public policy makers and interdisciplinary scientists in achieving sustainability of a threatened ecosystem.

Lubchenco, J. "Entering the Century of the Environment: A New Social Contract for Science." *Science*, January 23, 1998. Describes the challenge to scientists in working toward ecosystem sustainability.

Malakoff, D. "Atlantic Salmon Spawn Fight Over Species Protection." *Science*, February 6, 1998. An example of the many controversies over biodiversity.

Meffe, G. K., and C. R. Carroll. *Principles of Conservation Biology*, 2e. Sunderland, MA: Sinauer Associates. 1997. An authoritative, lucidly written text.

Myers, N. "Mass Extinction and Evolution." *Science*, October 24, 1997. Emphasizes the effect of the biodiversity crisis on the future of evolution.

O'Neill, R. V., et al. "Monitoring Environmental Quality at the Landscape Scale." *BioScience*, September 1997. Presents an overview of landscape ecology in analyzing environmental quality.

Parry-Jones, R., and A. Vincent. "Can We Tame Wild Medicine?" *New Scientist*, January 3, 1998. Provides a discussion of the threat to some species posed by overexploitation for herbal medicines.

Pimentel, D., C. Wilson, C. McCullum, R. Huang, P. Dwen, J. Flack, Q. Tran, F. Saltman, and B. Cliff. "Economic and Environmental Benefits of Biodiversity." *BioScience*, December 1997. A scholarly analysis of the potential dividends of saving biodiversity.

Weeks, W. W. *Beyond the Ark: Tools for an Ecosystem Approach to Conservation*. Washington, DC: Island Press. 1997. A brief introduction to modern concepts in conservation biology.

Wildt, D. E., W. F. Rall, J. K. Critser, S. L. Monfort, and U. S. Seal. "Genome Resource Banks." *BioScience*, November 1997. Discusses the need to institute gene banks for wildlife species.

WEB LINKS

Visit the special edition of *The Biology Place* for BIOLOGY, Fifth Edition, at http://www.biology.com/campbell. Go to Chapter 55 for online resources, including learning activities, practice exams, and links to the following web sites:

"The National Wildlife Federation"
The National Wildlife Federation is the largest member-supported conservation group in the U.S., uniting individuals, organizations, businesses, and government to protect wildlife, wild places, and the environment.

"The World Conservation Union"
The mission of this organization is to influence, encourage, and assist societies throughout the world to conserve the integrity and diversity of nature and to ensure that any use of natural resources is equitable and ecologically sustainable.

"Smithsonian Institution's Conservation and Research Center"
Visit one of the world's leading centers for conservation research and training.

"Africa Environment 2000"
This is the story of a conservation organization founded to save rhinoceroses by two young women cycling from Scotland to Zimbabwe.

SELF-QUIZ ANSWERS

CHAPTER 2

1. b	6. b
2. a	7. b
3. b	8. a
4. b	9. b
5. c	10. b

CHAPTER 3

1. d	6. c
2. c	7. c
3. b	8. d
4. c	9. c
5. b	10. c

CHAPTER 4

1. b	6. b
2. c	7. b
3. d	8. a
4. d	9. d
5. a	10. b

CHAPTER 5

1. d	6. a
2. c	7. d
3. d	
4. a	
5. b	

CHAPTER 6

1. b	6. a
2. c	7. c
3. b	8. c
4. b	9. a
5. e	10. c

CHAPTER 7

1. c	6. b
2. c	7. c
3. b	8. b
4. d	9. e
5. d	10. a

CHAPTER 8

1. b	6. fructose
2. c	7. glucose
3. a	8. cell contents
4. d	9. into cell
5. b	10. b

CHAPTER 9

1. d	6. a
2. b	7. b
3. c	8. d
4. c	9. b
5. a	10. b

CHAPTER 10

1. d	6. c
2. b	7. d
3. d	8. e
4. b	9. d
5. b	10. b

CHAPTER 11

1. c	6. c
2. d	7. a
3. a	8. b
4. c	9. c
5. c	10. a

CHAPTER 12

1. b	6. c
2. b	7. c
3. a	8. c
4. a	9. b
5. See Fig. 12.5	10. a

CHAPTER 13

1. d	6. d
2. b	7. a
3. d	8. c
4. d	9. c
5. c	10. d

CHAPTER 14

Genetics Problems

1. Incomplete dominance, with heterozygotes being gray in color. Mating a gray rooster with a black hen should yield approximately equal numbers of gray and black offspring.

2. F_1 cross is $AARR \times aarr$. Genotype of progeny is $AaRr$, phenotype is all axial-pink. F_2 cross is $AaRr \times AaRr$. Genotypes of progeny are 4 $AaRr$: 2 $AaRR$: 2 $AARr$: 2 $aaRr$: 2 $Aarr$: 1 $AARR$: 1 $aaRR$: 1 $AArr$: 1 $aarr$. Phenotypes of progeny are 6 axial-pink : 3 axial-red : 3 axial-white : 2 terminal-pink : 1 terminal-white : 1 terminal-red.

3. a. $^1/_{64}$ b. $^1/_{64}$ c. $^1/_8$ d. $^1/_{32}$

4. Albino is a recessive trait; black is dominant.

Parents	Gametes	Offspring
$BB \times bb$	B and b	All Bb
$bb \times Bb$	b and $^1/_2B$,	$^1/_2Bb$, $^1/_2bb$
	$^1/_2b$	

5. a. $PPLl \times PPLl$, $PpLl$, or $ppLl$
b. $ppLl \times ppLl$
c. $PPLL \times$ any of the 9 possible genotypes
d. $PpLl \times Ppll$
e. $PpLl \times PpLl$

6. Man I^Ai; woman I^Bi; child ii. Other genotypes for children are $^1/_4$, I^AI^B, $^1/_4 I^Ai$, $^1/_4 I^Bi$.

7. Four

8. a. $^3/_4 \times ^3/_4 \times ^3/_4 = {}^{27}/_{64}$
b. $1 - {}^{27}/_{64} = {}^{37}/_{64}$
c. $^1/_4 \times ^1/_4 \times ^1/_4 = {}^1/_{64}$
d. $1 - ^1/_{64} = {}^{63}/_{64}$

9. a. $^1/_{256}$ b. $^1/_{16}$ c. $^1/_{256}$
d. $^1/_{64}$ e. $^1/_{128}$

10. If the "curl" allele is dominant, then the original mutant crossed with noncurl cats will produce both curl and noncurl offspring. If the mutation is recessive, then only curl offspring will result from curl × curl matings. You know that cats are true-breeding when curl × curl matings produce only curl offspring. A pure-bred curl cat is homozygous (as it turns out, for the dominant allele, which causes the curled ears).

11. a. 1 b. $^1/_{32}$ c. $^1/_8$ d. $^1/_2$

12. $^1/_9$ 13. $^1/_{16}$

14. Twenty-five percent will be cross-eyed; all of the cross-eyed offspring will also be white.

15. The dominant allele I is epistatic to the p locus, and thus the F_1 generation will be:
9 $I\_P\_$: colorless
3 I_pp : colorless
3 $iiP\_$: purple
1 $iipp$: red
Overall, 12 colorless : 3 purple : 1 red.

16. Recessive; George = Aa, Arlene = aa, Sandra = AA or Aa, Tom = aa, Sam = Aa, Wilma = aa, Ann = Aa, Michael = Aa, Daniel = Aa, Alan = Aa, Tina = AA or Aa, Carla = aa, Christopher = AA or Aa

17. $^1/_2$ 18. $^1/_6$

19. 9 $B\_A\_$: agouti
3 B_aa : black
3 $bbA\_$: white
1 $bbaa$: white
Overall, 9 agouti : 3 black : 4 white.

20. The allele for the disorder is dominant. Individuals 1 and 2 are heterozygous, and individual 3 is homozygous for the recessive (normal) allele.

CHAPTER 15

Genetics Problems

1. 0; $^1/_2$, $^1/_{16}$

2. Recessive. If the disorder were dominant, it would affect at least one parent of a child born with the disorder. For a girl to have the disorder, she would have to inherit recessive alleles from *both* parents. This would be very rare, especially since males with the allele die in their early teens.

3. $^1/_4$ for each daughter ($^1/_2$ chance that child will be female × $^1/_2$ chance of a homozygous recessive genotype); $^1/_2$ for first son.

4. 17%

5. The disorder would always be inherited from the mother.

6. XXX

7. $D–A–B–C$

8. In meiosis, the combined 14-21 chromosome will behave as one chromosome. If a gamete receives the combined 14-21 chromosome and a normal copy of chromosome 21, trisomy 21 will result when this gamete combines with a normal gamete.

9. At some point during development, one of the embryo's cells may have failed to carry out mitosis after duplicating its chromosomes. Subsequent normal cell cycles would produce genetic copies of this tetraploid cell.

10. Fifty percent of the offspring would show phenotypes that resulted from crossovers. These results would be the same as those from a cross where *A* and *B* were not linked. Further crosses involving other genes on the same chromosome would reveal the linkage and map distances.

11. One hypothesis is that a translocation has moved one of the genes to a different chromosome.

12. 6%. Wild type (heterozygous for normal wings and red eyes) × recessive homozygote with vestigial wings and purple eyes.

13. Between *T* and *A*, 12%; between *A* and *S*, 5%.

14. Between *T* and *S*, 18%. Sequence of genes is *T-A-S*.

CHAPTER 16

1. c	6. a
2. d	7. c
3. b	8. d
4. c	9. a
5. b	10. b

CHAPTER 17

1. c	6. a
2. b	7. c
3. d	8. d
4. d	9. e
5. a	10. b

CHAPTER 18

1. e	6. d
2. d	7. a
3. b	8. c
4. a	9. a
5. e	10. e

CHAPTER 19

1. c	6. a
2. a	7. e
3. a	8. c
4. a	9. b
5. e	10. b

CHAPTER 20

1. b	6. c
2. b	7. e
3. c	8. c
4. b	9. d
5. a	10. b

CHAPTER 21

1. a	6. d
2. e	7. b
3. b	8. a
4. a	9. c
5. a	10. e

CHAPTER 22

1. a	6. b
2. b	7. b
3. c	8. c
4. d	9. c
5. c	10. d

CHAPTER 23

1. b	6. a
2. d	7. c
3. c	8. b
4. a	9. e
5. c	10. b

CHAPTER 24

1. b	6. c
2. b	7. e
3. b	8. a
4. a	9. d
5. b	10. b

CHAPTER 25

1. d	6. b
2. b	7. a
3. a	8. d
4. e	9. b
5. c	10. e

CHAPTER 26

1. b	6. b
2. e	7. a
3. d	8. b
4. c	9. d
5. c	10. c

CHAPTER 27

1. b	6. a
2. a	7. d
3. d	8. c
4. c	9. a
5. c	10. c

CHAPTER 28

1. a	6. e
2. c	7. b
3. e	8. c
4. a	9. c
5. b	10. b

CHAPTER 29

1. c	6. a
2. a	7. haploid
3. a	8. haploid
4. b	9. diploid
5. a	10. haploid

CHAPTER 30

1. d	6. d
2. a	7. b
3. b	8. d
4. a	9. c
5. b	10. a

CHAPTER 31

1. b	6. d
2. c	7. a
3. c	8. e
4. b	9. b
5. e	10. a

CHAPTER 32

1. c	6. b
2. e	7. b
3. d	8. a
4. c	9. e
5. c	10. b

CHAPTER 33

1. d	6. a
2. c	7. d
3. a	8. a
4. a	9. e
5. a	10. c

CHAPTER 34

1. e	6. a
2. c	7. b
3. d	8. e
4. d	9. c
5. c	10. a

CHAPTER 35

1. d	6. a
2. c	7. d
3. b	8. d
4. c	9. b
5. d	10. c

CHAPTER 36

1. e	6. c
2. c	7. a
3. d	8. b
4. c	9. c
5. b	10. c

CHAPTER 37

1. b	6. b
2. b	7. b
3. c	8. c
4. d	9. d
5. b	10. a

CHAPTER 38

1. d	6. c
2. a	7. e
3. c	8. b
4. a	9. c
5. b	10. c

CHAPTER 39

1. b	6. a
2. a	7. b
3. b	8. b
4. d	9. c
5. b	10. c

CHAPTER 40

1. a	6. c
2. c	7. b
3. e	8. b
4. d	9. c
5. d	10. c

CHAPTER 41

1. e	6. c
2. c	7. c
3. c	8. d
4. c	9. b
5. d	10. b

CHAPTER 42

1. c	6. c
2. b	7. b
3. d	8. a
4. c	9. a
5. b	10. c

CHAPTER 43

1. b	6. e
2. d	7. d
3. a	8. c
4. e	9. b
5. b	10. c

CHAPTER 44

1. d	6. d
2. a	7. b
3. e	8. d
4. e	9. c
5. b	10. a

CHAPTER 45

1. c	6. b
2. d	7. e
3. a	8. c
4. d	9. b
5. c	10. c

CHAPTER 46

1. d	6. a
2. b	7. a
3. a	8. a
4. b	9. d
5. c	10. b

CHAPTER 47

1. a	6. c
2. b	7. b
3. d	8. c
4. c	9. d
5. a	10. d

CHAPTER 48

1. c	6. a
2. b	7. c
3. a	8. c
4. d	9. c
5. d	10. b

CHAPTER 49

1. e	6. e
2. d	7. b
3. a	8. d
4. b	9. c
5. c	10. b

CHAPTER 50

1. c	6. d
2. e	7. e
3. e	8. c
4. d	9. d
5. a	10. a

CHAPTER 51

1. b	6. d
2. d	7. c
3. d	8. c
4. c	9. e
5. d	10. b

CHAPTER 52

1. c	6. b
2. d	7. c
3. c	8. d
4. d	9. a
5. c	10. c

CHAPTER 53

1. c	6. d
2. d	7. b
3. b	8. b
4. d	9. d
5. e	10. c

CHAPTER 54

1. c	6. a
2. e	7. b
3. b	8. c
4. e	9. d
5. d	10. c

CHAPTER 55

1. c	6. b
2. c	7. a
3. d	8. e
4. b	9. d
5. d	10. a

THE METRIC SYSTEM

MEASUREMENT	UNIT AND ABBREVIATION	METRIC EQUIVALENT	METRIC-TO-ENGLISH CONVERSION FACTOR	ENGLISH-TO-METRIC CONVERSION FACTOR
Length	1 kilometer (km)	= 1000 (10^3) meters	1 km = 0.62 mile	1 mile = 1.61 km
	1 meter (m)	= 100 (10^2) centimeters	1 m = 1.09 yards	1 yard = 0.914 m
		= 1000 millimeters	1 m = 3.28 feet	1 foot = 0.305 m
			1 m = 39.37 inches	
	1 centimeter (cm)	= 0.01 (10^{-2}) meter	1 cm = 0.394 inch	1 foot = 30.5 cm
				1 inch = 2.54 cm
	1 millimeter (mm)	= 0.001 (10^{-3}) meter	1 mm = 0.039 inch	
	1 micrometer (μm) (formerly micron, μ)	= 10^{-6} meter (10^{-3} mm)		
	1 nanometer (nm) (formerly millimicron, mμ)	= 10^{-9} meter (10^{-3} μm)		
	1 angstrom (Å)	= 10^{-10} meter (10^{-4} μm)		
Area	1 hectare (ha)	= 10,000 square meters	1 ha = 2.47 acres	1 acre = 0.0405 ha
	1 square meter (m^2)	= 10,000 square centimeters	1 m^2 = 1.196 square yards	1 square yard = 0.8361 m^2
			1 m^2 = 10.764 square feet	1 square foot = 0.0929 m^2
	1 square centimeter (cm^2)	= 100 square millimeters	1 cm^2 = 0.155 square inch	1 square inch = 6.4516 cm^2
Mass	1 metric ton (t)	= 1000 kilograms	1 t = 1.103 tons	1 ton = 0.907 t
	1 kilogram (kg)	= 1000 grams	1 kg = 2.205 pounds	1 pound = 0.4536 kg
	1 gram (g)	= 1000 milligrams	1 g = 0.0353 ounce	1 ounce = 28.35 g
			1 g = 15.432 grains	
	1 milligram (mg)	= 10^{-3} gram	1 mg = approx. 0.015 grain	
	1 microgram (μg)	= 10^{-6} gram		
Volume (solids)	1 cubic meter (m^3)	= 1,000,000 cubic centimeters	1 m^3 = 1.308 cubic yards	1 cubic yard = 0.7646 m^3
			1 m^3 = 35.315 cubic feet	1 cubic foot = 0.0283 m^3
	1 cubic centimeter (cm^3 or cc)	= 10^{-6} cubic meter	1 cm^3 = 0.061 cubic inch	1 cubic inch = 16.387 cm^3
	1 cubic millimeter (mm^3)	= 10^{-9} cubic meter (10^{-3} cubic centimeter)		
Volume (Liquids and Gases)	1 kiloliter (kl or kL)	= 1000 liters	1 kL = 264.17 gallons	1 gallon = 3.785 L
	1 liter (L)	= 1000 milliliters	1 L = 0.264 gallons	1 quart = 0.946 L
			1 L = 1.057 quarts	
	1 milliliter (mL)	= 10^{-3} liter	1 mL = 0.034 fluid ounce	1 quart = 946 mL
		= 1 cubic centimeter	1 mL = approx. $\frac{1}{4}$ teaspoon	1 pint = 473 mL
				1 fluid ounce = 29.57 mL
			1 ml = approx. 15–16 drops (gtt.)	1 teaspoon = approx. 5 mL
	1 microliter (μl or μL)	= 10^{-6} liter (10^{-3} milliliters)		
Time	1 second (s)	= $\frac{1}{60}$ minute		
	1 millisecond (ms)	= 10^{-3} second		
Temperature	Degrees Celsius (°C) (Absolute zero, when all molecular motion ceases, is −273 °C. The Kelvin (K) scale, which has the same size degrees as Celsius, has its zero point at absolute zero. Thus, 0° K = −273°C.)		°F = $\frac{9}{5}$°C + 32	°C = $\frac{5}{9}$(°F − 32)

CLASSIFICATION OF LIFE

This appendix presents the taxonomic classification used for the major groups of organisms discussed in this text; not all phyla are included. Plant and fungal divisions are the taxonomic equivalents of phyla. The classification reviewed here is based on the three-domain (superkingdom) system; in the traditional five-kingdom system, all prokaryotes are classified in a single kingdom, the Monera. The rationale for alternative taxonomic systems is discussed in Unit Five of the text.

DOMAIN ARCHAEA
Methanogens
Extreme halophiles
Thermoacidophiles

DOMAIN BACTERIA
Proteobacteria
    Purple bacteria
    Chemoautotrophic proteobacteria
    Chemoheterotrophic proteobacteria
Gram-positive eubacteria
Cyanobacteria
Spirochetes
Chlamydias

DOMAIN EUKARYA
The five-kingdom classification scheme unites all eukaryotes generally called protists in a single kingdom, the Protista. In this book we follow the lead of current research, classifying some protists in "candidate kingdoms," groups that are phylogenetically unified but not yet recognized as formal taxa. We also discuss some other protists whose affinities are less clear, and these are also listed in this appendix. We use the taxonomic category *phylum* for groups that are chiefly heterotrophic and *division* for those that are mainly autotrophic. Green algae (Division Chlorophyta) are also listed here, although many plant biologists classify them in the plant kingdom; see Chapter 26.

Candidate Kingdom Archaezoa
Phylum Diplomonada (*Giardia* and other diplomonads)
Phylum Trichomonada (trichomonads)
Phylum Microsporida (microsporidians)

Candidate Kingdom Euglenozoa
Division Euglenophyta (euglenoids)
Phylum Kinetoplastida (trypanosomes)

Candidate Kingdom Alveolata
Division Dinoflagellata (dinoflagellates)
Phylum Apicomplexa (*Plasmodium* and other apicomplexans)
Phylum Ciliophora (ciliates)

Candidate Kingdom Stramenopila
Division Phaeophyta (brown algae)
Phylum Oomycota (water molds)
Division Chrysophyta (golden algae)
Division Bacillariophyta (diatoms)

Candidate Kingdom Rhodophyta (red algae)

Groups whose affinities are less certain
Phylum Rhizopoda (some amoebas)
Phylum Actinopoda (heliozoans, radiolarians)
Phylum Foraminifera (forams)
Phylum Myxomycota (plasmodial slime molds)
Phylum Acrasiomycota (cellular slime molds)

Group with close ties to the plant kingdom
Division Chlorophyta (green algae)

Kingdom Plantae
Division Bryophyta (mosses)
Division Hepatophyta (liverworts)
Division Anthocerophyta (hornworts)
Division Lycophyta (club mosses)

Division Sphenophyta (horsetails)
Division Pterophyta (ferns)
Division Coniferophyta (conifers)
Division Cycadophyta (cycads)
Division Ginkgophyta (ginkgos)
Division Gnetophyta (gnetae)
Division Anthophyta (flowering plants)
    Class Monocotyledones (monocots)
    Class Dicotyledones (dicots)

Kingdom Fungi
Division Chytridiomycota (chytrids)
Division Zygomycota (zygomycetes)
Division Ascomycota (sac fungi)
Division Basidiomycota (club fungi)
Division Deuteromycota (imperfect fungi)
Lichens (symbiotic associations of algae and fungi)

Kingdom Animalia
Phylum Porifera (sponges)
Phylum Cnidaria
    Class Hydrozoa (hydrozoans)
    Class Scyphozoa (jellies)
    Class Anthozoa (sea anemones and coral animals)
Phylum Ctenophora (comb jellies)
Phylum Platyhelminthes (flatworms)
    Class Turbellaria (free-living flatworms)
    Class Trematoda (flukes)
    Class Monogenea (flukes)
    Class Cestoidea (tapeworms)
Phylum Nemertea (proboscis worms)
Phylum Rotifera (rotifers)
Phylum Nematoda (roundworms)
Phylum Mollusca (mollusks)
    Class Polyplacophora (chitons)
    Class Gastropoda (gastropods: snails and their relatives)
    Class Bivalvia (bivalves)
    Class Cephalopoda (cephalopods; squids and octopuses)
Phylum Annelida (segmented worms)
    Class Oligochaeta (oligochaetes)
    Class Polychaeta (polychaetes)

    Class Hirudinea (leeches)
Phylum Onychophora (walking worms; some schemes classify onychophorans as a subphylum or class in the Phylum Arthropoda)
Phylum Arthropoda (arthropods)
    Subphylum Trilobitomorpha (trilobites, all extinct)
    Subphylum Chelicerata (chelicerates)
        Class Eurypterida (water scorpions, all extinct)
        Class Arachnida (spiders, ticks, scorpions)
    Subphylum Uniramia (uniramians)
        Class Diplopoda (millipedes)
        Class Chilopoda (centipedes)
        Class Insecta (insects)
    Subphylum Crustacea (crustaceans)
    (*Note:* The validity of subphyla Uniramia and Crustacea is being debated; molecular systematics indicates that insects and crustaceans may constitute a monophyletic group distinct from diplopods and chilopods.)
Phylum Phoronida (phoronids)
Phylum Bryozoa (bryozoans)
Phylum Brachiopoda (brachiopods: lamp shells)
Phylum Echinodermata (echinoderms)
    Class Asteroidea (sea stars)
    Class Ophiuroidea (brittle stars)
    Class Echinoidea (sea urchins and sand dollars)
    Class Crinoidea (sea lilies)
    Class Concentricycloidea (sea daisies)
    Class Holothuroidea (sea cucumbers)
Phylum Chordata (chordates)
    Subphylum Urochordata (urochordates: tunicates)
    Subphylum Cephalochordata (cephalochordates: lancelets)
    Subphylum Vertebrata (vertebrates)
        Superclass Agnatha (jawless vertebrates)
            Class Myxini (hagfishes)
            Class Cephalospidomorphi (lampreys)
        Superclass Gnathostomata
            Class Placodermi (extinct jawed fishes)
            Class Chondrichthyes (cartilaginous fishes)
            Class Osteichthyes (bony fishes)
            Class Amphibia (amphibians)
            Class Reptilia (reptiles)
            Class Aves (birds)
            Class Mammalia (mammals)

A COMPARISON OF THE LIGHT MICROSCOPE AND THE ELECTRON MICROSCOPE

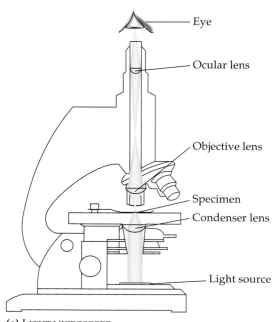

(a) LIGHT MICROSCOPE

In light microscopy, light is focused on a specimen by a glass condenser lens; the image is then magnified by an objective lens and an ocular lens, for projection on the eye or on photographic film.

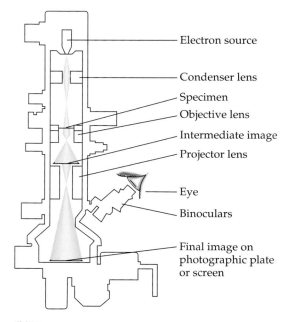

(b) ELECTRON MICROSCOPE

In electron microscopy, a beam of electrons (top of the microscope) is used instead of light, and electromagnets are used instead of glass lenses. The electron beam is focused on the specimen by a condenser lens; the image is magnified by an objective lens and a projector lens, for projection on a screen or on photographic film.

CREDITS

PHOTOGRAPHS

1.CO Courtesy of the Imogen Cunningham Trust. ©1974 Imogen Cunningham.
1.01a Courtesy of NYU/Strongin.
1.01b Photo by Tim White.
1.01c Courtesy of Mary-Claire King, University of Washington.
1.01d ©Paul Anderton/Addison Wesley Longman, Inc.
1.02a ©Robert Fletterick.
1.02b ©Dr. Jeremy Burgess/SPL/Photo Researchers, Inc.
1.02c ©Manfred Kage/Peter Arnold, Inc.
1.02d ©Dr. Jeremy Burgess/SPL/Photo Researchers, Inc.
1.02e ©John Shaw/Tom Stack and Associates.
1.02f ©1997 Photodisc.
1.03a ©Bob Stovall/Bruce Coleman, Inc.
1.03b ©Michio Hoshino/Minden Pictures.
1.03c ©Michael Fogden/Bruce Coleman, Inc.
1.03d ©Wolfgang Bayer/Bruce Coleman, Inc.
1.03e ©Jeff Lepore/Photo Researchers, Inc.
1.03f, g ©Tom and Pat Leeson/Photo Researchers, Inc.
1.05a ©1997 Photodisc.
1.06a ©1998 Photodisc.
1.06b ©Janice Sheldon.
1.06c ©Dr. Alfred Llinas/Peter Arnold, Inc.
1.06d Courtesy of Dr. Nicolae Simionescu.
1.07 ©Ric Ergenbright/Ric Ergenbright Photography.
1.09a ©Manfred Kage/Peter Arnold, Inc.
1.09b Courtesy W. L. Dentler, University of Kansas/BPS.
1.09c ©Omikron/Photo Researchers, Inc.
1.11a ©A.B. Dowsett/Science Source/Photo Researchers, Inc.
1.11b ©Ralph Robinson/Visuals Unlimited.
1.11c ©D.P. Wilson/Science Source/Photo Researchers, Inc.
1.11d, e, f ©1998 Photodisc.
1.12 ©Chip Clark.
1.13 Courtesy of Richard Milner.
1.14 ©Rudi Kuiter. Reprinted with permission of Discover Magazine.
1.15 Courtesy of David Reznick, University of California, Riverside.
1.18a ©Hank Morgan/Photo Researchers Inc.
1.18b ©Peter Menzel.
2.CO ©Stella Johnson.
2.EOC2 ©Phil Degginger/Color-Pic, Inc.
2.MB1a ©Terraphotographics/Biological Photo Service.
2.MB1c From M.C. Ratazzi et al., *Am J Human Genet* 28(1976):143–154.
2.02 ©E. R. Degginger/Color-Pic, Inc.
2.02 Stephen Frisch/Benjamin/Cummings.
2.03 ©Grant Heilman/Grant Heilman Photography, Inc.
2.04 ©Ivan Polunin/Bruce Coleman, Inc.
2.06 ©Igor Kostin/IMAGO/SYGMA.

2.13 ©Stephen Frisch/Benjamin/Cummings.
2.17 ©Annalisa Kraft/Benjamin/Cummings.
2.18 ©Runk Schoenberger/Grant Heilman Photography, Inc.
3.CO Courtesy of NASA.
3.02 ©E.R. Degginger/Color-Pic, Inc.
3.03 ©Stephen Dalton/NHPA.
3.04 ©1996 DUOMO/William Sallaz.
3.06 ©Flip Nicklin/Minden Pictures.
3.10 ©1991 Maresa Pryor/Earth Scenes/Animals Animals.
4.CO Courtesy of P. Shing Ho.
4.01 Roger Ressmeyer/©Corbis.
4.05 ©Manfred Kage/Peter Arnold, Inc.
4.08 (left) ©W.J. Weber/Visuals Unlimited.
4.08 (right) ©Stephen J. Krasemann/Photo Researchers, Inc.
5.CO ©Martin Shields.
5.MB1b, c, d Courtesy of Marie Green, University of California, Riverside.
5.01a Estate of Linus Pauling.
5.01b ©Louise Lockley/SCIRO/Science Photo Library/Photo Researchers, Inc.
5.06a ©Dr. Jeremy Burgess/Photo Researchers, Inc.
5.06b Courtesy of H. Shio and P.B. Lazarow.
5.08 ©J. Litray/Visuals Unlimited.
5.09a ©F. Collet/Photo Researchers, Inc.
5.09b ©George Disario/The Stock Market.
5.11a Courtesy of the American Dairy Association.
5.11b ©Lara Hartley.
5.17 Courtesy of the Graphics Systems Research Group, IBM U.K. Scientific Centre.
5.19a, b ©M. Murayama, Murayama Research Laboratory/BPS.
5.21 (left) ©Martin Shields.
5.21 (right) Vollrath & Edmunds, *Nature* 340: 305–317.
6.CO ©Jean-Marie Bassot/Photo Researchers, Inc.
6.02 ©Eunice Harris 1987/Photo Researchers, Inc.
6.03 ©Manfred Kage/Peter Arnold, Inc.
6.11 Courtesy of Thomas Steitz, Yale University.
6.18 ©R. Rodewald, University of Virginia/Biological Photo Service.
7.CO ©M. Schliwa/Visuals Unlimited.
7.T01.1 ©Biophoto Associates/Photo Researchers, Inc.
7.T01.2 ©David M. Phillips/Visuals Unlimited.
7.T01.3 ©Ed Reschke.
7.T01.4, 5 ©David M. Phillips/Visuals Unlimited.
7.T01.6 Courtesy of Noran Instruments.
7.T02.1 Courtesy of Dr. Mary Osborn, Max Planck Institute.
7.T02.2 Courtesy of Drs. Frank Solomon and J. Dinsmore, MIT.
7.T02.3 Mark S. Ladinsky and J. Richard McIntosh, University of Colorado.
7.02a, b ©William L. Dentler, University of Kansas/Biological Photo Service.
7.04b ©S.C. Holt, University of Texas Health Center/Biological Photo Service.
7.06a Courtesy of J. David Robertson.

7.09e U. Aebi. et al. *Nature* 323(1996):560–564, figure 1a. Used by permission.
7.10 ©D.W. Fawcett/Photo Researchers, Inc.
7.11 ©R. Bolender, D. Fawcett/Photo Researchers, Inc.
7.12 ©G.T. Cole, University of Texas, Austin/Biological Photo Service.
7.13a ©R. Rodewald, University of Virginia/Biological Photo Service.
7.13b Courtesy of Daniel S. Friend, Harvard Medical School.
7.15 Courtesy of E.H. Newcomb, University of Wisconsin.
7.17 Courtesy of Daniel S. Friend, Harvard Medical School.
7.18 ©WP Wergin and E.H. Newcomb, University of Wisconsin, Madison/Biological Photo Service.
7.19 Reproduced from S.E. Frederick and E.H. Newcomb, *The Journal of Cell Biology* 43 (1969):343 by copyright permission of The Rockefeller University Press. Provided by E.H. Newcomb.
7.20 Courtesy of Dr. John E. Heuser, Washington University, St. Louis.
7.22 Courtesy of Kent McDonald, University of California, Berkeley.
7.23a ©Richard Kessel/Visuals Unlimited.
7.23b ©1990 Dennis Kunkel.
7.24a ©OMIKRON/Science Source/Photo Researchers, Inc.
7.24b, c ©W. L. Dentler, University of Kansas/ Biological Photo Service.
7.26 Reproduced from Hirokawa Nobutaka, *The Journal of Cell Biology* 94(1982):425 by copyright permission of The Rockefeller University Press.
7.27 Courtesy of Dr. John E. Heuser, Washington University, St. Louis.
7.28 ©G.F. Leedale/Photo Researchers, Inc.
7.30a Reproduced from Douglas J. Kelly, *The Journal of Cell Biology* 28(1966):51 by permission of The Rockefeller University Press.
7.30c Reproduced from C. Peracchia and A.F. Dulhunty, *The Journal of Cell Biology* 70(1976):419 by permission of The Rockefeller University Press.
7.31 ©Boehringer Ingelheim International GmbH, photo Lennart Nilsson/Albert Bonniers Forlag AB, *The Body Victorious*, Delacorte Press, Dell Publishing Co., Inc.
8.MB1 Courtesy of Philippa Claude.
8.12a, b ©Cabisco/Visuals Unlimited.
8.18a ©R.N. Band and H.S. Pankratz, Michigan State University/Biological Photo Service.
8.18b ©D.W. Fawcett/Photo Researchers, Inc.
8.18c From M.M. Perry and A.B. Gilbert, *J. Cell Sci.* 39(1979):257. ©1979 by The Company of Biologists Ltd.
9.CO ©Gerry Ellis/ENP Images.
10.CO ©E.R. Degginger/Earth Scenes/Animals Animals.
10.01a ©Renee Lynn/Photo Researchers, Inc.
10.01b ©Bob Evans/Peter Arnold, Inc.
10.01c ©Dwight Kuhn.

27.T03.9 ©Moredon Animal Health/SPL/Photo Researchers, Inc.
27.02a ©Meckes/Ottawa/Photo Researchers, Inc.
27.02b ©Manfred Kage/Peter Arnold, Inc.
27.02c ©David Chase/CNRI/Phototake NYC.
27.03 Courtesy of Esther Angert, Harvard University.
27.04 Fran Heyl Associates, photo by David Hasty, computer enhancement by pixelation.
27.05 Courtesy of J. Adler.
27.06a Courtesy of S. W. Watson.
27.06b N. J. Lang/University of California/Biological Photo Service.
27.07 ©John Durham/SPL/Photo Researchers, Inc.
27.09a Courtesy of Frederick Atwood, Flint Hill School.
27.09b ©T. E. Adams/Visuals Unlimited.
27.10 ©Helen E. Carr/Biological Photo Service.
27.12 Courtesy of Exxon Corporation.
28.CO ©M. I. Walker/Photo Researchers, Inc.
28.04 ©E. White/Visuals Unlimited.
28.05 Courtesy of John Mansfield, University of Wisconsin, Madison.
28.06a ©Eric Grave/Photo Researchers, Inc.
28.06b Courtesy of JoAnn Burkholder, North Carolina State University.
28.07 Courtesy of Masamichi Aikawa, Case Western Reserve University.
28.08a ©Eric Grave/Photo Researchers, Inc.
28.08b ©Manfred Kage/Peter Arnold, Inc.
28.08c ©M. Abbey/Visuals Unlimited.
28.10 ©Peter Parks/Animals Animals.
28.11a, b ©Eric Grave/Photo Researchers, Inc.
28.12 ©Manfred Kage/Peter Arnold, Inc.
28.12b ©Paola Koch/Photo Researchers, Inc.
28.13 ©Ray Simmons/Photo Researchers, Inc.
28.13 ©R. Calentine/Visuals Unlimited.
28.14 Courtesy of Robert Kay, MRC Cambridge.
28.15a ©Eric Grave/Photo Researchers, Inc.
28.15b ©Fred Rhoades/Mycena Consulting.
28.16 ©Biological Photo Service.
28.17 ©Fred Rhoades/Mycena Consulting.
28.18 ©Anne Wertheim/Animals Animals.
28.19 ©W Lewis Trusty/Animals Animals.
28.20 Courtesy of J. R. Waaland, University of Washington/Biological Photo Service.
28.21a Courtesy of J. R. Waaland, University of Washington/Biological Photo Service.
28.21b ©D. P. Wilson and Eric and David Hosking/Photo Researchers, Inc.
28.21c ©Gary Robinson/Visuals Unlimited.
28.22a ©Manfred Kage/Peter Arnold, Inc.
28.22b Estate of Dr. J. Metzner/Peter Arnold, Inc.
28.22c ©Laurie Campbell/NHPA.
28.23 ©M. I. Walker/Science Source/Photo Researchers, Inc.
28.24 Courtesy of W. L. Dentler, University of Kansas.
28.25 ©D. P. Wilson and Eric and David Hosking/Photo Researchers, Inc.
29.CO ©Otto Rogge.
29.EOC1 ©Dale and Marian Zimmerman/Bruce Coleman, Inc.
29.01a (left) ©J. R. Waaland/Biological Photo Service.
29.01a (right) ©Biological Photo Service.
29.01b ©Graham Kent.
29.04a ©Martha Cook and Claudia Lipke.
29.04b ©Linda Graham.
29.06 ©Glenn Oliver/Visuals Unlimited.
29.07 ©Dwight Kuhn.
29.08 ©Science VU.
29.09 From the Botany Department Collection at the University of Wisconsin, Madison. Courtesy of David Hanson, photographed by Claudia Lipke.
29.10 ©Chip Clark, 1988.

29.11 ©Milton Rand/Tom Stack and Associates.
29.12 ©Robert and Linda Mitchell.
29.13 ©E. S. Ross, California Academy of Sciences.
29.14 ©The Field Museum, Neg # 75400c.
30.CO Courtesy of The National Museum of Natural History, Smithsonian Institute.
30.03a ©James L. Castner.
30.03b ©Runk Schoenberger/Grant Heilman Photography, Inc.
30.03c ©Michael Fogden/Bruce Coleman, Inc.
30.03d ©C. P. Hickman/Visuals Unlimited.
30.07 ©Gregory K. Scott/Photo Researchers, Inc.
30.09 ©D. Wilder.
31.01 ©Fred Rhoades/Mycena Consulting.
31.05 J. R. Waaland, University of Washington/Biological Photo Service.
31.05 Courtesy of William Barstow, University of Georgia, Athens.
31.06 Ed Reschke/Peter Arnold, Inc.
31.07a ©Fred Rhoades/Mycena Consulting.
31.07b ©Jacana/Photo Researchers, Inc.
31.07c ©J. L. Lepore/Photo Researchers, Inc.
31.08 E. R. Degginger/Animals Animals.
31.09a ©Kerry T. Givens/Tom Stack and Associates.
31.09b ©Frans Lanting/Minden Pictures.
31.09c ©Adrian Davies/Bruce Coleman, Inc.
31.10 ©Biophoto Associates/Photo Researchers, Inc.
31.11 (left) ©Jack Bostrack/Visuals Unlimited.
31.11 (right) ©M. F. Brown/Visuals Unlimited.
31.12 ©N. Allin and G. L. Barron, University of Guelph/Biological Photo Service.
31.13 Courtesy of Stephen J. Kron, University of Chicago.
31.14 ©Fred Rhoades/Mycena Consulting.
31.15 ©V. Ahmadijian/Visuals Unlimited.
31.16 ©R.L. Peterson, University of Guelf/Biological Photo Service.
31.17 ©Robb Walsh.
32.CO ©Fred Bavendam/Minden Pictures.
33.CO ©Gary Braasch.
33.01, 33.05a ©Andrew J. Martinez/Photo Researchers, Inc.
33.05b ©Robert Brons/Biological Photo Service.
33.05c ©Kevin McCarthy/Offshoot Stock.
33.05d ©Chris Huss/The Wildlife Collection.
33.06 ©Robert Brons/Biological Photo Service.
33.07 ©Fred Bavendam/Peter Arnold, Inc.
33.08 ©Bill Wood/Bruce Coleman, Inc.
33.10 Centers for Disease Control.
33.11 ©Stanley Fleger/Visuals Unlimited.
33.12 ©W. I. Walker/Photo Researchers, Inc.
33.13a, b ©L. S. Stepanowicz/Photo Researchers, Inc.
33.14 ©Bill Wodd/NHPA.
33.15a ©Colin Milkins, Oxford Scientific Films/Animals Animals.
33.15b ©Fred Bavendam/Peter Arnold, Inc.
33.17 ©Jeff Foott/Tom Stack and Associates.
33.19a ©Kevin Schafer.
33.19b ©Chris Huss.
33.20 ©H. W. Pratt/Biological Photo Service.
33.22a ©Tom McHugh/Steinhart Aquarium/Photo Researchers, Inc.
33.22b ©Fred Bavendam/Peter Arnold, Inc.
33.22c ©Douglas Faulkner/Photo Researchers, Inc.
33.24a ©Sea Studio.
33.24b ©Kjell Sandved.
33.24c ©Robert and Linda Mitchell.
33.26 ©Cliff B. Frith/Bruce Coleman, Inc.
33.27 ©Chip Clark.
33.28 ©Milton Tierney, Jr./Visuals Unlimited.
33.29a ©Frans Lantin/Minden Pictures.
33.29b ©David Scharf.

33.29c Courtesy of Diana Sammataro, Pennsylvania State University.
33.30a ©Paul Skelcher/Rainbow.
33.31a ©Robert and Linda Mitchell.
33.31b ©E. R. Degginger/Color-Pic, Inc.
33.32 ©George Grall/National Geographic Society.
33.34a, b, c, d, e ©John Shaw/Tom Stack and Associates.
33.35a ©Frans Lanting/Minden Pictures.
33.35b ©Tom McHugh/Photo Researchers, Inc.
33.35c ©C. R. Wyttenbach/University of Kansas/Biological Photo Service.
33.36a ©Jeffrey L. Rotman/Peter Arnold, Inc.
33.36b ©Gary Milburn/Tom Stack and Associates.
33.36c ©Dave Woodward/Tom Stack and Associates.
33.36d ©Marty Snyderman.
33.36e ©Carl Roessler/Animals Animals.
33.36f ©Fred Bavendam/Peter Arnold, Inc.
34.CO ©Biophoto Associates/Photo Researchers, Inc.
34.02a ©Scott Johnson/Animals Animals.
34.04a ©Runk Schoenenberg/Grant Heilman Photography.
34.04c ©Mike Neveux.
34.07 ©Herve Berthoule/Jacana/Photo Researchers, Inc.
34.07 (inset) ©Tom Hugh/Photo Researchers, Inc.
34.09a ©Steinhart Aquarium/Photo Researchers, Inc.
34.09b ©Fred Bavendam/Minden Pictures.
34.10a ©Patrice Ceisel/Visuals Unlimited.
34.10b ©J. M. Labat/Jacana/Photo Researchers, Inc.
34.12 ©Richard Ellis/Photo Researchers, Inc.
34.15a ©Dwight Kuhn.
34.15b, c ©Michael Fogden/Bruce Coleman, Inc.
34.16a, b, c ©Hans Pfletschinger/Peter Arnold, Inc.
34.18 Photograph by Jessie Cohen, National Zoological Park, Smithsonian Institution. ©Smithsonian Institution.
34.21a ©Mark Moffett/Minden Pictures.
34.21b ©A.N.T./NHPA.
34.21c ©Robert and Linda Mitchell.
34.21d ©Medford Taylor/National Geographic Society.
34.22b ©Janice Sheldon.
34.23 ©Stephen J. Kraseman/DRK Photo.
34.25a ©Mitsuaki Iwago/Minden Pictures.
34.25b ©John Henry Dick/Vireo.
34.25c ©Frans Lanting/Minden Pictures.
34.25d ©1997 Photodisc.
34.27a(inset) Courtesy of Mervyn Griffiths/CSIRO.
34.27a ©D. Parer and E. Parer Cook/Auscape.
34.27b ©Dan Hadden/Ardea Ltd.
34.27c ©Fritz Prenzel/Animals Animals.
34.29 ©Erwin and Peggy Bauer/Bruce Coleman, Inc.
34.31a ©Stephen Dalton/NHPA.
34.31b ©Mickey Gibson/Animals Animals.
34.32a ©E. R. Degginger/Animals Animals.
34.32b ©Frans Lanting/Minden Pictures.
34.32c ©Nancy Adams/Tom Stack and Associates.
34.32d ©Michael K. Nichols/National Geographic Society.
34.34a Cleveland Museum of Natural History.
34.34b ©John Reader/SPL/Photo Researchers, Inc.
34.34c ©Institute of Human Origins, photo by Donald Johanson.
35.01a, c Elliot M. Meyerowitz and John Bowman, Development 112(1991):1–2 31.2.
35.01b Courtesy of Elliot Meyerowitz, Caltech.
35.02 ©David Cavagnaro.
35.05, 35.06a, b, c ©Dwight Kuhn.
35.06d ©George Bernard/Animals Animals.

35.08a ©Dwight Kuhn.
35.08b, c ©Kevin Schafer.
35.08d ©Larry Mellichamp/Visuals Unlimited.
35.09a, b ©Micrograph by W. P. Wergin, provided by E. H. Newcomb.
35.09c ©G. F. Leedale/Photo Researchers, Inc.
35.10a ©Dwight Kuhn.
35.10b ©Biophoto/Science Source/Photo Researchers, Inc.
35.10c, d ©Bruce Iverson.
35.10d ©Ed Reschke/Peter Arnold, Inc.
35.10e (left) ©George J. Wilder/Visuals Unlimited.
35.10e (right) ©Randy Moore/BioPhot.
35.15 Carolina Biological Supply/Phototake NYC.
35.16a ©Ed Reschke.
35.16b Carolina Biological Supply/Phototake NYC.
35.17 ©Dwight Kuhn.
35.18, 35.19, 35.20b, 35.20c ©Ed Reschke.
35.22 Courtesy of Dr. Howard F. Towner, Loyola Marymount University.
35.24d ©Ed Reschke/Peter Arnold, Inc.
36.MB1a Courtesy of Gary Tallman, Pepperdine University.
36.07 ©Dana Richter/Visuals Unlimited.
36.12 ©John D. Cunningham/Visuals Unlimited.
36.15a, b, c, Photos by M. H. Zimmerman courtesy of Professor P. B. Tomlinson, Harvard University.
37.CO ©Kim Taylor/Burce Coleman, Inc.
37.03 ©Holt Studios/Nigel Cattlin/Photo Researchers, Inc.
37.04 ©John H. Hoffman/Bruce Coleman.
37.05 ©William E. Ferguson.
37.07 John Reganhold, US Department of Agriculture Soil Conservation Service.
37.09a ©Biophoto Associates/Photo Researchers, Inc.
37.09b E. H. Newcomb/Biological Photo Service.
37.12a ©Gerald van Dyke/Visuals Unlimited.
37.12b ©Carolina Biological Supply/Phototake NYC.
37.13a ©Kevin Schafer.
37.13a (inset) ©Biophoto Associates/Photo Researchers, Inc.
37.13b ©Biological Photo Service.
37.14a ©Jeff Lepore/Photo Researchers, Inc.
37.14b ©John Shaw/Tom Stack and Associates.
38.CO © Stephenie Ferguson.
38.T1.01 ©Harold Taylor/OSF/Earth Scenes.
38.T1.02 ©William J. Weber/Visuals Unlimited.
38.T1.03 ©Bob Gossington/Bruce Coleman, Inc.
38.03a ©Tom Branch, 1978/Photo Researchers, Inc.
38.03b ©Ed Reschke/Peter Arnold, Inc.
38.03c ©Link, 1985/Visuals Unlimited.
38.03d ©Stephen Dalton/Photo Researchers, Inc.
38.03e ©William Ferguson.
38.03f ©Ray Coleman/Photo Researchers, Inc.
38.04a ©Graham Kent.
38.04b ©Ed Reschke.
38.13a ©James L. Castner.
38.13b ©David Cavagnaro/DRK.
38.14a, b ©Bruce Iverson.
38.15a Courtesy of Dr. John C. Sanford/Cornell University.
38.16a ©Jack Bostrack/Visuals Unlimited.
38.16b ©John D. Cunningham/Visuals Unlimited.
38.17 Courtesy of Susan Wick, University of Minnesota.
38.18 ©B. Wells and Kay Roberts.
38.20 ©Bruce Iverson.
39.CO, 39.06a, b ©Malcolm Wilkins, Glasgow University, UK.
39.07 Courtesy of Tugio Sasaki, Institute for Agricultural Research, Japan.

39.08 Courtesy of Fred Jensen, Kearney Agricultural Center.
39.09 Courtesy of Stephen Gladfelter, Stanford University.
39.10 ©Ed Reschke.
39.12 Courtesy of Michael Evans, Ohio State University.
39.13 Courtesy of Janet Braam, from Cell 60 (9 February 1990): cover. ©1990 by Cell Press.
39.14a, b ©John Kaprielan/Photo Researchers.
39.14c From K. Esau, Anatomy of Seed Plants, 2nd ed. (New York: John Wiley and Sons, 1977), fig. 19.4, p. 358.
39.15 Courtesy of Frank B. Salisbury, Utah State University.
39.21a, b Courtesy of J. L. Basq and M. C. Drew.
39.24 Courtesy of Barbara Baker, University of California, Berkeley.
40.CO ©Dwight R. Kuhn.
40.MB1.1 Courtesy of Robert Full, University of California.
40.MB1.2 ©Yoav Levy/Phototake NYC.
40.04 ©Ed Reschke.
40.08 ©Jeff Foott/Tom Stack & Associates.
41.CO ©Marty Stouffer/Animals Animals.
41.02 ©Carol Hughes/Bruce Coleman, Inc.
41.04 ©Brandon Cole.
41.05 Courtesy of Thomas Eisner, Cornell University.
41.06 ©Lennart Nilsson/Albert Bonniers Forlag AB.
41.07 ©Gunter Ziesler/Peter Arnold, Inc.
41.17 (left) ©Brian Milne/Animals Animals.
41.17 (right) ©Hans and Judy Beste/Animals Animals.
42.CO ©Jane Burton/Bruce Coleman, Inc.
42.01 ©Norbert Wu/Mo Young Productions.
42.15b ©Boehringer Ingelheim International GmbH photo by Lennart Nilsson/Albert Bonniers Verlag AB, The Body Victorious, Delacorte Press.
42.16a ©Ed Reschke.
42.16b ©W. Ober/Visuals Unlimited.
42.21 Courtesy of Dr. Peng Chai, University of Texas and Dr. Hong Y. Yan, University of Kentucky.
42.22c (right) ©CNRI/Photo Researchers Inc.
42.24a ©Professor Hans Rainer Dunker, Justus Liebig University, Giessen.
42.29 ©Kevin Schafer.
43.CO ©Lennart Nilsson/Albert Bonniers Forlag AB, A Child Is Born, Dell Publishing Company.
43.02 ©Science Photo Library/Photo Researchers, Inc.
43.03, 43.12b ©Lennart Nilsson/Boehringer Ingelheim International GmbH.
43.15c ©Dr. A. J. Olson, The Scripps Research Institute.
43.19 ©Lennart Nilsson/Boehringer Ingelheim International GmbH.
44.CO ©John Shaw/Bruce Coleman, Inc.
44.03a ©Jeff Lepore/Photo Researchers, Inc.
44.03b ©Dave B. Fleetham/Visuals Unlimited.
44.04 ©Daniel Lyons/Bruce Coleman, Inc.
44.12a, b Courtesy of John Crowe, University of California.
44.13a ©Tom McHugh/Photo Researchers, Inc.
45.CO ©William E. Ferguson.
46.CO Hans Pfletschinger/Peter Arnold, Inc.
46.01 ©David Wrobel/Monterey Bay Aquarium.
46.02a Courtesy of David Crews, photo by P. de Vries.
46.03 ©Stephan Myers.
46.04 ©Dwight Kuhn.
46.05 ©William Ferguson.
46.10 ©C. Edelman/La Villette/Photo Researchers, Inc.

46.18a, b, c ©Lennart Nilsson/Albert Bonniers Vorlag AB.
46.22 ©Howard Sochurek.
47.CO ©Lennart Nilsson/Albert Bonniers Vorlag AB.
47.01 Historical Collections, College of Physicians, Philadelphia.
47.03.1, 2, 3, 4 J. Reproduced from C. Rilkey, L. F. Jaffe, E. B. Ridgeway, and G. T. Reynolds, The Journal of Cell Biology 76(1978):448–466 by copyright permission of The Rockefeller University Press.
47.06a, b, c, ©George Watchmaker.
47.09 Courtesy of Charles A Ettensohn, Carnegie Mellon University.
47.11a ©CABISCO/Visuals Unlimited.
47.11c Thomas Poole, SUNY Health Science Center.
47.13 Carolina Biological Supply/Phototake NYC.
47.18a Reproduced from Dr. Jean Paul Thiery The Journal of Cell Biology 96(1983):462–473 by copyright permission of the Rockefeller University Press.
47.18b1, 2 ©Richard Hynes, from Scientific American, June 1986.
47.19a, b Courtesy of Janet Heasman, University of Minnesota.
47.20b1, 2 From Hiroki Nishida, Dev. Biol. 121 (1987):526. Reprinted by permission of Academic Press.
47.23a, b Courtesy of Kathryn Tosney, University of Michigan.
47.24 Based on Honig and Summerbell, 1985. Photo courtesy of Dennis Summerbell.
48.CO ©V. I. Lab E. R. I. C./FPG.
48.MB1b Courtesy of W. F. Gilly, Hopkins Marine Station of Stanford University.
48.MB2a ©Howard Sochurek.
48.MB2b Courtesy of Marcus Raichle, MD, Washington University School of Medicine, St Louis, MO.
48.02b ©Manfred Kage/Peter Arnold, Inc.
48.11b Courtesy of E. R. Lewis, University of California, Berkeley.
48.18 ©Stouffer Productions/Animals Animals.
48.21a ©Alexander Tsiarias/Photo Researchers, Inc.
49.CO ©Stephen Dalton/NHPA.
49.02a ©OSF/Animals Animals.
49.02b Courtesy of R. A. Steinbrecht, Max Planck Institute.
49.03a ©Joe McDonald/Animals Animals.
49.03b ©Russ Kinne/Photo Researchers, Inc.
49.05a ©John L. Pontier/Animals Animals.
49.17 From Richard Elzinga, Fundamentals of Entomology 3rd ed. ©1987, p. 185. Reprinted by permission of Prentice-Hall, Upper Saddle River, NJ.
49.18 ©Joe Monroe/Photo Researchers, Inc.
49.22 ©John Cancalosi/Tom Stack and Associates.
49.26 Courtesy of Clara Franzini-Armstrong, University of Pennsylvania.
49.27a, b, c, Courtesy of Dr. H. E. Huxley.
49.32b ©Eric Grave/Photo Researchers, Inc.
50.CO Courtesy of NASA - LBJ Space Center.
50.01 Courtesy of Gary Atchison, Iowa State University.
50.02 ©Copyright 1995, Los Angeles Times. Reprinted with permission.
50.11a ©Boyd Norton.
50.11b ©Michael Gadomski/Earth Scenes/Animals Animals.
50.11c ©William H. Mullins/Photo Researchers, Inc.
50.12a ©Steve Solum/ Bruce Coleman, Inc.
50.12b ©M.E. Warre/Photo Researchers, Inc.

18.CO From James D. Watson et al., *Molecular Biology of the Gene* 4th ed., fig. 7.10 (Menlo Park, CA: Benjamin/Cummings, 1987). ©1987 James D. Watson.

19.03 (inset) ©Irving Geis.

21.04 Adapted from Alberts et al., *Molecular Biology of the Cell*, 2nd ed., fig. 16.32, p. 904 (New York: Garland Publishing, 1989). ©1989 Garland Publishing. Reprinted by permission.

21.14 Adapted from an illustration by William McGinnis.

21.18 (upper right illustration only) Adapted from E. Dennis et al., "Manipulating Floral Identity," *Current Biology* 3(1993):90–93. Reprinted by permission.

25.05 Data from M. J. Benton, "Diversification and Extinction in the History of Life" *Science* 268 (1995):55.

25.16 Adapted from Cladogram by Peggy Conversano, illustrations by Ed Heck and Frank Ippolito, courtesy of Natural History.

27.5 From Gerard J. Tortora, Berdell R. Funke, and Christine L. Case, *Microbiology: An Introduction* 6th ed. (Menlo Park, CA: Benjamin/Cummings, 1998). ©1998 Benjamin/Cummings an imprint of Addison Wesley Longman, Inc.

30.10 Data from Berner, Robert A. "The Rise of Plants and Their Effects on Weathering and Atmospheric CO_2" *Science*, 276(1997):545.

34.20 ©Donna Braginetz.

34.26 Stephen J. Gould et al., *The Book of Life* (London: Ebury Press), p. 96. Reprinted by permission of Random House UK Ltd.

34.35 Adapted from an illustration from Laurie Grace, "The Recent African Genesis of Humans" by A. C. Wilson, R. I. Cann, *Scientific American* 1992:73.

43.14, 43.15 From Gerard J. Tortora, Berdell R. Funke, and Christine L. Case, *Microbiology: An Introduction*, 6th ed. (Menlo Park, CA: Benjamin/Cummings, 1998). ©1998 Benjamin/Cummings, an imprint of Addison Wesley Longman, Inc.

43.17 Adapted from Lennart Nilsson and Jan Lindberg, *The Body Victorious* (New York: Delacorte Press, 1987), p. 27. Illustration by Urban Frank, Studio Frank and Co, Illustrator.

44.02 Adapted from P. T. Marshall and G. M. Hughes, *Physiology of Mammals and Other Vertebrates*, 2nd ed. (Cambridge: Cambridge University Press, 1980). Reprinted with the permission of Cambridge University Press.

44.05b Adapted from an illustration by Enid Kotschnig from "Thermoregulation in a Winter Moth" by Bernd Heinrich, *Scientific American* 1987:105.

44.10 Adapted from Lawrence G. Mitchell, John A. Mutchmor, and Warren D. Dolphin, *Zoology* (Menlo Park, CA: Benjamin/Cummings, 1988) ©1988 The Benjamin/Cummings Publishing Company.

44.13b Kangaroo rat data from Schmidt-Nielsen, *Animal Physiology Adaptation and Environment* 4th ed., p. 339 (Cambridge: Cambridge University Press, 1990).

45.04 Adapted from Alberts et al., *Molecular Biology of the Cell*, 2nd ed., fig. 15.9 (New York: Garland Publishing, 1989). ©1989 Garland Publishing. Reprinted by permission.

45.12 Adapted from Gilbert, *Developmental Biology*, 4th ed., fig. 7.39 p. 282. (Sunderland, MA: Sinauer Associates Inc.). Reprinted by permission.

47.17 From Wolpert et al., *Principles of Development*, fig, 8.25, p. 251 right (Oxford: Oxford University Press, 1988). By permission of Oxford University Press.

47.20 Adapted from Alberts et al., *Molecular Biology of the Cell*, 2nd ed., fig. 16.29a, p. 904. (New York: Garland Publishing, 1989). ©1989 Garland Publishing. Reprinted by permission.

47.22 *Left*: From Wolpert et al., *Principles of Development* (Oxford: Oxford University Press. 1988), fig. 1.10 (right). By permission of Oxford University Press. Right: Adapted from Gilbert, *Developmental Biology* 5th Ed., part of fig. 15.12, p. 604 (Sunderland, MA: Sinauer Associates Inc.). ©1997 Sinauer Associates. Reprinted by permission.

48.07 Adapted from G. Matthews, *Cellular Physiology of Nerve and Muscle* (Cambridge, MA: Blackwell Scientific Publications, 1986). Reprinted by permission of Blackwell Science, Inc.

49.25 Adapted from Lawrence G. Mitchell, John A. Mutchmor, and Warren D. Dolphin, *Zoology* (Menlo Park, CA; Benjamin/Cummings, 1988). ©1988 The Benjamin/Cummings Publishing Company.

51.02 Adapted from Lawrence G. Mitchell, John A. Mutchmor, and Warren D. Dolphin, *Zoology* (Menlo Park, CA; Benjamin/Cummings, 1988). ©1988 The Benjamin/Cummings Publishing Company.

51.03 Adapted from N. Tinberger, *The Study of Instinct* (Oxford University Press, Oxford, 1951). By permission of Oxford University Press.

51.08 Courtesy of Masakazu Konishi.

52.10 R. E. Rickleffs, in D. S. Farner, *Breeding Biology of Birds*, pp. 366–435 (National Academy of Sciences, Washington DC, 1973).

52.19 Data from Higgins et al., "Stochastic Dynamics and Deterministic Skeletons: Population Behavior of Dungeness Crab", *Science* May 30, 1997.

53.9 Adapted from Gerard J. Tortora, Berdell R. Funke, and Christine L. Case, *Microbiology: An Introduction*, 6th ed. (Menlo Park, CA: Benjamin/Cummings, 1998). ©1998 Benjamin/Cummings, an imprint of Addison Wesley Longman, Inc.

53.11a A. S. Rand and E. E. Williams, "The Anoles of La Palma: Aspects of Their Ecological Relationships," *Breviora* no. 327, 1969. Museum of Comparative Zoology, Harvard University. ©Presidents and Fellows of Harvard College.

54.02 Adapted from R. Leo Smith, *Ecology and Field Biology*, 4th ed. ©1990 by R. Leo Smith. Reprinted by permission of Addison-Wesley Educational Publishers.

54.09 From R. E. Ricklefs, *The Economy of Nature* 4th ed.©1997 by W. H. Freeman and Company. Used with permission.

54.16 From G. Tyler, *Living in the Environment*, 2nd ed., p. 87 (Belmont, CA: Wadsworth Publishing, 1979). ©1979 Wadsworth Publishing Company.

55.MB1a Adapted from an illustration by Tamara R. Sayre.

55.MB1b USGS-BRD-Gap Analysis.

55.02 Tom Moore ©1986 Discover Magazine. Reprinted by permission of Discover Magazine.

55.14 Adapted from W. Purves and G. Orians, *Life: The Science of Biology*, 5th ed., fig. 55.23, p. 1239. (Sunderland, MA: Sinauer, 1998). Copyright ©1998 by Sinauer and W. H. Freeman and Company. Reprinted by permission.

GLOSSARY

abscisic acid (ABA) *(ab-SIS-ik)* A plant hormone that generally acts to inhibit growth, promote dormancy, and help the plant tolerate stressful conditions.

absorption spectrum The range of a pigment's ability to absorb various wavelengths of light.

abyssal zone *(uh-BIS-ul)* The portion of the ocean floor where light does not penetrate and where temperatures are cold and pressures intense.

acclimatization *(uh-KLY-mih-ty-ZAY-shun)* Physiological adjustment to a change in an environmental factor.

accommodation The automatic adjustment of an eye to focus on near objects.

acetyl CoA The entry compound for the Krebs cycle in cellular respiration; formed from a fragment of pyruvate attached to a coenzyme.

acetylcholine One of the most common neurotransmitters; functions by binding to receptors and altering the permeability of the postsynaptic membrane to specific ions, either depolarizing or hyperpolarizing the membrane.

acid A substance that increases the hydrogen ion concentration in a solution.

acid precipitation Rain, snow, or fog that is more acidic than pH 5.6.

acoelomate *(a-SEEL-oh-mate)* A solid-bodied animal lacking a cavity between the gut and outer body wall.

acrosome *(AK-ruh-some)* An organelle at the tip of a sperm cell that helps the sperm penetrate the egg.

actin *(AK-tin)* A globular protein that links into chains, two of which twist helically about each other, forming microfilaments in muscle and other contractile elements in cells.

action potential A rapid change in the membrane potential of an excitable cell, caused by stimulus-triggered, selective opening and closing of voltage-sensitive gates in sodium and potassium ion channels.

active site The specific portion of an enzyme that attaches to the substrate by means of weak chemical bonds.

active transport The movement of a substance across a biological membrane against its concentration or electrochemical gradient, with the help of energy input and specific transport proteins.

adaptive peak An equilibrium state in a population when the gene pool has allele frequencies that maximize the average fitness of a population's members.

adaptive radiation The emergence of numerous species from a common ancestor introduced into an environment, presenting a diversity of new opportunities and problems.

adenylyl cyclase An enzyme that converts ATP to cyclic AMP in response to a chemical signal.

adrenal gland *(uh-DREE-nul)* An endocrine gland located adjacent to the kidney in mammals; composed of two glandular portions: an outer cortex, which responds to endocrine signals in reacting to stress and effecting salt and water balance, and a central medulla, which responds to nervous inputs resulting from stress.

aerobic *(air-OH-bik)* Containing oxygen; referring to an organism, environment, or cellular process that requires oxygen.

age structure The relative number of individuals of each age in a population.

agnathan *(AG-naa-thun)* A member of a jawless class of vertebrates represented today by the lampreys and hagfishes.

agonistic behavior *(ag-on-IS-tik)* A type of behavior involving a contest of some kind that determines which competitor gains access to some resource, such as food or mates.

AIDS (acquired immunodeficiency syndrome) The name of the late stages of HIV infection; defined by a specified reduction of T cells and the appearance of characteristic secondary infections.

aldehyde *(AL-duh-hyde)* An organic molecule with a carbonyl group located at the end of the carbon skeleton.

aldosterone *(al-DAH-stair-own)* An adrenal hormone that acts on the distal tubules of the kidney to stimulate the reabsorption of sodium (Na^+) and the passive flow of water from the filtrate.

alga (plural, **algae**) A photosynthetic, plantlike protist.

all-or-none event An action that occurs either completely or not at all, such as the generation of an action potential by a neuron.

allantois *(AL-an-TOH-iss)* One of four extraembryonic membranes; serves as a repository for the embryo's nitrogenous waste.

allele *(uh-LEEL)* An alternative form of a gene.

allometric growth *(AL-oh-MET-rik)* The variation in the relative rates of growth of various parts of the body, which helps shape the organism.

allopatric speciation *(AL-oh-PAT-rik)* A mode of speciation induced when the ancestral population becomes segregated by a geographical barrier.

allopolyploid *(AL-oh-POL-ee-ploid)* A common type of polyploid species resulting from two different species interbreeding and combining their chromosomes.

allosteric site *(AL-oh-STEER-ik)* A specific receptor site on an enzyme molecule remote from the active site. Molecules bind to the allosteric site and change the shape of the active site, making it either more or less receptive to the substrate.

alpha (α) helix A spiral shape constituting one form of the secondary structure of proteins, arising from a specific hydrogen-bonding structure.

alternation of generations A life cycle in which there is both a multicellular diploid form, the sporophyte, and a multicellular haploid form, the gametophyte; characteristic of plants.

altruistic behavior *(AL-troo-IS-tik)* The aiding of another individual at one's own risk or expense.

alveolus *(al-VEE-oh-lus)* (plural, **alveoli**) (1) One of the deadend, multilobed air sacs that constitute the gas exchange surface of the lungs. (2) One of the milk-secreting sacs of epithelial tissue in the mammary glands.

amino acid *(uh-MEE-noh)* An organic molecule possessing both carboxyl and amino groups. Amino acids serve as the monomers of proteins.

amino group A functional group that consists of a nitrogen atom bonded to two hydrogen atoms; can act as a base in solution, accepting a hydrogen ion and acquiring a charge of +1.

aminoacyl-tRNA synthetases A family of enzymes, at least one for each amino acid, that catalyze the attachment of an amino acid to its specific tRNA molecule.

amniocentesis *(AM-nee-oh-sen-TEE-sis)* A technique for determining genetic abnormalities in a fetus by the presence of certain chemi-

cals or defective fetal cells in the amniotic fluid, obtained by aspiration from a needle inserted into the uterus.

amnion *(AM-nee-on)* The innermost of four extraembryonic membranes; encloses a fluid-filled sac in which the embryo is suspended.

amniote A vertebrate possessing an amnion surrounding the embryo; reptiles, birds, and mammals are amniotes.

amniotic egg *(AM-nee-AH-tik)* A shelled, water-retaining egg that enables reptiles, birds, and egg-laying mammals to complete their life cycles on dry land.

Amphibia The vertebrate class of amphibians, represented by frogs, salamanders, and caecilians.

amphipathic molecule A molecule that has both a hydrophilic region and a hydrophobic region.

anaerobic *(an-air-OH-bik)* Lacking oxygen; referring to an organism, environment, or cellular process that lacks oxygen and may be poisoned by it.

anagenesis *(AN-uh-JEN-eh-sis)* A pattern of evolutionary change involving the transformation of an entire population, sometimes to a state different enough from the ancestral population to justify renaming it as a separate species; also called phyletic evolution.

analogy The similarity of structure between two species that are not closely related; attributable to convergent evolution.

androgens *(AN-droh-jens)* The principal male steroid hormones, such as testosterone, which stimulate the development and maintenance of the male reproductive system and secondary sex characteristics.

aneuploidy *(AN-yoo-ploy-dee)* A chromosomal aberration in which certain chromosomes are present in extra copies or are deficient in number.

angiosperm *(AN-jee-oh-spurm)* A flowering plant, which forms seeds inside a protective chamber called an ovary.

anion *(AN-eye-on)* A negatively charged ion.

annual A plant that completes its entire life cycle in a single year or growing season.

anterior Referring to the head end of a bilaterally symmetrical animal.

anther *(AN-thur)* The terminal pollen sac of a stamen, inside which pollen grains with male gametes form in the flower of an angiosperm.

antheridium *(an-theh-RID-ee-um)* In plants, the male gametangium, a moist chamber in which gametes develop.

antibiotic A chemical that kills bacteria or inhibits their growth.

antibody An antigen-binding immunoglobulin, produced by B cells, that functions as the effector in an immune response.

anticodon *(AN-tee-CO-don)* A specialized base triplet on one end of a tRNA molecule that recognizes a particular complementary codon on an mRNA molecule.

antidiuretic hormone **(ADH)** A hormone important in osmoregulation.

antigen *(AN-teh-jen)* A foreign macromolecule that does not belong to the host organism and that elicits an immune response.

aphotic zone *(ay-FOE-tik)* The part of the ocean beneath the photic zone, where light does not penetrate sufficiently for photosynthesis to occur.

apical dominance *(AY-pik-ul)* Concentration of growth at the tip of a plant shoot, where a terminal bud partially inhibits axillary bud growth.

apical meristem *(AY-pik-ul MARE-eh-stem)* Embryonic plant tissue in the tips of roots and in the buds of shoots that supplies cells for the plant to grow in length.

apomorphic character *(AP-oh-MORE-fik)* A derived phenotypic character, or homology, that evolved after a branch diverged from a phylogenetic tree.

apoplast *(AP-oh-plast)* In plants, the nonliving continuum formed by the extracellular pathway provided by the continuous matrix of cell walls.

apoptosis Programmed cell death brought about by signals that trigger the activation of a cascade of "suicide" proteins in the cells destined to die.

aposematic coloration *(AP-oh-so-MAT-ik)* The bright coloration of animals with effective physical or chemical defenses that acts as a warning to predators.

aquaporin A transport protein in the plasma membranes of a plant or animal cell that specifically facilitates the diffusion of water across the membrane (osmosis).

aqueous solution *(AY-kwee-us)* A solution in which water is the solvent.

Archaea One of two prokaryotic domains, the other being the Bacteria.

Archaezoa Primitive eukaryotic group that includes diplomonads, such as *Giardia*; some systematists assign kingdom status to archezoans.

archegonium *(ar-kih-GO-nee-um)* In plants, the female gametangium, a moist chamber in which gametes develop.

archenteron *(ark-EN-ter-on)* The endoderm-lined cavity, formed during the gastrulation process, that develops into the digestive tract of an animal.

arteriosclerosis A cardiovascular disease caused by the formation of hard plaques within the arteries.

artery A vessel that carries blood away from the heart to organs throughout the body.

artificial selection The selective breeding of domesticated plants and animals to encourage the occurrence of desirable traits.

ascus (plural, **asci**) A saclike spore capsule located at the tip of the ascocarp in dikaryotic hyphae; defining feature of the Ascomycota division of fungi.

asexual reproduction A type of reproduction involving only one parent that produces genetically identical offspring by budding or by the division of a single cell or the entire organism into two or more parts.

associative learning The acquired ability to associate one stimulus with another; also called classical conditioning.

assortative mating A type of nonrandom mating in which mating partners resemble each other in certain phenotypic characters.

asymmetric carbon A carbon atom covalently bonded to four different atoms or groups of atoms.

atomic number The number of protons in the nucleus of an atom, unique for each element and designated by a subscript to the left of the elemental symbol.

atomic weight The total atomic mass, which is the mass in grams of one mole of the atom.

ATP (adenosine triphosphate) *(uh-DEN-oh-sin try-FOS-fate)* An adenine-containing nucleoside triphosphate that releases free energy when its phosphate bonds are hydrolyzed. This energy is used to drive endergonic reactions in cells.

ATP synthase A cluster of several membrane proteins found in the mitochondrial cristae (and bacterial plasma membrane) that function in chemiosmosis with adjacent electron transport chains, using the energy of a hydrogen-ion concentration gradient to make ATP. ATP synthases provide a port through which hydrogen ions diffuse into the matrix of a mitrochondrion.

atrioventricular valve A valve in the heart between each atrium and ventricle that prevents a backflow of blood when the ventricles contract.

atrium *(AY-tree-um)* (plural, **atria**) A chamber that receives blood returning to the vertebrate heart.

autogenesis model According to this model, eukaryotic cells evolved by the specialization of internal membranes originally derived from prokaryotic plasma membranes.

autoimmune disease An immunological disorder in which the immune system turns against itself.

autonomic nervous system *(AWT-uh-NAHM-ik)* A subdivision of the motor nervous system of vertebrates that regulates the internal environment; consists of the sympathetic and parasympathetic divisions.

autopolyploid *(AW-toe-POL-ee-ploid)* A type of polyploid species resulting from one species doubling its chromosome number to become tetraploid, which may self-fertilize or mate with other tetraploids.

autosome *(AW-tuh-some)* A chromosome that is not directly involved in determining sex, as opposed to the sex chromosomes.

autotroph *(AW-toh-TROHF)* An organism that obtains organic food molecules without eating other organisms. Autotrophs use energy from the sun or from the oxidation of inorganic substances to make organic molecules from inorganic ones.

auxins *(AWK-sins)* A class of plant hormones, including indoleacetic acid (IAA), having a variety of effects, such as phototropic response through the stimulation of cell elongation, stimulation of secondary growth, and the development of leaf traces and fruit.

auxotroph *(AWK-soh-trohf)* A nutritional mutant that is unable to synthesize and that cannot grow on media lacking certain essential molecules normally synthesized by wild-type strains of the same species.

Aves The vertebrate class of birds, characterized by feathers and other flight adaptations.

axillary bud *(AKS-ill-air-ee)* An embryonic shoot present in the angle formed by a leaf and stem.

axon *(AKS-on)* A typically long extension, or process, from a neuron that carries nerve impulses away from the cell body toward target cells.

B cell A type of lymphocyte that develops in the bone marrow and later produces antibodies, which mediate humoral immunity.

Bacteria One of two prokaryotic domains, the other being the Archaea.

bacterium (plural, **bacteria**) A prokaryotic microorganism in Domain Bacteria.

balanced polymorphism A type of polymorphism in which the frequencies of the coexisting forms do not change noticeably over many generations.

bark All tissues external to the vascular cambium in a plant growing in thickness, consisting of phloem, phelloderm, cork cambium, and cork.

Barr body A dense object lying along the inside of the nuclear envelope in female mammalian cells, representing an inactivated X chromosome.

basal body *(BAY-sul)* A eukaryotic cell organelle consisting of a 9 + 0 arrangement of microtubule triplets; may organize the microtubule assembly of a cilium or flagellum; structurally identical to a centriole.

basal metabolic rate (BMR) The minimal number of kilocalories a resting animal requires to fuel itself for a given time.

base A substance that reduces the hydrogen ion concentration in a solution.

basement membrane The floor of an epithelial membrane on which the basal cells rest.

base-pair substitution A point mutation; the replacement of one nucleotide and its partner from the complementary DNA strand by another pair of nucleotides.

basidium (plural, **basidia**) A reproductive appendage that produces sexual spores on the gills of mushrooms. The fungal division Basidiomycota is named for this structure.

Batesian mimicry *(BAYTZ-ee-un MIM-ih-kree)* A type of mimicry in which a harmless species looks like a different species that is poisonous or otherwise harmful to predators.

behavioral ecology A heuristic approach based on the expectation that Darwinian fitness (reproductive success) is improved by optimal behavior.

benthic zone The bottom surfaces of aquatic environments.

biennial *(by-EN-ee-ul)* A plant that requires two years to complete its life cycle.

bilateral symmetry Characterizing a body form with a central longitudinal plane that divides the body into two equal but opposite halves.

bilateria *(BY-leh-TEER-ee-uh)* Members of the branch of eumetazoans possessing bilateral symmetry.

binary fission The type of cell division by which prokaryotes reproduce; each dividing daughter cell receives a copy of the single parental chromosome.

binomial The two-part Latinized name of a species, consisting of genus and specific epithet.

biodiversity hotspot A relatively small area with an exceptional concentration of species.

bioenergetics The study of how organisms manage their energy resources.

biogeochemical cycles The various nutrient circuits, which involve both biotic and abiotic components of ecosystems.

biogeography The study of the past and present distribution of species.

biological magnification A trophic process in which retained substances become more concentrated with each link in the food chain.

biological species A population or group of populations whose members have the potential to interbreed.

biomass The dry weight of organic matter comprising a group of organisms in a particular habitat.

biome *(BY-ome)* One of the world's major communities, classified according to the predominant vegetation and characterized by adaptations of organisms to that particular environment.

biosphere *(BY-oh-sfeer)* The entire portion of Earth that is inhabited by life; the sum of all the planet's communities and ecosystems.

biotechnology The industrial use of living organisms or their components to improve human health and food production.

biotic *(by-OT-ik)* Pertaining to the living organisms in the environment.

blastocoel *(BLAS-toh-seel)* The fluid-filled cavity that forms in the center of the blastula embryo.

blastocyst An embryonic stage in mammals; a hollow ball of cells produced one week after fertilization in humans.

blastopore *(BLAS-toh-por)* The opening of the archenteron in the gastrula that develops into the mouth in protostomes and the anus in deuterostomes.

blastula *(BLAS-tyoo-la)* The hollow ball of cells marking the end stage of cleavage during early embryonic development.

blood-brain barrier A specialized capillary arrangement in the brain that restricts the passage of most substances into the brain, thereby preventing dramatic fluctuations in the brain's environment.

blood pressure The hydrostatic force that blood exerts against the wall of a vessel.

bond energy The quantity of energy that must be absorbed to break a particular kind of chemical bond; equal to the quantity of energy the bond releases when it forms.

book lungs Organs of gas exchange in spiders, consisting of stacked plates contained in an internal chamber.

bottleneck effect Genetic drift resulting from the reduction of a population, typically by a natural disaster, such that the surviving population is no longer genetically representative of the original population.

Bowman's capsule *(BOH-munz)* A cup-shaped receptacle in the vertebrate kidney that is the initial, expanded segment of the nephron where filtrate enters from the blood.

brainstem The hindbrain and midbrain of the vertebrate central nervous system. In humans, it forms a cap on the anterior end of the spinal cord, extending to about the middle of the brain.

bryophytes *(BRY-oh-fites)* The mosses, liverworts, and hornworts; a group of nonvascular plants that inhabit the land but lack many of the terrestrial adaptations of vascular plants.

budding An asexual means of propagation in which outgrowths from the parent form and pinch off to live independently or else remain attached to eventually form extensive colonies.

buffer A substance that consists of acid and base forms in solution and that minimizes changes in pH when extraneous acids or bases are added to the solution.

bulk flow The movement of water due to a difference in pressure between two locations.

C₃ plant A plant that uses the Calvin cycle for the initial steps that incorporate CO_2 into organic material, forming a three-carbon compound as the first stable intermediate.

C₄ plant A plant that prefaces the Calvin cycle with reactions that incorporate CO_2 into four-carbon compounds, the end-product of which supplies CO_2 for the Calvin cycle.

calcitonin *(kal-sih-TOH-nin)* A mammalian thyroid hormone that lowers blood calcium levels.

calmodulin *(kal-MOD-yoo-lin)* An intracellular protein to which calcium binds in its function as a second messenger in hormone action.

calorie (cal) The amount of heat energy required to raise the temperature of 1 g of water 1°C; the amount of heat energy that 1 g of water releases when it cools by 1°C. The Calorie (with a capital C), usually used to indicate the energy content of food, is a kilocalorie.

Calvin cycle The second of two major stages in photosynthesis (following the light reactions), involving atmospheric CO_2 fixation and reduction of the fixed carbon into carbohydrate.

CAM plant A plant that uses crassulacean acid metabolism, an adaptation for photosynthesis in arid conditions, first discovered in the family Crassulaceae. Carbon dioxide entering open stomata during the night is converted into organic acids, which release CO_2 for the Calvin cycle during the day, when stomata are closed.

Cambrian explosion A burst of evolutionary origins when most of the major body plans of animals appeared in a relatively brief time in geological history; recorded in the fossil record about 545 to 525 million years ago.

capillary *(KAP-ill-air-ee)* A microscopic blood vessel that penetrates the tissues and consists of a single layer of endothelial cells that allows exchange between the blood and interstitial fluid.

capsid The protein shell that encloses the viral genome; rod-shaped, polyhedral, or more completely shaped.

carbohydrate *(KAR-bo-HY-drate)* A sugar (monosaccharide) or one of its dimers (disaccharides) or polymers (polysaccharides).

carbon fixation The incorporation of carbon from CO_2 into an organic compound by an autotrophic organism (a plant, another photosynthetic organism, or a chemoautotrophic bacterium).

carbonyl group *(KAR-buh-nil)* A functional group present in aldehydes and ketones, consisting of a carbon atom double-bonded to an oxygen atom.

carboxyl group *(kar-BOX-ul)* A functional group present in organic acids, consisting of a single carbon atom double-bonded to an oxygen atom and also bonded to a hydroxyl group.

carcinogen *(kar-SIN-oh-jen)* A chemical agent that causes cancer.

cardiac muscle *(KAR-dee-ak)* A type of muscle that forms the contractile wall of the heart; its cells are joined by intercalated discs that relay each heartbeat.

cardiac output The volume of blood pumped per minute by the left ventricle of the heart.

carnivore An animal, such as a shark, hawk, or spider, that eats other animals.

carotenoids *(keh-ROT-en-oydz)* Accessory pigments, yellow and orange, in the chloroplasts of plants; by absorbing wavelengths of light that chlorophyll cannot, they broaden the spectrum of colors that can drive photosynthesis.

carpel *(KAR-pel)* The female reproductive organ of a flower, consisting of the stigma, style, and ovary.

carrier In human genetics, an individual who is heterozygous at a given genetic locus, with one normal allele and one potentially harmful recessive allele. The heterozygote is phenotypically normal for the character determined by the gene but can pass on the harmful allele to offspring.

carrying capacity The maximum population size that can be supported by the available resources, symbolized as K.

cartilage *(KAR-til-ij)* A type of flexible connective tissue with an abundance of collagenous fibers embedded in chondrin.

Casparian strip *(kas-PAR-ee-un)* A water-impermeable ring of wax around endodermal cells in plants that blocks the passive flow of water and solutes into the stele by way of cell walls.

catabolic pathway *(KAT-uh-BOL-ik)* A metabolic pathway that releases energy by breaking down complex molecules into simpler compounds.

catabolite activator protein (CAP) *(ka-TAB-ul-LITE)* In *E. coli*, a helper protein that stimulates gene expression by binding within the promoter region of an operon and enhancing the promoter's ability to associate with RNA polymerase.

cation *(KAT-eye-on)* An ion with a positive charge, produced by the loss of one or more electrons.

cation exchange A process in which positively charged minerals are made available to a plant when hydrogen ions in the soil displace mineral ions from the clay particles.

cell center A region in the cytoplasm near the nucleus from which microtubules originate and radiate.

cell cycle An ordered sequence of events in the life of a dividing eukaryotic cell, composed of the M, G_1, S, and G_2 phases.

cell fractionation The disruption of a cell and separation of its organelles by centrifugation.

cell-mediated immunity The type of immunity that functions in defense against fungi, protists, bacteria, and viruses inside host cells and against tissue transplants, with highly specialized cells that circulate in the blood and lymphoid tissue.

cell plate A double membrane across the midline of a dividing plant cell, between which the new cell wall forms during cytokinesis.

cell wall A protective layer external to the plasma membrane in plant cells, bacteria, fungi, and some protists. In the case of plant cells, the wall is formed of cellulose fibers embedded in a polysaccharide-protein matrix. The primary cell wall is thin and flexible, whereas the secondary cell wall is stronger and more rigid, and is the primary constituent of wood.

cellular differentiation The structural and functional divergence of cells as they become specialized during a multicellular organism's development; dependent on the control of gene expression.

cellular respiration The most prevalent and efficient catabolic pathway for the production of ATP, in which oxygen is consumed as a reactant along with the organic fuel.

cellulose *(SELL-yoo-lose)* A structural polysaccharide of cell walls, consisting of glucose monomers joined by β-1, 4-glycosidic linkages.

Celsius scale *(SELL-see-us)* A temperature scale (°C) equal to $\frac{5}{9}$ (°F − 32) that measures the freezing point of water at 0°C and the boiling point of water at 100°C.

central nervous system (CNS) In vertebrate animals, the brain and spinal cord.

centriole *(SEN-tree-ole)* A structure in an animal cell, composed of cylinders of microtubule triplets arranged in a 9 + 0 pattern. An animal cell usually has a pair of centrioles, which are involved in cell division.

centromere *(SEN-troh-mere)* The centralized region joining two sister chromatids.

centrosome Material present in the cytoplasm of all eukaryotic cells and important during cell division; also called microtubule-organizing center.

cephalochordate A chordate without a backbone, represented by lancelets, tiny marine animals.

cerebellum *(SEH-reh-BELL-um)* Part of the vertebrate hindbrain (rhombencephalon) located dorsally; functions in unconscious coordination of movement and balance.

cerebral cortex *(seh-REE-brul)* The surface of the cerebrum; the largest and most complex part of the mammalian brain, containing sensory and motor nerve cell bodies of the cerebrum; the part of the vertebrate brain most changed through evolution.

cerebrum *(seh-REE-brum)* The dorsal portion, composed of right and left hemispheres, of the vertebrate forebrain; the integrating center for memory, learning, emotions, and other highly complex functions of the central nervous system.

chaparral (*SHAP-uh-RAL*) A scrubland biome of dense, spiny evergreen shrubs found at mid-latitudes along coasts where cold ocean currents circulate offshore; characterized by mild, rainy winters and long, hot, dry summers.

chemical equilibrium In a reversible chemical reaction, the point at which the rate of the forward reaction equals the rate of the reverse reaction.

chemiosmosis (*KEM-ee-oz-MOH-sis*) The production of ATP using the energy of hydrogen-ion gradients across membranes to phosphorylate ADP; powers most ATP synthesis in cells.

chemoautotroph (*KEE-moh-AW-toh-trohf*) An organism that needs only carbon dioxide as a carbon source but that obtains energy by oxidizing inorganic substances.

chemoheterotroph (*KEE-moh-HET-er-oh-trohf*) An organism that must consume organic molecules for both energy and carbon.

chemoreceptor A receptor that transmits information about the total solute concentration in a solution or about individual kinds of molecules.

chiasma (*KY-as-muh*) (plural, **chiasmata**) The X-shaped, microscopically visible region representing homologous chromatids that have exchanged genetic material through crossing over during meiosis.

chitin (*KY-tin*) A structural polysaccharide of an amino sugar found in many fungi and in the exoskeletons of all arthropods.

chlorophyll A green pigment located within the chloroplasts of plants; chlorophyll *a* can participate directly in the light reactions, which convert solar energy to chemical energy.

chloroplast (*KLOR-oh-plast*) An organelle found only in plants and photosynthetic protists that absorbs sunlight and uses it to drive the synthesis of organic compounds from carbon dioxide and water.

cholesterol (*kol-ESS-teh-rol*) A steroid that forms an essential component of animal cell membranes and acts as a precursor molecule for the synthesis of other biologically important steroids.

Chondrichthyes The vertebrate class of cartilaginous fishes, represented by sharks and their relatives.

chondrin A protein-carbohydrate complex secreted by chondrocytes; chondrin and collagen fibers form cartilage.

chordate (*KOR-date*) A member of a diverse phylum of animals that possess a notochord; a dorsal, hollow nerve cord; pharyngeal gill slits; and a postanal tail as embryos.

chorion (*KOR-ee-on*) The outermost of four extraembryonic membranes; contributes to the formation of the mammalian placenta.

chorionic villus sampling (CVS) (*KOR-ee-on-ik VILL-us*) A technique for diagnosing genetic and congenital defects while the fetus is in the uterus. A small sample of the fetal portion of the placenta is removed and analyzed.

chromatin The complex of DNA and proteins that makes up a eukaryotic chromosome. When the cell is not dividing, chromatin exists as a mass of very long, thin fibers that are not visible with a light microscope.

Chromista In some classification systems, a kingdom consisting of brown algae, golden algae, and diatoms.

chromosome (*KRO-muh-some*) A threadlike, gene-carrying structure found in the nucleus. Each chromosome consists of one very long DNA molecule and associated proteins. *See* chromatin.

chytrid Fungus with flagellated stage; possible evolutionary link between fungi and protists.

cilium (*SILL-ee-um*) (plural, **cilia**) A short cellular appendage specialized for locomotion, formed from a core of nine outer doublet microtubules and two inner single microtubules ensheathed in an extension of plasma membrane.

circadian rhythm (*sur-KAY-dee-un*) A physiological cycle of about 24 hours, present in all eukaryotic organisms, that persists even in the absence of external cues.

cladistics (*kluh-DIS-tiks*) A taxonomic approach that classifies organisms according to the order in time at which branches arise along a phylogenetic tree, without considering the degree of morphological divergence.

cladogenesis (*KLAY-doh-GEN-eh-sis*) A pattern of evolutionary change that produces biological diversity by budding one or more new species from a parent species that continues to exist; also called branching evolution.

cladogram A dichotomous phylogenetic tree that branches repeatedly, suggesting a classification of organisms based on the time sequence in which evolutionary branches arise.

classical conditioning A type of associative learning; the association of a normally irrelevant stimulus with a fixed behavioral response.

cleavage The process of cytokinesis in animal cells, characterized by pinching of the plasma membrane; specifically, the succession of rapid cell divisions without growth during early embryonic development that converts the zygote into a ball of cells.

cleavage furrow The first sign of cleavage in an animal cell; a shallow groove in the cell surface near the old metaphase plate.

cline Variation in features of individuals in a population that parallels a gradient in the environment.

cloaca (*kloh-AY-kuh*) A common opening for the digestive, urinary, and reproductive tracts in all vertebrates except most mammals.

clonal selection (*KLOH-nul*) The mechanism that determines specificity and accounts for antigen memory in the immune system; occurs because an antigen introduced into the body selectively activates only a tiny fraction of inactive lymphocytes, which proliferate to form a clone of effector cells specific for the stimulating antigen.

clone (1) A lineage of genetically identical individuals or cells. (2) In popular usage, a single individual organism that is genetically identical to another individual. (3) As a verb, to make one or more genetic replicas of an individual or cell. Also, *see* gene cloning.

cloning vector An agent used to transfer DNA in genetic engineering, such as a plasmid that moves recombinant DNA from a test tube back into a cell, or a virus that transfers recombinant DNA by infection.

closed circulatory system A type of internal transport in which blood is confined to vessels.

cochlea (*KOH-klee-uh*) The complex, coiled organ of hearing that contains the organ of Corti.

codominance A phenotypic situation in which both alleles are expressed in the heterozygote.

codon (*KOH-don*) A three-nucleotide sequence of DNA or mRNA that specifies a particular amino acid or termination signal; the basic unit of the genetic code.

coelom (*SEE-lome*) A body cavity completely lined with mesoderm.

coelomate (*SEE-loh-mate*) An animal whose body cavity is completely lined by mesoderm, the layers of which connect dorsally and ventrally to form mesenteries.

coenocytic (*SEN-oh-SIT-ik*) Referring to a multinucleated condition resulting from the repeated division of nuclei without cytoplasmic division.

coenzyme (*ko-EN-zyme*) An organic molecule serving as a cofactor. Most vitamins function as coenzymes in important metabolic reactions.

coevolution The mutual influence on the evolution of two different species interacting with each other and reciprocally influencing each other's adaptations.

cofactor Any nonprotein molecule or ion that is required for the proper functioning of an enzyme. Cofactors can be permanently bound to the active site or may bind loosely with the substrate during catalysis.

cohesion The binding together of like molecules, often by hydrogen bonds.

cohesion species concept The idea that specific evolutionary adaptations and discrete complexes of genes define species.

collagen A glycoprotein in the extracellular matrix of animal cells that forms strong fibers, found extensively in connective tissue and bone; the most abundant protein in the animal kingdom.

collecting duct The location in the kidney where filtrate from renal tubules is collected; the filtrate is now called urine.

collenchyma cell (*koal-EN-keh-muh*) A flexible plant cell type that occurs in strands or cylinders that support young parts of the plant without restraining growth.

commensalism (*kuh-MEN-sul-iz-um*) A symbiotic relationship in which the symbiont benefits but the host is neither helped nor harmed.

community All the organisms that inhabit a particular area; an assemblage of populations of different species living close enough together for potential interaction.

companion cell A type of plant cell that is connected to a sieve-tube member by many plasmodesmata and whose nucleus and ribosomes may serve one or more adjacent sieve-tube members.

competitive exclusion principle The concept that when the populations of two species compete for the same limited resources, one population will use the resources more efficiently and have a reproductive advantage that will eventually lead to the elimination of the other population.

competitive inhibitor A substance that reduces the activity of an enzyme by entering the active site in place of the substrate whose structure it mimics.

complement fixation An immune response in which antigen-antibody complexes activate complement proteins.

complement system A group of at least 20 blood proteins that cooperate with other defense mechanisms; may amplify the inflammatory response, enhance phagocytosis, or directly lyse pathogens; activated by the onset of the immune response or by surface antigens on microorganisms or other foreign cells.

complementary DNA (cDNA) A DNA molecule made in vitro using mRNA as a template and the enzyme reverse transcriptase. A cDNA molecule therefore corresponds to a gene, but lacks the introns present in the DNA of the genome.

complete digestive tract A digestive tube that runs between a mouth and an anus; also called alimentary canal. An incomplete digestive tract has only one opening.

complete flower A flower that has sepals, petals, stamens, and carpels.

compound A chemical combination, in a fixed ratio, of two or more elements.

compound eye A type of multifaceted eye in insects and crustaceans consisting of up to several thousand light-detecting, focusing ommatidia; especially good at detecting movement.

condensation reaction A reaction in which two molecules become covalently bonded to each other through the loss of a small molecule, usually water; also called dehydration reaction.

cone cell One of two types of photoreceptors in the vertebrate eye; detects color during the day.

conidium (plural, **conidia**) A naked, asexual spore produced at the ends of hyphae in ascomycetes.

conifer A gymnosperm whose reproductive structure is the cone. Conifers include pines, firs, redwoods, and other large trees.

conjugation (*KON-joo-GAY-shun*) In bacteria, the transfer of DNA between two cells that are temporarily joined.

connective tissue Animal tissue that functions mainly to bind and support other tissues, having a sparse population of cells scattered through an extracellular matrix.

conservation biology A goal-oriented science that seeks to counter the biodiversity crisis, the current rapid decrease in Earth's variety of life.

contraception The prevention of pregnancy.

convection The mass movement of warmed air or liquid to or from the surface of a body or object.

convergent evolution The independent development of similarity between species as a result of their having similar ecological roles and selection pressures.

cooperativity (*koh-OP-ur-uh-TIV-eh-tee*) An interaction of the constituent subunits of a protein causing a conformational change in one subunit to be transmitted to all the others.

cork cambium (*KAM-bee-um*) A cylinder of meristematic tissue in plants that produces cork cells to replace the epidermis during secondary growth.

corpus luteum (*KOR-pus LOO-tee-um*) A secreting tissue in the ovary that forms from the collapsed follicle after ovulation and produces progesterone.

cortex The region of the root between the stele and epidermis filled with ground tissue.

cotransport The coupling of the "downhill" diffusion of one substance to the "uphill" transport of another against its own concentration gradient.

cotyledons (*KOT-eh-LEE-dons*) The one (monocot) or two (dicot) seed leaves of an angiosperm embryo.

countercurrent exchange The opposite flow of adjacent fluids that maximizes transfer rates; for example, blood in the gills flows in the opposite direction in which water passes over the gills, maximizing oxygen uptake and carbon dioxide loss.

covalent bond (*koh-VAY-lent*) A type of strong chemical bond in which two atoms share one pair of electrons in a mutual valence shell.

crista (*KRIS-tuh*) (plural, **cristae**) An infolding of the inner membrane of a mitochondrion that houses the electron transport chain and the enzyme catalyzing the synthesis of ATP.

crossing over The reciprocal exchange of genetic material between nonsister chromatids during synapsis of meiosis I.

cryptic coloration (*KRIP-tik*) A type of camouflage that makes potential prey difficult to spot against its background.

cuticle (*KYOO-teh-kul*) (1) A waxy covering on the surface of stems and leaves that acts as an adaptation to prevent desiccation in terrestrial plants. (2) The exoskeleton of an arthropod, consisting of layers of protein and chitin that are variously modified for different functions.

cyanobacteria (*sy-AN-oh-bak-TEER-ee-uh*) Photosynthetic, oxygen-producing bacteria (formerly known as blue-green algae).

cyclic AMP (cAMP) Cyclic adenosine monophosphate, a ring-shaped molecule made from ATP that is a common intracellular signaling molecule (second messenger) in eukaryotic cells, for example, in vertebrate endocrine cells. It is also a regulator of some bacterial operons.

cyclic electron flow A route of electron flow during the light reactions of photosynthesis that involves only photosystem I and produces ATP but not NADPH or oxygen.

cyclin (*SY-klin*) A regulatory protein whose concentration fluctuates cyclically.

cyclin-dependent kinase (Cdk) A protein kinase that is active only when attached to a particular cyclin.

cytochrome (*SY-toh-krome*) An iron-containing protein, a component of electron transport chains in mitochondria and chloroplasts.

cytokines In the vertebrate immune system, protein factors secreted by macrophages and helper T cells as regulators of neighboring cells.

cytokinesis (*SY-toh-kin-EE-sis*) The division of the cytoplasm to form two separate daughter cells immediately after mitosis.

cytokinins (*SY-toh-KY-nins*) A class of related plant hormones that retard aging and act in concert with auxins to stimulate cell division, influence the pathway of differentiation, and control apical dominance.

cytoplasm (*SY-toh-plaz-um*) The entire contents of the cell, exclusive of the nucleus, and bounded by the plasma membrane.

cytoplasmic determinants In animal development, substances deposited by the mother in the eggs she produces that regulate the expression of genes affecting the early development of the embryo.

cytoplasmic streaming A circular flow of cytoplasm, involving myosin and actin filaments, that speeds the distribution of materials within cells.

cytoskeleton (*SY-toh-SKEL-eh-ton*) A network of microtubules, microfilaments, and intermediate filaments that branch throughout the cytoplasm and serve a variety of mechanical and transport functions.

cytosol (*SY-toh-sol*) The semifluid portion of the cytoplasm.

cytotoxic T cell (T_C) A type of lymphocyte that kills infected cells and cancer cells.

dalton (*DAWL-ton*) The atomic mass unit; a measure of mass for atoms and subatomic particles.

Darwinian fitness A measure of the relative contribution of an individual to the gene pool of the next generation.

day-neutral plant A plant whose flowering is not affected by photoperiod.

decomposers Saprotrophic fungi and bacteria that absorb nutrients from nonliving organic material such as corpses, fallen plant material, and the wastes of living organisms, and convert them into inorganic forms.

dehydration reaction A chemical reaction in which two molecules covalently bond to one another with the removal of a water molecule.

deletion (1) A deficiency in a chromosome resulting from the loss of a fragment through breakage. (2) A mutational loss of a nucleotide from a gene.

demography The study of statistics relating to births and deaths in populations.

denaturation For proteins a process in which a protein unravels and loses its native conformation, thereby becoming biologically inactive. For DNA, the separation of the two strands of the double helix. Denaturation occurs under extreme conditions of pH, salt concentration, and temperature.

dendrite (DEN-dryt) One of usually numerous, short, highly branched processes of a neuron that conveys nerve impulses toward the cell body.

density The number of individuals per unit area or volume.

density-dependent factor Any factor influencing population regulation that has a greater impact as population density increases.

density-dependent inhibition The phenomenon observed in normal animal cells that causes them to stop dividing when they come into contact with one another.

density-independent factor Any factor influencing population regulation that acts to reduce population by the same percentage, regardless of size.

deoxyribonucleic acid (DNA) (DEE-oks-ee-ry-boh-noo-KLAY-ik) A double-stranded, helical nucleic acid molecule capable of replicating and determining the inherited structure of a cell's proteins.

deoxyribose The sugar component of DNA, having one less hydroxyl group than ribose, the sugar component of RNA.

depolarization An electrical state in an excitable cell whereby the inside of the cell is made less negative relative to the outside than at the resting membrane potential. A neuron membrane is depolarized if a stimulus decreases its voltage from the resting potential of −70 mV in the direction of zero voltage.

deposit-feeder A heterotroph, such as an earthworm, that eats its way through detritus, salvaging bits and pieces of decaying organic matter.

dermal tissue system The protective covering of plants; generally a single layer of tightly packed epidermal cells covering young plant organs formed by primary growth.

desmosome (DEZ-muh-some) A type of intercellular junction in animal cells that functions as an anchor.

determinate cleavage A type of embryonic development in protostomes that rigidly casts the developmental fate of each embryonic cell very early.

determinate growth A type of growth characteristic of animals, in which the organism stops growing after it reaches a certain size.

determination The progressive restriction of developmental potential, causing the possible fate of each cell to become more limited as the embryo develops.

detritus (deh-TRY-tis) Dead organic matter.

deuterostomes (DOO-ter-oh-stomes) One of two distinct evolutionary lines of coelomates, consisting of the echinoderms and chordates and characterized by radial, indeterminate cleavage, enterocoelous formation of the coelom, and development of the anus from the blastopore.

diaphragm A sheet of muscle that forms the bottom wall of the thoracic cavity in mammals; active in ventilating the lungs.

diastole (dy-ASS-toh-lee) The stage of the heart cycle in which the heart muscle is relaxed, allowing the chambers to fill with blood.

dicot (DY-kot) A subdivision of flowering plants whose members possess two embryonic seed leaves, or cotyledons.

differentiation See cellular differentiation.

diffusion The spontaneous tendency of a substance to move down its concentration gradient from a more concentrated to a less concentrated area.

digestion The process of breaking down food into molecules small enough for the body to absorb.

dihybrid cross (DY-HY-brid) A breeding experiment in which parental varieties differing in two traits are mated.

dikaryon (dy-KAH-ree-on) A mycelium of certain septate fungi that possesses two separate haploid nuclei per cell.

dioecious (dy-EE-shus) Referring to a plant species that has staminate and carpellate flowers on separate plants.

diploid cell (DIP-loyd) A cell containing two sets of chromosomes (2n), one set inherited from each parent.

directional selection Natural selection that favors individuals on one end of the phenotypic range.

disaccharide (dy-SAK-ur-ide) A double sugar, consisting of two monosaccharides joined by dehydration synthesis.

dispersion The distribution of individuals within geographical population boundaries.

diversifying selection Natural selection that favors extreme over intermediate phenotypes.

DNA ligase (LY-gaze) A linking enzyme essential for DNA replication; catalyzes the covalent bonding of the 3' end of a new DNA fragment to the 5' end of a growing chain.

DNA methylation The addition of methyl groups (—CH_3) to bases of DNA after DNA synthesis; may serve as a long-term control of gene expression.

DNA polymerase An enzyme that catalyzes the elongation of new DNA at a replication fork by the addition of nucleotides to the existing chain.

DNA probe A chemically synthesized, radioactively labeled segment of nucleic acid used to find a gene of interest by hydrogen-bonding to a complementary sequence.

domain A taxonomic category above the kingdom level; the three domains are Archaea, Bacteria, and Eukarya.

dominance hierarchy A linear "pecking order" of animals, where position dictates characteristic social behaviors.

dominant allele In a heterozygote, the allele that is fully expressed in the phenotype.

double circulation A circulation scheme with separate pulmonary and systemic circuits, which ensures vigorous blood flow to all organs.

double fertilization A mechanism of fertilization in angiosperms, in which two sperm cells unite with two cells in the embryo sac to form the zygote and endosperm.

double helix The form of native DNA, referring to its two adjacent polynucleotide strands wound into a spiral shape.

Down syndrome A human genetic disease resulting from having an extra chromosome 21, characterized by mental retardation and heart and respiratory defects.

duodenum (doo-oh-DEE-num) The first section of the small intestine, where acid chyme from the stomach mixes with digestive juices from the pancreas, liver, gallbladder, and gland cells of the intestinal wall.

duplication An aberration in chromosome structure resulting from an error in meiosis or mutagens; duplication of a portion of a chromosome resulting from fusion with a fragment from a homologous chromosome.

dynein (DY-nin) A large contractile protein forming the sidearms of microtubule doublets in cilia and flagella.

ecdysone (EK-deh-sone) A steroid hormone that triggers molting in arthropods.

ecological efficiency The ratio of net productivity at one trophic level to net productivity at the next lower level.

ecological niche *(nich)* The sum total of an organism's utilization of the biotic and abiotic resources of its environment.

ecological species concept The idea that ecological roles (niches) define species.

ecological succession Transition in the species composition of a biological community, often following ecological disturbance of the community; the establishment of a biological community in an area virtually barren of life.

ecology The study of how organisms interact with their environments.

ecosystem A level of ecological study that includes all the organisms in a given area as well as the abiotic factors with which they interact; a community and its physical environment.

ectoderm *(EK-tuh-durm)* The outermost of the three primary germ layers in animal embryos; gives rise to the outer covering and, in some phyla, the nervous system, inner ear, and lens of the eye.

ectotherm *(EK-toh-thurm)* An animal, such as a reptile, fish, or amphibian, that must use environmental energy and behavioral adaptations to regulate its body temperature.

effector cell A muscle cell or gland cell that performs the body's responses to stimuli; responds to signals from the brain or other processing center of the nervous system.

electrochemical gradient The diffusion gradient of an ion, representing a type of potential energy that accounts for both the concentration difference of the ion across a membrane and its tendency to move relative to the membrane potential.

electrogenic pump An ion transport protein generating voltage across the membrane.

electromagnetic spectrum The entire spectrum of radiation; ranges in wavelength from less than a nanometer to more than a kilometer.

electron microscope (EM) A microscope that focuses an electron beam through a specimen, resulting in resolving power a thousandfold greater than that of a light microscope. A transmission electron microscope (TEM) is used to study the internal structure of thin sections of cells. A scanning electron microscope (SEM) is used to study the fine details of cell surfaces.

electron transport chain A sequence of electron-carrier molecules (membrane proteins) that shuttle electrons during the redox reactions that release energy used to make ATP.

electronegativity The tendency for an atom to pull electrons toward itself.

element Any substance that cannot be broken down to any other substance.

embryo sac The female gametophyte of angiosperms, formed from the growth and division of the megaspore into a multicellular structure with eight haploid nuclei.

enantiomer *(eh-NAN-she-uh-mer)* One of a pair of molecules that are mirror-image isomers of each other.

endangered species A species that is in danger of extinction throughout all or a significant portion of its range.

endemic species Species that are confined to a specific, relatively small geographic area.

endergonic reaction *(EN-dur-GON-ik)* A nonspontaneous chemical reaction in which free energy is absorbed from the surroundings.

endocrine gland *(EN-doh-krin)* A ductless gland that secretes hormones directly into the bloodstream.

endocrine system The internal system of chemical communication involving hormones, the ductless glands that secrete hormones, and the molecular receptors on or in target cells that respond to hormones; functions in concert with the nervous system to effect internal regulation and maintain homeostasis.

endocytosis *(EN-doh-sy-TOH-sis)* The cellular uptake of macromolecules and particulate substances by localized regions of the plasma membrane that surround the substance and pinch off to form an intracellular vesicle.

endoderm *(EN-doh-durm)* The innermost of the three primary germ layers in animal embryos; lines the archenteron and gives rise to the liver, pancreas, lungs, and the lining of the digestive tract.

endodermis *(EN-doh-DUR-mis)* The innermost layer of the cortex in plant roots; a cylinder one cell thick that forms the boundary between the cortex and the stele.

endomembrane system The collection of membranes inside and around a eukaryotic cell, related either through direct physical contact or by the transfer of membranous vesicles.

endometrium *(EN-doh-MEE-tree-um)* The inner lining of the uterus, which is richly supplied with blood vessels.

endoplasmic reticulum (ER) *(EN-doh-plaz-mik reh-TIK-yoo-lum)* An extensive membranous network in eukaryotic cells, continuous with the outer nuclear membrane and composed of ribosome-studded (rough) and ribosome-free (smooth) regions.

endorphin *(en-DOR-fin)* A hormone produced in the brain and anterior pituitary that inhibits pain perception.

endoskeleton *(EN-doh-SKEL-eh-ton)* A hard skeleton buried within the soft tissues of an animal, such as the spicules of sponges, the plates of echinoderms, and the bony skeletons of vertebrates.

endosperm *(EN-doh-spurm)* A nutrient-rich tissue formed by the union of a sperm cell with two polar nuclei during double fertilization, which provides nourishment to the developing embryo in angiosperm seeds.

endospore A thick-coated, resistant cell produced within a bacterial cell exposed to harsh conditions.

endosymbiotic theory *(EN-doh-SIM-by-OT-ik)* A hypothesis about the origin of the eukaryotic cell, maintaining that the forerunners of eukaryotic cells were symbiotic associations of prokaryotic cells living inside larger prokaryotes.

endothelium *(EN-doh-THEEL-ee-um)* The innermost, simple squamous layer of cells lining the blood vessels; the only constituent structure of capillaries.

endotherm *(EN-doh-thurm)* An animal that uses metabolic energy to maintain a constant body temperature, such as a bird or mammal.

endotoxin *(EN-doh-TOKS-in)* A component of the outer membranes of certain gram-negative bacteria responsible for generalized symptoms of fever and ache.

energy The capacity to do work by moving matter against an opposing force.

enhancer A DNA sequence that recognizes certain transcription factors that can stimulate transcription of nearby genes.

entropy *(EN-truh-pee)* A quantitative measure of disorder or randomness, symbolized by S.

environmental grain An ecological term for the effect of spatial variation, or patchiness, relative to the size and behavior of an organism.

enzymes A class of proteins serving as catalysts, chemical agents that change the rate of a reaction without being consumed by the reaction.

epidermis *(EP-eh-DER-mis)* (1) The dermal tissue system in plants. (2) The outer covering of animals.

epigenesis *(EP-eh-JEN-eh-sis)* The progressive development of form in an embryo.

epiglottis A cartilaginous flap that blocks the top of the windpipe, the glottis, during swallowing, which prevents the entry of food or fluid into the respiratory system.

epinephrine A hormone produced as a response to stress; also called adrenaline.

epiphyte *(EP-eh-fite)* A plant that nourishes itself but grows on the surface of another plant for support, usually on the branches or trunks of tropical trees.

episome *(EP-eh-some)* A plasmid capable of integrating into the bacterial chromosome.

epistasis A phenomenon in which one gene alters the expression of another gene that is independently inherited.

epithelial tissue *(EP-eh-THEEL-ee-ul)* Sheets of tightly packed cells that line organs and body cavities.

epitope A localized region on the surface of an antigen that is chemically recognized by antibodies; also called antigenic determinant.

erythrocyte (*er-RITH-roh-site*) A red blood cell; contains hemoglobin, which functions in transporting oxygen in the circulatory system.

esophagus (*eh-SOF-eh-gus*) A channel that conducts food, by peristalsis, from the pharynx to the stomach.

essential amino acids The amino acids that an animal cannot synthesize itself and must obtain from food. Eight amino acids are essential in the human adult.

estivation (*ES-teh-VAY-shun*) A physiological state characterized by slow metabolism and inactivity, which permits survival during long periods of elevated temperature and diminished water supplies.

estrogens (*ES-troh-jens*) The primary female steroid sex hormones, which are produced in the ovary by the developing follicle during the first half of the cycle and in smaller quantities by the corpus luteum during the second half. Estrogens stimulate the development and maintenance of the female reproductive system and secondary sex characteristics.

estrous cycle (*ES-trus*) A type of reproductive cycle in all female mammals except higher primates, in which the nonpregnant endometrium is reabsorbed rather than shed, and sexual response occurs only during midcycle at estrus.

ethylene (*ETH-ul-een*) The only gaseous plant hormone, responsible for fruit ripening, growth inhibition, leaf abscission, and aging.

euchromatin (*yoo-KROH-muh-tin*) The more open, unraveled form of eukaryotic chromatin, which is available for transcription.

eukaryotic cell (*YOO-kar-ee-OT-ik*) A type of cell with a membrane-enclosed nucleus and membrane-enclosed organelles, present in protists, plants, fungi, and animals; also called eukaryote.

eumetazoa (*YOO-met-uh-ZOH-uh*) Members of the subkingdom that includes all animals except sponges.

eutherian mammals Placental mammals; those whose young complete their embryonic development within the uterus, joined to the mother by the placenta.

eutrophic lake A highly productive lake, having a high rate of biological productivity supported by a high rate of nutrient cycling.

evaporative cooling The property of a liquid whereby the surface becomes cooler during evaporation, owing to a loss of highly kinetic molecules to the gaseous state.

evolution All the changes that have transformed life on Earth from its earliest beginnings to the diversity that characterizes it today.

evolutionary species concept The idea that evolutionary lineages and ecological roles can form the basis of species identification.

exaptation A structure that evolves and functions in one environmental context but that can perform additional functions when placed in some new environment.

excitatory postsynaptic potential (EPSP) (*POST-sin-AP-tik*) An electrical change (depolarization) in the membrane of a postsynaptic neuron caused by the binding of an excitatory neurotransmitter from a presynaptic cell to a postsynaptic receptor; makes it more likely for a postsynaptic neuron to generate an action potential.

excretion The disposal of nitrogen-containing waste products of metabolism.

exergonic reaction (*EKS-ur-GON-ik*) A spontaneous chemical reaction in which there is a net release of free energy.

exocytosis (*EKS-oh-sy-TOH-sis*) The cellular secretion of macromolecules by the fusion of vesicles with the plasma membrane.

exon A coding region of a eukaryotic gene that is expressed. Exons are separated from each other by introns.

exoskeleton A hard encasement on the surface of an animal, such as the shells of mollusks or the cuticles of arthropods, that provides protection and points of attachment for muscles.

exotoxin (*EKS-oh-TOKS-in*) A toxic protein secreted by a bacterial cell that produces specific symptoms even in the absence of the bacterium.

exponential population growth The geometric increase of a population as it grows in an ideal, unlimited environment.

extracellular matrix (ECM) The substance in which animal tissue cells are embedded; consists of protein and polysaccharides.

extraembryonic membranes (*EKS-truh-EM-bree-AHN-ik*) Four membranes (yolk sac, amnion, chorion, allantois) that support the developing embryo in reptiles, birds, and mammals.

F factor A fertility factor in bacteria, a DNA segment that confers the ability to form pili for conjugation and associated functions required for the transfer of DNA from donor to recipient. May exist as a plasmid or integrated into the bacterial chromosome.

F_1 generation The first filial or hybrid offspring in a genetic cross-fertilization.

F_2 generation Offspring resulting from interbreeding of the hybrid F_1 generation.

facilitated diffusion The spontaneous passage of molecules and ions, bound to specific carrier proteins, across a biological membrane down their concentration gradients.

facultative anaerobe (*FAK-ul-tay-tiv AN-uh-robe*) An organism that makes ATP by aerobic respiration if oxygen is present but that switches to fermentation under anaerobic conditions.

fat (triacylglycerol) (*tri-AH-sil-GLIS-er-all*) A biological compound consisting of three fatty acids linked to one glycerol molecule.

fatty acid A long carbon chain carboxylic acid. Fatty acids vary in length and in the number and location of double bonds; three fatty acids linked to a glycerol molecule form fat.

feedback inhibition A method of metabolic control in which the end-product of a metabolic pathway acts as an inhibitor of an enzyme within that pathway.

fermentation A catabolic process that makes a limited amount of ATP from glucose without an electron transport chain and that produces a characteristic end-product, such as ethyl alcohol or lactic acid.

fertilization The union of haploid gametes to produce a diploid zygote.

fiber A lignified cell type that reinforces the xylem of angiosperms and functions in mechanical support; a slender, tapered sclerenchyma cell that usually occurs in bundles.

fibrin (*FY-brin*) The activated form of the blood-clotting protein fibrinogen, which aggregates into threads that form the fabric of the clot.

fibroblast (*FY-broh-blast*) A type of cell in loose connective tissue that secretes the protein ingredients of the extracellular fibers.

first law of thermodynamics (*THUR-moh-dy-NAM-iks*) The principle of conservation of energy. Energy can be transferred and transformed, but it cannot be created or destroyed.

fixed action pattern (FAP) A highly stereotypical behavior that is innate and must be carried to completion once initiated.

flaccid (*FLAS-id*) Limp; walled cells are flaccid in isotonic surroundings, where there is no tendency for water to enter.

flagellum (*fluh-JEL-um*) (plural, **flagella**) A long cellular appendage specialized for locomotion, formed from a core of nine outer doublet microtubules and two inner single microtubules, ensheathed in an extension of plasma membrane.

fluid-feeder An animal that lives by sucking nutrient-rich fluids from another living organism.

fluid mosaic model The currently accepted model of cell membrane structure, which envisions the membrane as a mosaic of individually inserted protein molecules drifting laterally in a fluid bilayer of phospholipids.

follicle (*FOL-eh-kul*) A microscopic structure in the ovary that contains the developing ovum and secretes estrogens.

food chain The pathway along which food is transferred from trophic level to trophic level, beginning with producers.

food web The elaborate, interconnected feeding relationships in an ecosystem.

founder effect A cause of genetic drift attributable to colonization by a limited number of individuals from a parent population.

fragile X syndrome A hereditary mental disorder, partially explained by genomic imprinting and the addition of nucleotides to a triplet repeat near the end of an *X* chromosome.

frameshift mutation A mutation occurring when the number of nucleotides inserted or deleted is not a multiple of 3, thus resulting in improper grouping into codons.

free energy A quantity of energy that interrelates entropy *(S)* and the system's total energy *(H)*; symbolized by *G*. The change in free energy of a system is calculated by the equation $G = \Delta H - T\Delta S$, where *T* is absolute temperature.

free energy of activation The initial investment of energy necessary to start a chemical reaction; also called activation energy.

frequency-dependent selection A decline in the reproductive success of a morph resulting from the morph's phenotype becoming too common in a population; a cause of balanced polymorphism in populations.

fruit A mature ovary of a flower that protects dormant seeds and aids in their dispersal.

functional group A specific configuration of atoms commonly attached to the carbon skeletons of organic molecules and usually involved in chemical reactions.

G protein A GTP-binding protein that relays signals from a plasma-membrane signal receptor, known as a G-protein linked receptor, to other signal-transduction proteins inside the cell. When such a receptor is activated, it in turn activates the G protein, causing it to bind a molecule of GTP in place of GDP. Hydrolysis of the bound GTP to GDP inactivates the G protein.

G-protein linked receptor A signal receptor protein in the plasma membrane that responds to the binding of a signal molecule by activating a G protein.

G$_1$ phase The first growth phase of the cell cycle, consisting of the portion of interphase before DNA synthesis begins.

G$_2$ phase The second growth phase of the cell cycle, consisting of the portion of interphase after DNA synthesis occurs.

gametangium *(GAM-eh-TANJ-ee-um)* (plural, **gametangia**) The reproductive organ of bryophytes, consisting of the male antheridium and female archegonium; a multichambered jacket of sterile cells in which gametes are formed.

gamete *(GAM-eet)* A haploid egg or sperm cell; gametes unite during sexual reproduction to produce a diploid zygote.

gametophyte *(guh-MEE-toh-fite)* The multicellular haploid form in organisms undergoing alternation of generations, which mitotically produces haploid gametes that unite and grow into the sporophyte generation.

ganglion *(GANG-lee-un)* (plural, **ganglia**) A cluster (functional group) of nerve cell bodies in a centralized nervous system.

gap junction A type of intercellular junction in animal cells that allows the passage of material or current between cells.

gastrin A digestive hormone, secreted by the stomach, that stimulates the secretion of gastric juice.

gastrovascular cavity The central digestive compartment, usually with a single opening that functions as both mouth and anus.

gastrula *(GAS-troo-la)* The two-layered, cup-shaped embryonic stage.

gastrulation *(GAS-truh-LAY-shun)* The formation of a gastrula from a blastula.

gated ion channel A specific ion channel that opens and closes to allow the cell to alter its membrane potential.

gel electrophoresis *(JELL eh-LEK-troh-for-EE-sis)* The separation of nucleic acids or proteins, on the basis of their size and electrical charge, by measuring their rate of movement through an electrical field in a gel.

gene A discrete unit of hereditary information consisting of a specific nucleotide sequence in DNA (or RNA, in some viruses).

gene amplification The selective synthesis of DNA, which results in multiple copies of a single gene, thereby enhancing expression.

gene cloning The production of multiple copies of a gene.

gene flow The loss or gain of alleles from a population due to the emigration or immigration of fertile individuals, or the transfer of gametes, between populations.

gene pool The total aggregate of genes in a population at any one time.

genetic drift Changes in the gene pool of a small population due to chance.

genetic map An ordered list of genetic loci (genes or other genetic markers) along a chromosome.

genetic recombination The general term for the production of offspring that combine traits of the two parents.

genome *(JEE-nome)* The complete complement of an organism's genes; an organism's genetic material.

genomic imprinting The parental effect on gene expression. Identical alleles may have different effects on offspring, depending on whether they arrive in the zygote via the ovum or via the sperm.

genomic library A set of thousands of DNA segments from a genome, each carried by a plasmid, phage, or other cloning vector.

genotype *(JEE-noh-type)* The genetic makeup of an organism.

genus *(JEE-nus)* (plural, **genera**) A taxonomic category above the species level, designated by the first word of a species' binomial Latin name.

geographical range The geographic area in which a population lives.

geological time scale A time scale established by geologists that reflects a consistent sequence of historical periods, grouped into four eras: Precambrian, Paleozoic, Mesozoic, and Cenozoic.

gibberellins *(JIB-ur-EL-ins)* A class of related plant hormones that stimulate growth in the stem and leaves, trigger the germination of seeds and breaking of bud dormancy, and stimulate fruit development with auxin.

gill A localized extension of the body surface of many aquatic animals, specialized for gas exchange.

glial cell *(GLEE-ul)* A nonconducting cell of the nervous system that provides support, insulation, and protection for the neurons.

glomerulus *(glum-AIR-yoo-lus)* A ball of capillaries surrounded by Bowman's capsule in the nephron and serving as the site of filtration in the vertebrate kidney.

glucagon A peptide hormone secreted by pancreatic endocrine cells that raises blood glucose levels; an antagonistic hormone to insulin.

glucocorticoid A corticosteroid hormone secreted by the adrenal cortex that influences glucose metabolism and immune function.

glycocalyx *(GLY-koh-KAY-liks)* A fuzzy coat on the outside of animal cells, made of sticky oligosaccharides.

glycogen *(GLY-koh-jen)* An extensively branched glucose storage polysaccharide found in the liver and muscle of animals; the animal equivalent of starch.

glycolysis *(gly-KOL-eh-sis)* The splitting of glucose into pyruvate. Glycolysis is the one metabolic pathway that occurs in all living cells, serving as the starting point for fermentation or aerobic respiration.

glycoprotein A protein with covalently attached carbohydrate.

Golgi apparatus *(GOAL-jee)* An organelle in eukaryotic cells consisting of stacks of flat membranous sacs that modify, store, and route products of the endoplasmic reticulum.

gonadotropins *(goh-NAD-oh-TROH-pinz)* Hormones that stimulate the activities of the testes and ovaries; a collective term for follicle-stimulating and luteinizing hormones.

gonads *(GOH-nadz)* The male and female sex organs; the gamete-producing organs in most animals.

graded potential A local voltage change in a neuron membrane induced by stimulation of a neuron, with strength proportional to the strength of the stimulus and lasting about a millisecond.

gradualism A view of Earth's history that attributes profound change to the cumulative product of slow but continuous processes.

Gram stain A staining method that distinguishes between two different kinds of bacterial cell walls.

granum *(GRAN-um)* (plural, **grana**) A stacked portion of the thylakoid membrane in the chloroplast. Grana function in the light reactions of photosynthesis.

gravitropism *(GRAV-eh-TROH-piz-um)* A response of a plant or animal in relation to gravity.

greenhouse effect The warming of planet Earth due to the atmospheric accumulation of carbon dioxide, which absorbs infrared radiation and slows its escape from the irradiated Earth.

gross primary productivity (GPP) The total primary productivity of an ecosystem.

ground meristem A primary meristem that gives rise to ground tissue in plants.

ground tissue system A tissue of mostly parenchyma cells that makes up the bulk of a young plant and fills the space between the dermal and vascular tissue systems.

growth factor A protein that must be present in the extracellular environment (culture medium or animal body) for the growth and normal development of certain types of cells.

guard cell A specialized epidermal plant cell that forms the boundaries of the stomata.

guttation The exudation of water droplets caused by root pressure in certain plants.

gymnosperm *(JIM-noh-spurm)* A vascular plant that bears naked seeds not enclosed in any specialized chambers.

habituation A simple kind of learning involving a loss of sensitivity to unimportant stimuli, allowing an animal to conserve time and energy.

haploid cell *(HAP-loid)* A cell containing only one set of chromosomes *(n).*

Hardy-Weinberg theorem An axiom maintaining that the sexual shuffling of genes alone cannot alter the overall genetic make-up of a population.

haustorium (plural, **haustoria**) In parasitic fungi, a nutrient-absorbing hyphal tip that penetrates the tissues of the host but remains outside the host cell membranes.

Haversian system *(ha-VER-shun)* One of many structural units of vertebrate bone, consisting of concentric layers of mineralized bone matrix surrounding lacunae, which contain osteocytes, and a central canal, which contains blood vessels and nerves.

heat The total amount of kinetic energy due to molecular motion in a body of matter. Heat is energy in its most random form.

heat-shock protein A protein that helps protect other proteins during heat stress, found in plants, animals, and microorganisms.

helper T cell (T$_H$) A type of T cell that is required by some B cells to help them make antibodies or that helps other T cells respond to antigens or secrete lymphokines or interleukins.

hemoglobin *(HEE-moh-gloh-bin)* An iron-containing protein in red blood cells that reversibly binds oxygen.

hemolymph In invertebrates with an open circulatory system, the body fluid that bathes tissues.

hepatic portal vessel A large circulatory channel that conveys nutrient-laden blood from the small intestine to the liver, which regulates the blood's nutrient content.

herbivore A heterotrophic animal that eats plants.

hermaphrodite *(her-MAF-roh-dite)* An individual that functions as both male and female in sexual reproduction by producing both sperm and eggs.

heterochromatin *(HET-ur-oh-KROH-muh-tin)* Nontranscribed eukaryotic chromatin that is so highly compacted that it is visible with a light microscope during interphase.

heterochrony Evolutionary changes in the timing or rate of development.

heterocyst *(HET-ur-oh-sist)* A specialized cell that engages in nitrogen fixation on some filamentous cyanobacteria.

heteromorphic *(HET-ur-oh-MOR-fik)* A condition in the life cycle of all modern plants in which the sporophyte and gametophyte generations differ in morphology.

heterosporous *(HET-ur-OS-pur-us)* Referring to plants in which the sporophyte produces two kinds of spores that develop into unisexual gametophytes, either female or male.

heterotroph *(HET-ur-oh-TROHF)* An organism that obtains organic food molecules by eating other organisms or their by-products.

heterozygote advantage *(HET-ur-oh-ZY-gote)* A mechanism that preserves variation in eukaryotic gene pools by conferring greater reproductive success on heterozygotes over individuals homozygous for any one of the associated alleles.

heterozygous *(HET-ur-oh-ZY-gus)* Having two different alleles for a given genetic character.

hibernation A physiological state that allows survival during long periods of cold temperatures and reduced food supplies, in which metabolism decreases, the heart and respiratory system slow down, and body temperature is maintained at a lower level than normal.

histamine *(HISS-tuh-meen)* A substance released by injured cells that causes blood vessels to dilate during an inflammatory response.

histone *(HISS-tone)* A small protein with a high proportion of positively charged amino acids that binds to the negatively charged DNA and plays a key role in its chromatin structure.

HIV (human immunodeficiency virus) The infectious agent that causes AIDS; HIV is an RNA retrovirus.

holoblastic cleavage *(HOH-loh-BLAS-tik)* A type of cleavage in which there is complete divi-

sion of the egg, as in eggs having little yolk (sea urchin) or a moderate amount of yolk (frog).

homeobox *(HOME-ee-oh-BOX)* A 180-nucleotide sequence within a homeotic gene encoding the part of the protein that binds to the DNA of the genes regulated by the protein.

homeosis Evolutionary alteration in the placement of different body parts.

homeostasis *(HOME-ee-oh-STAY-sis)* The steady-state physiological condition of the body.

homeotic genes *(HOME-ee-OT-ik)* Genes that control the overall body plan of animals by controlling the developmental fate of groups of cells.

homologous chromosomes *(home-OL-uh-gus)* Chromosome pairs of the same length, centromere position, and staining pattern that possess genes for the same characters at corresponding loci. One homologous chromosome is inherited from the organism's father, the other from the mother.

homologous structures Structures in different species that are similar because of common ancestry.

homology Similarity in characteristics resulting from a shared ancestry.

homosporous *(home-OS-pur-us)* Referring to plants in which a single type of spore develops into a bisexual gametophyte having both male and female sex organs.

homozygous *(HOME-oh-ZY-gus)* Having two identical alleles for a given trait.

hormone One of many types of circulating chemical signals in all multicellular organisms that are formed in specialized cells, travel in body fluids, and coordinate the various parts of the organism by interacting with target cells.

Human Genome Project An international collaborative effort to map and sequence the DNA of the entire human genome.

humoral immunity *(HYOO-mur-al)* The type of immunity that fights bacteria and viruses in body fluids with antibodies that circulate in blood plasma and lymph, fluids formerly called humors.

hybrid zone A region where two related populations that diverged after becoming geographically isolated make secondary contact and interbreed where their geographical ranges overlap.

hydrocarbon *(HY-droh-kar-bon)* An organic molecule consisting only of carbon and hydrogen.

hydrogen bond A type of weak chemical bond formed when the slightly positive hydrogen atom of a polar covalent bond in one molecule is attracted to the slightly negative atom of a polar covalent bond in another molecule.

hydrogen ion A single proton with a charge of +1. The dissociation of a water molecule (H_2O)

leads to the generation of a hydroxide ion (OH^-) and a hydrogen ion (H^+).

hydrolysis *(hy-DROL-eh-sis)* A chemical process that lyses or splits molecules by the addition of water; an essential process in digestion.

hydrophilic *(HY-droh-FIL-ik)* Having an affinity for water.

hydrophobic *(HY-droh-FOH-bik)* Having an aversion to water; tending to coalesce and form droplets in water.

hydrophobic interaction A type of weak chemical bond formed when molecules that do not mix with water coalesce to exclude the water.

hydrostatic skeleton *(HY-droh-STAT-ik)* A skeletal system composed of fluid held under pressure in a closed body compartment; the main skeleton of most cnidarians, flatworms, nematodes, and annelids.

hydroxyl group *(hy-DROKS-ul)* A functional group consisting of a hydrogen atom joined to an oxygen atom by a polar covalent bond. Molecules possessing this group are soluble in water and are called alcohols.

hyperpolarization An electrical state whereby the inside of the cell is made more negative relative to the outside than at the resting membrane potential. A neuron membrane is hyperpolarized if a stimulus increases its voltage from the resting potential of -70 mV, reducing the chance that the neuron will transmit a nerve impulse.

hypertonic solution A solution with a greater solute concentration than another, a hypotonic solution.

hypha *(HY-fa)* (plural, **hyphae**) A filament that collectively makes up the body of a fungus.

hypothalmus *(HY-poh-THAL-uh-mus)* The ventral part of the vertebrate forebrain; functions in maintaining homeostasis, especially in coordinating the endocrine and nervous systems; secretes hormones of the posterior pituitary and releasing factors, which regulate the anterior pituitary.

hypotonic solution A solution with a lesser solute concentration than another, a hypertonic solution.

imaginal disk *(i-MAJ-in-ul)* An island of undifferentiated cells in an insect larva, which are committed (determined) to form a particular organ during metamorphosis to the adult.

immunoglobulin (Ig) *(IM-myoo-noh-GLOB-yoo-lin)* One of the class of proteins comprising the antibodies.

imprinting A type of learned behavior with a significant innate component, acquired during a limited critical period.

incomplete dominance A type of inheritance in which F_1 hybrids have an appearance that is intermediate between the phenotypes of the parental varieties.

incomplete flower A flower lacking sepals, petals, stamens, or carpels.

incomplete metamorphosis *(MET-uh-MOR-foh-sis)* A type of development in certain insects, such as grasshoppers, in which the larvae resemble adults but are smaller and have different body proportions. The animal goes through a series of molts, each time looking more like an adult, until it reaches full size.

indeterminate cleavage A type of embryonic development in deuterostomes, in which each cell produced by early cleavage divisions retains the capacity to develop into a complete embryo.

indeterminate growth A type of growth characteristic of plants, in which the organism continues to grow as long as it lives.

induced fit The change in shape of the active site of an enzyme so that it binds more snugly to the substrate, induced by entry of the substrate.

induction The ability of one group of embryonic cells to influence the development of another.

inflammatory response A line of defense triggered by penetration of the skin or mucous membranes, in which small blood vessels in the vicinity of an injury dilate and become leakier, enhancing the infiltration of leukocytes; may also be widespread in the body.

ingestion A heterotrophic mode of nutrition in which other organisms or detritus are eaten whole or in pieces.

inhibitory postsynaptic potential (IPSP) *(POST-sin-AP-tik)* An electrical charge (hyperpolarization) in the membrane of a postsynaptic neuron caused by the binding of an inhibitory neurotransmitter from a presynaptic cell to a postsynaptic receptor; makes it more difficult for a postsynaptic neuron to generate an action potential.

inner cell mass A cluster of cells in a mammalian blastocyst that protrudes into one end of the cavity and subsequently develops into the embryo proper and some of the extraembryonic membranes.

inositol trisphosphate (IP₃) *(in-NOS-i-tahl)* The second messenger, which functions as an intermediate between certain nonsteroid hormones and the third messenger, a rise in cytoplasmic Ca^{2+} concentration.

insertion A mutation involving the addition of one or more nucleotide pairs to a gene.

insertion sequence The simplest kind of a transposon, consisting of inserted repeats of DNA flanking a gene for transposase, the enzyme that catalyzes transposition.

insight learning The ability of an animal to perform a correct or appropriate behavior on the first attempt in a situation with which it has had no prior experience.

insulin *(IN-sul-in)* A vertebrate hormone that lowers blood glucose levels by promoting the uptake of glucose by most body cells and the synthesis and storage of glycogen in the liver; also stimulates protein and fat synthesis; secreted by endocrine cells of the pancreas called islets of Langerhans.

interferon *(IN-tur-FEER-on)* A chemical messenger of the immune system, produced by virus-infected cells and capable of helping other cells resist the virus.

interleukin-1 *(IN-tur-loo-kin)* A chemical regulator (cytokin) secreted by macrophages that have ingested a pathogen or foreign molecule and have bound with a helper T cell; stimulates T cells to grow and divide and elevates body temperature. Interleukin-2, secreted by activated T cells, stimulates helper T cells to proliferate more rapidly.

intermediate filament A component of the cytoskeleton that includes all filaments intermediate in size between microtubules and microfilaments.

interneuron *(IN-tur-NOOR-ahn)* An association neuron; a nerve cell within the central nervous system that forms synapses with sensory and motor neurons and integrates sensory input and motor output.

internode The segment of a plant stem between the points where leaves are attached.

interphase The period in the cell cycle when the cell is not dividing. During interphase, cellular metabolic activity is high, chromosomes and organelles are duplicated, and cell size may increase. Interphase accounts for 90% of the time of each cell cycle.

interstitial cells *(IN-tur-STISH-ul)* Cells scattered among the seminiferous tubules of the vertebrate testis that secrete testosterone and other androgens, the male sex hormones.

interstitial fluid The internal environment of vertebrates, consisting of the fluid filling the spaces between cells.

intertidal zone The shallow zone of the ocean where land meets water.

intrinsic rate of increase The difference between the number of births and the number of deaths, symbolized as r_{max}; the maximum population growth rate.

introgression *(IN-troh-GRES-shun)* The transplantation of genes between species resulting from fertile hybrids mating successfully with one of the parent species.

intron *(IN-tron)* A noncoding, intervening sequence within a eukaryotic gene.

inversion An aberration in chromosome structure resulting from an error in meiosis or from mutagens; reattachment in a reverse orientation of a chromosomal fragment to the chromosome from which the fragment originated.

invertebrate An animal without a backbone; invertebrates make up 95% of animal species.

in vitro fertilization *(VEE-troh)* Fertilization of ova in laboratory containers followed by artifi-

cial implantation of the early embryo in the mother's uterus.

ion *(EYE-on)* An atom that has gained or lost electrons, thus acquiring a charge.

ionic bond *(eye-ON-ik)* A chemical bond resulting from the attraction between oppositely charged ions.

isogamy *(eye-SOG-uh-mee)* A condition in which male and female gametes are morphologically indistinguishable.

isomer *(EYE-sum-ur)* One of several organic compounds with the same molecular formula but different structures and therefore different properties. The three types are structural isomers, geometric isomers, and enantiomers.

isomorphic generations Alternating generations in which the sporophytes and gametophytes look alike, although they differ in chromosome number.

isotonic solutions Solutions of equal solute concentration.

isotope *(EYE-so-tope)* One of several atomic forms of an element, each containing a different number of neutrons and thus differing in atomic mass.

joule (J) A unit of energy: 1 J = 0.239 cal; 1 cal = 4.184 J.

juvenile hormone (JH) A hormone in arthropods, secreted by the corpora allata glands, that promotes the retention of larval characteristics.

juxtaglomerular apparatus (JGA) Specialized tissue located near the afferent arteriole that supplies blood to the kidney glomerulus; the JGA raises blood pressure by producing renin, which activates angiotensin.

***K*-selection** The concept that in certain (*K*-selected) populations, life history is centered around producing relatively few offspring that have a good chance of survival.

karyogamy The fusion of nuclei of two cells, as part of syngamy.

karyotype *(KAR-ee-oh-type)* A method of organizing the chromosomes of a cell in relation to number, size, and type.

keystone predator A predatory species that helps maintain species richness in a community by reducing the density of populations of the best competitors so that populations of less competitive species are maintained.

kilocalorie (kcal) A thousand calories; the amount of heat energy required to raise the temperature of 1 kg of water 1°C.

kin selection A phenomenon of inclusive fitness, used to explain altruistic behavior between related individuals.

kinesis *(kih-NEE-sis)* A change in activity rate in response to a stimulus.

kinetic energy *(kih-NET-ik)* The energy of motion, which is directly related to the speed of that motion. Moving matter does work by

transferring some of its kinetic energy to other matter.

kinetochore *(kih-NET-oh-kor)* A specialized region on the centromere that links each sister chromatid to the mitotic spindle.

kingdom A taxonomic category, the second broadest after domain.

Koch's postulates A set of four criteria for determining whether a specific pathogen is the cause of a disease.

Krebs cycle A chemical cycle involving eight steps that completes the metabolic breakdown of glucose molecules to carbon dioxide; occurs within the mitochondrion; the second major stage in cellular respiration.

lacteal *(lak-TEEL)* A tiny lymph vessel extending into the core of an intestinal villus and serving as the destination for absorbed chylomicrons.

lagging strand A discontinuously synthesized DNA strand that elongates in a direction away from the replication fork.

larva *(LAR-vuh)* (plural, **larvae**) A free-living, sexually immature form in some animal life cycles that may differ from the adult in morphology, nutrition, and habitat.

lateral line system A mechanoreceptor system consisting of a series of pores and receptor units (neuromasts) along the sides of the body of fishes and aquatic amphibians; detects water movements made by an animal itself and by other moving objects.

lateral meristem *(MARE-eh-stem)* The vascular and cork cambium, a cylinder of dividing cells that runs most of the length of stems and roots and is responsible for secondary growth.

law of independent assortment Mendel's second law, stating that each allele pair segregates independently during gamete formation; applies when genes for two traits are located on different pairs of homologous chromosomes.

law of segregation Mendel's first law, stating that allele pairs separate during gamete formation, and then randomly re-form pairs during the fusion of gametes at fertilization.

leading strand The new continuous complementary DNA strand synthesized along the template strand in the mandatory 5' → 3' direction.

leukocyte *(LOO-koh-site)* A white blood cell; typically functions in immunity, such as phagocytosis or antibody production.

lichen *(LY-ken)* An organism formed by the symbiotic association between a fungus and a photosynthetic alga.

life table A table of data summarizing mortality in a population.

ligament A type of fibrous connective tissue that joins bones together at joints.

ligand *(LIG-und)* A molecule that binds specifically to a receptor site of another molecule.

ligand-gated ion channel receptor A signal receptor protein in a cell membrane that can act as a channel for the passage of a specific ion across the membrane. When activated by a signal molecule, the receptor either allows or blocks passage of the ion, resulting in a change in ion concentration that usually affects cell functioning.

light microscope (LM) An optical instrument with lenses that refract (bend) visible light to magnify images of specimens.

light reactions The steps in photosynthesis that occur on the thylakoid membranes of the chloroplast and convert solar energy to the chemical energy of ATP and NADPH, evolving oxygen in the process.

lignin *(LIG-nin)* A hard material embedded in the cellulose matrix of vascular plant cell walls that functions as an important adaptation for support in terrestrial species.

limbic system *(LIM-bik)* A group of nuclei (clusters of nerve cell bodies) in the lower part of the mammalian forebrain that interact with the cerebral cortex in determining emotions; includes the hippocampus and the amygdala.

linkage map A genetic map *(see)* based on the frequencies of recombination between markers during crossing over of homologous chromosomes. The greater the frequency of recombination between two genetic markers, the farther apart they are assumed to be.

linked genes Genes that are located on the same chromosome.

lipid *(LIH-pid)* One of a family of compounds, including fats, phospholipids, and steroids, that are insoluble in water.

lipoprotein A protein bonded to a lipid; includes the low-density lipoproteins (LDLs) and high-density lipoproteins (HDLs) that transport fats and cholesterol in blood.

locus *(LOH-kus)* (plural, **loci**) A particular place along the length of a certain chromosome where a given gene is located.

logistic population growth A model describing population growth that levels off as population size approaches carrying capacity.

long-day plant A plant that flowers, usually in late spring or early summer, only when the light period is longer than a critical length.

loop of Henle The long hairpin turn, with a descending and ascending limb, of the renal tubule in the vertebrate kidney; functions in water and salt reabsorption.

lungs The invaginated respiratory surfaces of terrestrial vertebrates, land snails, and spiders that connect to the atmosphere by narrow tubes.

lymph *(limf)* The colorless fluid, derived from interstitial fluid, in the lymphatic system of vertebrate animals.

lymphatic system *(lim-FAT-ik)* A system of vessels and lymph nodes, separate from the cir-

culatory system, that returns fluid and protein to the blood.

lymphocyte A white blood cell. The lymphocytes that complete their development in the bone marrow are called B cells, and those that mature in the thymus are called T cells.

lysogenic cycle A type of phage replication cycle in which the viral genome becomes incorporated into the bacterial host chromosome as a prophage.

lysosome (*LY-so-some*) A membrane-enclosed bag of hydrolytic enzymes found in the cytoplasm of eukaryotic cells.

lysozyme (*LY-so-zime*) An enzyme in perspiration, tears, and saliva that attacks bacterial cell walls.

lytic cycle (*LIT-ik*) A type of viral replication cycle resulting in the release of new phages by death or lysis of the host cell.

M phase The mitotic phase of the cell cycle, which includes mitosis and cytokinesis.

macroevolution Evolutionary change on a grand scale, encompassing the origin of novel designs, evolutionary trends, adaptive radiation, and mass extinction.

macromolecule A giant molecule of living matter formed by the joining of smaller molecules, usually by condensation synthesis. Polysaccharides, proteins, and nucleic acids are macromolecules.

macrophage (*MAK-roh-fage*) An amoeboid cell that moves through tissue fibers, engulfing bacteria and dead cells by phagocytosis.

major histocompatibility complex (**MHC**) A large set of cell surface antigens encoded by a family of genes. Foreign MHC markers trigger T-cell responses that may lead to the rejection of transplanted tissues and organs.

Malpighian tubule (*mal-PIG-ee-un*) A unique excretory organ of insects that empties into the digestive tract, removes nitrogenous wastes from the blood, and functions in osmoregulation.

Mammalia The vertebrate class of mammals, characterized by body hair and mammary glands that produce milk to nourish the young.

mantle A heavy fold of tissue in mollusks that drapes over the visceral mass and may secrete a shell.

marsupial (*mar-SOOP-ee-ul*) A mammal, such as a koala, kangaroo, or opossum, whose young complete their embryonic development inside a maternal pouch called the marsupium.

matrix The nonliving component of connective tissue, consisting of a web of fibers embedded in homogeneous ground substance that may be liquid, jellylike, or solid.

matter Anything that takes up space and has mass.

mechanoreceptor A sensory receptor that detects physical deformations in the body's

environment associated with pressure, touch, stretch, motion, and sound.

medulla oblongata (*meh-DOO-luh OBB-long-GAH-tuh*) The lowest part of the vertebrate brain; a swelling of the hindbrain dorsal to the anterior spinal cord that controls autonomic, homeostatic functions, including breathing, heart and blood vessel activity, swallowing, digestion, and vomiting.

medusa (*meh-DOO-suh*) The floating, flattened, mouth-down version of the cnidarian body plan. The alternate form is the polyp.

megapascal (**MPa**) (*MEG-uh-pass-KAL*) A unit of pressure equivalent to 10 atmospheres of pressure.

meiosis (*my-OH-sis*) A two-stage type of cell division in sexually reproducing organisms that results in gametes with half the chromosome number of the original cell.

membrane potential The charge difference between the cytoplasm and extracellular fluid in all cells, due to the differential distribution of ions. Membrane potential affects the activity of excitable cells and the transmembrane movement of all charged substances.

memory cell A clone of long-lived lymphocytes, formed during the primary immune response, that remains in a lymph node until activated by exposure to the same antigen that triggered its formation. Activated memory cells mount the secondary immune response.

menstrual cycle (*MEN-stroo-ul*) A type of reproductive cycle in higher female primates, in which the nonpregnant endometrium is shed as a bloody discharge through the cervix into the vagina.

meristem (*MARE-eh-stem*) Plant tissue that remains embryonic as long as the plant lives, allowing for indeterminate growth.

meroblastic cleavage (*MARE-oh-BLAS-tik*) A type of cleavage in which there is incomplete division of yolk-rich egg, characteristic of avian development.

mesentery (*MEZ-en-ter-ee*) A membrane that suspends many of the organs of vertebrates inside fluid-filled body cavities.

mesoderm (*MEZ-oh-durm*) The middle primary germ layer of an early embryo that develops into the notochord, the lining of the coelom, muscles, skeleton, gonads, kidneys, and most of the circulatory system.

mesophyll (*MEZ-oh-fil*) The ground tissue of a leaf, sandwiched between the upper and lower epidermis and specialized for photosynthesis.

messenger RNA (**mRNA**) A type of RNA synthesized from DNA in the genetic material that attaches to ribosomes in the cytoplasm and specifies the primary structure of a protein.

metabolism (*meh-TAB-oh-liz-um*) The totality of an organism's chemical processes, consisting of catabolic and anabolic pathways.

metamorphosis (*MET-uh-MOR-fuh-sis*) The resurgence of development in an animal larva that transforms it into a sexually mature adult.

metanephridium (*MET-uh-neh-FRID-ee-um*) (plural, **metanephridia**) In annelid worms, a type of excretory tubule with internal openings called nephrostomes that collect body fluids and external openings called nephridiopores.

metapopulation A subdivided population of a single species.

metastasis (*meh-TAS-teh-sis*) The spread of cancer cells beyond their original site.

microevolution A change in the gene pool of a population over a succession of generations.

microfilament A solid rod of actin protein in the cytoplasm of almost all eukaryotic cells, making up part of the cytoskeleton and acting alone or with myosin to cause cell contraction.

microtubule A hollow rod of tubulin protein in the cytoplasm of all eukaryotic cells and in cilia, flagella, and the cytoskeleton.

microvillus (plural, **microvilli**) One of many fine, fingerlike projections of the epithelial cells in the lumen of the small intestine that increase its surface area.

middle lamella (*luh-MEL-uh*) A thin layer of adhesive extracellular material, primarily pectins, found between the primary walls of adjacent young plant cells.

mimicry A phenomenon in which one species benefits by a superficial resemblance to an unrelated species. A predator or species of prey may gain a significant advantage through mimicry.

mineralocorticoid A corticosteroid hormone secreted by the adrenal cortex that regulates salt and water homeostasis.

minimum dynamic area The amount of suitable habitat needed to sustain a viable population.

minimum viable population size (**MVP**) The smallest number of individuals needed to perpetuate a population.

missense mutation The most common type of mutation involving a base-pair substitution within a gene that changes a codon, but the new codon makes sense in that it still codes for an amino acid.

mitochondrial matrix The compartment of the mitochondrion enclosed by the inner membrane and containing enzymes and substrates for the Krebs cycle.

mitochondrion (*MY-toh-KON-dree-un*) (plural, **mitochondria**) An organelle in eukaryotic cells that serves as the site of cellular respiration.

mitosis (*my-TOH-sis*) A process of nuclear division in eukaryotic cells conventionally divided into five stages: prophase, prometaphase, metaphase, anaphase, and telophase. Mitosis conserves chromosome number by equally allocating replicated chromosomes to each of the daughter nuclei.

modern synthesis A comprehensive theory of evolution emphasizing natural selection, gradualism, and populations as the fundamental units of evolutionary change; also called neo-Darwinism.

molarity A common measure of solute concentration, referring to the number of moles of solute in 1 L of solution.

mold A rapidly growing, asexually reproducing fungus.

mole The number of grams of a substance that equals its molecular weight in daltons and contains Avogadro's number of molecules.

molecular formula A type of molecular notation indicating only the quantity of the constituent atoms.

molecule Two or more atoms held together by covalent bonds.

molting A process in arthropods in which the exoskeleton is shed at intervals to allow growth by the secretion of a larger exoskeleton.

monoclonal antibody *(MON-oh-KLONE-ul)* A defensive protein produced by cells descended from a single cell; an antibody that is secreted by a clone of cells and, consequently, is specific for a single antigenic determinant.

monocot *(MON-oh-kot)* A subdivision of flowering plants whose members possess one embryonic seed leaf, or cotyledon.

monoculture Cultivation of large land areas with a single plant variety.

monoecious *(mon-EE-shus)* Referring to a plant species that has both staminate and carpellate flowers on the same individual.

monohybrid cross A breeding experiment that uses parental varieties differing in a single character.

monomer *(MON-uh-mer)* The subunit that serves as the building block of a polymer.

monophyletic *(MON-oh-fy-LEH-tik)* Pertaining to a taxon derived from a single ancestral species that gave rise to no species in any other taxa.

monosaccharide *(MON-oh-SAK-ur-ide)* The simplest carbohydrate, active alone or serving as a monomer for disaccharides and polysaccharides. Also known as simple sugars, the molecular formulas of monosaccharides are generally some multiple of CH_2O.

monotreme *(MON-uh-treem)* An egg-laying mammal, represented by the platypus and echidna.

morphogen A substance, such as bicoid protein, that provides positional information in the form of a concentration gradient along an embryonic axis.

morphogenesis *(MOR-foh-JEN-eh-sis)* The development of body shape and organization during ontogeny.

morphological species concept The idea that species are defined by measurable anatomical criteria.

morphospecies A species defined by its anatomical features.

mosaic development A pattern of development, such as that of a mollusk, in which the early blastomeres each give rise to a specific part of the embryo. In some animals, the fate of the blastomeres is established in the zygote.

mosaic evolution The evolution of different features of an organism at different rates.

motor neuron A nerve cell that transmits signals from the brain or spinal cord to muscles or glands.

motor unit A single motor neuron and all the muscle fibers it controls.

MPF (M-phase promoting factor) A protein complex required for a cell to progress from late interphase to mitosis; the active form consists of cyclin and *cdc2*, a protein kinase.

Müllerian mimicry *(myoo-LER-ee-un)* A mutual mimicry by two unpalatable species.

multigene family A collection of genes with similar or identical sequences, presumably of common origin.

mutagen *(MYOOT-uh-jen)* A chemical or physical agent that interacts with DNA and causes a mutation.

mutagenesis *(MYOOT-uh-JEN-uh-sis)* The creation of mutations.

mutation *(myoo-TAY-shun)* A rare change in the DNA of genes that ultimately creates genetic diversity.

mutualism *(MYOO-choo-ul-iz-um)* A symbiotic relationship in which both the host and the symbiont benefit.

mycelium *(my-SEEL-ee-um)* The densely branched network of hyphae in a fungus.

mycorrhizae *(MY-koh-RY-zee)* Mutualistic associations of plant roots and fungi.

myelin sheath *(MY-eh-lin)* In a neuron, an insulating coat of cell membrane from Schwann cells that is interrupted by nodes of Ranvier where saltatory conduction occurs.

myofibril *(MY-oh-FY-brill)* A fibril collectively arranged in longitudinal bundles in muscle cells (fibers); composed of thin filaments of actin and a regulatory protein and thick filaments of myosin.

myoglobin *(MY-uh-glow-bin)* An oxygen-storing, pigmented protein in muscle cells.

myosin *(MY-uh-sin)* A type of protein filament that interacts with actin filaments to cause cell contraction.

NAD⁺ (nicotinamide adenine dinucleotide) A coenzyme present in all cells that helps enzymes transfer electrons during the redox reactions of metabolism.

natural killer cell A nonspecific defensive cell that attacks tumor cells and destroys infected body cells, especially those harboring viruses.

natural selection Differential success in the reproduction of different phenotypes resulting from the interaction of organisms with their environment. Evolution occurs when natural selection causes changes in relative frequencies of alleles in the gene pool.

negative feedback A primary mechanism of homeostasis, whereby a change in a physiological variable that is being monitored triggers a response that counteracts the initial fluctuation.

nephron *(NEF-ron)* The tubular excretory unit of the vertebrate kidney.

neritic zone *(neh-RIT-ik)* The shallow regions of the ocean overlying the continental shelves.

net primary productivity (NPP) The gross primary productivity minus the energy used by the producers for cellular respiration; represents the storage of chemical energy in an ecosystem available to consumers.

neural crest A band of cells along the border where the neural tube pinches off from the ectoderm; the cells migrate to various parts of the embryo and form the pigment cells in the skin, bones of the skull, the teeth, the adrenal glands, and parts of the peripheral nervous system.

neuron *(NOOR-on)* A nerve cell; the fundamental unit of the nervous system, having structure and properties that allow it to conduct signals by taking advantage of the electrical charge across its cell membrane.

neurosecretory cells Hypothalamus cells that receive signals from other nerve cells, but instead of signaling to an adjacent nerve cell or muscle, they release hormones into the bloodstream.

neurotransmitter A chemical messenger released from the synaptic terminal of a neuron at a chemical synapse that diffuses across the synaptic cleft and binds to and stimulates the postsynaptic cell.

neutral variation Genetic diversity that confers no apparent selective advantage.

niche *See* ecological niche.

nitrogen fixation The assimilation of atmospheric nitrogen by certain prokaryotes into nitrogenous compounds that can be directly used by plants.

nitrogenase *(nih-TRAH-juh-nayz)* An enzyme, unique to certain prokaryotes, that reduces N_2 to NH_3.

node A point along the stem of a plant at which leaves are attached.

nodes of Ranvier *(ran-VEER)* The small gaps in the myelin sheath between successive glial cells along the axon of a neuron; also, the site of high concentration of voltage-gated ion channels.

noncompetitive inhibitor A substance that reduces the activity of an enzyme by binding to a location remote from the active site, changing its conformation so that it no longer binds to the substrate.

noncyclic electron flow A route of electron flow during the light reactions of photosynthesis that involves both photosystems and pro-

duces ATP, NADPH, and oxygen; the net electron flow is from water to $NADP^+$.

noncyclic photophosphorylation (*FO-toh-fos-FOR-eh-LAY-shun*) The production of ATP by noncyclic electron flow.

nondisjunction An accident of meiosis or mitosis, in which both members of a pair of homologous chromosomes or both sister chromatids fail to move apart properly.

nonpolar covalent bond A type of covalent bond in which electrons are shared equally between two atoms of similar electronegativity.

nonsense mutation A mutation that changes an amino acid codon to one of the three stop codons, resulting in a shorter and usually nonfunctional protein.

norm of reaction The range of phenotypic possibilities for a single genotype, as influenced by the environment.

notochord (*NO-toh-kord*) A longitudinal, flexible rod formed from dorsal mesoderm and located between the gut and the nerve cord in all chordate embryos.

nuclear envelope The membrane in eukaryotes that encloses the nucleus, separating it from the cytoplasm.

nucleic acid (polynucleotide) (*PAHL-ee-NOO-klee-oh-tide*) A polymer consisting of many nucleotide monomers; serves as a blueprint for proteins and, through the actions of proteins, for all cellular activities. The two types are DNA and RNA.

nucleic acid probe In DNA technology, a labeled single-stranded nucleic acid molecule used to tag a specific nucleotide sequence in a nucleic acid sample. Molecules of the probe hydrogen-bond to the complementary sequence wherever it occurs; radioactive or other labeling of the probe allows its location to be detected.

nucleoid (*NOO-klee-oid*) A dense region of DNA in a prokaryotic cell.

nucleoid region The region in a prokaryotic cell consisting of a concentrated mass of DNA.

nucleolus (*noo-KLEE-oh-lus*) (plural, **nucleoli**) A specialized structure in the nucleus, formed from various chromosomes and active in the synthesis of ribosomes.

nucleoside (*NOO-klee-oh-side*) An organic molecule consisting of a nitrogenous base joined to a five-carbon sugar.

nucleosome (*NOO-klee-oh-some*) The basic, beadlike unit of DNA packaging in eukaryotes, consisting of a segment of DNA wound around a protein core composed of two copies of each of four types of histone.

nucleotide (*NOO-klee-oh-tide*) The building block of a nucleic acid, consisting of a five-carbon sugar covalently bonded to a nitrogenous base and a phosphate group.

nucleus (1) An atom's central core, containing protons and neutrons. (2) The chromosome-containing organelle of a eukaryotic cell. (3) A cluster of neurons.

obligate aerobe (*OB-lig-it AIR-obe*) An organism that requires oxygen for cellular respiration and cannot live without it.

obligate anaerobe (*AN-ur-obe*) An organism that cannot use oxygen and is poisoned by it.

oceanic zone The region of water lying over deep areas beyond the continental shelf.

oligotrophic lake A nutrient-poor, clear, deep lake with minimum phytoplankton.

omnivore A heterotrophic animal that consumes both meat and plant material.

oncogene (*ON-koh-jeen*) A gene found in viruses or as part of the normal genome that is involved in triggering cancerous characteristics.

ontogeny (*on-TOJ-en-ee*) The embryonic development of an organism.

oogamy (*oh-OG-um-ee*) A condition in which male and female gametes differ, such that a small, flagellated sperm fertilizes a large, non-motile egg.

oogenesis (*OO-oh-JEN-eh-sis*) The process in the ovary that results in the production of female gametes.

open circulatory system An arrangement of internal transport in which blood bathes the organs directly and there is no distinction between blood and interstitial fluid.

operant conditioning (*OP-ur-ent*) A type of associative learning that directly affects behavior in a natural context; also called trial-and-error learning.

operon (*OP-ur-on*) A unit of genetic function common in bacteria and phages, consisting of coordinately regulated clusters of genes with related functions.

opsonization An immune response in which the binding of antibodies to the surface of a microbe facilitates phagocytosis of the microbe by a macrophage.

organ A specialized center of body function composed of several different types of tissues.

organ-identity gene A plant gene in which a mutation causes a floral organ to develop in the wrong location.

organ of Corti The actual hearing organ of the vertebrate ear, located in the floor of the cochlear canal in the inner ear; contains the receptor cells (hair cells) of the ear.

organelle (*OR-guh-NEL*) One of several formed bodies with a specialized function, suspended in the cytoplasm and found in eukaryotic cells.

organic chemistry The study of carbon compounds (organic compounds).

organogenesis (*or-GAN-oh-JEN-eh-sis*) An early period of rapid embryonic development in which the organs take form from the primary germ layers.

orgasm Rhythmic, involuntary contractions of certain reproductive structures in both sexes during the human sexual response cycle.

osmoconformer An animal that does not actively adjust its internal osmolarity because it is isotonic with its environment.

osmolarity (*OZ-moh-LAR-eh-tee*) Solute concentration expressed as molarity.

osmoregulation Adaptations to control the water balance in organisms living in hypertonic, hypotonic, or terrestrial environments.

osmoregulator An animal whose body fluids have a different osmolarity than the environment, and that must either discharge excess water if it lives in a hypotonic environment or take in water if it inhabits a hypertonic environment.

osmosis (*oz-MOH-sis*) The diffusion of water across a selectively permeable membrane.

osmotic pressure (*oz-MOT-ik*) A measure of the tendency of a solution to take up water when separated from pure water by a selectively permeable membrane.

Osteichthyes The vertebrate class of bony fishes, characterized by a skeleton reinforced by calcium phosphate; the most abundant and diverse vertebrates.

ostracoderm (*os-TRAK-uh-durm*) An extinct agnathan; a fishlike creature encased in an armor of bony plates.

outgroup A species or group of species that is closely related to the group of species being studied, but clearly not as closely related as any study-group members are to each other.

ovarian cycle (*oh-VAIR-ee-un*) The cyclic recurrence of the follicular phase, ovulation, and the luteal phase in the mammalian ovary, regulated by hormones.

ovary (*OH-vur-ee*) (1) In flowers, the portion of a carpel in which the egg-containing ovules develop. (2) In animals, the structure that produces female gametes and reproductive hormones.

oviduct (*OH-veh-dukt*) A tube passing from the ovary to the vagina in invertebrates or to the uterus in vertebrates.

oviparous (*oh-VIP-ur-us*) Referring to a type of development in which young hatch from eggs laid outside the mother's body.

ovoviviparous (*OH-voh-vy-VIP-ur-us*) Referring to a type of development in which young hatch from eggs that are retained in the mother's uterus.

ovulation The release of an egg from ovaries. In humans, an ovarian follicle releases an egg during each menstrual cycle.

ovule (*OV-yool*) A structure that develops in the plant ovary and contains the female gametophyte.

ovum (*OH-vum*) The female gamete; the haploid, unfertilized egg, which is usually a relatively large, nonmotile cell.

oxidation The loss of electrons from a substance involved in a redox reaction.

oxidative phosphorylation *(FOS-for-eh-LAY-shun)* The production of ATP using energy derived from the redox reactions of an electron transport chain.

oxidizing agent The electron acceptor in a redox reaction.

pacemaker A specialized region of the right atrium of the mammalian heart that sets the rate of contraction; also called the sinoatrial (SA) node.

paedogenesis *(pee-doh-JEN-eh-sis)* The precocious development of sexual maturity in a larva.

paedomorphosis *(PEE-doh-mor-FOH-sis)* The retention in an adult organism of the juvenile features of its evolutionary ancestors.

paleontology *(PAY-lee-un-TOL-uh-jee)* The scientific study of fossils.

Pangaea *(pan-JEE-uh)* The supercontinent formed near the end of the Paleozoic era when plate movements brought all the land masses of Earth together.

paraphyletic *(PAR-uh-FY-leh-tik)* Pertaining to a taxon that excludes some members that share a common ancestor with members included in the taxon.

parasite *(PAR-uh-site)* An organism that absorbs nutrients from the body fluids of living hosts.

parasitism A symbiotic relationship in which the symbiont (parasite) benefits at the expense of the host by living either within the host (endoparasite) or outside the host (ectoparasite).

parasympathetic division One of two divisions of the autonomic nervous system; generally enhances body activities that gain and conserve energy, such as digestion and reduced heart rate.

parathyroid glands Four endocrine glands, embedded in the surface of the thyroid gland, that secrete parathyroid hormone and raise blood calcium levels.

parazoa *(PAR-uh-ZOH-uh)* Members of the subkingdom of animals consisting of the sponges.

parenchyma *(pur-EN-kim-uh)* A relatively unspecialized plant cell type that carries most of the metabolism, synthesizes and stores organic products, and develops into more differentiated cell types.

parthenogenesis *(PAR-then-oh-JEN-eh-sis)* A type of reproduction in which females produce offspring from unfertilized eggs.

partial pressure The concentration of gases; a fraction of total pressure.

passive transport The diffusion of a substance across a biological membrane.

pattern formation The ordering of cells into specific three-dimensional structures, an essential part of shaping an organism and its individual parts during development.

pedigree A family tree describing the occurrence of heritable characters in parents and off-spring across as many generations as possible.

pelagic zone *(pel-AY-jik)* The area of the ocean past the continental shelf, with areas of open water often reaching to very great depths.

peptide bond The covalent bond between two amino acid units, formed by condensation synthesis.

peptidoglycan *(PEP-tid-oh-GLY-kan)* A type of polymer in bacterial cell walls consisting of modified sugars cross-linked by short polypeptides.

perception The interpretation of sensations by the brain.

perennial *(pur-EN-ee-ul)* A plant that lives for many years.

pericycle *(PAIR-eh-sy-kul)* A layer of cells just inside the endodermis of a root that may become meristematic and begin dividing again.

periderm *(PAIR-eh-durm)* The protective coat that replaces the epidermis in plants during secondary growth, formed of the cork and cork cambium.

peripheral nervous system The sensory and motor neurons that connect to the central nervous system.

peristalsis *(PAIR-is-TAL-sis)* Rhythmic waves of contraction of smooth muscle that push food along the digestive tract.

peroxisome *(pur-OKS-eh-some)* A microbody containing enzymes that transfer hydrogen from various substrates to oxygen, producing and then degrading hydrogen peroxide.

petiole *(PET-ee-ole)* The stalk of a leaf, which joins the leaf to a node of the stem.

pH scale A measure of hydrogen ion concentration equal to $-\log [H^+]$ and ranging in value from 0 to 14.

phage *(fage)* A virus that infects bacteria; also called a bacteriophage.

phagocytosis *(FAY-goh-sy-TOH-sis)* A type of endocytosis involving large, particulate substances.

pharynx *(FAH-rinks)* An area in the vertebrate throat where air and food passages cross; in flatworms, the muscular tube that protrudes from the ventral side of the worm and ends in the mouth.

phenetics *(feh-NEH-tiks)* An approach to taxonomy based entirely on measurable similarities and differences in phenotypic characters, without consideration of homology, analogy, or phylogeny.

phenotype *(FEE-nuh-type)* The physical and physiological traits of an organism.

pheromone *(FAIR-uh-mone)* A small, volatile chemical signal that functions in communication between animals and acts much like a hormone in influencing physiology and behavior.

phloem *(FLOH-um)* The portion of the vascular system in plants consisting of living cells arranged into elongated tubes that transport sugar and other organic nutrients throughout the plant.

phosphate group *(FOS-fate)* A functional group important in energy transfer.

phospholipids *(FOS-foh-LIP-ids)* Molecules that constitute the inner bilayer of biological membranes, having a polar, hydrophilic head and a nonpolar, hydrophobic tail.

photic zone *(FOH-tik)* The narrow top slice of the ocean, where light permeates sufficiently for photosynthesis to occur.

photoautotroph *(FOH-toh-AW-toh-trohf)* An organism that harnesses light energy to drive the synthesis of organic compounds from carbon dioxide.

photoheterotroph *(FOH-toh-HET-ur-oh-trohf)* An organism that uses light to generate ATP but that must obtain carbon in organic form.

photon *(FOH-tahn)* A quantum, or discrete amount, of light energy.

photoperiodism *(FOH-toh-PEER-ee-od-iz-um)* A physiological response to day length, such as flowering in plants.

photophosphorylation *(FOH-toh-fos-for-uh-LAY-shun)* The process of generating ATP from ADP and phosphate by means of a proton-motive force generated by the thylakoid membrane of the chloroplast during the light reactions of photosynthesis.

photorespiration A metabolic pathway that consumes oxygen, releases carbon dioxide, generates no ATP, and decreases photosynthetic output; generally occurs on hot, dry, bright days, when stomata close and the oxygen concentration in the leaf exceeds that of carbon dioxide.

photosynthesis The conversion of light energy to chemical energy that is stored in glucose or other organic compounds; occurs in plants, algae, and certain prokaryotes.

photosystem The light-harvesting unit in photosynthesis, located on the thylakoid membrane of the chloroplast and consisting of the antenna complex, the reaction-center chlorophyll *a*, and the primary electron acceptor. There are two types of photosystems, I and II; they absorb light best at different wavelengths.

phototropism *(FOH-toh-TROH-piz-um)* Growth of a plant shoot toward or away from light.

phylogeny *(fih-LOJ-en-ee)* The evolutionary history of a species or group of related species.

phylum A taxonomic category; phyla are divided into classes.

phytoalexin *(fy-toh-ah-LEK-sin)* An antibiotic, produced by plants, that destroys microorganisms or inhibits their growth.

phytochrome *(FY-tuh-krome)* A pigment involved in many responses of plants to light.

pilus *(PILL-us)* (plural, **pili**) A surface appendage in certain bacteria that functions in adherence and the transfer of DNA during conjugation.

pineal gland *(PIN-ee-ul)* A small endocrine gland on the dorsal surface of the vertebrate forebrain; secretes the hormone melatonin, which regulates body functions related to seasonal day length.

pinocytosis *(PY-noh-sy-TOH-sis)* A type of endocytosis in which the cell ingests extracellular fluid and its dissolved solutes.

pith The core of the central vascular cylinder of monocot roots, consisting of parenchyma cells, which are ringed by vascular tissue; ground tissue interior to vascular bundles in dicot stems.

pituitary gland *(pih-TOO-ih-tair-ee)* An endocrine gland at the base of the hypothalamus; consists of a posterior lobe (neurohypophysis), which stores and releases two hormones produced by the hypothalamus, and an anterior lobe (adenohypophysis), which produces and secretes many hormones that regulate diverse body functions.

placenta *(pluh-SEN-tuh)* A structure in the pregnant uterus for nourishing a viviparous fetus with the mother's blood supply; formed from the uterine lining and embryonic membranes.

placental mammal A member of a group of mammals, including humans, whose young complete their embryonic development in the uterus, joined to the mother by a placenta.

placoderm *(PLAK-oh-durm)* A member of an extinct class of fishlike vertebrates that had jaws and were enclosed in a tough, outer armor.

plankton Mostly microscopic organisms that drift passively or swim weakly near the surface of oceans, ponds, and lakes.

plasma *(PLAZ-muh)* The liquid matrix of blood in which the cells are suspended.

plasma cell A derivative of B cells that secretes antibodies.

plasma membrane The membrane at the boundary of every cell that acts as a selective barrier, thereby regulating the cell's chemical composition.

plasmid *(PLAZ-mid)* A small ring of DNA that carries accessory genes separate from those of a bacterial chromosome. Also found in some eukaryotes, such as yeast.

plasmodesma *(PLAZ-moh-DEZ-muh)* (plural, **plasmodesmata**) An open channel in the cell wall of plants through which strands of cytosol connect from adjacent cells.

plasmogamy The fusion of the cytoplasm of cells from two individuals; occurs as one stage of syngamy.

plasmolysis *(plaz-MOL-eh-sis)* A phenomenon in walled cells in which the cytoplasm shrivels and the plasma membrane pulls away from the

cell wall when the cell loses water to a hypertonic environment.

plastid One of a family of closely related plant organelles, including chloroplasts, chromoplasts, and amyloplasts (leucoplasts).

platelet A small enucleated blood cell important in blood clotting; derived from large cells in the bone marrow.

pleated sheet One form of the secondary structure of proteins in which the polypeptide chain folds back and forth, or where two regions of the chain lie parallel to each other and are held together by hydrogen bonds.

pleiotropy *(PLY-eh-troh-pee)* The ability of a single gene to have multiple effects.

plesiomorphic character *(PLEEZ-ee-oh-MOR-fik)* A primitive phenotypic character possessed by a remote ancestor.

pluripotent stem cell A cell within bone marrow that is a progenitor for any kind of blood cell.

point mutation A change in a gene at a single nucleotide pair.

polar covalent bond A type of covalent bond between atoms that differ in electronegativity. The shared electrons are pulled closer to the more electronegative atom, making it slightly negative and the other atom slightly positive.

polar molecule A molecule (such as water) with opposite charges on opposite sides.

pollen grain An immature male gametophyte that develops within the anthers of stamens in a flower.

pollination *(POL-eh-NAY-shun)* The placement of pollen onto the stigma of a carpel by wind or animal carriers, a prerequisite to fertilization.

polyandry *(POL-ee-AN-dree)* A polygamous mating system involving one female and many males.

polygenic inheritance *(POL-ee-JEN-ik)* An additive effect of two or more gene loci on a single phenotypic character.

polygyny *(pol-IJ-en-ee)* A polygamous mating system involving one male and many females.

polymer *(POL-eh-mur)* A large molecule consisting of many identical or similar monomers linked together.

polymerase chain reaction (**PCR**) A technique for amplifying DNA in vitro by incubating with special primers, DNA polymerase molecules and nucleotides.

polymorphic *(POL-ee-MOR-fik)* Referring to a population in which two or more physical forms are present in readily noticeable frequencies.

polymorphism *(POL-ee-MOR-fiz-um)* The coexistence of two or more distinct forms of individuals (polymorphic characters) in the same population.

polyp *(POL-ip)* The sessile variant of the cnidarian body plan. The alternate form is the medusa.

polypeptide *(POL-ee-PEP-tide)* A polymer (chain) of many amino acids linked together by peptide bonds.

polyphyletic Pertaining to a taxon whose members were derived from two or more ancestral forms not common to all members.

polyploidy *(POL-ee-ploid-ee)* A chromosomal alteration in which the organism possesses more than two complete chromosome sets.

polyribosome *(POL-ee-RY-boh-some)* An aggregation of several ribosomes attached to one messenger RNA molecule.

polysaccharide *(POL-ee-SAK-ur-ide)* A polymer of up to over a thousand monosaccharides, formed by condensation synthesis.

population A group of individuals of one species that live in a particular geographic area.

population viability analysis (**PVA**) A method of predicting whether or not a species will persist in a particular environment.

positional information Signals, to which genes regulating development respond, indicating a cell's location relative to other cells in an embryonic structure.

positive feedback A physiological control mechanism in which a change in some variable triggers mechanisms that amplify the change.

postsynaptic membrane *(post-sin-AP-tik)* The surface of the cell on the opposite side of the synapse from the synaptic terminal of the stimulating neuron that contains receptor proteins and degradative enzymes for the neurotransmitter.

postzygotic barrier *(POST-zy-GOT-ik)* Any of several species-isolating mechanisms that prevent hybrids produced by two different species from developing into viable, fertile adults.

potential energy The energy stored by matter as a result of its location or spatial arrangement.

prezygotic barrier *(PREE-zy-GOT-ik)* A reproductive barrier that impedes mating between species or hinders fertilization of ova if interspecific mating is attempted.

primary consumer An herbivore; an organism in the trophic level of an ecosystem that eats plants or algae.

primary germ layers The three layers (ectoderm, mesoderm, endoderm) of the late gastrula, which develop into all parts of an animal.

primary growth Growth initiated by the apical meristems of a plant root or shoot.

primary immune response The initial immune response to an antigen, which appears after a lag of several days.

primary producer An autotroph, which collectively make up the trophic level of an ecosystem that ultimately supports all other levels; usually a photosynthetic organism.

primary productivity The rate at which light energy or inorganic chemical energy is converted to the chemical energy of organic compounds by autotrophs in an ecosystem.

primary structure The level of protein structure referring to the specific sequence of amino acids.

primary succession A type of ecological succession that occurs in an area where there were originally no organisms.

primer An already existing RNA chain bound to template DNA to which DNA nucleotides are added during DNA synthesis.

principle of allocation The concept that each organism has an energy budget, or a limited amount of total energy available for all of its maintenance and reproductive needs.

prion An infectious form of protein that may increase in number by converting related proteins to more prions.

probe *See* nucleic acid probe.

procambium *(pro-KAM-bee-um)* A primary meristem of roots and shoots that forms the vascular tissue.

prokaryotic cell *(pro-KAR-ee-OT-ik)* A type of cell lacking a membrane-enclosed nucleus and membrane-enclosed organelles; found only in the domains Bacteria and Archaea.

promoter A specific nucleotide sequence in DNA that binds RNA polymerase and indicates where to start transcribing RNA.

prophage *(PRO-fage)* A phage genome that has been inserted into a specific site on the bacterial chromosome.

prostaglandin (PG) *(PROS-tuh-GLAN-din)* One of a group of modified fatty acids secreted by virtually all tissues and performing a wide variety of functions as messengers.

protein *(PRO-teen)* A three-dimensional biological polymer constructed from a set of 20 different monomers called amino acids.

protein kinase An enzyme that transfers phosphate groups from ATP to a protein.

protein phosphatase An enzyme that removes phosphate groups from proteins, often functioning to reverse the effect of a protein kinase.

proteoglycans *(pro-tee-oh-GLY-kanz)* A glycoprotein in the extracellular matrix of animal cells, rich in carbohydrate.

proteasome A giant protein complex that recognizes and destroys proteins tagged for elimination by the small protein ubiquitin.

protoderm *(PRO-toh-durm)* The outermost primary meristem, which gives rise to the epidermis of roots and shoots.

proton-motive force The potential energy stored in the form of an electrochemical gradient, generated by the pumping of hydrogen ions across biological membranes during chemiosmosis.

proton pump *(PRO-tahn)* An active transport mechanism in cell membranes that consumes ATP to force hydrogen ions out of a cell and, in the process, generates a membrane potential.

protonephridium *(PRO-toh-nef-RID-ee-um)* An excretory system, such as the flame-cell system of flatworms, consisting of a network of closed tubules having external openings called nephridiopores and lacking internal openings.

proto-oncogene *(PRO-toh-ONK-oh-jeen)* A normal cellular gene corresponding to an oncogene; a gene with a potential to cause cancer, but that requires some alteration to become an oncogene.

protoplast The contents of a plant cell exclusive of the cell wall.

protostome *(PRO-toh-stome)* A member of one of two distinct evolutionary lines of coelomates, consisting of the annelids, mollusks, and arthropods, and characterized by spiral, determinate cleavage, schizocoelous formation of the coelom, and development of the mouth from the blastopore.

protozoan (plural, **protozoa**) A protist that lives primarily by ingesting food, an animal-like mode of nutrition.

provirus Viral DNA that inserts into a host genome.

proximate causation The immediate mechanisms underlying an organism's behavioral, physiological, or morphological response, in contrast to ultimate, or evolutionary causation.

pseudocoelomate *(SOO-doh-SEEL-oh-mate)* An animal whose body cavity is not completely lined by mesoderm.

pseudopodium *(SOO-doh-POH-dee-um)* (plural, **pseudopodia**) A cellular extension of amoeboid cells used in moving and feeding.

punctuated equilibrium A theory of evolution advocating spurts of relatively rapid change followed by long periods of stasis.

quantitative character A heritable feature in a population that varies continuously as a result of environmental influences and the additive effect of two or more genes (polygenic inheritance).

quaternary structure *(KWAT-ur-nair-ee)* The particular shape of a complex, aggregate protein, defined by the characteristic three-dimensional arrangement of its constituent subunits, each a polypeptide.

quiescent center A region located within the zone of cell division in plant roots, containing meristematic cells that divide very slowly.

***r*-selection** The concept that in certain (*r*-selected) populations, a high reproductive rate is the chief determinant of life history.

radial cleavage A type of embryonic development in deuterostomes in which the planes of cell division that transform the zygote into a ball of cells are either parallel or perpendicular to the polar axis, thereby aligning tiers of cells one above the other.

radial symmetry Characterizing a body shaped like a pie or barrel, with many equal parts radiating outward like the spokes of a wheel; present in cnidarians and echinoderms.

radiata Members of the radially symmetrical animal phyla, including cnidarians.

radicle An embryonic root of a plant.

radioactive dating A method of determining the age of fossils and rocks using half-lives of radioactive isotopes.

radioactive isotope An isotope, an atomic form of a chemical element, that is unstable; the nucleus decays spontaneously, giving off detectable particles and energy.

radiometric dating A method paleontologists use for determining the ages of rocks and fossils on a scale of absolute time, based on the half-life of radioactive isotopes.

receptor-mediated endocytosis *(EN-doh-sy-TOH-sis)* The movement of specific molecules into a cell by the inward budding of membranous vesicles containing proteins with receptor sites specific to the molecules being taken in; enables a cell to acquire bulk quantities of specific substances.

receptor potential An initial response of a receptor cell to a stimulus, consisting of a change in voltage across the receptor membrane proportional to the stimulus strength. The intensity of the receptor potential determines the frequency of action potentials traveling to the nervous system.

recessive allele In a heterozygote, the allele that is completely masked in the phenotype.

reciprocal altruism *(AL-troo-IZ-um)* Altruistic behavior between unrelated individuals; believed to produce some benefit to the altruistic individual in the future when the current beneficiary reciprocates.

recognition species concept The idea that specific mating adaptations become fixed in a population and form the basis of species identification.

recombinant An offspring whose phenotype differs from that of the parents.

recombinant DNA A DNA molecule made in vitro with segments from different sources.

redox reaction *(REE-doks)* A chemical reaction involving the transfer of one or more electrons from one reactant to another; also called oxidation-reduction reaction.

reducing agent The electron donor in a redox reaction.

reduction The gaining of electrons by a substance involved in a redox reaction.

reflex An automatic reaction to a stimulus, mediated by the spinal cord or lower brain.

refractory period *(ree-FRAK-tor-ee)* The short time immediately after an action potential in which the neuron cannot respond to another stimulus, owing to an increase in potassium permeability.

regulative development A pattern of development, such as that of a mammal, in which the early blastomeres retain the potential to form the entire animal.

relative fitness The contribution of one genotype to the next generation compared to that of alternative genotypes for the same locus.

releaser A signal stimulus that functions as a communication signal between individuals of the same species.

releasing hormone A hormone produced by neurosecretory cells in the hypothalamus of the vertebrate brain that stimulates or inhibits the secretion of hormones by the anterior pituitary.

repetitive DNA Nucleotide sequences, usually noncoding, that are present in many copies in a eukaryotic genome. The repeated units may be short and arranged tandemly (in series) or long and dispersed in the genome.

replication fork A Y-shaped point on a replicating DNA molecule where new strands are growing.

repressible enzyme An enzyme whose synthesis is inhibited by a specific metabolite.

repressor A protein that suppresses the transcription of a gene.

Reptilia The vertebrate class of reptiles, represented by lizards, snakes, turtles, and crocodilians.

resolving power A measure of the clarity of an image; the minimum distance that two points can be separated and still be distinguished as two separate points.

resource partitioning The division of environmental resources by coexisting species populations such that the niche of each species differs by one or more significant factors from the niches of all coexisting species populations.

resting potential The membrane potential characteristic of a nonconducting, excitable cell, with the inside of the cell more negative than the outside.

restriction enzyme A degradative enzyme that recognizes and cuts up DNA (including that of certain phages) that is foreign to a bacterium.

restriction fragment length polymorphisms (RFLPs) Differences in DNA sequence on homologous chromosomes that result in different patterns of restriction fragment lengths (DNA segments resulting from treatment with restriction enzymes); useful as genetic markers for making linkage maps.

restriction site A specific sequence on a DNA strand that is recognized as a "cut site" by a restriction enzyme.

retina (REH-tin-uh) The innermost layer of the vertebrate eye, containing photoreceptor cells (rods and cones) and neurons; transmits images formed by the lens to the brain via the optic nerve.

retinal The light-absorbing pigment in rods and cones of the vertebrate eye.

retrovirus (REH-troh-VY-rus) An RNA virus that reproduces by transcribing its RNA into

DNA and then inserting the DNA into a cellular chromosome; an important class of cancer-causing viruses.

reverse transcriptase (trans-KRIP-tase) An enzyme encoded by some RNA viruses that uses RNA as a template for DNA synthesis.

rhodopsin A visual pigment consisting of retinal and opsin. When rhodopsin absorbs light, the retinal changes shape and dissociates from the opsin, after which it is converted back to its original form.

ribonucleic acid (RNA) (ry-boh-noo-KLAY-ik) A type of nucleic acid consisting of nucleotide monomers with a ribose sugar and the nitrogenous bases adenine (A), cytosine (C), guanine (G), and uracil (U); usually single-stranded; functions in protein synthesis and as the genome of some viruses.

ribose The sugar component of RNA.

ribosomal RNA (rRNA) The most abundant type of RNA. Together with proteins, it forms the structure of ribosomes that coordinate the sequential coupling of tRNA molecules to the series of mRNA codons.

ribosome A cell organelle constructed in the nucleolus, functioning as the site of protein synthesis in the cytoplasm. Consists of rRNA and protein molecules, which make up two subunits.

ribozyme An enzymatic RNA molecule that catalyzes reactions during RNA splicing.

RNA polymerase (pul-IM-ur-ase) An enzyme that links together the growing chain of ribonucleotides during transcription.

RNA processing Modification of RNA before it leaves the nucleus, a process unique to eukaryotes.

RNA splicing The removal of noncoding portions (introns) of the RNA molecule after initial synthesis.

rod cell One of two kinds of photoreceptors in the vertebrate retina; sensitive to black and white and enables night vision.

root cap A cone of cells at the tip of a plant root that protects the apical meristem.

root hair A tiny projection growing just behind the root tips of plants, increasing surface area for the absorption of water and minerals.

root pressure The upward push of water within the stele of vascular plants, caused by active pumping of minerals into the xylem by root cells.

rough ER That portion of the endoplasmic reticulum studded with ribosomes.

R plasmid A bacterial plasmid carrying genes that confer resistance to certain antibiotics.

rubisco Ribulose carboxylase, the enzyme that catalyzes the first step (the addition of CO_2 to

RuBP, or ribulose bisphosphate) of the Calvin cycle.

ruminant An animal, such as a cow or a sheep, with an elaborate, multicompartmentalized stomach specialized for an herbivorous diet.

S phase The synthesis phase of the cell cycle, constituting the portion of interphase during which DNA is replicated.

SA (sinoatrial) node The pacemaker of the heart, located in the wall of the right atrium. At the base of the wall separating the two atria is another patch of nodal tissue called the atrioventricular node (AV).

saltatory conduction (SAHL-tuh-TOR-ee) Rapid transmission of a nerve impulse along an axon resulting from the action potential jumping from one node of Ranvier to another, skipping the myelin-sheathed regions of membrane.

saprobe An organism that acts as a decomposer by absorbing nutrients from dead organic matter.

sarcomere (SAR-koh-meer) The fundamental, repeating unit of striated muscle, delimited by the Z lines.

sarcoplasmic reticulum (SAR-koh-PLAZ-mik reh-TIK-yoo-lum) A modified form of endoplasmic reticulum in striated muscle cells that stores calcium used to trigger contraction during stimulation.

saturated fatty acid A fatty acid in which all carbons in the hydrocarbon tail are connected by single bonds, thus maximizing the number of hydrogen atoms that can attach to the carbon skeleton.

savanna (suh-VAN-uh) A tropical grassland biome with scattered individual trees, large herbivores, and three distinct seasons based primarily on rainfall, maintained by occasional fires and drought.

Schwann cells A chain of supporting cells enclosing the axons of many neurons and forming an insulating layer called the myelin sheath.

sclereid (SKLER-ee-id) A short, irregular sclerenchyma cell in nutshells and seed coats and scattered through the parenchyma of some plants.

sclerenchyma cell (skler-EN-kim-uh) A rigid, supportive plant cell type usually lacking protoplasts and possessing thick secondary walls strengthened by lignin at maturity.

second law of thermodynamics The principle whereby every energy transfer or transformation increases the entropy of the universe. Ordered forms of energy are at least partly converted to heat, and in spontaneous reactions, the free energy of the system also decreases.

second messenger A small, nonprotein, water-soluble molecule or ion, such as calcium ion or cyclic AMP, that relays a signal to a cell's interior in response to a signal received by a signal receptor protein.

secondary compound A chemical compound synthesized through the diversion of products of major metabolic pathways for use in defense by prey species.

secondary consumer A member of the trophic level of an ecosystem consisting of carnivores that eat herbivores.

secondary growth The increase in girth of the stems and roots of many plants, especially woody, perennial dicots.

secondary immune response The immune response elicited when an animal encounters the same antigen at some later time. The secondary immune response is more rapid, of greater magnitude, and of longer duration than the primary immune response.

secondary productivity The rate at which all the heterotrophs in an ecosystem incorporate organic material into new biomass, which can be equated to chemical energy.

secondary structure The localized, repetitive coiling or folding of the polypeptide backbone of a protein due to hydrogen bond formation between peptide linkages.

secondary succession A type of succession that occurs where an existing community has been severely cleared by some disturbance.

sedimentary rock *(SED-eh-MEN-tar-ee)* Rock formed from sand and mud that once settled in layers on the bottom of seas, lakes, and marshes. Sedimentary rocks are often rich in fossils.

seed An adaptation for terrestrial plants consisting of an embryo packaged along with a store of food within a resistant coat.

selection coefficient The difference between two fitness values, representing a relative measure of selection against an inferior genotype.

selective permeability A property of biological membranes that allows some substances to cross more easily than others.

self-incompatibility The capability of certain flowers to block fertilization by pollen from the same or a closely related plant.

semen *(SEE-men)* The fluid that is ejaculated by the male during orgasm; contains sperm and secretions from several glands of the male reproductive tract.

semicircular canals A three-part chamber of the inner ear that functions in maintaining equilibrium.

semilunar valve A valve located at the two exits of the heart, where the aorta leaves the left ventricle and the pulmonary artery leaves the right ventricle.

seminiferous tubules *(SEM-in-IF-er-us)* Highly coiled tubes in the testes in which sperm are produced.

sensation An impulse sent to the brain from activated receptors and sensory neurons.

sensory neuron A nerve cell that receives information from the internal and external environments and transmits the signals to the central nervous system.

sensory receptor A specialized structure that responds to specific stimuli from an animal's external or internal environment; transmits the information of an environmental stimulus to the animal's nervous system by converting stimulus energy to the electrochemical energy of action potentials.

sepal *(SEE-pul)* A whorl of modified leaves in angiosperms that encloses and protects the flower bud before it opens.

sex chromosomes The pair of chromosomes responsible for determining the sex of an individual.

sex-linked gene A gene located on a sex chromosome.

sexual dimorphism *(dy-MOR-fiz-um)* A special case of polymorphism based on the distinction between the secondary sex characteristics of males and females.

sexual reproduction A type of reproduction in which two parents give rise to offspring that have unique combinations of genes inherited from the gametes of the two parents.

sexual selection Selection based on variation in secondary sex characteristics, leading to the enhancement of sexual dimorphism.

shoot system The aerial portion of a plant body, consisting of stems, leaves, and flowers.

short-day plant A plant that flowers, usually in late summer, fall, or winter, only when the light period is shorter than a critical length.

sieve-tube member A chain of living cells that form sieve tubes in phloem.

sign stimulus An external sensory stimulus that triggers a fixed action pattern.

signal peptide A stretch of amino acids on polypeptides that targets proteins to specific destinations in eukaryotic cells.

signal-transduction pathway A mechanism linking a mechanical or chemical stimulus to a cellular response.

sink habitat A habitat where mortality exceeds reproduction.

sister chromatids *(KROH-muh-tidz)* Replicated forms of a chromosome joined together by the centromere and eventually separated during mitosis or meiosis II.

skeletal muscle Striated muscle generally responsible for the voluntary movements of the body.

sliding-filament model The theory explaining how muscle contracts, based on change within a sarcomere, the basic unit of muscle organization, stating that thin (actin) filaments slide across thick (myosin) filaments, shortening the sarcomere; the shortening of all sarcomeres in a myofibril shortens the entire myofibril.

small nuclear ribonucleoprotein (snRNP) *(RY-boh-NOO-klee-oh-pro-teen)* One of a variety of small particles in the cell nucleus, composed of RNA and protein molecules; functions are not fully understood, but some form parts of spliceosomes, active in RNA splicing.

smooth ER That portion of the endoplasmic reticulum that is free of ribosomes.

smooth muscle A type of muscle lacking the striations of skeletal and cardiac muscle because of the uniform distribution of myosin filaments in the cell.

sociobiology The study of social behavior based on evolutionary theory.

sodium-potassium pump A special transport protein in the plasma membrane of animal cells that transports sodium out of and potassium into the cell against their concentration gradients.

solute *(SOL-yoot)* A substance that is dissolved in a solution.

solution A homogeneous, liquid mixture of two or more substances.

solvent The dissolving agent of a solution. Water is the most versatile solvent known.

somatic cell *(soh-MAT-ik)* Any cell in a multicellular organism except a sperm or egg cell.

somatic nervous system The branch of the motor division of the vertebrate peripheral nervous system composed of motor neurons that carry signals to skeletal muscles in response to external stimuli.

source habitat A habitat where reproduction exceeds mortality and from which excess individuals disperse.

Southern blotting A hybridization technique that enables researchers to determine the presence of certain nucleotide sequences in a sample of DNA.

speciation *(SPEE-see-AY-shun)* The origin of new species in evolution.

species A particular kind of organism; members possess similar anatomical characteristics and have the ability to interbreed.

species diversity The number and relative abundance of species in a biological community.

species richness The number of species in a biological community.

species selection A theory maintaining that species living the longest and generating the greatest number of species determine the direction of major evolutionary trends.

specific heat The amount of heat that must be absorbed or lost for 1 g of a substance to change its temperature 1°C.

spectrophotometer An instrument that measures the proportions of light of different wavelengths absorbed and transmitted by a pigment solution.

spermatogenesis The continuous and prolific production of mature sperm cells in the testis.

sphincter (*SFINK-ter*) A ringlike valve, consisting of modified muscles in a muscular tube, such as a digestive tract; closes off the tube like a drawstring.

spindle An assemblage of microtubules that orchestrates chromosome movement during eukaryotic cell division.

spiral cleavage A type of embryonic development in protostomes, in which the planes of cell division that transform the zygote into a ball of cells occur obliquely to the polar axis, resulting in cells of each tier sitting in the grooves between cells of adjacent tiers.

spliceosome (*SPLY-see-oh-some*) A complex assembly that interacts with the ends of an RNA intron in splicing RNA; releases an intron and joins two adjacent exons.

sporangium (plural, **sporangia**) A capsule in fungi and plants in which meiosis occurs and haploid spores develop.

spore In the life cycle of a plant or alga undergoing alternation of generations, a meiotically produced haploid cell that divides mitotically, generating a multicellular individual, the gametophyte, without fusing with another cell.

sporophyte The multicellular diploid form in organisms undergoing alternation of generations that results from a union of gametes and that meiotically produces haploid spores that grow into the gametophyte generation.

sporopollenin A secondary product, a polymer synthesized by a side branch of a major metabolic pathway of plants that is resistant to almost all kinds of environmental damage; especially important in the evolutionary move of plants onto land.

stabilizing selection Natural selection that favors intermediate variants by acting against extreme phenotypes.

stamen The pollen-producing male reproductive organ of a flower, consisting of an anther and filament.

starch A storage polysaccharide in plants consisting entirely of glucose.

statocyst (*STAT-eh-SIST*) A type of mechanoreceptor that functions in equilibrium in invertebrates through the use of statoliths, which stimulate hair cells in relation to gravity.

stele The central vascular cylinder in roots where xylem and phloem are located.

stereoisomer A molecule that is a mirror image of another molecule with the same molecular formula.

steroids A class of lipids characterized by a carbon skeleton consisting of four rings with various functional groups attached.

stoma (plural, **stomata**) A microscopic pore surrounded by guard cells in the epidermis of leaves and stems that allows gas exchange between the environment and the interior of the plant.

strict aerobe (*AIR-obe*) An organism that can survive only in an atmosphere of oxygen, which is used in aerobic respiration.

strict anaerobe An organism that cannot survive in an atmosphere of oxygen. Other substances, such as sulfate or nitrate, are the terminal electron acceptors in the electron transport chains that generate their ATP.

stroma The fluid of the chloroplast surrounding the thylakoid membrane; involved in the synthesis of organic molecules from carbon dioxide and water.

stromatolite Rock made of banded domes of sediment in which are found the most ancient forms of life: prokaryotes dating back as far as 3.5 billion years.

structural formula A type of molecular notation in which the constituent atoms are joined by lines representing covalent bonds.

substrate The substance on which an enzyme works.

substrate-level phosphorylation The formation of ATP by directly transferring a phosphate group to ADP from an intermediate substrate in catabolism.

summation A phenomenon of neural integration in which the membrane potential of the postsynaptic cell in a chemical synapse is determined by the total activity of all excitatory and inhibitory presynaptic impulses acting on it at any one time.

suppressor T cell (T_s) A type of T cell that causes B cells as well as other cells to ignore antigens.

surface tension A measure of how difficult it is to stretch or break the surface of a liquid. Water has a high surface tension because of the hydrogen bonding of surface molecules.

survivorship curve A plot of the number of members of a cohort that are still alive at each age; one way to represent age-specific mortality.

suspension-feeder An aquatic animal, such as a clam or a baleen whale, that sifts small food particles from the water.

sustainable agriculture Long-term productive farming methods that are environmentally safe.

sustainable development The long-term prosperity of human societies and the ecosystems that support them.

swim bladder An adaptation, derived from a lung, that enables bony fishes to adjust their density and thereby control their buoyancy.

symbiont (*SIM-by-ont*) The smaller participant in a symbiotic relationship, living in or on the host.

symbiosis An ecological relationship between organisms of two different species that live together in direct contact.

sympathetic division One of two divisions of the autonomic nervous system of vertebrates; generally increases energy expenditure and prepares the body for action.

sympatric speciation A mode of speciation occurring as a result of a radical change in the genome that produces a reproductively isolated subpopulation in the midst of its parent population.

symplast In plants, the continuum of cytoplasm connected by plasmodesmata between cells.

synapomorphies Shared derived characters; homologies that evolved in an ancestor common to all species on one branch of a fork in a cladogram, but not common to species on the other branch.

synapse (*SIN-aps*) The locus where one neuron communicates with another neuron in a neural pathway; a narrow gap between a synaptic terminal of an axon and a signal-receiving portion (dendrite or cell body) of another neuron or effector cell. Neurotransmitter molecules released by synaptic terminals diffuse across the synapse, relaying messages to the dendrite or effector.

synapsis The pairing of replicated homologous chromosomes during prophase I of meiosis.

synaptic terminal A bulb at the end of an axon in which neurotransmitter molecules are stored and released.

syngamy (*SIN-gam-ee*) The process of cellular union during fertilization.

systematics The branch of biology that studies the diversity of life; encompasses taxonomy and is involved in reconstructing phylogenetic history.

systemic acquired resistance (SAR) A defensive response in infected plants that helps protect healthy tissue from pathogenic invasion.

systole (*SIS-toh-lee*) The stage of the heart cycle in which the heart muscle contracts and the chambers pump blood.

T cell A type of lymphocyte responsible for cell-mediated immunity that differentiates under the influence of the thymus.

taiga (*TY-guh*) The coniferous or boreal forest biome, characterized by considerable snow, harsh winters, short summers, and evergreen trees.

taxis (*TAKS-iss*) A movement toward or away from a stimulus.

taxon (plural, **taxa**) The named taxonomic unit at any given level.

taxonomy The branch of biology concerned with naming and classifying the diverse forms of life.

telomerase An enzyme that catalyzes the lengthening of telomeres; the enzyme includes a molecule of RNA that serves as a template for new telomere segments.

telomere The protective structure at each end of a eukaryotic chromosome. Specifically, the tandemly repetitive DNA (*see* repetitive DNA) at the end of the chromosome's DNA molecule.

temperate deciduous forest A biome located throughout midlatitude regions where there is sufficient moisture to support the growth of large, broad-leaf deciduous trees.

temperate virus A virus that can reproduce without killing the host.

temperature A measure of the intensity of heat in degrees, reflecting the average kinetic energy of the molecules.

tendon A type of fibrous connective tissue that attaches muscle to bone.

tertiary consumer A member of a trophic level of an ecosystem consisting of carnivores that eat mainly other carnivores.

tertiary structure (*TUR-shee-air-ee*) Irregular contortions of a protein molecule due to interactions of side chains involved in hydrophobic interactions, ionic bonds, hydrogen bonds, and disulfide bridges.

testcross Breeding of an organism of unknown genotype with a homozygous recessive individual to determine the unknown genotype. The ratio of phenotypes in the offspring determines the unknown genotype.

testis (plural, **testes**) The male reproductive organ, or gonad, in which sperm and reproductive hormones are produced.

testosterone The most abundant androgen hormone in the male body.

tetanus (*TET-un-us*) The maximal, sustained contraction of a skeletal muscle, caused by a very fast frequency of action potentials elicited by continual stimulation.

tetrapod A vertebrate possessing two pairs of limbs, such as amphibians, reptiles, birds, and mammals.

thalamus (*THAL-uh-mus*) One of two integrating centers of the vertebrate forebrain. Neurons with cell bodies in the thalamus relay neural input to specific areas in the cerebral cortex and regulate what information goes to the cerebral cortex.

thermoregulation The maintenance of internal temperature within a tolerable range.

thick filament A filament composed of staggered arrays of myosin molecules; a component of myofibrils in muscle fibers.

thigmomorphogenesis A response in plants to chronic mechanical stimulation, resulting from increased ethylene production; an example is thickening stems in response to strong winds.

thigmotropism (*THIG-moh-TROH-piz-um*) The directional growth of a plant in relation to touch.

threatened species Species that are likely to become endangered in the foreseeable future

throughout all or a significant portion of their range.

threshold potential The potential an excitable cell membrane must reach for an action potential to be initiated.

thylakoid (*THY-luh-koid*) A flattened membrane sac inside the chloroplast, used to convert light energy to chemical energy.

thymus (*THY-mus*) An endocrine gland in the neck region of mammals that is active in establishing the immune system; secretes several messengers, including thymosin, that stimulate T cells.

thyroid gland An endocrine gland that secretes iodine-containing hormones (T_3 and T_4), which stimulate metabolism and influence development and maturation in vertebrates, and cacitonin, which lowers blood calcium levels in mammals.

thyroid-stimulating hormone (**TSH**) A hormone produced by the anterior pituitary that regulates the release of thyroid hormones.

Ti plasmid A plasmid of a tumor-inducing bacterium that integrates a segment of its DNA into the host chromosome of a plant; frequently used as a carrier for genetic engineering in plants.

tight junction A type of intercellular junction in animal cells that prevents the leakage of material between cells.

tissue An integrated group of cells with a common structure and function.

tonoplast A membrane that encloses the central vacuole in a plant cell, separating the cytosol from the cell sap.

torpor In animals, a physiological state that conserves energy by slowing down the heart and respiratory systems.

totipotency The ability of embryonic cells to retain the potential to form all parts of the animal.

trace element An element indispensable for life but required in extremely minute amounts.

trachea (*TRAY-kee-uh*) The windpipe; that portion of the respiratory tube that has C-shaped cartilagenous rings and passes from the larynx to two bronchi.

tracheae (*TRAY-kee-ee*) Tiny air tubes that branch throughout the insect body for gas exchange.

tracheal system A gas exchange system of branched, chitin-lined tubes that infiltrate the body and carry oxygen directly to cells in insects.

tracheid (*TRAY-kee-id*) A water-conducting and supportive element of xylem composed of long, thin cells with tapered ends and walls hardened with lignin.

transcription The synthesis of RNA on a DNA template.

transcription factor A regulatory protein that binds to DNA and stimulates transcription of specific genes.

transfer RNA (**tRNA**) An RNA molecule that functions as an interpreter between nucleic acid and protein language by picking up specific amino acids and recognizing the appropriate codons in the mRNA.

transformation (1) The conversion of a normal animal cell to a cancerous cell. (2) A phenomenon in which external DNA is assimilated by a cell.

translation The synthesis of a polypeptide using the genetic information encoded in an mRNA molecule. There is a change of "language" from nucleotides to amino acids.

translocation (1) An aberration in chromosome structure resulting from an error in meiosis or from mutagens; attachment of a chromosomal fragment to a nonhomologous chromosome. (2) During protein synthesis, the third stage in the elongation cycle when the RNA carrying the growing polypeptide moves from the A site to the P site on the ribosome. (3) The transport via phloem of food in a plant.

transpiration The evaporative loss of water from a plant.

transposon (*trans-POH-son*) A transposable genetic element; a mobile segment of DNA that serves as an agent of genetic change.

triplet code A set of three-nucleotide-long words that specify the amino acids for polypeptide chains.

triploblastic Possessing three germ layers: the endoderm, mesoderm, and ectoderm. Most eumetazoa are triploblastic.

trophic level The division of species in an ecosystem on the basis of their main nutritional source. The trophic level that ultimately supports all others consists of autotrophs, or primary producers.

trophic structure The different feeding relationships in an ecosystem that determine the route of energy flow and the pattern of chemical cycling.

trophoblast The outer epithelium of the blastocyst, which forms the fetal part of the placenta.

tropic hormone A hormone that has another endocrine gland as a target.

tropical rain forest The most complex of all communities, located near the equator where rainfall is abundant; harbors more species of plants and animals than all other terrestrial biomes combined.

tropism A growth response that results in the curvature of whole plant organs toward or away from stimuli due to differential rates of cell elongation.

tumor A mass that forms within otherwise normal tissue, caused by the uncontrolled growth of a transformed cell.

tumor-suppressor gene A gene whose protein products inhibit cell division, thereby preventing uncontrolled cell growth (cancer).

tundra A biome at the extreme limits of plant growth; at the northernmost limits, it is called arctic tundra, and at high altitudes, where plant forms are limited to low shrubby or matlike vegetation, it is called alpine tundra.

turgid (*TUR-jid*) Firm; walled cells become turgid as a result of the entry of water from a hypotonic environment.

turgor pressure The force directed against a cell wall after the influx of water and the swelling of a walled cell due to osmosis.

tyrosine kinase An enzyme that catalyzes the transfer of phosphate groups from ATP to the amino acid tyrosine in a substrate protein.

tyrosine kinase receptor A receptor protein in the plasma membrane that responds to the binding of a signal molecule by catalyzing the transfer of phosphate groups from ATP to tyrosines on the cytoplasmic side of the receptor. The phosphorylated tyrosines activate other signal-transduction proteins within the cell.

ultimate causation The evolutionary explanation for a behavioral, physiological, or morphological response, in contrast to proximate causation, the immediate mechanisms that underlie a response.

unsaturated fatty acid A fatty acid possessing one or more double bonds between the carbons in the hydrocarbon tail. Such bonding reduces the number of hydrogen atoms attached to the carbon skeleton.

urea A soluble form of nitrogenous waste excreted by mammals and most adult amphibians.

ureter A duct leading from the kidney to the urinary bladder.

urethra A tube that releases urine from the body near the vagina in females or through the penis in males; also serves in males as the exit tube for the reproductive system.

uric acid An insoluble precipitate of nitrogenous waste excreted by land snails, insects, birds, and some reptiles.

urochordate A chordate without a backbone, commonly called a tunicate, a sessile marine animal.

uterus A female organ where eggs are fertilized and/or development of the young occurs.

vaccine A harmless variant or derivative of a pathogen that stimulates a host's immune system to mount defenses against the pathogen.

vacuole A membrane-enclosed sac taking up most of the interior of a mature plant cell and containing a variety of substances important in plant reproduction, growth, and development.

valence shell The outermost energy shell of an atom, containing the valence electrons involved in the chemical reactions of that atom.

Van der Waals interactions Weak attractions between molecules or parts of molecules that are brought about by localized charge fluctuations.

vascular cambium A continuous cylinder of meristematic cells surrounding the xylem and pith that produces secondary xylem and phloem.

vascular plants Plants with vascular tissue, consisting of all modern species except the mosses and their relatives.

vascular tissue Plant tissue consisting of cells joined into tubes that transport water and nutrients throughout the plant body.

vascular tissue system A system formed by xylem and phloem throughout the plant, serving as a transport system for water and nutrients, respectively.

vas deferens The tube in the male reproductive system in which sperm travel from the epididymis to the urethra.

vegetative reproduction Cloning of plants by asexual means.

vein A vessel that returns blood to the heart.

ventilation Any method of increasing contact between the respiratory medium and the respiratory surface.

vertebrate A chordate animal with a backbone: the mammals, birds, reptiles, amphibians, and various classes of fishes.

vessel element A specialized short, wide cell in angiosperms; arranged end to end, they form continuous tubes for water transport.

vestigial organ A type of homologous structure that is rudimentary and of marginal or no use to the organism.

viroid (*VY-roid*) A plant pathogen composed of molecules of naked RNA only several hundred nucleotides long.

visceral muscle Smooth muscle found in the walls of the digestive tract, bladder, arteries, and other internal organs.

visible light That portion of the electromagnetic spectrum detected as various colors by the human eye, ranging in wavelength from about 400 nm to about 700 nm.

vitalism The belief that natural phenomena are governed by a life force outside the realm of physical and chemical laws.

vitamin An organic molecule required in the diet in very small amounts; vitamins serve primarily as coenzymes or parts of coenzymes.

viviparous (*vy-VIP-er-us*) Referring to a type of development in which the young are born alive after having been nourished in the uterus by blood from the placenta.

voltage-gated channel Ion channel in a membrane that opens and closes in response to changes in membrane potential (voltage); the sodium and potassium channels of neurons are examples.

water potential The physical property predicting the direction in which water will flow, governed by solute concentration and applied pressure.

water vascular system A network of hydraulic canals unique to echinoderms that branches into extensions called tube feet, which function in locomotion, feeding, and gas exchange.

wavelength The distance between crests of waves, such as those of the electromagnetic spectrum.

wild type An individual with the normal phenotype.

wobble A violation of the base-pairing rules in that third nucleotide (5' end) of a tRNA anticodon can form hydrogen bonds with more than one kind of base in the third position (3' end) of a codon.

xylem (*ZY-lum*) The tube-shaped, nonliving portion of the vascular system in plants that carries water and minerals from the roots to the rest of the plant.

yeast A unicellular fungus that lives in liquid or moist habitats, primarily reproducing asexually by simple cell division or by budding of a parent cell.

yolk sac One of four extraembryonic membranes that supports embryonic development; the first site of blood cells and circulatory system function.

zoned reserve systems Habitat areas that are protected from human alteration and surrounded by lands that are used and more extensively altered by human activity.

zygote The diploid product of the union of haploid gametes in conception; a fertilized egg.

INDEX

Coacervates, 495
Coal forests of Carboniferous period, 558f, 559
Coarse-grained environment, 1083
Cocci bacteria, 503, 504f
Cochlea, 1002, 1003f
    pitch distinguished by, 1004f
Codominance, 248
Codons, 298
    protein synthesis and binding of RNA
        anticodons and, 304–5
    recognition of, 308
    start and stop, 298, 299f
Coefficient of relatedness, 1077
Coelocanths, 640
Coelom, 593, 614
    formation of, in protostomes versus
        deuterostomes, 594
Coelomates, 593, 608–24, 627t
    deuterostomes, 624–27
    protostome and deuterostome split in, 593–95
    protostomes, 608–24
    split between acoelomates and, 593
Coenocytic fungi, 575f, 576
Coevolution, 1110
    relationship between angiosperms and
        pollinators as, 570
Cofactors, enzyme, 94
Cognition, 1064–67
Cognitive ethology, 1065
Cognitive maps, 1065
Cohesion, 38
Cohesion species concept, 450
    hybrid zones and, 456
Cohort, 1086
Coitus, 922
Coitus interruptus, 932
Cold, plant response to, 771
Coleochaete, 550, 551f
Coleoptera (beetles, weevils), 620t
Coleoptile, 738, 740
Coleorhiza, 738
Collagen
    in extracellular matrix of animal cell, 125f, 126
    quaternary structure of protein, 74, 75f
Collagenous fibers, 780f
Collecting duct, 885
    transport properties of nephron and, 884f
Collenchyma cells, 679f, 680
Colloblasts, 604
Colon, 806
Coloration, defensive, 1112–13
Color blindness, 269–70
Colorectal cancer, 359, 361f
Color vision, 1000
Comb jellies (Ctenophora), 592, 603–4
Commensalism, 516, 1117–18
Commercial applications/uses
    of angiosperms, 570–71
    of fungi, 582–83
    pharmaceuticals production, 582–83
    of plant secondary products, 572t
    of prokaryotes, 517
Communication, animal social interactions
        dependent on, 1072–76
Communities, 1107–30
    biogeography and, 1126–28
    boundaries between, 1109f
    commensalism and mutualism in, 1117–18
    conservation of species at level of, 1167–72
    defined, 1107
    disturbance and nonequilibrium in, 1121–26
    ecological research in, 1028
    ecological succession in, 1124
    feeding relationships in, 1119
    individualistic versus interactive hypotheses
        on structure of, 1107–9

interspecific competition in, 1114–17
interspecific interactions in, and evolution of,
    1109–10
interspecific interactions in, and population
    density of, 1110–11
interspecific interactions in, and structure of,
    1118–21
predation and parasitism in, 1111–14
stability in, 1121
Compaction, mammalian development, 949
Companion cells, 681
Comparative anatomy and embryology as
    evidence for evolution, 423–25
Competition, interspecific, 1114–17
    ecological niches and, 1115
    effect of, on populations and community
        structure, 1120–21
    evidence for, in nature, 1115–17
    exploitative, 1114
    interference, 1114
    principle of competitive exclusion, 1114–15
Competitive exclusion principle, 1114–15
Competitive inhibitors, 94, 95f
Competitive social behaviors, 1068–70
Complementarity, DNA, 79, 284–85
Complementary DNA (cDNA), 369f, 370
    gene libraries and, 370–71
Complement fixation, 853, 854f, 855f
Complement system (complement proteins), 844
Complete digestive tract, 606, 799. See also
    Alimentary canal, digestion in
Complete dominance, 248
Complete flowers, 731
Complete metamorphosis, 622, 623f
Composite (complex) transposons, 336
Compound(s), 23
Compound eyes, 616, 996f, 997
Computed tomography (CT), 987b
Computer mapping, 1169b
Concentration gradient, 137
    active transport and pumping of solutes
        against, 140–41
    membrane potential, potassium and sodium
        and, 965–66
Conception, 928
Condensation reactions, 58, 59f
Conditioning, classical versus operant, 1063–64
Condom, contraceptive, 932
Conduction, 866
Cone cells, 998
Confocal microscopy, 104t
Conformation of protein, 68, 70–76
Conformers, 1048
Conidia, 580
Conifers (Coniferophyta), 564, 565f
    forest biome of, 1047f
    life history of pine, 566f
    reproduction in, 564–65
Conjugation
    antibiotic resistance and R plasmids, 335
    in bacteria, 333–35, 507
    in ciliate Paramecium, 530f
    in green algae Spirogyra, 541f
    plasmids and, 333–35
Conjunctiva, 998
Connective tissue, 780–82
    blood as, 782 (see also Blood)
    collagen fibers of, 780f
    types of, 781f
Consciousness
    animal, 1066–67
    human, 988–89
Conservation biology, 1154–74
    biodiversity crisis and, 1154–57
    at community, ecosystem, and landscape
        levels, 1167–72

emergence and focus in field of, 1157–58
geographic distribution of biodiversity and,
    1158–60
at population and species levels, 1160–67
Conservation of energy, 85
Conservative model of DNA replication, 285f
Consumers, biospheric, 8, 168
    primary, secondary, and tertiary, 1132
Consumption in ecosystems, 1132
Continental drift, 469, 470f
Contraception, 931–33
    mechanisms of some methods of, 931f
Contractile vacuoles, 115
Control center, homeostatic control system, 789
Control elements, eukaryotic gene, 354
Control group, 15
Controlled experiment, 15
Control systems. See Animal regulatory systems;
    Plant control systems
Convection, 866
Convergent evolution, 476–77
Convergent extension, 950, 951f
Cooksonia sp., fossils of, 555f
Cooperativity
    in animal social behavior, 1067–68
    enzyme activity and, 96, 97f
    origins of molecular, 497f
Coordinate gene expression, 355–56
Copepods, 624
Coral reef, 1040, 1041f, 1155–56
Corals (Anthozoa), 602
Corepressor, 339
Cork cambium, 689, 690–92
Corn
    B. McClintock's research on genetics of kernel
        color in, 336–37
    nitrogen deficiency in, 24f
    speciation and hybridization of, 450
    transposons in genome of, 336–37, 350
Cornea, 998
Corpus callosum, 983
Corpus luteum, 920
Correns, Karl, 275
Corridors between ecosystems, 1168–69
Cortex, plant tissue, 685, 702–3
Cortical granules, 938
Cortical nephrons, 882, 883f
Cortical reaction, 938f, 939f
Corticosteroids, 908–9
Cortisol, 908
Cortisone, 909
Coruzzi, Gloria, on molecular biology studies in
    plants, 668–69
Cotransport, 142, 143f, 696
Cotyledons, 569, 736, 738, 740
Countercurrent exchange
    in blood vessels of fish gills, 828, 829f
    thermoregulation and, 867–68
Countercurrent heat exchanger, 867, 868f
Courtship behaviors, 447f, 650f, 916, 1070–72
Covalent bonds, 28–30
    double, 29
    nonpolar and polar, 29–30
    in organic molecules, 50
Cowpox, 326
Crabs, 623
    horseshoe, 617f
    population fluctuations in Dungeness, 1100f
Cranial nerves, 978
Cranium, vertebrate, 634
Crassulacean acid metabolism (CAM), 184, 708–9,
    1049
Crayfish, 623, 827f
Creatine phosphate, 1017
Cretaceous period mass extinctions, 472–73, 646
    mammal diversification following, 650–56

Cretinism, 903, 904
Creutzfeldt-Jacob disease, 329
Crick, Francis, discovery of DNA structure by J. Watson and, 79, 279, 281–83
Cri du chat syndrome, 274
Crinoidea (sea lilies), 625*f*, 626
Cristae, 117
Critical period for behavioral imprinting, 1061
Crocodilia (alligators, crocodiles), 646, 647*f*
Cro-Magnons, 663
Crop plants, 570–71. *See also* Agriculture
    heterozygote advantage and crossbreeding of, 438–39
    improving protein yield in, 721
    monoculture and lack of genetic diversity in, 742–43
Cross-bridge, 1016*f*
Crossing over, 236
    chiasmata as sign of, 235, 236*f*
    genetic recombination of linked genes by, 265, 266*f*
Cross pollination, 568
    Mendel's studies using, 239–47
Crustaceans, 616, 623–24
    chelicerates compared to uniramians and, 616
    compound eyes in, 997
    exoskeleton in, 623
    external anatomy of, 615*f*
    gills of, 827*f*
    hormones in, 894
Cryptic coloration, 1112
Ctenophora (comb jellies), 592, 603–4
Cultural eutrophication of lakes, 1146
Cultural evolution, human, 664–65
Cuticle, 615, 1012
    plant, 547, 681
Cuttings, plant, 741–42
Cuvier, Georges, paleontological studies of, 415–16
Cyanobacteria, 515*t*
    bloom of, 511*f*
    lichens and, 584
    origins of cellular respiration and, 511–12
Cycads (Cycadophyta), 564, 565*f*
Cyclic AMP (cAMP)
    positive gene regulation and role of, 340–41
    as second messenger, 197, 198*f*
Cyclic electron flow, photosynthesis, 178–79
Cyclic guanosine monophosphate (cGMP), 999
Cyclic photophosphorylation, 178–79
Cyclin, 218
Cyclin-dependent kinases (Cdks), 218
Cystic fibrosis
    abnormal protein degradation and, 358
    as recessively inherited disorder, 254
Cystinuria, 140
Cysts, protist, 521
Cytochromes (cyt), 158*f*, 159
    cytochrome *c*, 478
Cytokines, 849
Cytokinesis, 208, 213
    in animal and plant cells, 214*f*
    in plants and charophytes, 550
Cytokinins, 754*t*, 755–57
    control of apical dominance by, 756, 757*f*
    control of cell division and differentiation by, 756
    root nodules and, 725
Cytological map, 268
Cytology, microscopes as tool in, 104–5
Cytoplasm, 106
    cytokinesis and division of, 213, 214*f*
    developmental fate of animal cells linked to organization of, 395–97, 952–54
    fusion of (plasmogamy), in fungi, 576
    genes located in, 275–76
    response of, to signaling, 200–201

Cytoplasmic determinants, 396, 397*f*
Cytoplasmic streaming, 123, 124*f*, 532, 799*f*
Cytosine (C), 77, 78*f*, 79
Cytoskeleton, 119–24
    animal morphogenesis and changes in, 950
    intermediate filaments of, 120*t*, 124
    membrane proteins and, 135*f*
    microfilaments of, 120*t*, 123–24
    microtubules of, 120–23
    motor molecules in, 119*f*
    plant cell division and expansion guided by, 744–46
    structure and function of, 120*t*
Cytosol, 106, 310
    lateral transport in plants and, 700*f*
Cytotaxis, 529
Cytotoxic T cells (T$_C$), 847
    CD8 cell surface protein on, 850
    function of, against intracellular pathogens, 850–51

Dalton, 25
Dalton, John, 25
Danielli, James, 131
Dark reactions, photosynthetic. *See* Calvin cycle, photosynthesis
Dart, Raymond, 660
Darwin, Charles, 417–22, 489
    adaptation as focus of research by, 418–19
    Beagle voyage and field research of, 417–18
    descent-by-modification as theory of, 419–20
    historical context of life and theory of, 415*f*
    modern synthesis of Mendelian inheritance and evolutionary theory of, 428–29
    natural selection and adaptation as theory of, 12–13, 420, 421–22
    studies of phototropism, 420–21
    summary of evolutionary theory by, 420–21
Darwin, Francis, 752–53
Darwinian fitness, 440
Daughter cells, distribution of chromosomes to, 208*f*, 209–13
Davson, Hugh, 132
Davson-Danielli membrane model, 131*f*
Dawkins, Richard, on evolutionary biology, 412–13
Dawson, Terence, on kangaroos, 776–77
Day-neutral plants, 766
DDT, 1120
    biological magnification of, in food webs, 1147
    gene mutations and, 437
Death rate in populations, 1085
Decapods, 623
Decomposers, 169, 1132
    bacteria as, 516
    fungi as, 574–75, 581, 585–86
    slime molds as, 532
Decomposition in ecosystems, 1132, 1134
    rates of, and nutrient cycling, 1143–44
Deep-sea vents, 498, 1041*f*, 1042
Deforestation, 571–72
Dehydration reactions, 58, 59*f*
Deletion
    chromosomal, 272
    of nucleotides in genes, 312
Demography, 1084–87
    age structure and sex ratio as factors in, 1085–86
    life tables and survivorship curves in, 1086–87
Denaturation
    of DNA, 368
    of proteins, 75, 76*f*
Dendrites, 961, 962*f*
Density, population, 1083
    effects of interspecific interactions on, 1110–11

factors of, affecting population growth, 1097–1101
    measuring, 1083
Density-dependent inhibition of cell division, 220*f*
Density-dependent population factors, 1097–99
Density-independent population factors, 1099–1100
Dentition, vertebrate, 807*f*
Deoxyribonucleic acid. *See* DNA (deoxyribonucleic acid)
Deoxyribose, 77, 78*f*
Depolarization, 967
Deposit-feeders, 797
Dermal tissue system, plant epidermis, 681, 688*f*
Dermaptera (earwigs), 620*t*
Descent with modification, 419–20. *See also* Natural selection
Desert, 1045*f*
    plants adapted to, 708–9, 1049
Desmosomes, 126*f*, 127
Determinate cleavage, 593, 594*f*
Determination, cell, 395, 396*f*
Detritus, 1035, 1132
Detritivores, 1132. *See also* Decomposers
Deuteromycetes (imperfect fungi), 582
Deuterostomes, 593, 627*t*
    chordates as, 626
    cleavage in, 593–94, 942
    coelom formation in, 594
    fate of blastopore in, 594–95
Development, 388–92. *See also* Animal development; Plant development
    cell division, differentiation, and morphogenesis during, 389, 390*f*
    differential gene expression in, 392–97
    genetic and cellular mechanisms of pattern formation in, 397–410
    genetic control of animal, and evolutionary novelty, 458–60
    model organisms for study of, 389–92
    pattern formation mechanisms in process of, 397–410
Developmentally-fixed behavior, 1054–55
Devonian period, radiations of fishes in, 641*f*
De Vries, Hugo, 453
Diabetes mellitus, 859, 905–6
Diacylglycerol (DAG), 199
Diaphragm, contraceptive, 932
Diaphragm, respiratory, 831, 832*f*
Diapsids, 644, 645*f*
Diastole, cardiac cycle, 816
Diatoms (bacillariophyta), 534, 535*f*
Dicots (Dicotyledones), 565, 672
    anatomy of winter twig of, 683*f*
    cotyledons of, 569
    development of embryo in, 737*f*
    leaves of, 676
    monocots compared to, 673*f*
    root tissue in, 685*f*
    taproot system of, 674
Diencephalon, 980
Diet
    dentition and, 807*f*
    disease and, 66
    ecosystem energy flows and efficient, 1138
    evolutionary adaptations of vertebrate digestive systems and, 807–8
    required nutrients in, 792–96
    vegetarian, 794*f*
Differential-interference-contrast (Nomarski) microscopy, 104*t*
Differentiation, cell, 744
    cell-cell induction and, 952, 954–57
    cytoplasmic determinants affecting, 952, 953–54

embryonic development and, 350, 352, 389, 390*f*, 950–57
nuclear transplantation and, 393–95
in plants, 744–47, 756
tissue-specific proteins linked to cell, 395, 396*f*
Diffusion, 137
facilitated, 140
Digestion, 798–800
in alimentary canals, 799, 800*f*
in gastrovascular cavities, 799
hormones and, 805, 806*t*
intracellular, in food vacuoles, 798–99
in small intestine, 803–5
in stomach, 783*f*, 802–3
Digestive system, mammalian, 800–807
diet and length of, 807–8
esophagus, 801–2
hormones and, 805–6
large intestine, 806–7
oral cavity, 800–801
pharynx, 801
small intestine, 803–5
stomach, 783*f*, 802–3
symbiotic microorganisms in, 808
Digestive system, vertebrate, evolutionary adaptations of, 807–8
Digestive tract, 799–800
annelid, 800*f*
bird, 800*f*
diet and, 807–8
of herbivores versus carnivores, 807*f*
insect, 800*f*
mammalian (*see* Digestive system, mammalian)
rotifer, 606
ruminant, 807*f*
Digger wasp nest-locating behavior, 1056*f*
Dihybrid cross, 244
testing for segregation in, 245*f*
Dikaryon, 576
Dinoflagellates, 527
Dinosaurs, 645–46
Cretaceous crisis and extinction of, 646
phylogenetic tree of, 484*f*
social behavior and parental care among, 646*f*
Dioecious plant species, 732
Dipeptidases, 804
Diploblastic animals, 592
Diploid cells, 228. *See also* Meiosis
genetic variation preserved in, 438
reduction of chromosomes from, to haploid cells, 228, 230*f*, 231–35
Diplomonads, 524, 526
Diplopoda (millipedes), 618, 619*f*
Diptera (flies, mosquitos), 620*t*
Directional selection, 440, 441*f*
Direct repeat sequences, 336
Disaccharides, 61–62. *See also* Lactose; Maltose; Sucrose
Discrete characters, 436
Diseases and disorders. *See also* Genetic disorders
abnormal immune function leading to, 858–61
African sleeping sickness, 526, 622, 1114*f*, 1120
AIDS (*see* AIDS (acquired immunodeficiency syndrome))
allergies as, 858–59
atherosclerosis, 66, 143, 824, 825*f*
autoimmune, 847, 859
cancer (*see* Cancer)
cardiovascular, 256, 824–26
cholera, 197–98
cystinuria, 140
diabetes mellitus, 859, 905–6

DNA technology for diagnosis of, 380
gene therapy for, 380–81
Giardia and, 524, 526
goiter, 24*f*
hemophilia, 270, 824
hormone-related, 902
hypercholesterolemia, 143
immune system (*see* Immune system)
immunodeficiency, 859–61
malaria, 255, 528, 1120
opportunistic, 516, 859
parasites as cause of, 1120
Parkinson's, 52*f*, 974
pathogens as cause of (*see* Pathogens)
in plants (*see* Plant disease)
Schistosoma, 605
sickle-cell disease, 72*f*, 250, 254*f*, 255
viral, in animals, 326–28
viroids and prions as cause of, 329
Disease vectors, insects as, 622. *See also* Pathogens
Dispersion, patterns of population, 1083–84
within geographical range, 1084*f*, 1126
uniform, 1084
Dispersive model of DNA replication, 285*f*
Displays, animal, 1073
Dissociation curve, 835
Distal tubule, 882, 883*f*, 885
Disturbances as abiotic factor, 1030
effects of, on communities, 1121–22, 1125
humans as agents of, 1122–24
nonequilibrial model of, 1124–26
succession resulting from, 1124
Disulfide bridges, 73, 74*f*
Diversifying selection, 441
Diversity and unity, biological, 9–11
Diving mammals, respiratory and circulatory adaptations of, 836–37
Division, 577
DNA (deoxyribonucleic acid), 6*f*, 7
antisense, 381–82
chromatin packing in, 344–46
chromosomes formed from, 227 (*see also* Chromosome(s))
cloning (*see* Recombinant DNA)
complementary (cDNA), 369, 370, 371
denaturation of, 368
discovery of, as key genetic material, 278–83
DNA-protein complex (*see* Chromatin)
double helix structure of, 78, 79*f*
inheritance based on replication of, 226–27
intron and exon segments of, 302–3 (*see also* Exons; Introns)
leading and lagging strands of, 287–88
length of, 207, 346
libraries of, 370–71
methylation of, 271, 353
molecule ends of, 290–91
nitrogenous bases, 77–78 (*see also* Nitrogenous bases)
packing of, into chromatin, 344–46
proteins specified by, 294–300 (*see also* Protein synthesis)
repair of, 289–91
replication of (*see* DNA replication)
restriction mapping of, 478
satellite, 347
sequences of (*see* DNA sequences)
sequencing of, 377, 378*b*
strand polarity, 287–88
structure of, 77–78, 79*f*, 281*f*–83
template strand of, 297–98
transcription of RNA under direction of, 296–97, 300–302
triplet code of nucleotides in, 297, 298*f*
DNA-binding domain, 355, 356*f*
DNA-DNA hybridization, 478, 479*f*

DNA fingerprinting
forensic investigations and, 382*f*, 383
paternity in red-wing blackbirds established by, 1073*b*
DNA gun, 743*f*
DNA ligase, 288
DNA repair by, 289–90
using restriction enzyme and, to make recombinant DNA, 366*f*, 367
DNA methylation, 271
control of gene expression and, 353
DNA microarray assays, 379
DNA nucleotide sequence. *See* DNA sequences
DNA polymerases, 286, 287*f*
DNA viruses and, 322
DNA replication, 284–91
antiparallel DNA strands as problem in, 287–88
base pairing and, 284–85
enzymes and proteins in process of, 286–89
enzymes as proofreaders in, 289–90
leading and lagging DNA strands in, 287, 288
models of, 284, 285*f*
origins of, 286
priming, 288–89
strand elongation in, 286–87
summary of, 289*f*
DNA sequences
analysis of, 377, 378*b*, 478–80
direct repeats, 336
homologous, 479–80
introns and exons, 302, 303*f*
inverted repeats, 335
mutations in (*see* Mutations)
in phylogenetically related species, 477–80
phylogenetic hypothesis based on, 480*f*
repetitive, 346–48
TATA box , 301
terminator, 302
DNA sequencing, 377, 378*b*, 478–80
DNA technology, 18*f*, 364–87
forensic, environmental, and agricultural applications of, 382–85
Human Genome Project and, 376, 380
medical and pharmaceutical applications of, 379–82
methods for analysis of DNA nucleotide sequences by, 372–79
methods of gene cloning by, 364–72
safety and ethical questions related to, 381, 385
DNA virus, 320, 321*f*
Dobzhansky, Theodosius, 429
Domains, protein, 304
DNA-binding, 355, 356*f*
looped, 346
Domains, systematics, 475, 503, 512–13
comparisons of three, 512*t*
three-domain classification system, 499*f*, 500, 503*f*
Domains of life, 10, 11*f*
Dombeck, Michael, on ecological management of public lands, 1024–25
Dominance hierarchy, 1068–69
Dominant allele, 242
incomplete, 247–48
Dominant trait
genetic disorder as, 255, 256*f*
widow's peak as, 252, 253*f*
Dopamine, 974, 975*t*
Dorsal lip, blastopore, 945
as induction organizer, 954, 955*f*
Dorsal side, body, 592
Double circulation, 814
in mammals, 814–17
Double covalent bond, 29
Double fertilization, 568–69, 736

increased atmospheric carbon dioxide due to combustion of, 1140
Fossil record, 464–73. *See also* Fossil(s)
  continental drift and, 469–70
  as evidence for evolution, 12*f*, 423, 468–69
  mass extinctions, survivor adaptive radiation, and, 470–73
  in sedimentary rock, 415–16, 464–66
Founder effect, 434
Fovea, 998
F plasmid, conjugation and, 333–35
Fragile X syndrome, 274, 347
Fragmentation
  asexual reproduction by, 914
  of habitats, 1161, 1162
  plant, 741
Frameshift mutation, 312
Franklin, Rosalind, contribution of, to discovery of DNA structure, 281, 282*f*
Free energy, 86–88
  defined, 86–87
  equilibrium and, 87*f*, 88
  metabolism and, 88, 89*f*
Free energy of activation, 91. *See also* Activation energy
Free ribosomes, 111, 310
Freeze-fracture method of cell preparation, 132, 138*b*
Frequency-dependent selection, 439
Freshwater animals, osmoregulation in, 877
Freshwater biomes, 1034–39
  estuaries as, 1038*f*, 1039
  ponds and lakes as, 1033, 1034*f*, 1036*f*, 1037*f*
  streams and rivers as, 1037*f*
  wetlands as, 1038–39
Frogs (Anura), 642, 643*f*
  circulatory system, 813, 814*f*
  cleavage in embryo of, 942*f*
  cryptic coloration in, 1112*f*
  diet and digestion in, 808
  fate map of cells in embryo of, 953*f*
  gastrulation in embryo of, 944*f*
  organogenesis in, 946*f*
  skin color in, 896–97, 903
Fructose, hydrolysis of glucose and, 93*f*
Fruit, 568, 738–39
  characteristics of fleshy, 738*t*
  ethylene and ripening of, 759
  gibberellins and growth of, 758
  plant and animal relationships and, 570
  seed dispersal by, 568
  types of, 738
Fruit fly. *See Drosophila melanogaster; Drosophila* sp.
Fuel, food as, 792–96
Functional groups, 53–55
Function and structure, biological organization and correlation of, 7–8
Fundamental niche, 1115
Fungi, 574–88
  chytrids (Chytridiomycota), 577
  club fungi (Basidiomycota), 581, 582*f*
  as decomposers, 585–86
  ecological impact of, 585–86
  as food, 586
  lichens, 584–85
  molds, 581–83
  mycorrhizae, 585, 724–26
  nutrition in, 574–75
  as pathogens, 579, 583, 586
  phylogeny of, 577*f*, 587
  reproduction in, 574–77
  sac fungi (Ascomycota), 579–80
  sexual life cycle in, 230, 231*f*
  yeasts, 583
  zygote (Zygomycota), 578–79

Fungi (kingdom), 11*f*. *See also* Fungi
Fusiform initials, 690

G$_0$ phase of cell cycle, 218
G$_1$ phase of cell cycle, 209
G$_2$ phase of cell cycle, 209, 218*f*
Galápagos Islands
  adaptive radiation and evolution in, 452
  beak evolution in finches of, 422*f*
  character displacement in finches of, 1116, 1117*f*
  C. Darwin's studies on, 418–19
Gallbladder, 800, 801*f*, 806
Gametangia, 548
  moss, 547*f*
Gametes, 208, 228. *See also* Egg; Sperm
  animal, 913
  chromosomes of, 228–30
  differing size or morphology of (anisogamy), 541–42
  evolution of, 543
  fertilization of animal, 916–17
  isolation of, as reproductive barrier, 447
  law of independent assortment and segregation of alleles into, 244–46
  law of segregation and alleles for genetic character in separate, 241–44
Gametophyte, algae, 231, 539
Gametophyte, plant, 231, 548, 561, 562*f*, 730
  in bryophytes, 552, 553*f*
  development of, within anthers and ovaries, 730–34
  pollination and fertilization of, 734, 736
Gamma aminobutyric acid (GABA), 974, 975*t*
Ganglion (ganglia cells), 963
  visual information and, 1001
Gap analysis, 1169*b*
Gap genes, 402
Gap junctions, 126*f*, 127
Garrod, Archibald, 294
Gaseous signals of nervous system, 975–76
Gas exchange in animals, 826–37
  in aquatic animals, 827–28
  in arthropods, 615, 616, 622
  brain control centers and, 832–33
  breathing and, 830–33
  circulatory system and, 811–26
  in deep-diving mammals, 836–37
  gills and, 827–28
  lungs and tracheal systems for, 828–32
  oxygen uptake and carbon dioxide disposal in, 826–27
  pressure gradients and, 833–34
  respiratory pigments and, 834–36
  in terrestrial animals, 828–32
  tracheal system for, 622, 829–30
Gas exchange in plants, 696*f*, 704*f*, 706–9
Gastric juice, 802
Gastrin, 806
Gastropods (Gastropoda), 610, 611*f*
  torsion in embryo of, 610*f*
Gastrovascular cavity
  cnidarian, 601–2
  digestion in, 799
Gastrula, 590
Gastrulation, 589, 590*f*, 943–45
  in bird embryo, 947*f*
  embryonic tissue layers formed by, 592, 943
  in frog embryo, 944*f*, 945
  of sea urchin embryo, 943*f*
Gated channels, 140, 696, 700
Gated ion channels in neurons, 967, 968*f*
Gel electrophoresis, 372
  of macromolecules, 374*b*
Gemmules, 914
Gene(s), 76, 208, 226. *See also* Chromosome(s); DNA (deoxyribonucleic acid)

alternative versions of (*see* Alleles)
association of, with specific chromosome, 261–63
BRCA1, and breast cancer, 224–25, 361
cloning of (*see* Gene clones)
DNA technology and determining function of, 379
egg-polarity, 399–402
evolving definition of, 314–16
expression of (*see* Gene expression, eukaryotic; Gene expression, prokaryotic)
extranuclear, and non-Mendelian inheritance, 275–76
first, 496–97
gap, 402
homeotic, 403–4, 460
Hox, 404, 460*f*, 596, 957
idea of, and Gregor Mendel's studies, 239
immunoglobulin, 350, 351*f*
inheritance and, 226–27
jumping (*see* Transposons)
linked, 263–66
location of, on chromosomes (*see* Gene locus)
multigene families, 348–49
mutations in (*see* Mutations)
natural selection centered in, R. Dawkins on, 412–13
organ-identity, 408, 409*f*, 748
organization of typical eukaryotic, 353, 354*f*
p53, 359
pattern formation in animal embryo and, 956, 957
point mutations in, 312–14
proteins specified by, 294–300 (*see also* Protein synthesis)
pseudogenes, 349
regulatory, 338–39
S-, and self-incompatibility in plants, 735
segmentation, 402
sex-linked, 263, 264*f*
split (RNA splicing), 302–3
tumor-suppressor, 359, 361
XIST, on Barr bodies, 271
Gene amplification, 349–51
Gene clones
  identification of, 368
  libraries of, 370–71
Gene cloning, 365
  bacterial plasmids and production of, 365*f*, 366, 367*f*–69
  expression vectors and, 369–70
Gene expression, eukaryotic, 344–63
  cancer as result of abnormal, 358–61
  cellular differentiation dependent upon, 352, 952
  chromatin modifications and control of, 353
  chromatin structural organization and, 344–46
  control of, 351–58
  coordinate, 355–56
  development and differential, 392–97
  DNA technology and study of patterns of, 377–79
  opportunities for control of, in gene-to-protein pathway, 352*f*, 353
  plant development and, 746–47
  regulation of, as response to signal, 200, 201*f*
  RNA processing, 302–4
  RNA synthesis, 300–2
  steroid hormones and, 356
Gene expression, prokaryotic, control of, 337–41
Gene expression, synthesis of RNA and protein, 294–311
Gene flow, 434
Gene-for-gene recognition, plant-pathogen, 772
Gene locus, 227
  mapping of, using recombination data, 267–68

Learning, 1060–64
    associative, 1063–64
    classical conditioning as, 1063
    habituation as, 1061
    imprinting as, 1061–63
    maturation versus, 1060–61
    memory and, 988
    operant conditioning as, 1063–64
    play and, 1064
Leeches (Hirudinea), 614
    nervous system, 976, 977f
Leeuwenhoek, Anton van, 4
Leghemoglobin, 722
Legumes, symbiotic nitrogen fixation between
        bacteria and, 722–24
Lek, 1071
Lens, eye, 998
Lenticels, 690
Lepidoptera (butterflies, moths), 621t. See also
        Butterflies
Leptin, 793
Leukemia, 274, 328, 824
Leukocytes, 782, 823. See also White blood cells
        (leukocytes)
    nonspecific defense by, 841–43
Lewis, Edward, 403
Leydig cells, 918
Lichens, 540, 584–85
Life, 490–501
    cells, as basic units of, 4–6
    cells, first, 492–93
    chemical evolution and origin of, 492–95
    classification of, 10f, 11f (see also Taxonomy)
    dates of origin of, 491–92
    debate about origins of, 497–98
    diversity and unity of, 9–11
    domains of, 11f
    elements required by, 23–24
    emergent properties of, 4, 5f
    evolution of, 12–13 (see also Evolution)
    hierarchy in biological order of, 1–4
    inheritance and continuity of, 6–7
    major episodes in history of, 492, 493f
    major lineages of, 498–500, 503f (see also
        Systematics)
    organisms as open systems of, 8 (see also
        Organisms)
    origins of hereditary information and
        Darwinian evolution in, 497
    properties of, 5f
    protobionts and origins of, 495
    regulatory mechanisms of, 8–9
    RNA as first genetic material of, 495–97
    science and study of, 13–19
    structure and function in, 7–8
Life cycle, 227. See also Sexual life cycle
    of algae, 230f, 231, 537, 538f, 539, 541f, 542f
    of angiosperm, 568, 569f, 730, 731f
    of animals, 589
    of apicomplexan Plasmodium sp., 528f
    of cellular slime mold, 534f
    of fern, 556f
    of fungi, 576f, 578f, 580f, 582f
    of hydrozoan, 603f
    of pine (gymnosperm), 566f
    of plants, 548, 566, 568–69
    of plasmodial slime mold, 533f
    of trematode blood flukes, 605f
    virus, 321–24
    of water mold, 536f
Life history, 1087–92
    age at first reproduction in, 1091–92
    of guppies, and evolutionary adaptations, 16
    number of offspring per reproductive episode
        in, 1090–91
    number of reproductive episodes in, 1089–90

patterns in, 1088
    population growth models and strategies of,
        1096–97
    reproduction versus survival considerations in,
        1088–89
Life tables, population, 1086, 1087t
Ligaments, 781
Ligand, 143, 192
Ligand-gated ion channels, 194, 195f
Light. See also Sunlight
    as abiotic factor, 1029–30
    characteristics of, 173
    circadian rhythms and, 765
    effect of, on nocturnal animals, 982f
    harvesting of, in thylakoid membrane, 172,
        173–79
    opening/closing of leaf stomata and, 707
    photoperiodism and, 765–67
    photoreceptors for detection of, 995, 996–1002
    phototropism as plant growth toward, 752–53,
        762
    phytochromes and receptor of, in plants,
        767–69
Light chain, antibody molecule, 852f, 853
Light-independent reactions. See Calvin cycle,
        photosynthesis
Light microscopes (LMs), 103, A-7
Light microscopy, types of, 104t, A-7
Light reactions, photosynthesis, 172–79
    chemiosmosis during, 178, 179
    cyclic electron flow during, 178–79
    mechanical analogy of, 178f
    nature of sunlight and, 173
    noncyclic electron flow during, 177–78
    photoexcitation of chlorophyll during, 175
    photosynthetic pigments and, 173–75
    photosystems of, 175–77
Light receptors, photosynthetic pigments as,
        173–75
Lignin, 547, 555
Limb development, pattern formation during
        vertebrate, 955–57
Limbic system, 986f
Limiting nutrient, 1136
Linkage map, 268f, 269, 376
    RFLPs as genetic markers for producing, 373
Linked genes, 263–65
    crossing over and recombination of, 265, 266f
    evidence for, in Drosophila, 265f
Linnaeus, Carolus, taxonomy developed by, 415,
        420, 475
Lipase, 804
Lipids, 65–68
    fats, 65–66 (see also Fat(s))
    phospholipids, 67–68
    steroids, 68
Lipoproteins, high and low density, 143, 826
Liposomes, 495
Littoral zone, 1036
Liver, 800, 801f, 803, 805
    role of, in homeostasis, 890
Liverworts (Hepatophyta), 554
Lizards (Squamata), 646, 647f
    parthenogenic reproduction in, 914, 915f
    resource partitioning among sympatric,
        1116f
Loams, soil, 717
Lobe-finned fishes, 640
Lobsters, 623–24
    anatomy of, 615f
Local chemical signaling, 189, 190f
Local regulators, chemical signals as, 189–90,
        895–98
Locomotion, 1009–11. See also Movement
Locus, gene. See Gene locus
Logging, deforestation and, 571–72

Logistic population growth, 1094
    carrying capacity and, 1094–97
Long-day plants, 766
Long-term depression (LTD), 988
Long-term memory, 988
Long-term potentiation (LTP), 988
Looped domains, 346
Loop of Henle, 882, 883f, 885
Loose connective tissue, 780, 781f
Lophophorate animals, 608, 609f
Lophophore, 608
Lorenz, Konrad, 1061
Low-density lipoproteins (LDLs), 143, 826
Lungfishes, 640
Lungs, 830
    automatic control of breathing and, 832–33
    loading/uploading of respiratory gases in,
        833–34
    ventilation of, 830–32
Luteal phase, ovarian cycle, 926
Luteinizing hormone (LH), 902, 910, 927
Lycophyta (lycophytes), 557
Lycopods (Lycophyta), 557
Lyell, Charles, 416
Lymph, 820
Lymphatic system, 820–22
    human, 842f
    as nonspecific defense, 820, 842
Lymph nodes, 820
Lymphocytes, 822f, 823, 844–55
    antigen interaction with, and induction of
        immune response, 845–46
    B cells (see B lymphocytes (B cells))
    clonal selection of, 845
    development of, 846f, 847
    differentiation of, 824f
    immune system specificity provided by,
        844–45
    T cells (see T lymphocytes (T cells))
Lynx, population cycles of snowshoe hare and,
        1101f
Lysis, humoral immunity and cell, 853, 854f, 855f
Lysogenic cycle, 323, 324f
Lysosome, 114–15, 798
    formation and function of, 115f
    genetic disorders involving, 115
Lysozyme, 841
    functional conformation and structure of,
        71f
Lytic cycle, 322, 323f, 324f

M, N, and MN blood groups, 248
MacArthur, Robert, on island biogeography,
        1126–28
McCarty, Maclyn, 279
McClintock, Barbara, genetics research by, 336
MacLeod, Colin, 279
Macroevolution, 445
    mass extinctions and adaptive radiations in,
        470–73
    non-goal orientation of trends in, 460–62
    origin of evolutionary novelty and, 458–62
    speciation as, 446–58
    E. Vrba on, 488–89
Macromolecules, 58–82
    carbohydrates as, 60–65
    coacervate as aggregate of, 495
    computer modeling and graphics of, 80b
    gel electrophoresis of, 374b
    lipids as, 65–68
    lysosome digestion of, 114–15
    nucleic acids as, 76–80
    as polymers, 58–60
    proteins as, 68–76
    transport of, in and out of cells, 143–44
Macronutrients, plant, 715–16

Macrophage, 127f, 781
    as antigen-presenting cell, 851–52
    phagocytosis by, 842–43
Magnesium as plant nutrient, 716–17
Magnetic resonance imaging (MRI), 987b
Magnetoreceptors, 995, 996
Major histocompatibility complex (MHC), 847
    Class I, 847, 848, 849
    Class II, 847, 851
    rejection of tissue grafts and organ transplants
        due to, 847, 858
Malaria, 1120
    mosquitos as vector for, 622
    Plasmodium life history and, 528f
    sickle-cell disease and, 255, 438
Males
    hormones affecting reproduction and sexual
        maturation in, 925
    reproductive anatomy of human, 918, 919f,
        920
    sexual response in, 922
    spermatogenesis in, 922, 923f
    XXY disorder in, 273
    XY sex chromsomes of, 268
    XYY disorder in, 273
Malignant tumor, 221
Malleus, 1002, 1003f
Malnourishment, 794
Malpighian tubules, 622, 881
Maltose, 61f
Mammals (Mammalia), 650–56
    characteristics of, 651
    circulatory (cardiovascular) system of, 814–26
    cloning of, 394f, 395
    commensalism between bird and, 1118f
    countercurrent heat exchange in marine, 867,
        868f
    digestive system of, 800–807
    embryonic development in, 948–50
    embryos and amniotic egg of, 643–44
    as endotherms, 785
    eutherian (placental), 655f, 656
    evolution of, 651
    excretory system and kidney of, 881–89
    fertilization of eggs in, 917, 939, 940f
    hearing and ear of, 1002–5
    inactivation of X-chromosome in female,
        270–71
    jaw and earbones of, 651f
    marsupials, 654, 655f, 776–77
    monotremes, 652t, 654, 776
    orders of, 652–53t
    reproduction in, 918–33
    respiratory adaptations of deep-diving,
        836–37
    respiratory system of, 830–37
    thermoregulation in, 870–71
    urea production by, 874, 875f
Mammary glands, 922
    lactation and, 930
Mandibles, 616
Mangold, Hilde, 954–55
Mantle, mollusks, 609
Mantle cavity, mollusks, 609
Marine animals
    coral, 1040, 1041f
    countercurrent heat exchange in marine
        mammals, 867, 868f
    at deep-sea vent communities, 1041f, 1042
    in intertidal zones, 1040, 1041f
    osmoregulation in, 876–77
    respiratory adaptations of diving mammals,
        836–37
    salt excretion in birds, 874f
Marine biomes, 1034–35
    animals of (*see* Marine animals)

benthos zone, 1041f, 1042
    coral reefs, 1040
    estuaries and, 1038f, 1039
    intertidal zone of, 1040, 1041f
    oceanic pelagic biome, 1040–42
    zonation in, 1039–40
Marine ecosystems, food chains in, 1132f
Marine worms. *See* Polychaetes (marine worms)
Mark-recapture method, 1085b
Marsupials, 652t, 654
    T. Dawson on kangaroos, 776–77
    eutherians compared to, 655f
Mass extinctions, 470–73
    adaptive radiations following, 471
    catastrophism theory and, 416
    in Cretaceous period, 472–73, 646
    in current era, 1154–58
    examples of, 471–73
Mass number, 25
Mast cells, 843
    allergic response and, 858f
Maternal effect genes, 399–402
Mating, 1070–72. *See also* Fertilization
    assortive, 435
    courtship behaviors, 447f, 650f, 916, 1070–72
    human sexual response and, 922
    nonrandom, in populations, 434–35
    random, as source of genetic variation, 430
    systems of, 1072, 1073b
Matter, 22–23
    atomic structure of, 24–28
    chemical bonding and molecule formation in,
        28–33
    chemical reactions and, 33–34
    cycling of, in ecosystems (*see* Chemical cycling
        in ecosystems)
Maturation versus learning, 1060–61
Mayer, Alfred, 319–20
Mayr, Ernst, 429
    on logic of natural selection theory, 420
Mechanical isolation as reproductive barrier, 447
Mechanoreceptors, 994
    for equilibrium, 1005
    for gravity, 1006–7
    for hearing, 1002–5
    lateral line system as, 638, 1005, 1006f
    for touch, 994f
Medicine
    DNA technology and, 379–82
    Koch's postulates on pathogens used by, 516
Medulla oblongata, 981
    breathing controlled in, 833
Medusa (cnidarian), 601
Megapascals, 697
Megasporangium, 563
Megaspores, 556, 563, 732, 734f
Meiosis, 208, 227–35
    alternation of fertilization and, in sexual life
        cycle, 228–31
    chromosomal basis of inheritance and, 262f,
        268–71
    evolution of, 524
    mitosis compared to, 231, 234f, 235
    nondisjunction of chromosomes in, 271f
    in plants, 548
    reduction of chromosome number during,
        228, 230f, 231–35
    stages of meiotic cell division, 232–33, 235
Meiosis I, 231, 235f
Meiosis II, 231
Melanocyte-stimulating hormone (MSH), 896–97,
        902, 903
Melatonin, 902–3
Membrane(s), biological, 130–45. *See also* Plasma
        membrane
    artificial, 131f

extraembryonic, 643–44, 948f, 949f
    internal, in eukaryotic cell, 107
    nuclear envelope as, 110
    in prokaryotes, 506, 507f
    rough endoplasmic reticulum and production
        of, 113
    structure of, 67–68, 130–35
    transport across, 136–44
Membrane antibodies, 844
Membrane attack complex (MAC), 854, 855f
Membrane potentials, 141–42, 964–70
    action potential and changes in, 966–69
    action potential propagation along axons and,
        969–70
    basis of, 965f
    measuring, 966b
    in plant cells, 696, 707
    resting, 967
Membrane proteins, 131f, 132
    cotransport of solutes facilitated by, 142–43
    drifting of, 133f
    functions of, 133–34
    as receptor proteins, 192–95
    structure of, 133, 134f
Memes, 413
Memory
    human brain and, 988
    immunological, 845, 846f
Memory cells, 845
Mendel, Gregor Johann, 239–47. *See also*
        Mendelian inheritance
Mendelian inheritance, 239–60
    chromosomal behavior during sexual life
        cycles as basis of, 261–68
    genetic testing and counseling based on,
        256–58
    genotype and phenotype relationship, 247–52
    in humans, 252–58
    law of independent assortment, 244–46, 262f
    law of segregation, 241–44, 262f
    Mendel's research approach, 239–41
    modern synthesis of Darwinism and, 428–29
    particulate behavior of genes reviewed, 247
    patterns of, and human genetic disorders,
        252–56
    patterns of, in human inheritance, 252, 253f
    rules of probability reflected in, 246–47
Meninges, 978
Meniscus, 704
Menopause, 927
Menstrual cycle, 925, 926f, 927
Menstrual flow phase, menstrual cycle, 926
Menstruation, 925
Meristems, 682
    apical, 389, 682, 683–89
    lateral, 689–92
    location of major, 682f
    transition of, from vegetative to flowering, 767
Meroblastic cleavage, 943
Meselson, Matthew, experiments on DNA
        replication by F. Stahl and, 285f
Mesencephalon, 980
Mesenteries, 784
Mesoderm, 943–45
    gastrulation and formation of, 592, 943
    organs formed from, 945–46
Mesohyl, 600
Mesophyll, 170, 687, 688f
Mesophyll cells, 184
Mesotrophic lakes, 1036
Mesozoic era
    gymnosperms in, 564
    radiation of angiosperms between Cenozoic
        era and, 569–70
Messenger RNA (mRNA), 77, 296
    codons of, 298

Mosaic evolution, 660
Mosquitos
    as fluid feeders, 797*f*
    malaria and, 528*f*, 622, 1120
Mosses (Bryophyta), 552–54
    gametangia of, 547*f*
    life cycle of, 553*f*
Motility, 119*f*. *See also* Movement
    prokaryotic cell, 505–6
Motor division, peripheral nervous system, 978
Motor mechanisms in animals, 1009–20
    in annelids, 613*f*
    in lancelets, 632
    locomotion and, 1009–11
    muscle contraction as, 1014–20
    skeletons as essential for, 1011–13
Motor mechanisms in plants, 763, 764*f*
Motor molecules
    chromosome migration and, 212, 213*f*
    cytoskeleton, cell motility and, 119*f*
Motor neurons, 962, 963*f*, 978
    muscle contraction stimulated by, 1017–18
    recruitment of, 1018
Motor proteins, chromosome migration and, 212, 213*f*
Motor unit of vertebrate muscle, 1018, 1019*f*
Mouse
    as model organism, 391
    pattern formation in, 404*f*
    speciation among deer, 449*f*
Movement, 1009–20
    animal cognition and, 1065–66
    animal development and cell, 389, 950–52
    bioenergetic cost of, 1010*f*
    cell motility, 119*f*, 123, 124*f*
    locomotion as, 1009–11
    mechanisms of, in animals (*see* Motor mechanisms in animals)
    in plants, 761–64
    prokaryotic cell, 505–6
    in protists, 521, 530–32
    skeletons as essential for, 1011–13
    in slime molds, 531*t*
Movement corridor, 1168–69
MPF (maturation promoting factor), 218
Mucous membrane, 780
    as body defense mechanism, 840–41
Muller, Hermann, 313
Müllerian mimicry, 1113
Multicellularity, 2–3
    origins of, 542–43
Multifactorial characters, 251
    as genetic disorders, 255–56
Multigene family, 348–39
Multiple fruit, 738
Multiple sclerosis, 859
Multiplication, rule of, and Mendelian inheritance, 246, 430
Multiregional model of human origins, 663*f*
Muscle(s)
    body movements and requirements on, 1018–20
    cardiac, 782*f*, 783, 1019–20
    cooperation of skeleton and, for movement, 1014*f*
    determination and differentiation cells of, 395, 396*f*
    fast and slow fibers in, 1018–19
    lactic acid fermentation in cells of, 162
    motor unit neuron in, 1018, 1019*f*
    myosin and actin interaction and contractions of, 1014–17
    role of calcium and regulatory proteins in contraction of, 1017–18
    skeletal, 782*f*, 783, 1014, 1015*f*
    sliding-filament model of contracting, 1015*f*

smooth, 782*f*, 783, 1020
    summation of contractions in cells of, 1018*f*
    tissue of, 589, 782*f*, 783
Muscle spindle, 994
Mushroom, 581, 582*f*
Mussels (Bivalvia), 611
Mutagenesis, in vitro, 379
Mutagens, 313–14
    Ames test for measuring strength of, 313, 314*b*
Mutant phenotypes, 263
Mutations, 312
    in bacteria, 330–31, 437, 507
    cancer and, 224, 359–61
    as cause of microevolution in populations, 434
    chromosomal, 271–74
    deletions, 312
    in DNA, 290
    frameshift, 312
    genetic variation generated by, in populations, 437–38
    in homologous DNA sequences, 479, 480*f*
    insertions, 312
    insertion sequences as cause of, 336
    missense, 312
    mutagens causing, 313–14
    nonsense, 312
    point, 312 (*see also* Point mutations)
    proto-oncogenes transformed into oncogenes by, 358–59
    repetitive DNA sequences and, 347
    silent, 312
    spontaneous, 313
Mutualism, 516, 1117, 1118
    community structure affected by, 1119–20
    legumes and nitrogen-fixing bacteria, 722, 723*f*
    roots and mycorrhizae fungi, 585, 724–25
Mutualistic fungi, 574–75
Mycelium (fungi), 575, 576
Mycorrhizae, 578, 585, 675, 702, 724–26
    agricultural importance of, 725
    evolutionary relationship of root nodules to, 725–26
    two types of, 724, 725*f*
    water absorption and, 701–2
Myelencephalon, 980
Myelin sheath, 961, 962*f*
Myofibrils, 782*f*, 1014, 1015*f*
Myofilaments, 1014, 1015*f*
Myoglobin, storage of oxygen in, 836
Myosin
    cell motility, actin filaments and, 123–24
    cytokinesis and, 213
    muscle contraction and, 1014–17
Myotonia, 922

NAD+ (nicotinamide adenine dinucleotide), as oxidizing agent and electron shuttle during cellular respiration, 150–52
NADH
    electron transfer from, in cellular respiration, 150–52, 161
    glycolysis and, 152, 153, 155*f*, 156
    Krebs cycle and, 156, 157*f*
NADP+ (nicotinamide adenine dinucleotide phosphate), 172
NADP+ reductase, 178
NADPH
    Calvin cycle and conversion of carbon dioxide to glucose using, 179–82
    synthesis of, in photosynthetic light reactions, 172
Naked mole rats, 1076, 1077*f*
Natural family planning, 932
Natural killer cells (NK), 843
Natural selection, 414, 440–42

as cause of microevolution in population, 435
    C. Darwin's theory of adaptation and, 12–13, 420–22
    R. Dawkins on, 412
    evolutionary fitness and, 440
    in finch populations, 422
    frequency-dependent, 439
    gene-centered, 412–13
    genetic variation as substrate for, 435–40
    in guppy populations, 15–17
    interspecific interactions as factors in, 1109–10
    modes of, 440–41
    perfection not created by, 442
    sexual selection and, 441–42
Natural theology, 415
Nature, scale of, 415
Nature reserves, 1169–70
Navigation, bird migration and, 1065, 1066*f*
Neanderthals, 663–64
Negative feedback, 9
    kidney regulation by, 888*f*
    as mechanism of homeostasis, 789
Negative pressure breathing, 830–31, 832*f*
Nematocysts, 601
Nematoda (nematodes, roundworms), 593, 607
    cell lineages of, 392*f*
    cell signaling and induction in, 404–6
    hydrostatic skeleton in, 1011
    as model organism, 391
Nemertea (proboscis worms/ribbonworms), 608
Nephron, 882–84
    production of urine from blood filtrate in, 884–85
    structure and function of, 882, 883*f*
    transport epithelium and, 884*f*
Neritic zone, 1040
Nerve(s), 961. *See also* Neuron(s)
    cranial, 978
    spinal, 978
Nerve chord, 631, 976
Nerve growth factor (NGF), 896
Nerve impulse (action potential), integration of, at cellular level, 972–74. *See also* Action potential; Neuron(s)
Nerve net, 976
Nervous system, 893, 960–91. *See also* Motor mechanisms in animals; Sensory reception
    body symmetry correlated with, 976–77
    cognition and function of, 1064–65
    endocrine system integration with, 894, 960
    functions of, 960–64
    human brain (*see* Human brain)
    imaging of, 987*b*
    insect, 976, 977*f*
    invertebrate, 976, 977*f*
    kidney function regulated by hormones and, 887–89
    nervous system organization, 976–79
    neural signaling in, 964–76
    neurons and supporting cells of, 961–64
    tissue of, 782–83
    vertebrate brain, structure and function of, 979–89
    vertebrate central nervous system, 961, 77–78
    vertebrate peripheral nervous system, 961, 978–99
Nervous tissue, 589. *See also* Neuron(s)
    in animals, 782–83 (*see also* Nervous system)
    in invertebrates, 976–77
Net primary productivity (NPP), 1134–35
    idealized pyramid of, 1137*f*
Neural crest, 633, 945
    derivation of endocrine cells from, 907*f*
Neural signals, 964–76
    action potentials and, 966–70

Proboscis worms (Nemertea), 608
Procambium, 684, 686
Producers, biospheric, 8
   primary, 1131–33
Production in ecosystem, 1132
Productivity
   ecosystem energy budget and primary, 1134–36
   ecosystem energy flow and secondary, 1136–37
   pyramid of, 1137
   of select ecosystems, 1135*f*
Products of chemical reactions, 34
Profundal zone, 1036
Progesterone, 897, 908*f*, 910
Progestins, 910
Programmed cell death, 846. *See also* Apoptosis
Prokaryotes, 502–19
   bacteria and archaea as evolutionary branches
     of, 503
   domains, 10, 11*f*
   ecological impact of, 513–17
   eukaryotes versus, 506–7
   fossil, 491*f*
   genome of, 506–7
   growth, reproduction, and rapid adaptation
     by, 507–8
   membranes of, 506, 507*f*
   motility of, 505–6
   nutritional and metabolic diversity among,
     508–12
   overview of, 502–3
   as pathogens, 504, 508, 516–17
   phylogeny of, 512–13, 514–15*t*
   structure of, 503–5
   symbiosis among, 516–17
Prokaryotic cell, 6, 105–7. *See also* Bacteria
   action of antibiotics on, 504–5, 507
   cell wall, 504–5
   circular DNA molecules in, 291
   eukaryotic cell versus, 105–7, 506–7
   flagella of, 505, 506*f*
   protein synthesis in, versus in eukaryotes, 296,
     297*f*, 311*f*
   reproduction in, 213–16, 330, 507
   shapes of, 503, 504*f*
Prolactin (PRL), 902
Proliferative phase, menstrual cycle, 926
Prometaphase, mitosis, 209
Promiscuous mating systems, 1072
Promoter sequences
   in eukaryotic genes, 353–54
   TATA box, 301*f*
Prophage, 323, 324*f*
Prophase, mitosis, 209
Prosimians (Prosimii), 656, 657*f*
Prostaglandins (PGs), 843, 896, 994
Prostate gland, 919*f*, 920
Protandrous species, 915
Proteasome, degradation of protein by, 357*f*, 358
Protein(s), 68–76
   amino acids of, (*see also* Amino acid(s))
   antimicrobial, 844
   catabolism of, 164*f*
   catalytic (*see* Enzyme(s))
   cell determination/differentiation and
     production of specific, 395, 396*f*
   chaperone, 76, 309
   complement, 844
   conformation, structure, and function of, 68,
     70–76
   control of gene expression and
     processing/degradation of, 357*f*, 358
   denaturation and renaturation of, 75, 76*f*
   digestion of, 803
   DNA replication and role of, 286–89
   domains of (*see* Domains, protein)
   folding problem, 76

functions of, overview, 68*t*
G (*see* G protein)
gene specification of, 294–300 (*see also* Protein
   synthesis)
heat-shock, 771, 872
human deficiency of, 721, 794
improving yield of, in crop plants, 721
infectious (prions), 329
integral, 133, 134*f*
as measure of evolutionary relationships, 425*f*
membrane (*see* Membrane proteins)
neutral variations in, 439
peripheral, 133, 134*f*
phosphorylation of, 195–97
in phylogenetically related species, 478
point mutations and effects on, 312–14
polypeptide chains of 68–70 (*see also*
   Polypeptides)
PR, 773
receptor (*see* Receptor proteins)
regulatory, 403, 1017, 1018
secretory (*see* Secretory proteins)
signal mechanism for targeting, 310–11
solubility of, in water, 42*f*
stress-induced, 872
synthesis of (*see* Protein synthesis)
tissue-specific, 395
transport (*see* Transport proteins)
Protein folding, 76
Protein kinases, 195, 218
   as relay in signal transduction pathway, 195,
     196*f*
Proteinoids, 495
Protein phosphatases, 196–97
Protein synthesis, 77*f*, 304–16, 496
   gene concept related to knowledge about,
     314–16
   gene expression and specification of, 294–300
   nucleotide triplets as specifiers of amino acids
     in, 297–98
   nucleus control of, 111
   overview of transcription and translation steps
     in, 296–97, 315*f*
   point mutations and, 312–14
   polypeptide signal sequences and, 310–11
   post-transcription processing of RNA and,
     302–4
   in prokaryotes versus eukaryotes, 311
   ribosomes and, 111
   RNA's role in, 311
   transcription and RNA synthesis phase of,
     300–302
   translation and polypeptide synthesis phase of,
     304–10
Proteobacteria, 514*t*
Proteoglycans, 126
Protist(s), 11*f*, 492, 520–25
   actinopods (radiolarians, heliozoans), 531–32
   alternation of generations in some, 537–39
   Alveolata, 527–30
   amoebas (rhizopods), 530–31
   apicomplexans, 527–28
   Archaezoa, 524–26
   brown algae (Phaeophyta) seaweeds, 536, 537*f*
   candidate kingdoms of, 543*t*
   ciliates (ciliophorans), 529–30
   as decomposers, 532
   diatoms (Bacillariophyta), 534–35
   dinoflagellates, 527
   diversity of, 520–22
   Euglenozoa, 526
   flagellate, 526
   foraminiferans (forams), 532
   golden algae (Chrysophyta), 535
   green algae (Chlorophyta), 540–42
   locomotion by pseudopodia in, 530–32

mitochondria lacking in some, 524–26
monophyletic taxa emerging from systematics
   of, 524
multicellularity and, 542–43
origin of animals from flagellated, 590*f*
origin of animals and fungi from common
   ancestral, 587
as pathogens, 524–26, 528*f*, 531
red algae (Rhodophyta), 539
slime molds, 532, 533*f*, 534*f*
Stramenopila, 533–37
systematics and phylogeny of, 499–500, 524,
   525*f*
water molds (Oomycota), 535, 536*f*
Protista (kingdom), 11*f*, 524. *See also* Protist(s)
Protobionts, formation of, 493, 495
Protoderm, 684, 686
Protogynous species, 915
Proton, 24, 25
Protonephridium, 879, 880*f*
Proton-motive force, 160
Proton pump, 142
   plant cell growth in reponse to auxin and, 755
   signal-transduction pathways in plant cells
     and, 761*f*
   transport in plants using, 696–97
Proto-oncogenes, 328, 358
   conversion of, into oncogenes, 358*f*
   ras, 359, 360*f*
Protoplast, 678
Protoplast fusion, 742
Protostomes, 593, 627*t*
   cleavage in, 593–94, 942
   coelom formation in, 594
   fate of blastophore in, 594–95
   phyla of, 595*t*
Protozoa, 521
Provirus, 326
Proximal tubule, 882, 883*f*, 884–85
Proximate questions, 1049
PR proteins, 773
Pseudocoelom, 593
Pseudocoelomates, 593, 606–7, 627*t*
Pseudogenes, 349
Pseudopodia, 123, 124*f*, 530–32
P site, tRNA binding, 306, 307*f*
Pterophyta (ferns), 556*f*, 558
Pterosaurs, 645–46
Public lands management, 1157–58
   M. Dombeck on, 1024–25
Puffballs (basidiomycetes), 581
Pulmocutaneous circuit, 813, 814*f*
Pulmonary circuit, 814
Pulse, heart and, 815, 816
Punctuated equilibrium, evolution by, 457–58, 489
Punnett square, 250
Pupa, 894
Pupil, eye, 998
Purines, nucleic acid structure and, 77, 78*f*
Pyloric sphincter, 803
Pyramid of numbers, 1138
Pyramid of productivity, 1137
Pyrimidines, nucleic acid structure and, 77, 78*f*
Pyrogens, 844
Pyruvate
   conversion of, to acetyl CoA, 156
   as key juncture in catabolism, 163*f*
   oxidation of glucose to, during glycolysis,
     153–56

Quantitative characters, 250, 436
Quaternary structure, protein, 74, 75*f*
Quiescent center, 684

Racemization, 468, 481–82
Radial cleavage, 594

RNA polymerase, 300
    binding of, and initiation of transcription, 301
    control of eukaryotic gene expression and, 353, 354
RNA processing, 296–97, 302–4
    alteration of mRNA ends, 302
    control of eukaryotic gene expression during, 356
    intron function and importance in, 303–4
    ribozyme function during, 303
    RNA splicing during, 302, 303f
RNA splicing, 302, 303f
RNA viruses, 320, 321f
    replication of, 325f, 326
Rocks as abiotic factor, 1030
Rod cells, bacilli, 503, 504f
Rod cells, eye, 998
Rodentia (squirrels, rats, beavers, etc.), 653t, 656
    activity levels in nocturnal squirrel, 982f
Root. See also Root system
    lateral, 686f
    nitrogen-fixing bacteria on, 720, 721f, 722–24, 1141
    nodules on, 722–26
    primary growth of, 683–86
    primary tissues of, 684–86
    secondary growth of, 692
Root cap, 683
Root hairs, 675, 701–2
Root pressure, ascent of xylem sap and, 703
Root system, 672, 673f, 674–75
    lateral transport in, 701f
    primary growth in, 683–86
    response of, to oxygen deprivation, 770
    secondary growth in, 692
    water and mineral absorption by, 701–3
Rotifera (rotifers), 593, 606–7
Rough ER (endoplasmic reticulum), 112
    membrane production and, 113
    secretory protein synthesis and, 112–13
Round window, ear, 1004
Roundworms (Nematoda), 404–6, 593, 607
R plasmids, antibiotic resistance and, 335
r-selected populations, 1097
Rubisco (RuBP carboxylase), 180
Ruminants, digestion in, 808f
Rusts (basidiomycetes), 581

Saccharomyces cerevisiae (baker's yeast), 583
    cell signaling mechanisms in, 188, 189f
Saccule, 1005
Sac fungi (Ascomycota), 579–80
Safety concerns of DNA technology, 385
Salamanders (Urodela), 643
    paedomorphosis in, 459f
Salicylic acid, 773
Saliva, 800
Salivary amylase, 801
Salivary glands, 800, 801f
Salmon
    life history of, 1090
    migratory behavior and smell sense in, 1007f
Salmonella sp., 517
Saltatory conduction, 970
Salts. See also Sodium chloride (NaCl)
    excretion of, by birds, 874f
    ionic compounds as, 31
    mineralocorticoids and balance of, 909
    plant response to excessive, 770–71
Sanger, Frederick, 72
Sanger method of DNA sequencing, 378b
Saprobes, 508
Saprobic fungi, 574
Sarcomeres, 1014, 1015f
Sarcoplasmic reticulum, 1017

Sarcopterygii (fleshy-finned fishes), 640
Satellite DNA, 347
Saturated fatty acid, 66f
Sauropsids, 644, 645f
Savanna, 1044f
Scallops (Bivalvia), 611
Scanning electron microscope (SEM), 103–4
Schistosoma mansoni (blood fluke), 605, 843
Schizocoelous development, 594
Schleiden, Matthias, 4
Schwann, Theodor, 4
Schwann cells, 961, 962f, 970
Science, 13–19
    B. Alberts on, 100–101
    controlled experiments in, 15
    hypothetico-deductive thinking in, 13–18
    technology and, 18–19
    theory in, 425–26
Science as process, 13–18
    analyzing species viability, 1165–67
    behavioral ecology, 1057–60
    cell signaling and transcriptional regulation in plant development, 406–10
    chemical cycling, vegetative regulation of, 1144–45
    community structure hypotheses, 1107–9
    C. Darwin's field research, 417–18
    DNA as genetic material, 278–81
    DNA structure, 281–83
    gene-chromosome associations, 261–63
    gene-directed protein synthesis, 294–96
    hypotheses on community structure, 1107–9
    membrane models, 130–32
    G. Mendel's studies in genetics, 239–41
    model organisms for study of development, 389–92
    plant hormones, discovery of, 752–53
    search for fossilized DNA, 481–82
    testable hypotheses as hallmark of, 13–18
    tracking atoms through photosynthesis, 170–72
    viruses, discovery of, 319–20
Scientific method. See Biological methods
Scion, plant, 741
Sclera, 997–98
Sclerenchyma cells, 679f, 680
Scorpions, 617f
Scrotum, 919
Scutellum, 738
Scyphozoa (jellies), 592, 602, 603
Sea anemones (Anthozoa), 602, 603
    asexual reproduction in, 914f
Sea cucumbers (Holothuroidea), 625f, 626
Sea lilies (Crinoidea), 625f, 626
Search image, 1058
Seasons
    animal behaviors and, 981–83
    causes of, 1031f
    effects of, on climate, 1033–34
    plant responses to, 765–67
Sea squirt (tunicate), 631–32, 953f
Sea stars (Asteroidea), 624, 625f, 626
    anatomy, 626f
    gills, 827f
    nervous system, 976, 977f
    reproduction, 914
Sea urchins (Echinoidea), 592
    egg fertilization in, 937–39
    gastrulation in embryo of, 943f
    zygote cleavage in, 940, 941f
Seaweeds
    adaptations of, structural and reproductive, 536–37
    alternation of generations in life cycle of, 538f
    brown algae as, 536
    green algae as, 540–42

Secondary cell wall, plant, 125
Secondary consumers, 1132
Secondary growth, plants, 682, 689–92. See also Wood
    auxin as stimulant to, 755
    in roots, 692
    in stems, 689–92
Secondary immune response, 846
Secondary plant body, 689
Secondary productivity, 1136–37
Secondary products, plant, 547, 572t
Secondary structure, protein, 72–73
Secondary succession, 1124
Second law of thermodynamics, 85–86
Second messenger, 197–200
Secretin, 806
Secretion, excretory system and phase of, 879, 882
Secretory phase, menstrual cycle, 926
Secretory proteins
    insulin as (see Insulin)
    from ribosomes, 310
    rough endoplasmic reticulum and synthesis of, 112–13
Sedimentary rocks, fossils in, 415, 416f, 464–66
Seed, 562–63
    asexual production of (apomixis), 741
    crop size of, 1091f
    dispersion of, 568
    dormancy of, 739, 758
    evolution of, 549
    germination of, 739–40
    overcrowding and reduced production of, 1097, 1098f
    structure of mature, 737–38
Seed coat, 737
Seedless vascular plants, 555–59
    carboniferous coal forests and, 558–59
    ferns, 556f, 558
    horsetails, 557
    life cycle, 555, 556f
    lycophytes, 557
Seedling, 739–40
    disease in, 757f
Seed plants, 561–73
    angiosperms, 549, 565–71
    global impact of, 571–72
    gymnosperms, 549, 563–65
    reproductive adaptations of, 561–63
    sporophyte and gametophyte generations of, 561, 562f, 730, 731f
Segmentation, 614
    in arthropods, 402–4
    in chordates, 633f
    in worms, 612–14
Segmentation genes, 402
Segment-polarity genes, 403
Segregation of alleles
    fertilization and, as chance events, 246
    law of, into gametes, 241–44
Selective channels, 696
Selective permeability of membranes, 130, 136–37
    in plant cells, 695–96
Self-incompatibility
    in animals, 735 (see also Immune system)
    in plants, molecular basis of, 734–36
Self-pollination, 734
Self-recognition
    in animal immune system, 846–47, 857–58
    in plants, 734–36
Self-tolerance, 847
Semelparity, 1089–90
Semen, 920
Semicircular canals, 1005
Semiconservative model of DNA replication, 284, 285f
Semilunar valves, 815

Sulfhydryl group, 54*f*, 55
Summation, postsynaptic potential, 973–74
    of muscle cell contractions, 1018*f*
Sunfish, feeding behavior in bluegill, 1059*f*, 1060
Sunlight
    as abiotic factor, 1029–30
    characteristics of, 173
    Earth latitudes and, 1031*f*
    global energy budget and, 1134
Superchiasmatic nucleus (SCN), 903
Superior colliculi, 981
Supporting cells of nervous system (glia), 964
Suppressor T cell (T$_S$), 849–50
Suprachiasmatic nuclei (SCN), 982
Surface tension, 38, 39*f*
Survival
    age at maturity and rates of, 1090, 1091*f*
    of cohorts, 1086
    effects of genetic diversity on, 1165
Survivorship curve, 1086, 1087*f*
Suspension-feeders, 797
Sustainable agriculture, 720
Sustainable Biosphere Initiative, 1172
Sustainable development, 1171–72
Sutherland, Earl W., 190–91, 197
Swallowing reflex, 802*f*
Sweden, age structure of population in, 1102, 1103*f*
Swim bladder, 639, 640, 1006
Swimming, 1010
Symbionts, 516, 585–86, 1117
Symbiosis, 516, 1117
    between animals and digestive bacteria, 808
    commensalism as, 516, 1117–18
    among fungi, 585–86
    lichens as example of, 584
    mutualism as, 516 (*see also* Mutualism)
    between nitrogen-fixing bacteria and plants,
        722–26
    parasitism as, 516 (*see also* Parasites;
        Parasitism)
    plant nutrition and, 675, 701–2
    between plant roots and fungi (*see*
        Mycorrhizae)
    prokaryotic, 516–17
    prokaryotic, and origins of eukaryotes, 502–3,
        522–24
Sympathetic division of autonomic nervous
    system, 979*f*
Sympatric populations, 455
    resource partitioning by, 1116
Sympatric speciation, 451, 452–55
Symplast, 700, 701*f*
Synapomorphies, 483
Synapse(s), 961–62
    chemical, 971–72
    electrical, 970
Synapsids, 644, 645*f*
Synapsis, 235
Synaptic cleft, 971
Synaptic terminals, 961, 962*f*
Synaptic vesicles, 971
Syngamy, 228. *See also* Fertilization
    in fungi, 576–77
    in protists, 521
Systematics, 464, 473–85
    cladistic analysis and, 482–84
    contribution of morphology and molecular
        biology to phylogenetic, 485
    major life lineages and, 498–500, 503*f*
    molecular biology as tool for, 477–81,
        512–13
    monophyletic taxa and, 476–77
    phenetics and, 482
    phylogenetic trees and, 475–76 (*see also*
        Phylogenetic trees)
    prokaryotic, 512–13

taxonomy and classification in, 474–77 (*see
    also* Taxonomy)
Systemic acquired resistance (SAR), 773
Systemic circuit, 814
Systole, cardiac cycle, 816

Tail, muscular and postanal, in chordates, 631
Tandemly repetitive DNA, 347
Tapeworms (Cestoidea), 606
Taproot system, 674
Tardigrades (water bears), 878*f*
Target cells
    of animal hormones, 896–98
    of cytotoxic T cells, 850
Taste, receptors for, 995, 1007–9
Taste buds, 1008
TATA box, 301
Tatum, Edward, one gene-one enzyme hypothesis
    of G. Beadle and, 295–96
Taxis, 506, 1065
Taxon, 475
    monophyletic, polyphyletic, and paraphyletic,
        476–77
Taxonomy, 9–10, 415
    of animals, 595*t*, 627*t*
    of arthropods, 615–16
    different systems of, 498–500
    domains, 11*f*
    hierarchical classification system of, 474–75
    Linnaeus on, 415, 420, 475
    objectives of, 475
    phylogeny and, 475–76 (*see also* Phylogeny)
    of plants, 549, 550*t*
    of protists, 499–500
    species concepts and, 446–50
Tay-Sachs disease, 115, 248, 254
T cell receptors, 844
T cells. *See* T lymphocytes (T cells)
T-dependent antigens, 851
    response to, 851*f*
Technology, science and, 18–19
    B. Alberts on, 100–101
    DNA (*see* DNA technology)
Teeth
    diet and, 807–8
    mammalian, 807*f*
Telencephalon, 980
Telomerase, 291
Telomeres, 291, 347
Telophase, mitosis, 209
Temperate deciduous forest, 1046*f*
Temperate grasslands, 1046*f*
Temperate viruses, 323
Temperature, 39
    as abiotic factor, 1029
    acclimation to changes in, 871–72
    effect of, on enzyme activity, 94
    increased atmospheric (*see* Global warming)
    maintenance of body (*see* Thermoregulation)
    moderating effect of water on Earth's, 39–40
    plant responses to, 771
Template strand, 297–98
Temporal isolation as reproductive barrier, 447
Tendons, 781
Tension, water, 698
Terminal bud, 675
Terminator sequence, 302
Terrestrial animals
    gas exchange and respiration in, 828–32
    locomotion by, 1010
    osmoregulation in, 878–79
Terrestrial biomes, 1044–47*f*
    climate and, 1042–43
    distribution of major, 1043*f*
Terrestrial ecosystems
    food chain in, 1132*f*

    food web in, 1132, 1133*f*
    primary consumers in, 1133–34
    soil as key factor in, 717–20
Terrestrial life. *See* Land, colonization of
Territoriality, 1069–70
    bird song as communication of, 1073–74
    in stickleback fish, 1056, 1057*f*
Tertiary structure, protein, 73–74
Testcross, 244, 265
Testes, 918, 919*f*
    hormonal control of, 925*f*
Testosterone, 908*f*, 910, 925
    as chemical messenger, 194
    estrone compared to, 53*f*
Tetanus, 1018
Tetrad, chromatin, 235
Tetrapods, 634, 640–56
    amniotic egg in, 643–44
    amphibians, 640–43
    birds, 647–50
    mammals, 650–56
    origin of, 641*f*
    reptiles, 644–47
Thalamus, 981
Thallus, seaweed, 537
Theory, meaning of, 425–26
Therapsids, 651
Thermocline, 1035
Thermodynamics, energy transformations and
    laws of, 85–86
Thermophiles, extreme, 513
Thermoreceptors, 994
Thermoregulation, 865–73
    acclimatization and, 871–72
    ectothermic, 644, 866–67, 868–72
    endothermic, and 646, 866–67, 868–72
    feedback mechanisms in, 871, 872*f*
    heat gain/loss between organisms and
        environment, 866
    physiological and behavioral adjustments in,
        867–68
    in plants, 771
    temperature range adjustments and, 871–72
    thermoreceptors and, 994
    torpor and, 873
Thick filaments, 1014, 1015*f*
Thigmomorphogenesis, 763
Thigmotropism, 763
Thin filaments, 1014, 1015*f*
Thiols, 54*f*, 55
30-nm chromatin fiber, 345*f*, 346
Thoracic cavity, 784
Threatened species, 1160
Threshold potential, 967
Thrombus, 824
Thylakoids, 117, 118*f*
    light reactions in, 172, 173–79
    model for organization of, 180*f*
    photosystems as light-harvesting complexes in,
        175–77
Thymine (T), 77, 78*f*, 79
Thymus, 899*t*
Thyroid gland, 899*t*, 903
    hormones secreted by, 897–98, 903–4
Thyroid-stimulating hormone (TSH), 902
Thyroxine, 896, 903
Tidal volume, breathing, 832
Tight junctions, 126*f*, 127
T-independent antigens, 851
Ti plasmid, 384
Tissue plasminogen activator (TPA), 381
Tissues, animal, 589, 779
    connective, 780–82
    coordination and structure and function in,
        779–83
    embryonic, 943

Whales
  suspension-feeding in baleen, 797*f*
  terrestrial origins of, 423*f*, 424
Wheat (*Triticum* sp.), evolution of, 453, 455*f*
Whisk fern, 560*f*
White blood cells (leukocytes), 782, 822*f*, 823
  differentiation of, 824*f*
  eosinophils of, 822*f*, 823, 843
  lymphocytes (*see* Lymphocytes)
  lysosomes of, 114–15, 798
  monocytes, 822*f*, 823, 842
White matter, nervous system, 978
White rusts (Oomycota), 535
Whittaker, Robert H., 499, 524
  community hypotheses tested by, 1108*f*
Wieschaus, Eric, 399, 400–401*b*
Wild type, phenotype, 263
Wilkins, Maurice, 281
Wilson, E. O., 1026, 1067, 1156
  on island biogeography, 1126–28
Wind
  as abiotic factor, 1030
  global patterns of, 1032*f*
Wings
  bird, 648*f*, 649*f*
  insect, 619
Wiskott-Aldrich syndrome (WAS), 203
Wobble, base pair-rule relaxation, 305
Woese, Carl, 503
Wolf, social behavior in, 1069

Wood, as secondary plant growth, 689–92
Worms
  annelids, 612–14
  flatworms, 604–6
  marine, 608, 613–14
  proboscis worms/ribbonworms, 608
  roundworms, 593, 607
  walking, 615, 616*f*

X chromosome, 228, 263, 268–69
  extra, in males and females, 273
  fragile X syndrome, 274, 347
  genetic disorders linked to, 269*f*, 270
  inactivation of, in females, 270–71
Xeroderma pigmentosum, 290
Xerophytes, reduction of transpiration in, 708–9
X-rays, discovery of DNA double helix using, 281–83
Xylem, 555, 672, 679*f*
  ascent of sap in, 703–5
  cell evolution in, 567*f*
  water conduction by vessel elements and tracheids of, 679*f*, 680*f*, 681
Xylem vessels, 681
Y chromosome, 228, 263, 268–69
  males with extra, 273
  studies in human evolution and, 664
Yeasts, 583
  alcohol fermentation by, 162
  cell signaling in, 188, 189*f*

food production by, 583
  gene cloning and, 370
Yellowstone National Park
  fires in, 1122, 1123*f*
  grizzly bear populations in, 1167*f*
Yolk, egg, 941, 948
Yolk plug, 945
Yolk sac, 643*f*, 948, 949

Zeatin, 756
Zebrafish as model organism, 391
Zebra mussel, 1120
Zero population growth (ZPG), 1093
Z lines, 1014, 1015*f*
Zona pellucida, 940
Zone of cell division, 684
Zone of elongation, 684
Zone of maturation, 684
Zone of polarizing activity (ZPA), 956, 957*f*
Zoned reserve systems in landscape management, 1170
Zygomycota (zygote fungi), 578–79
Zygote, 228
  animal, 589, 590*f*, 593–94, 913, 928*f*
  cellular potency of, 953–54
  cleavage in, 928, 940–42
  development of, 388–92
  plant, 548*f*, 736
Zygote fungi (Zygomycota), 578–79